The Sense of Fiction

PRENTICE-HALL ENGLISH LITERATURE SERIES
Maynard Mack, *Editor*

PRENTICE-HALL INTERNATIONAL, INC., *London*
PRENTICE-HALL OF AUSTRALIA, PTY., LTD., *Sydney*
PRENTICE-HALL OF CANADA, LTD., *Toronto*
PRENTICE-HALL OF INDIA (PRIVATE) LTD., *New Delhi*
PRENTICE-HALL OF JAPAN, INC., *Tokyo*

The Sense of Fiction

Edited by

ROBERT L. WELKER
University of Alabama, Huntsville

HERSCHEL GOWER
Vanderbilt University

Prentice-Hall, Inc.
Englewood Cliffs, New Jersey

Library of Congress Catalog Card Number: 66-10135

Printed in the United States of America
[*C-80663*]

Acknowledgments

Besides our indebtedness
to the authors and publishers
whose kind permissions
have made this collection possible
and who are acknowledged elsewhere
individually,
we are indeed grateful
for the guidance and criticism
of the following colleagues
and friends:
Maynard Mack,
Leslie Cram Puryear,
Eleanor Graham,
Arnold Tibbetts,
Preston Frazer,
Albert E. Elmore,
and Marie Hudson Gower.

Contents

Notes on the Short Story

Scope and Effect

The thirty examples selected for this book indicate the range and scope of the short story written in English during the past century and a quarter. Once these selections have been examined in depth, the reader will form his own ideas of the flexibility and variety of the genre. He will also discover that the effects the short story can achieve may range from small to large, from simple to complex, from sustained drama to quiet understatement, from subtle humor to stark, compelling tragedy.

As editors we have grouped the stories in what seems to us a purposeful arrangement. To cite one example, the unprepared reader who meets Miss Emily Grierson in "A Rose for Emily" for the first time may have more difficulty in reaching a full understanding of that lady and her world than the reader of this book, who, on his way to Miss Emily, will have met other memorable individualists like Dan Bride in "The Majesty of the Law" and Munsie in "What You Hear From 'Em?". This is another way of saying that stories often complement each other in their characters, themes, and techniques. The discovery of an idea or the understanding of a technique in one story should heighten our awareness when we read the next, and we will be engaged in the continuing process of significant discovery. So the editors have ordered and arranged the selections in this book to make clear the universal overtones of a successful story.

Discussion and Analysis

Aside from our interest in the scope which complementary stories can provide, we have been concerned with each story as a distinctive and individual work of art. In analyzing the parts and discussing their combined effect, we have consistently applied the aesthetic principle of the unified whole. This suggest that the ultimate success of a story depends on the interrelationship of all its parts in a unified whole calculated to achieve a given effect. Since this is the underlying principle of the modern short story, we have attempted to use it as the basis for discussions which introduce and link the several sections of the book. Thus the headnotes and analyses point the way to meaning, for meaning is totality.

Although sound criticism will never lose sight of all the parts that contribute to the total effect, some necessary limitations restrict most of our discussions here to one or two outstanding aspects of a story—atmosphere, theme, character, or plot—and in any case the ability to read with full appreciation can best be learned one step at a time. However, readers will note that among the critical discussions there are fairly detailed analyses of four stories—"The Fall of the House of Usher," "An Imaginative Woman," "The Majesty of the Law," and "The Grave." (But these analyses do not preclude further commentaries. Rather they should suggest to the student how to read a story in its totality. They may also serve as models for student themes and investigations.) After other of the stories there are brief study guides and questions which invite further interpretations and longer treatments. Throughout the book there are sixteen stories with no commentary from the editors, for surely by his own powers the earnest critic will reap his greatest rewards.

Conventions and "Reality" in Fiction

The final pleasure of exploring fiction comes from the reader's independent discovery of the "truth" or "reality" existing in each story. Indeed, each detail of good fiction carries us toward this ultimate pleasure. The skillful writer leads us to it by carefully arranging his material so we will have the illusion of discovering reality ourselves instead of being commanded to accept a second-hand version of what experience means. In order to achieve these aims, the writer must rely on, and the reader must learn to accept, certain literary conventions. For example, the printed page becomes a speaking voice; from a given premise in a story a certain logical construction may follow which we call "true"; stream-of-consciousness becomes a character's internal thoughts and impressions; images convey a meaning as well as a picture. Gradually we come to accept literary conventions with a "willing suspension of disbelief" and we enjoy an illusion of reality, not reality itself. We enjoy art, not nature. In addition to photographic or realistic techniques an author may present the illusion of reality through fantasy, allegory, fable, or dreams. And when the conventions are used with much skill, we have the illusion that what is before our eyes is genuine. However unreal in itself, the illusion makes clear some valid and important aspect of experience.

This is not to say, of course, that any story is an actual substitute for the experience it relates. No author and no critic would make such a claim. Reading about life is not advocated as an improvement on living or as a substitute for reality. But the short story is about life—about the recurring emotions, situations, problems, dilemmas, ironies, values, sorrows, and joys which most men meet from time to time. And even though fiction is not a direct encounter, it does provide an imaginary experience which may be more meaningful than life itself, for we know that disordered events mean very little until we have decided what was particularly relevant and have arranged all the facts and impressions in an interrelationship which constitutes meaning.

Then these are the aims of fiction: to arrange human experience in such a way that it is readily accessible for interpretation. All relevancies will be included, all irrelevancies omitted, and the parts will be so ordered that, without wandering in a maze of distractions, we are permitted to grasp the significance of what has happened. A short story therefore may have meaning more intense than what we have felt or known in our own acts; and for that matter, a short story is "real" if meaning is the ultimate reality of life. So reading a short story should provide us, among other things, with the experience of discovering and exploring those ultimate realities which the ordinary world obscures.

The final result of a story, however, may not be necessarily a pat answer to a problem, a great moral truth, a precept for behavior, or a profound insight. It may mean any or all of these things, or it may mean the presentation of a problem, the discovery of a dilemma, the asking rather than the answering of a question. Here again we can equate meaning and theme, for the theme may be an exploration as well as a discovery, a hint instead of a pronouncement, a question as well as an answer, a complication of life rather than a simplification. Certainly no short story of merit is an evasion; it is an honest confrontation of the mysteries of reality.

Criteria of Difficulty and Totality

Obviously there are criteria for evaluating one good thing as opposed to another good thing, and these may be called "the criteria of difficulty and totality." When a story attempts to handle complex ideas, situations, or emotions and succeeds to a high degree, it must be judged of greater value than one which deals with the lesser complexities of man and the world, even though the latter may also achieve its modest aims with considerable success. Both types will be worthy of our attention, and each will have its place, but few good readers will fail to perceive that the story which tries to make us more fully aware by its breadth and intensity —the story which involves itself in subtleties as well as the obvious surfaces —is the finer of the two. Thus in our final evaluation of a work of fiction we should talk about it from the standpoint of its total truth beyond the mere enumeration of its parts—however attractive and compelling the parts may be in isolation. Using this total approach in our criticism, we come to talk about fiction objectively, not about our subjective likes and dislikes. With increasing confidence we learn to appreciate the art of fiction for its own sake, and our responses will thereafter transcend the bounds of individual taste.

Glossary of Literary Terms

Most of the elements and conventions of literature have been given names, some of them dating from classical Greek. These and later crtical terms can be adequately defined and illustrated to good effect. We can agree, more or less, on terminology and set up a working vocabulary useful to our critical discussions. These terms, listed and defined in the Glossary, help us to examine the short story, survey its several parts, and point the way to its meaning. Thus they help us to express with fair accuracy the measures of its art. And although we may be hard put to define the genre with much satisfaction or to account for the genius of the author and the inspired cerebrations which produced the story, we can nevertheless make known our delight and voice our critical satisfaction with what its art reveals.

Bibliographies and Criticism

As a convenient guide to scholarly interpretations since 1925 of some of the short stories in this collection, the editors recommend *Short Story Criticism,* compiled by Jarvis Thurston, O. B. Emerson, Carl Hartman, and Elizabeth V. Wright (Denver, Col.: Alan Swallow, 1960). This bibliography was brought up to date by Elizabeth V. Wright in *Studies in Short Fiction,* Vol. I (Summer 1964), a quarterly devoted to informed discussions of the short story and published since 1963 by Newberry College, Newberry, South Carolina. For further critical discussions, checklists of authors, and many useful materials for the student of American, English, and European fiction, consult *Modern Fiction Studies,* published since 1955 by the Modern Fiction Club of Purdue University, Lafayette, Indiana.

R. L. W.

H. G.

The Sense of Fiction

Unity of Effect

First published in 1839, "The Fall of the House of Usher" is historically one of the most famous stories in English. Appearing at a time when the short story as an art form was beginning to take shape in Europe and America, this story illustrates Edgar Allan Poe's important and seminal concept of the *unity of effect* in fiction, especially as obtained through *setting* and *atmosphere*. Significant in historical perspective and illustrative of Poe's critical theory, "The Fall of the House of Usher" has become a classic example of the "atmosphere story."

Actually Poe's concept of unity of effect was stated directly for the first time in 1842 in his critical review of Nathaniel Hawthorne's *Twice-Told Tales:*

> A skilful literary artist has constructed a tale. If wise, he has not fashioned his thoughts to accomodate his incidents; but having conceived, with deliberate care, a certain unique or single *effect* to be wrought out, he then invents such incidents—he then combines such events as may best aid him in establishing this preconceived effect. If his very initial sentence tend not to the outbringing of this effect, then he has failed in his first step. In the whole composition there should be no word written, of which the tendency, direct or indirect, is not to the one pre-established design. And by such means, with such care and skill, a picture is at length painted which leaves in the mind of him who contemplates it with a kindred art, a sense of the fullest satisfaction. The idea of the tale has been presented unblemished, because undisturbed. . . .

With Poe's observations we can date the beginning of the modern short story as a conscious literary genre distinct from the ancient tale or the budding novel. What Poe states—directly or indirectly—is a theory concerning the art of the short story. His insistence upon concentration, sometimes called the law of economy, sets the short story apart from other prose fiction. This principle insists that a short story have a high degree of intensity. There should be no word which does not function to the fullest in creating a very powerful effect in a very limited space.

Atmosphere is usually a direct means of contributing to a unified effect, and it is concerned with setting, with imagery and metaphor, and sometimes with the very idiom and language in which a character or narrator speaks. Atmosphere is the air (*atmos,* vapor) in which an idea and an action can live and breathe; it is the condition of mood, time, place, general disposition, environmental and emotional flavor, even general philosophical orientation, in which given acts and characters can plausibly occur and exist. Thus atmosphere is the surrounding environment—physical, intellectual, and spiritual—in which a fictional world (sphere) can thrive in its own manner. We may speak of an atmosphere of high sophistication, of innocent simplicity, of violence, of brooding danger, of bright cheerfulness, of mystery, of brittle gaiety, of Gothic horror, of decay and degeneration, or dynamic vitality, and so forth.

Often the atmosphere of a story is a direct clue to the nature of the characters or a foreshadowing of events or a symbolic configuration of the theme. Sometimes the atmosphere is developed for purposes of irony, as in "My Kinsman, Major Molineux," where a healthy character is placed in a setting of depravity to provide contrast. Each of the protagonists in "The Blue Hotel" and "Bartleby the Scrivener" is "foreign" to the world about him and stands against that world in bitter conflict.

Keeping in mind the principle of unity, the reader may now look at "The Fall of the House of Usher" and note the function of atmosphere and setting. A critical discussion follows on page 16.

EDGAR ALLAN POE

(1809–1849)

The Fall of the House of Usher

Son coeur est un luth suspendu;
Sitôt qu'on le touche il résonne.
—DE BÉRANGER

During the whole of a dull, dark, and soundless day in the autumn of the year, when the clouds hung oppressively low in the heavens, I had been passing alone, on horseback, through a singularly dreary tract of country; and at length found myself, as the shades of the evening drew on, within view of the melancholy House of Usher. I know not how it was—but, with the first glimpse of the building, a sense of insufferable gloom pervaded my spirit. I say insufferable; for the feeling was unrelieved by any of that half-pleasurable, because poetic, sentiment, with which the mind usually receives even the sternest natural images of the desolate or terrible. I looked upon the scene before me—upon the mere house, and the simple landscape features of the domain, upon the bleak walls, upon the vacant eye-like windows, upon a few rank sedges, and upon a few white trunks of decayed trees—with an utter depression of soul which I can compare to no earthly sensation more properly than to the after-dream of the reveller upon opium: the bitter lapse into everyday life, the hideous dropping off of the veil. There was an iciness, a sinking, a sickening of the heart, an unredeemed dreariness of thought which no goading of the imagination could torture into aught of the sublime. What was it—I paused to think—what was it that so unnerved me in the contemplation of the House of Usher? It was a mystery all insoluble; nor could I grapple with the shadowy fancies that crowded upon me as I pondered. I was forced to fall back upon the unsatisfactory conclusion, that while, beyond doubt, there *are* combinations of very simple natural objects which have the power of thus affecting us, still the analysis of this power lies among considerations beyond our depth. It was possible, I reflected, that a mere different arrangement of the particulars of the scene, of the details of the picture, would be sufficient to modify, or perhaps to annihilate its capacity for sorrowful impression; and, acting upon this idea, I reined my horse to the precipitous brink of a black and lurid tarn that lay in unruffled lustre by the dwelling, and gazed down—but with a shudder even more thrilling than before—upon the remodelled and inverted images of the gray sedge, and the ghastly tree-stems, and the vacant and eye-like windows.

Nevertheless, in this mansion of gloom I now proposed to myself a sojourn of some weeks. Its proprietor, Roderick Usher, had been one of my boon companions in boyhood; but many years had elapsed since our last meeting. A letter, however, had lately reached me in a distant part of the country—a letter from him—which, in its wildly importunate nature, had admitted of no other than a personal reply. The MS. gave evidence of nervous agitation. The writer spoke of acute bodily illness, of a mental disorder which oppressed him, and of an earnest desire to see me, as his best, and indeed his only personal friend, with a view of attempting, by the cheerfulness of my society, some alleviation of his malady. It was the manner in which all this, and much more, was said—it was the apparent *heart* that went with his request—which allowed me no room for hesitation; and I accordingly obeyed forthwith what I still considered a very singular summons.

Although, as boys, we had been even intimate associates, yet I really knew little of my friend. His reserve had been always excessive and habitual. I was aware, however, that his very ancient family had been noted, time out of mind, for a peculiar sensibility of temperament, displaying itself, through long ages, in many works of exalted art, and manifested, of late, in repeated deeds of munificent yet unobtrusive charity, as well as in a passionate devotion to the intricacies, perhaps even more than to the orthodox and easily recognizable beauties, of musical science. I had learned, too, the very remarkable fact, that the stem of the Usher race, all time-honored as it was, had put forth, at no period, any enduring branch; in other words, that the entire family lay in the direct line of descent, and had always, with very trifling and very temporary variation, so lain. It was this deficiency, I considered, while running over in thought the perfect keeping of the character of the premises with the accredited character of the people, and while speculating upon the possible influence which the one, in the long lapse of centuries, might have exercised upon the other—it was this deficiency, perhaps, of collateral issue, and the consequent undeviating transmission, from sire to son, of the patrimony with the name, which had, at length, so identified the two as to merge the original title of the estate in the quaint and equivocal appellation of the "House of Usher"—an appellation which seemed to include, in the minds of the peasantry who used it, both the family and the family mansion.

I have said that the sole effect of my somewhat childish experiment, that of looking down within the tarn, had been to deepen the first singular impression. There can be no doubt that the consciousness of the rapid increase of my superstition—for why should I not so term it?—served mainly to accelerate the increase itself. Such, I have long known, is the paradoxical law of all sentiments having terror as a basis. And it might have been for this reason only, that, when I again uplifted my eyes to the house itself, from its image in the pool, there grew in my mind a strange fancy—a fancy so ridiculous, indeed, that I but mention it to show the vivid force of the sensations which oppressed me. I had so worked upon my imagination as really to believe that about the whole mansion and domain there hung an atmosphere peculiar to themselves and their immediate vicinity: an atmosphere which had no affinity with the air of heaven, but which had reeked up from the decayed trees, and the gray wall, and the silent tarn: a pestilent and mystic vapor, dull, sluggish, faintly discernible, and leaden-hued.

Shaking off from my spirit what *must* have been a dream, I scanned more narrowly the real aspect of the building. Its principal feature seemed to be that of an excessive antiquity. The discoloration of ages had been great. Minute fungi overspread the whole exterior, hanging in a fine tangled web-work from the eaves. Yet all this was apart from any extraordinary dilapidation. No portion of the masonry had fallen; and there appeared to be a wild inconsistency between its still perfect adaptation of parts and the crumbling condition of the individual stones. In this there was much that reminded me of the specious totality of old wood-work which has rotted for long years in some neglected vault, with no disturbance from the breath of the external air. Beyond this indication of extensive decay, however, the fabric gave little token of instability. Perhaps the eye of a scrutinizing observer might have discovered a barely perceptible fissure, which, extending from the roof of the building in front, made its way down the wall in a zigzag direction, until it became lost in the sullen waters of the tarn.

Noticing these things, I rode over a short causeway to the house. A servant in waiting took my horse, and I entered the Gothic archway of the hall. A valet, of stealthy step, thence conducted me, in silence, through many dark and intricate passages in my progress to the *studio* of his master. Much that I encountered on the way contributed, I know not how, to heighten the vague sentiments of which I have already spoken. While the objects around me—while the carvings of the ceilings, the sombre tapestries of the walls, the ebon blackness of the floors, and the phantasmagoric armorial trophies which rattled as I strode, were but matters to which, or to such as which, I had been accustomed from my infancy—while I hesitated not to acknowledge how familiar was all this—I still wondered to find how unfamiliar were the fancies which ordinary images were stirring up. On one of the staircases, I met the physician of the family. His countenance, I thought, wore a mingled expression of low cunning and perplexity. He accosted me with trepidation and passed on. The valet now threw open a door and ushered me into the presence of his master.

The room in which I found myself was very large and lofty. The windows were long, narrow, and pointed, and at so vast a distance from the black oaken floor as to be altogether inaccessible from within. Feeble gleams of encrimsoned light made their way through the trellised panes, and served to render sufficiently distinct the more prominent objects around; the eye, however, struggled in vain to reach the remoter angles of the chamber, or the recesses of the vaulted and fretted ceiling. Dark draperies hung upon the walls. The general furniture was profuse, comfortless, antique, and tattered. Many books and musical instruments lay scattered about, but failed to give any vitality to the scene. I felt that I breathed an atmosphere of sorrow. An air of stern, deep, and irredeemable gloom hung over and pervaded all.

Upon my entrance, Usher arose from a sofa on which he had been lying at full length, and greeted me with a vivacious warmth which had much in it, I at first thought, of an overdone cordiality—of the constrained effort of the *ennuyé* man of the world. A glance, however, at his countenance, convinced me of his perfect sincerity. We sat down; and for some moments, while he spoke not, I gazed upon him with a feeling half of pity, half of awe. Surely, man had never before so terribly altered, in so brief a period, as had Roderick Usher! It was with difficulty that I could bring myself to admit the identity of the wan being before me with the companion of my early boyhood. Yet the character of his face had been at all times remarkable. A cadaverousness of complexion; an eye large, liquid, and luminous beyond comparison, lips somewhat thin and very pallid, but of a surpassingly beautiful curve; a nose of a delicate Hebrew model, but with a breadth of nostril unusual in similar formations; a finely moulded chin, speaking, in its want of prominence, of a want of moral energy; hair of a more than web-like softness and tenuity; these features, with an inordinate expansion above the regions of the temple, made up altogether a countenance not easily to be forgotten. And now in the mere exaggeration of the prevailing character of these features, and of the expression they were wont to convey, lay so much of change that I doubted to whom I spoke. The now ghastly pallor of the skin, and the now miraculous lustre of the eye, above all things startled and even awed me. The silken hair, too, had been suffered to grow all unheeded, and as, in its wild gossamer texture, it floated rather than fell about the face, I could not, even with effort, connect its Arabesque expression with any idea of simple humanity.

In the manner of my friend I was at once struck with an incoherence, an inconsistency; and I soon found this to arise from a series of feeble and futile struggles to overcome an habitual trepidancy, an excessive nervous agitation. For something of this nature I had indeed been prepared, no less by his letter, than by reminiscences of certain boyish traits, and by conclusions deduced from his peculiar physical conformation and temperament. His action was alternately vivacious and sullen. His voice varied rapidly from a tremulous indecision (when the animal spirits seemed utterly in abeyance) to that species of energetic concision—that abrupt, weighty, unhurried, and hollow-sounding enunciation—that leaden, self-balanced and perfectly modulated guttural utterance, which may be observed in the lost drunkard, or the irreclaimable eater of opium, during the period of his most intense excitement.

It was thus that he spoke of the object of my visit, of his earnest desire to see me, and of the solace he expected me to afford him. He entered, at some length, into what he conceived to be the nature of his malady. It was, he said, a constitutional and a family evil, and one for which he despaired to find a remedy—a mere nervous affection, he immediately added, which would undoubtedly soon pass off. It displayed itself in a host of unnatural sensations. Some of these, as he detailed them, interested and bewildered me; although, perhaps the terms, and the general manner of the narration had their weight. He suffered much from a morbid acuteness of the senses; the most insipid food was alone endurable; he could wear only garments of certain texture; the odors of all flowers were oppressive; his eyes were tortured by even a faint light; and there were but peculiar sounds, and these from stringed instruments, which did not inspire him with horror.

To an anomalous species of terror I found him a bounden slave. "I shall perish," said he, "I *must* perish in this deplorable folly. Thus, thus, and not otherwise, shall I be lost. I dread the events of the future, not in themselves, but in their results. I shudder at the thought of any, even the most trivial, incident, which may operate upon this intolerable agitation of soul. I have, indeed, no abhorrence of danger, except in its absolute effect—in terror. In this unnerved—in this pitiable condition, I feel that the period will sooner or later arrive when I must abandon life and reason together, in some struggle with the grim phantasm, FEAR."

I learned, moreover, at intervals, and through broken and equivocal hints, another singular feature of his mental condition. He was enchained by certain superstitious impressions in regard to the dwelling which he tenanted, and whence, for many years, he had never ventured forth—in regard to an influence whose suppositious force was conveyed in terms too shadowy here to be re-stated—an influence which some peculiarities in the mere form and substance of his family mansion, had, by dint of long sufferance, he said, obtained over his spirit—an effect which the *physique* of the gray walls and turrets, and of the dim tarn into which they all looked down, had, at length, brought about upon the *morale* of his existence.

He admitted, however, although with hesitation, that much of the peculiar gloom which thus afflicted him could be traced to a more natural and far more palpable origin—to the severe and long-continued illness, indeed to the evidently approaching dissolution, of a tenderly beloved sister—his sole companion for long years, his last and only relative on earth. "Her decease," he said, with a bitterness which I can never forget, "would leave him (him the hopeless and the frail) the last of the ancient race of the Ushers." While he spoke, the lady Madeline (for so was she called) passed slowly through a remote portion of the apartment, and, without having noticed my presence, disappeared. I regarded her with an utter astonishment not unmingled with dread, and yet I found it impossible to account for such feelings. A sensation of stupor oppressed me, as my eyes followed her retreating steps. When a door, at length, closed upon her, my glance sought instinctively and eagerly the countenance of the brother; but he had buried his face in his hands, and I could only perceive that a far more than ordinary wanness had overspread the emaciated fingers through which trickled many passionate tears.

The disease of the lady Madeline had long baffled the skill of her physicians. A settled apathy, a gradual wasting away of the person, and frequent although transient affections of a partially cataleptical character, were the unusual diagnosis. Hitherto she had steadily borne up against the pressure of her malady, and had not betaken herself finally to bed; but, on the closing in of the evening of my arrival at the house, she succumbed (as her brother told me at night with inexpressible agitation) to the prostrating power of the destroyer; and I learned that the glimpse I had obtained of her person would thus probably be the last I should obtain—that the lady, at least while living, would be seen by me no more.

For several days ensuing, her name was unmentioned by either Usher or myself: and during this period I was busied in earnest endeavors to alleviate the melancholy of my friend. We painted and read together; or I listened, as if in a dream, to the wild improvisations of his speaking guitar. And thus, as a closer and still closer intimacy admitted me more unreservedly into the recesses of his spirit, the more bitterly did I perceive the futility of all attempt at cheering a mind from which darkness, as if an inherent positive quality, poured forth upon all objects of the moral and physical universe, in one unceasing radiation of gloom.

I shall ever bear about me a memory of the many solemn hours I thus spent alone with the master of the House of Usher. Yet I should fail in any attempt to convey an idea of the exact character of the studies, or of the occupations, in which he involved me, or led me the way. An excited and highly distempered ideality threw a sulphureous lustre over all. His long improvised dirges will ring forever in my ears. Among other things, I hold painfully in mind a certain singular perversion and amplification of the wild air of the last waltz of von Weber. From the paintings over which his elaborate fancy brooded, and which grew, touch by touch, into vaguenesses at which I shuddered the more thrillingly, because I shuddered knowing not why;—from these paintings (vivid as their images now are before me) I would in vain endeavor to educe more than a small portion which should lie within the compass of merely written words. By the utter simplicity, by the nakedness of his designs, he arrested and overawed attention. If ever mortal painted an idea, that mortal was Roderick Usher. For me at least, in the circumstances then surrounding me, there arose out of the pure abstractions which the hypochondriac contrived to throw upon his canvas, an intensity of intolerable awe, no shadow of which felt I ever yet in the contemplation of the certainly glowing yet too concrete reveries of Fuseli.

One of the phantasmagoric conceptions of my friend, partaking not so rigidly of the spirit of abstraction, may be shadowed forth, although feebly, in words. A small picture presented the interior of an immensely long and rectangular vault or tunnel, with low walls, smooth, white, and without interruption or device. Certain accessory points of the design served well to convey the idea that this excavation lay at an exceeding depth below the surface of the earth. No outlet was observed in any portion of its vast extent, and no torch, or other artificial source of light was discernible; yet a flood of intense rays rolled throughout, and bathed the whole in a ghastly and inappropriate splendor.

I have just spoken of that morbid condition of the auditory nerve which rendered all music intolerable to the sufferer, with the exception of certain effects of stringed instruments. It was, perhaps, the narrow limits to which he thus confined himself upon the guitar, which gave birth, in great measure, to the fantastic character of his performances. But the fervid *facility* of his *impromptus* could not be so accounted for. They must have been, and were, in the notes, as well as in the words of his wild fantasias (for he not unfrequently accompanied himself with rhymed verbal improvisations), the result of that intense mental collectedness and concentration to which I have previously alluded as observable only in particular moments of the highest artificial excitement. The words of one of these rhapsodies I have easily remembered. I was, perhaps, the more forcibly impressed with it, as he gave it, because, in the under or mystic current of its meaning, I fancied that I perceived, and for the first time, a full consciousness on the part of Usher, of the tottering of his lofty reason upon her throne. The verses, which were entitled "The Haunted Palace," ran very nearly, if not accurately, thus:

In the greenest of our valleys
  By good angels tenanted,
Once a fair and stately palace—
  Radiant palace—reared its head.
In the monarch Thought's dominion,
  It stood there!
Never seraph spread a pinion
  Over fabric half so fair!

Banners yellow, glorious, golden,
  On its roof did float and flow
(This—all this—was in the olden
  Time long ago)
And every gentle air that dallied,
  In that sweet day,
Along the ramparts plumed and pallid,
  A wingèd odor went away.

Wanderers in that happy valley,
  Through two luminous windows, saw
Spirits moving musically
  To a lute's well-tunèd law,
Round about a throne where, sitting,
  Porphyrogene!
In state his glory well befitting,
  The ruler of the realm was seen.

And all with pearl and ruby glowing
  Was the fair palace door,
Through which came flowing, flowing, flowing
  And sparkling evermore,
A troop of Echoes, whose sweet duty
  Was but to sing,
In voices of surpassing beauty,
  The wit and wisdom of their king.

But evil things, in robes of sorrow,
  Assailed the monarch's high estate;
(Ah, let us mourn!—for never morrow
  Shall dawn upon him, desolate!)
And round about his home the glory
  That blushed and bloomed
Is but a dim-remembered story
  Of the old time entombed.

And travellers, now, within that valley,
  Through the red-litten windows see
Vast forms that move fantastically
  To a discordant melody;
While, like a ghastly rapid river,
  Through the pale door
A hideous throng rush out forever,
  And laugh—but smile no more.

I well remember that suggestions arising from this ballad, led us into a train of thought wherein there became manifest an opinion of Usher's which I mention not so much on account of its novelty (for other men have thought thus) as on account of the pertinacity with which he maintained it. This opinion, in its general form, was that of the sentience of all vegetable things. But, in his disordered fancy, the idea had assumed a more daring character, and trespassed, under certain conditions, upon the kingdom of inorganization. I lack words to express the full extent, or the earnest *abandon* of his persuasion. The belief, however, was connected (as I have previously hinted) with the gray stones of the home of his forefathers. The conditions of the sentience had been here, he imagined, fulfilled in the method of collocation of these stones—in the order of their arrangement, as well as in that of the many *fungi* which overspread them, and of the decayed trees which stood around—above all, in the long undisturbed endurance of this arrangement, and in its reduplication in the still waters of the tarn. Its evidence—the evidence of the sentience—was to be seen, he said (and I here started as he spoke), in the gradual yet certain condensation of an atmosphere of their own about the waters and the walls. The result was discoverable, he added, in that silent, yet importunate and terrible influence which for centuries had moulded the destinies of his family, and which made *him* what I now saw him—what he was. Such opinions need no comment, and I will make none.

Our books—the books which, for years, had formed no small portion of the mental existence of the invalid—were, as might be supposed, in strict keeping with this character of phantasm. We pored together over such works as the *Ververt et Chartreuse* of Gresset; the *Belphegor* of Machiavelli; the *Heaven and Hell* of Swedenborg; the *Subterranean Voyage of Nicholas Klimm* by Holberg; the *Chiromancy* of Robert Flud, of Jean D'Indaginé, and of De la Chambre; the *Journey into the Blue Distance* of Tieck; and the *City of the Sun* of Campanella. One favorite volume was a small octavo edition of the *Directorium Inquisitorum,* by the Dominican Eymeric de Gironne; and there were passages in Pomponius Mela, about the old African Satyrs and Ægipans, over which Usher would sit dreaming for hours. His chief delight, however, was found in the perusal of an exceedingly rare and curious book in quarto Gothic—the manual of a forgotten church—the *Vigiliæ Mortuorum Secundum Chorum Ecclesiæ Maguntinæ.*

I could not help thinking of the wild ritual of this work, and of its probable influence upon the hypochondriac, when, one evening, having informed me abruptly that the lady Madeline was no more, he stated his intention of preserving her corpse for a fortnight (previously to its final interment) in one of the numerous vaults within the main walls of the building. The worldly reason, however, assigned for this singular proceeding, was one which I did not feel at liberty to dispute. The brother had been led to his resolution (so he told me) by consideration of the unusual character of the malady of the deceased, of certain obtrusive and eager inquiries on the part of her medical men, and of the remote and exposed situation of the burial ground of the family. I will not deny that when I called to mind the sinister countenance of the person whom I met upon the staircase, on the day of my arrival at the house, I had no desire to oppose what I regarded as at best but a harmless, and by no means an unnatural, precaution.

At the request of Usher, I personally aided him in the arrangements for the temporary entombment. The body having been encoffined, we two alone bore it to its rest. The vault in which we placed it (and which had been so long unopened that our torches, half smothered in its oppressive atmosphere, gave us little opportunity for investigation) was small, damp, and entirely without means of admission for light; lying, at great depth, immediately beneath that portion of the building in which was my own sleeping apartment. It had been used, apparently, in remote feudal times, for the worst purpose of a donjon-keep, and, in later days, as a place of deposit for powder, or some other highly combustible substance, as a portion of its floor, and the whole interior of a long archway through which we reached it, were carefully sheathed with copper. The door, of massive iron, had been, also, similarly protected. Its immense weight caused an unusually sharp grating sound, as it moved upon its hinges.

Having deposited our mournful burden upon trestles within this region of horror, we partially turned aside the yet unscrewed lid of the coffin, and looked upon the face of the tenant. A striking similitude between the brother and sister now first arrested my attention; and Usher, divining, perhaps, my thoughts, murmured out some few words from which I learned that the deceased and himself had been twins, and that sympathies of a scarcely intelligible nature had always existed between them. Our glances, however, rested not long upon the dead—for we could not regard her unawed. The disease which had thus entombed the lady in the maturity of youth, had left, as usual in all maladies of a strictly cataleptical character, the mockery of a faint blush upon the bosom and the face, and that suspiciously lingering smile upon the lip which is so terrible in death. We replaced and screwed down the lid, and, having secured the door of iron, made our way, with toil, into the scarcely less gloomy apartments of the upper portion of the house.

And now, some days of bitter grief having elapsed, an observable change came over the features of the mental disorder of my friend. His ordinary manner had vanished. His ordinary occupations were neglected or forgotten.

He roamed from chamber to chamber with hurried, unequal, and objectless step. The pallor of his countenance had assumed, if possible, a more ghastly hue—but the luminousness of his eye had utterly gone out. The once occasional huskiness of his tone was heard no more; and a tremulous quaver, as if of extreme terror, habitually characterized his utterance. There were times, indeed, when I thought his unceasingly agitated mind was laboring with some oppressive secret, to divulge which he struggled for the necessary courage. At times, again, I was obliged to resolve all into the mere inexplicable vagaries of madness, for I beheld him gazing upon vacancy for long hours, in an attitude of the profoundest attention, as if listening to some imaginary sound. It was no wonder that his condition terrified—that it infected me. I felt creeping upon me, by slow yet certain degrees, the wild influences of his own fantastic yet impressive superstitions.

It was, especially, upon retiring to bed late in the night of the seventh or eighth day after the placing of the lady Madeline within the donjon, that I experienced the full power of such feelings. Sleep came not near my couch, while the hours waned and waned away. I struggled to reason off the nervousness which had dominion over me. I endeavored to believe that much, if not all of what I felt, was due to the bewildering influence of the gloomy furniture of the room—of the dark and tattered draperies, which, tortured into motion by the breath of a rising tempest, swayed fitfully to and fro upon the walls, and rustled uneasily about the decorations of the bed. But my efforts were fruitless. An irrepressible tremor gradually pervaded my frame; and, at length, there sat upon my very heart an incubus of utterly causeless alarm. Shaking this off with a gasp and a struggle, I uplifted myself upon the pillows, and, peering earnestly within the intense darkness of the chamber, hearkened—I know not why, except that an instinctive spirit prompted me—to certain low and indefinite sounds which came, through the pauses of the storm, at long intervals I knew not whence. Overpowered by an intense sentiment of horror, unaccountable yet unendurable, I threw on my clothes with haste (for I felt that I should sleep no more during the night), and endeavored to arouse myself from the pitiable condition into which I had fallen, by pacing rapidly to and fro through the apartment.

I had taken but few turns in this manner, when a light step on an adjoining staircase arrested my attention. I presently recognized it as that of Usher. In an instant afterward he rapped, with a gentle touch, at my door, and entered, bearing a lamp. His countenance was, as usual, cadaverously wan—but, moreover, there was a species of mad hilarity in his eyes—an evidently restrained *hysteria* in his whole demeanor. His air appalled me—but anything was preferable to the solitude which I had so long endured, and I even welcomed his presence as a relief.

"And you have not seen it?" he said abruptly, after having stared about him for some moments in silence—"you have not then seen it?—but, stay!

you shall." Thus speaking, and having carefully shaded his lamp, he hurried to one of the casements and threw it freely open to the storm.

The impetuous fury of the entering gust nearly lifted us from our feet. It was, indeed, a tempestuous yet sternly beautiful night, and one wildly singular in its terror and its beauty. A whirlwind had apparently collected its force in our vicinity; for there were frequent and violent alterations in the direction of the wind; and the exceeding density of the clouds (which hung so low as to press upon the turrets of the house) did not prevent our perceiving the life-like velocity with which they flew careering from all points against each other, without passing away into the distance. I say that even their exceeding density did not prevent our perceiving this; yet we had no glimpse of the moon or stars, nor was there any flashing forth of the lightning. But the under surfaces of the huge masses of agitated vapor, as well as all terrestrial objects immediately around us, were glowing in the unnatural light of a faintly luminous and distinctly visible gaseous exhalation which hung about and enshrouded the mansion.

"You must not—you shall not behold this!" said I, shudderingly, to Usher, as I led him, with a gentle violence, from the window to a seat. "These appearances, which bewilder you, are merely electrical phenomena not uncommon—or it may be that they have their ghastly origin in the rank miasma of the tarn. Let us close this casement; the air is chilling and dangerous to your frame. Here is one of your favorite romances. I will read, and you shall listen;—and so we will pass away this terrible night together."

The antique volume which I had taken up was the *Mad Trist* of Sir Launcelot Canning; but I had called it a favorite of Usher's more in sad jest than in earnest; for, in truth, there is little in its uncouth and unimaginative prolixity which could have had interest for the lofty and spiritual ideality of my friend. It was, however, the only book immediately at hand; and I indulged a vague hope that the excitement which now agitated the hypochondriac might find relief (for the history of mental disorder is full of similar anomalies) even in the extremeness of the folly which I should read. Could I have judged, indeed, by the wild overstrained air of vivacity with which he hearkened, or apparently hearkened, to the words of the tale, I might well have congratulated myself upon the success of my design.

I had arrived at that well-known portion of the story where Ethelred, the hero of the *Trist,* having sought in vain for peaceable admission into the dwelling of the hermit, proceeds to make good an entrance by force. Here, it will be remembered, the words of the narrative run thus:

> And Ethelred, who was by nature of a doughty heart, and who was now mighty withal, on account of the powerfulness of the wine which he had drunken, waited no longer to hold parley with the hermit, who, in sooth, was of an obstinate and maliceful turn, but, feeling the rain upon his shoulders, and fearing the rising of the tempest, uplifted his mace outright, and with blows, made

> quickly room in the plankings of the door for his gauntleted hand; and now pulling therewith sturdily, he so cracked and ripped, and tore all asunder, that the noise of the dry and hollow-sounding wood alarumed and reverberated throughout the forest.

At the termination of this sentence I started, and for a moment, paused; for it appeared to me (although I at once concluded that my excited fancy had deceived me)—it appeared to me that, from some very remote portion of the mansion, there came, indistinctly, to my ears, what might have been, in its exact similarity of character, the echo (but a stifled and dull one certainly) of the very cracking and ripping sound which Sir Launcelot had so particularly described. It was, beyond doubt, the coincidence alone which had arrested my attention; for, amid the rattling of the sashes of the casements, and the ordinary commingled noises of the still increasing storm, the sound, in itself, had nothing, surely, which should have interested or disturbed me. I continued the story:

> But the good champion Ethelred, now entering with the door, was sore enraged and amazed to perceive no signal of the maliceful hermit; but, in the stead thereof, a dragon of a scaly and prodigious demeanor, and of a fiery tongue, which sate in guard before a palace of gold, with a floor of silver; and upon the wall there hung a shield of shining brass with this legend enwritten—
>
> *Who entereth herein, a conqueror hath bin;*
> *Who slayeth the dragon, the shield he shall win;*
>
> And Ethelred uplifted his mace, and struck upon the head of the dragon, which fell before him, and gave up his pesty breath, with a shriek so horrid and harsh, and withal so piercing, that Ethelred had fain to close his ears with his hands against the dreadful noise of it, the like whereof was never before heard.

Here again I paused abruptly, and now with a feeling of wild amazement—for there could be no doubt whatever that, in this instance, I did actually hear (although from what direction it proceeded I found it impossible to say) a low and apparently distant, but harsh, protracted, and most unusual screaming or grating sound—the exact counterpart of what my fancy had already conjured up for the dragon's unnatural shriek as described by the romancer.

Oppressed, as I certainly was, upon the occurrence of the second and most extraordinary coincidence, by a thousand conflicting sensations, in which wonder and extreme terror were predominant, I still retained sufficient presence of mind to avoid exciting, by any observation, the sensitive nervousness of my companion. I was by no means certain that he had noticed the sounds in question; although, assuredly, a strange alteration had, during the last few minutes, taken place in his demeanor. From a position fronting my own, he had gradually brought round his chair, so as to sit with his face to the door of the chamber; and thus I could but partially perceive his features, although I saw that his lips trembled as if he were murmuring inaudibly. His head had dropped upon his breast—yet I knew that he was not asleep, from the wide and rigid opening of the eye as I caught a glance of it in profile. The motion of his body, too, was at variance with this idea—for he rocked from side to side with a gentle yet constant and uniform sway. Having rapidly taken notice of all this, I resumed the narrative of Sir Launcelot, which thus proceeded:

> And now, the champion, having escaped from the terrible fury of the dragon, bethinking himself of the brazen shield, and of the breaking up of the enchantment which was upon it, removed the carcass from out of the way before him, and approached valorously over the silver pavement of the castle to where the shield was upon the wall; which in sooth tarried not for his full coming, but fell down at his feet upon the silver floor, with a mighty great and terrible ringing sound.

No sooner had these syllables passed my lips, than—as if a shield of brass had indeed, at the moment, fallen heavily upon a floor of silver—I became aware of a distinct, hollow, metallic and clangorous yet apparently muffled reverberation. Completely unnerved, I leaped to my feet; but the measured rocking movement of Usher was undisturbed. I rushed to the chair in which he sat. His eyes were bent fixedly before him, and throughout his whole countenance there reigned a stony rigidity. But as I placed my hand upon his shoulder, there came a strong shudder over his whole person; a sickly smile quivered about his lips; and I saw that he spoke in a low, hurried, and gibbering murmur, as if unconscious of my presence. Bending closely over him, I at length drank in the hideous import of his words.

"Not hear it?—yes, I hear it, and *have* heard it. Long—long—long—many minutes, many hours, many days, have I heard it—yet I dared not—oh, pity me, miserable wretch that I am!—I dared not—I *dared* not speak! *We have put her living in the tomb!* Said I not that my senses were acute? I *now* tell you that I heard her first feeble movements in the hollow coffin. I heard them—many, many days ago—yet I dared not—*I dared not speak!* And now—to-night—Ethelred—ha! ha!—the breaking of the hermit's door, and the death-cry of the dragon, and the clangor of the shield!—say, rather, the rending of her coffin, and the grating of the iron hinges of her prison, and her struggles within the coppered archway of the vault! Oh whither shall I fly? Will she not be here anon? Is she not hurrying to upbraid me for my haste? Have I not heard her footstep on the stair? Do I not distinguish that heavy and horrible beating of her heart? MADMAN!" here he sprang furiously to his feet, and shrieked out his syllables, as if in the effort he were giving up his soul—*"Madman! I tell you that she now stands without the door!"*

As if in the superhuman energy of his utterance there had been found the potency of a spell, the huge antique panels to which the speaker pointed, threw slowly back, upon the instant, their ponderous and ebony jaws. It was the work of the rushing gust—but then without those doors there DID stand the lofty and enshrouded figure of the lady Madeline of Usher. There was blood upon her white robes, and the evidence of some bitter struggle upon every portion of her emaciated frame. For a moment she remained trembling and reeling to and fro upon the threshold—then, with a low moaning cry, fell heavily inward upon the person of her brother, and in her violent and now final death-agonies, bore him to the floor a corpse, and a victim to the terrors he had anticipated.

From that chamber, and from that mansion, I fled aghast. The storm was still abroad in all its wrath as I found myself crossing the old causeway. Suddenly there shot along the path a wild light, and I turned to see whence a gleam so unusual could have issued; for the vast house and its shadows were alone behind me. The radiance was that of the full, setting, and blood-red moon which now shone vividly through that once barely-discernible fissure of which I have before spoken as extending from the roof of the building, in a zigzag direction, to the base. While I gazed, this fissure rapidly widened—there came a fierce breath of the whirlwind—the entire orb of the satellite burst at once upon my sight—my brain reeled as I saw the mighty walls rushing asunder—there was a long tumultuous shouting sound like the voice of a thousand waters—and the deep and dank tarn at my feet closed sullenly and silently over the fragments of the House of Usher.

Investigation and Comment

Atmosphere in "The Fall of the House of Usher" is particularly significant, not only in establishing a mood of melancholy decay, suffocating oppression, and weird perversion, but also in contributing to the illusion of reality, wherein the reader momentarily suspends disbelief to such a degree that he accepts fantastic coincidences and preposterous events as possible actualities. In Poe's story atmosphere has a prime relationship to theme, for couched in the images, in the tone of the language, in the seemingly casual references to trivial circumstance, and in the highly rarified intellectual milieu of the characters, we find the ultimate meaning of the story. Atmosphere, far more than plot, delivers the effect, and so pervading is its role that many readers have assumed that mere mood is the final, total effect—a false contention that does injustice to the story. The diffusion of horror, the mood of intense melancholy, and the emotion of revulsion are only part of the effect, are only an aspect of a great unity in which idea itself assumes a larger, more proportionate share of the total design. It is the powerful atmosphere plus idea that create the final effect, but it is primarily atmosphere that delivers the theme of isolation, solipsism, and tragic narcissism in "The Fall of the House of Usher."

"If his very initial sentence tend not to the outbringing of this effect, then he has failed in his first step." We find that Poe has practiced his dictum with fidelity in the first sentence of the story: "During the whole of a dull, dark, and soundless day in the autumn of the year, when the clouds hung oppressively low in the heavens, I had been passing alone on horseback, through a singularly dreary tract of country; and at length found myself, as the shades of the evening drew on, within view of the melancholy House of Usher." This sentence relies heavily on those rhetorical devices we associate with poetry. Here we find alliteration, consonance, and assonance coupled with strong images to produce a sensation of heavy monotony, isolation, loneliness, oppressive silence—indeed the very sensation that is melancholy. The heavy alliteration of the *d*'s in *during, dull, dark, day, dreary,* and *drew* establishes a strong, stressed rhythm. The combinations of *u, o, m,* and *n* sounds draw out the lines and foster a monotonous repetition for the ear. The "moaning" syllables are perfectly suited to the atmosphere surrounding the House of Usher. So dreary is the insufferable gloom that it begins to affect the narrator who, we soon learn, is an intelligent, reasonable visitor in search of rational explanations of unusual phenomena. Because the reality of this gloom affects a person as sane and rational as the narrator himself, the reader is also disposed to accept it. Therefore, *tone,* which is the expression of the narrator's attitude toward his material and toward the audience, serves to heighten the reality and the meaning of the atmosphere.

The narrator next introduces another detail which Poe has couched in a metaphor of significant power: the "vacant eye-like windows" of the house. This image is repeated at the end of the paragraph, and further references to windows and vacant eyes are interspersed in a recurring pattern of imagery throughout the story. The windows of Roderick Usher's study admit no view of the world outside the house; hence they too are vacant; Roderick's eyes are at first strangely lustrous but become blank, empty, vacant; they stare fixedly, wide and rigid, like one in a trance, an opium dream, or one completely fixed upon an inner vision. What Roderick's eyes "see" is significant: he "sees" nothing but abstractions, horrors, terrors; he can "see" the lady Madeline through closed doors and in remote parts of the house; he "sees" vast, empty vaults which, illumined by their own self-generated light, admit no access to, or from, the world beyond. Roderick, then, like the house, is isolated from the world of reality. Both are enclosed in an atmosphere which is self-generated and self-isolating. Man and mansion are symbolically equated; both have turned their eyes inward upon themselves.

In the Usher family this introspection has prevailed for generations. Now Roderick Usher is caught in the trap of merely reflecting himself to himself, over and over in an endless process. Man creates his image (his house), and in turn he is influenced and re-created by the very image itself. The house, inverted and distorted, but otherwise an exact duplicate reflected in the black and lurid tarn, is a parallel to Roderick and his twin Madeline, each of whom is a mirror of the other. This inbred, incestuous entombment is the Usher family's illness—the madness that finally brings destruction. This is the evil atmosphere, which is represented literally by the miasmic fog and the smothering fungi. Madeline and Roderick are spiritually entombed within themselves, within the "house" they have created.

The tensions of the story are drawn to a climax when Roderick makes a last desperate effort to break through the walls of self, or ego, and to establish contact with something that is not himself. In other words, he tries to break out of his opium-dream world of pure idealism and pure abstraction. This is his attempt, feeble though it may be, to escape the horror his self-love has created. It is to this end that he calls for the assistance of his boyhood friend, the narrator, who, as a man of the real world, finds himself entering the House of Usher and the Ushers' world of almost complete solipsism.

Notice at this point a few of the details that clarify Roderick's sickness and the atmosphere in which it has developed. Roderick is excessively and habitually reserved. His charities, though munificent, are lacking in human contact, and hence are abstract. He is devoted to the *idea* of music, the intricacies rather than the sensory pleasure, and thus he indulges in the most abstract aspect of the most abstract of all arts. He paints canvases with abstract visions of his own mind which have no connection with a real, concrete world. Suffering from a morbid and egocentric sensitivity, he cannot tolerate anything that is not himself. Thus Roderick Usher has so concentrated on his own perceptions and developed his own sense of self that anything which is non-self is violently distasteful and unbearable. He can tolerate no taste but his own saliva, no smell but his own odor, no sound but his own voice, no light that lets the world intrude, no touch but the touch of his own skin. Further, he lives in constant dread that some fragment of otherness will penetrate his isolation. "I dread the events of the future, not in themselves, but in their results. I shudder at the thought of any, even the most trivial, incident, which may operate upon this intolerable agitation of soul." Even his fears are abstractions.

The Usher malady manifests itself in two ways: first, hypersensitivity and consequent revulsion to all that is otherness; and second, catalepsy, wherein one's inward retreat is so absolute that no stimulation from the outside world can be received. Catalepsy is, of course, manifest in Madeline, the image of Roderick and the self he entombs, wanting burial yet knowing the very thing he wants will destroy what he most loves—himself.

This mood of horror, melancholy, and intolerable madness—the atmosphere of the story—serves to intensify and clarify the dark theme of self-destroying solipsism. And in spite of all the "old-fashioned" trappings that we asociate with Gothic romances, ghost stories, and tales of the macabre, Poe's story treats the universal theme of man's isolation in a manner that is eminently successful. (You will note this same theme recurs in some of the other stories in this text and is given various treatments by such modern writers as William Faulkner in "A Rose for Emily," D. H. Lawrence in "The Rocking-Horse Winner," and Peter Taylor in "What You Hear From 'Em?")

For a better insight into atmosphere and setting as they contribute to the unity of effect in "The Fall of the House of Usher," the student should attempt to answer the following questions:

1. What is the function of the frequent allusions to the opium addict and drunkard?
2. What is the narrator's attitude toward Roderick's preposterous theory about the mysterious control that the house exerts on his spirit? Is this theory, in terms of the implied symbolism and in relation to the theme, really preposterous? If so, why?
3. Roderick enjoys improvising lyrics and accompanying himself on the guitar with a monotonous strumming—much in the manner of a modern jazz or blues singer. What might this suggest about Roderick and his modern counterpart? Why does Roderick enjoy such a lyric art and what is its significance?
4. What is the significance of the long list of books in the library? Is there a characteristic quality about this collection?
5. What is the function of the whirlwind? Is its function symbolic, atmospheric, or merely mechanistic to help make believable the sudden collapse of the house? Does the whirlwind function in all these capacities? What, in this same connection, is the function of the "barely perceptible fissure" in the wall of the Usher mansion?
6. Literally Roderick and Madeline cause each other's death—he by prematurely entombing his sister and not attempting to correct his deed, and she by frightening her brother to death. What is the larger significance of these acts and why does Poe give us the melodramatic picture of the twins dying in each other's arms?
7. The story has perhaps one very serious flaw. The atmosphere and the theme are not sufficiently unified with plot; that is, the plot is developed through some rather incredible coincidences. Discuss these coincidences and any other weaknesses you may find in the story.

ELIZABETH MADOX ROBERTS

(1886–1941)

The Haunted Palace

The House stood at the head of a valley where the hollow melted away into the rolling uplands. The high trees about the place so confined the songs of the birds that on a spring morning the jargoning seemed to emerge from the walls. The birds seemed to be indoors or within the very bricks of the masonry. In winter the winds blew up the hollow from the valley and lashed at the old house that stood square before the storms. The place was called Wickwood. It had been the abode of a family, Wickley, a group that had once clustered about the hearths there or had tramped over the courtyard or ridden through the pastures.

From a road that ran along the top of a ridge two miles to the east, the House could be seen as a succession of rhomboids and squares that flowed together beneath the vague misty reds of the mass. Or from the valley road to the west, looking up the hollow into the melting hills, in winter one could see it as a distant brick wall set with long windows, beneath a gray sloping roof. Sometimes a traveler, allured by the name of the place or by the aloof splendor of the walls as seen vaguely from one or the other of these highways, would cross the farmlands by the way of the uneven roads. He would trundle over the crooked ways and mount through the broken woodland to come at last to the House. Leaving his conveyance, he would cross the wide courtyard on the smooth flagstones, and he would hear the strange report his footfalls made as they disturbed the air that had, but for the birds and the wind, been quiet for so great a length of time that it had assumed stillness. He would wonder at the beauty of the doorways and deplore the waste that let the House stand unused and untended. He would venture up the stone steps at the west front and peer through the glass of the side lights. The strange quality of the familiar fall of his own shoe on stone would trouble his sense of all that he had discovered, so that he would at last come swiftly away.

The country rolled in changing curves and lines and spread toward the river valleys, where it dropped suddenly into a basin. The farms were owned by men and women who had labored to win them. But among these were younger men who worked for hire or as share-owners in the yield.

One of these last, Hubert, lived with Jess, his wife, in a small whitewashed shelter behind a cornfield. Jess spoke more frequently than the man and thus she had more memory. She had been here two years, but before that time she had lived beside a creek, and before that again in another place, while farther back the vista was run together in a fog of forgetting. She had courted Hubert in a cabin close beside a roadway. She remembered another place where there was a plum tree that bore large pink-red fruits, and a place where her father had cut his foot with an ax. Now, as a marker, her own children ran a little way into a cornfield to play. Beyond these peaks in memory, going backward, the life there rested in a formless level out of which only self emerged. She met any demand upon this void with a contempt in which self was sheltered.

Hubert was a share-laborer, but he wanted to be able to rent some land. He wanted to use land as if he were the owner, and yet to be free to go to fresh acres when he had exhausted a tract as he willed. After the first child, Albert, was born, he said to Jess:

"If a person could have ahead, say, four hundred dollars and against the Dean land might come idle. . . ."

His fervor had the power of a threat. He was knotty and bony and his muscles were dry and lean. He had learned at school to write his name and to make a few slow marks that signified numbers or quantities, but later he had used this knowledge so infrequently that most of it was lost to him. He wrote his name painfully and, writing, he drew his fingers together about the pen. His breath would flow hard and fast under the strain, his hand trembling. If there were other men standing about he would, if he were asked to write his name, sometimes say that he could not, preferring to claim complete illiteracy rather than to undergo the ordeal.

"Against the Dean land might come idle. . . ." He had a plan over which he brooded, wanting to get a power over some good land that he might drain money out of it. He was careful, moving forward through the soil, taking from it.

When the second child came they lived at the Dean land, behind the cornfield. Jess would fling a great handful of grain toward her hens and they would come with reaching bills and outthrust necks, their wings spread. She would throw ears of corn to the sow and it would chew away the grains while the sucklings would drag milk, the essence of the corn, from the dark udders.

"We ought, it seems, to build the sow a little shed against winter comes," Jess said to Hubert.

"We might eat the sow. I might fatten up the sow and get me another."

"She always was a no-account sow. Has only five or six to a litter. It's hardly worth while to pester yourself with a lazy hog."

"Fannie Burt asked me what was the name of the sow or to name what kind or breed she was. 'Name?' I says. As if folks would name the food they eat!"

Hubert laughed at the thought of naming the food. Names for the swine, either mother or species, gave him laughter. To write with one's hand the name of a sow in a book seemed useless labor. Instead of giving her a name he fastened her into a closed pen and gave her all the food he could find. When she was sufficiently fat he stuck her throat with a knife and prepared her body for his own eating.

Jess yielded to the decision Hubert made, being glad to have decisions made for her, and thus she accepted the flesh of the brood sow. Of this she ate heavily. She was large and often of a placid temper, sitting in unbrooding inattention, but often she flamed to sudden anger and thrust about her then with her hands or her fists. She did not sing about the house or the dooryard. Singing came to her from a wooden box that was charged by a small battery. She adjusted the needle of this to a near sending station and let the sound pour over the cabin. Out of the abundant jargon that flowed from the box she did not learn, and before it she did not remember. . . .

Jess had a few friends who came sometimes to see her. They were much like herself in what they knew and in what they liked. She would look curiously at their new clothing.

But one of them, named Fannie Burt, would come shouting to the children as she drove up the lane in a small cart, and her coming filled the day with remembered sayings and finer arrangements. When Fannie came Jess would call Albert, the oldest child, and send him on his hands and knees under the house to rob the hen's nest if there were not enough eggs in the basket, for the day called for a richer pudding. Fannie had no children as yet and she could be light and outflowing. She went here and there and she knew many of the people.

"Miss Anne mended the cover to the big black sofa in the parlor. . . ." She would tell of many things—of tapestry on a wall, blue and gold. Words seemed light when she talked, as being easily made to tell of strange and light matters. Jess was not sure that Fannie knew more of these things than she knew herself, since the words conveyed but an undefined sense. The lightness of bubbles floated about Fannie, things for which Jess had no meanings. Fannie had lived the year before at a farm where the owner had been as a neighbor to her. She often went back to call there, staying all day as a friend.

"Miss Anne mended the cover to the sofa where it was worn." Jess laughed with Fannie, and she scarcely knew whether she laughed at the sofa or at the mended place. She herself could not sew, and thus she could not mend any broken fabric of any kind. She laughed, however, Fannie's call being just begun. She was not yet hostile to it. She tried for the moment to stretch her imaginings to see something desired or some such thing as grace or beauty in the person who leaned over the ancient tapestry to mend it. The effort was spent in wonder and finally in anger. Fannie laughed at the sullenness that came to Jess. The sofa had come from Wickwood, she said. It had been given to Miss Anne at her marriage, for she was somehow related to the Wickleys. Laughing, Fannie tossed the least child and settled to tell again. Her tales would be, all together, a myth of houses and families, of people marrying and settling into new abodes. She was gay and sharp, and her face was often pointed with smiles. Or she would be talking now with the children and telling them the one story she had from a book.

"Then a great ogre lived in the place . . . a Thing that threatens to get you . . . a great Thing . . . destroys . . . eats up Life itself. Drinks the blood out of Life. It came with a club in its hand. . . . It was a fine place, but had a Thing inside it. . . . That would be when little Blue Wing went to the woods to play. She found this place in the woods. . . ."

"What was that?" Jess asked suddenly. "What kind was that you named?"

"A giant. Ogry or ogre. A Thing. Comes to eat up a man and to eat Life itself. . . ."

Fannie would be gone and Jess would be glad to have an end of her. As if too much had been asked of her she would sit now in vague delight, and she would forget to run her radio instrument while she saw Fannie's bright pointed face as something slipping past her. The stories that had been told had become a blend of indistinct mental colorings that would drop out of memory at length, as a spent pleasure no longer wanted. She would reject the visit completely and turn to anger, thrusting Fannie out. Then, complete hostility to the visitor having come to her, she would set roughly upon her tasks. If the children spoke of the stories that had been told she would order them to be quiet.

Some of the farms had lost their former owners. A house here and there was shut and still while the acres were farmed by the shifting men who lived in the cabins or in the town. A man came searching for Hubert at the end of the harvest to offer him a part of the Wickley place to farm.

"It's said fine people once lived there," Hubert said when he told Jess of his offer.

"If they're gone now I wouldn't care."

"It's not like any place ever you saw in life. It's good land, howsoever."

Other tenants would be scattered over the acres, laborers who would farm by sharing the crops. Hubert would rent the acres about the house and he would live there.

"Is there a good well of water?"

"Two wells there are," he answered her.

"I never heard of two wells."

"One has got a little fancy house up over it."

"What would I do with a little fancy house built up over a well? I can't use such a house." As if more might be required of her than she could perform, Jess was uneasy in thinking of the new place to which they would go. She did not want to go there. "It's a place made for some other," she said. She could not see the women of the place going about their labors. She could not discover what they might carry in their hands and what their voices might call from the doorways, or how they would sleep or dress themselves or find themselves food. In her troubled thought, while she came and went about the cabin room where the least child lay, shapes without outline, the women of the Wickleys, went into vague distances where doors that were not defined were opened and closed into an uncomprehended space.

But the next day Fannie Burt came and there was something further to know. The Wickley farm was called Wickwood, she said. Miss Anne's father had gone there in old Wickley's lifetime. Together these two men had made experiments in the growing of fine animals. Sometimes it would be a horse old Wickley wanted. "Egad!" he would say, or "I'm not dead yet!" Another story running into a comic ending, "A good colt she is, but a leetle matter of interference. Look at her hind feet." Fannie had something that Miss Anne had in mind. It was told imperfectly, thrown out in a hint and retained in a gesture, put back upon Miss Anne, who could tell with fluent words and meaning gestures. She would be sitting over the last of the dessert in the old, faded dining room. She would be telling for the pure joy of talking, laughing with the past. "Pappy went over to Wickwood. . . . It was Tuesday. . . . Came Sunday then and we all said, 'Where's Pappy?' Came to find out and he's still over to Wickwood with Cousin Bob. All that time to get the brown mare rightly in foal. And all still on paper."

Fannie would seem to be talking fast, and one thing would seem to be entangled with another, although she spoke with Miss Anne's quiet, slow cadence. In her telling men would be sitting together in a library. One would be making a drawing of a horse, such a horse as he would be devising. A horse would be sketched on paper before it was so much as foaled. This would be old Robert Wickley, a pen between his thumb and his fingers. "What we want after all is a good Kentucky saddle horse, fifteen hands high and two inches over. Take Danbury II, say, over at Newmarket. . . ."

"You take Danbury and you'll plumb get a jackass."

"Pappy laughed over a thing once for a week before he told us," Miss Anne's speaking through Fannie's speaking. "Pappy in a big tellen way one day and he let it be known what he was so amused about."

A man had come in at the door at Wickwood, a hurried man with money in cash saved by. He wanted the Wickley land on which to grow something. He wanted to buy, offering cash.

"Do you think you could live in my house and on my land?" old Wickley asked.

Fannie would be telling as Miss Anne had told and, beyond again, the father who had told in a moment of amusement. Men who came on business were let in at a side door. "Business was a Nobody then," Miss Anne said. Mollie would be off somewhere in the house singing. Carline had run off to get married. Old Wickley, father to Robert, rolling back his shirt-sleeves because the day was hot, and walking barefoot out into the cool grass, or he would be standing under the shower in the bath house while somebody pumped the water that sprayed over him. Miss Sallie made the garden with her own hands and designed the sundial. They made things for themselves with their hands. Bob Wickley sketching for himself the horse he wanted on a large sheet of manila paper. His grandmother had, as a bride, set the house twelve feet back of the builder's specifications in order to save a fine oak tree that still grew before the front door. A man wanting to plow his pastures. . . .

"Two hundred dollars an acre for the creek bottom, cash money."

Wickley had called him a hog and sent him away.

"Pappy laughed over it for a week. ' "You think you could live in my house? Come back three generations from now." . . . And, egad, he couldn't,' Pappy said."

"Hogs want to root in my pasture," Bob Wickley said. He was angry.

. . . Miss Anne speaking through Fannie's speaking, reports fluttering about, intermingled, right and wrong, the present and the past. Fannie could scarcely divide one Wickley from another. One had gathered the books. One had held a high public office. One had married a woman who pinned back her hair with a gold comb. Their children had read plentifully from the books. Justus, William, and Robert had been names among them. Miss Anne now owned the portrait of the lady of the golden comb. There had been farewells and greetings, dimly remembered gifts, trinkets, portraits to be made, children to be born. . . .

In this telling as it came from the telling of Miss Anne, there was one, a Robert, who danced along the great parlor floor with one named Mollie. Mollie was the wife of Andrew. She had come from a neighboring farm. When they danced the music from the piano had crashed and tinkled under the hands of Miss Lizette, Robert's mother, or of Tony Barr, a young man who came to visit at Wickwood. Down would fling the chords on the beat and at the same instant up would fling the dancers, stepping upward on the rhythm and treading the air. Mollie's long slim legs would flash from beneath her flying skirts, or one would lie for an instant outstretched while the pulse of the music beat, then off along the shining floor, gliding and swaying with the gliding of Robert, until it seemed as if the two of them were one, and as if they might float out the window together, locked into the rhythms, and thus dance away across the world.

"Where are they now?" Jess asked.

Fannie did not know. Miss Anne had not told her.

"Where would be Andrew, the one that was her husband?" She was angry and she wanted to settle blame somewhere.

He would be beside the wall. He would look at Mollie with delight. His head would move, or his hands, with the rhythm, and his eyes would be bright. Mollie loved him truly.

Sometimes it would be the old fast waltzes that were danced, and then Miss Lizette and old Bob would come into it. Then they would whirl swiftly about the floor and the music would be "Over the Waves." The young would try it, dizzy and laughing, or they would change the steps to their own.

"What did they do?" Jess asked. "I feel staggered to try to know about such a house."

"They had a wide scope of land," Fannie answered her. "They burned the bricks and made the house. They cut the timber for the beams of the house off their own fields."

The House had become an entity, as including the persons and the legends of it. All the Wickleys were blurred into one, were gathered into one report.

"There was a woman, Mollie Wickley. She was the mother of Andrew, or maybe she was his wife," Fannie said. "I don't recall. It's all one. There was a Sallie Wickley. I don't know whe'r she was his daughter or his wife."

"Iffen he couldn't keep it for his children," Jess called out, "why would he build such a place?"

"He lived in the house *himself*."

Jess and Hubert would be going to the place where these had been. All these were gone now. The land was still good. Hubert would be able to take money out of it. He would hold the plow into the soil and his tongue would hang from the side of his mouth in his fervor to plant more and to have a large yield. The people would be gone. Jess dismissed them with the clicking of her tongue. They seemed, nevertheless, to be coming nearer. In Fannie's presence, while she sat in the chair beside the door, they came nearer, to flit as shapes about her fluttering tongue while Jess fixed her gaze upon the mouth that was speaking or shifted to look at the familiar cups and plates on the table. Shapes fluttered then over the cups. Vague forms, having not the shapes of defined bodies, but the ends of meanings, appeared and went. Fannie knew little beyond the myths she had made, and Jess knew much less, knew nothing beyond the bright tinkle of Fannie's chatter.

"It was the horse then," Fannie said, in part explaining. "Now nobody wants enough horses. . . . Now it's tobacco."

Hubert and Jess came to the place, Wickwood, at sundown of an early winter afternoon. Hubert talked of the land, of the fields, growing talkative as their small truck rolled slowly through the ruts of the old driveway. When they had passed through the woodland, which was now in part denuded of its former growth, they came near to the house. It seemed to Jess that there was a strange wideness about the place, as if space were spent outward without bounds. They went under some tall oaks and maples while Hubert muttered of his plans.

A great wall arose in the dusk. The trees stretched their boughs toward the high wall in the twilight. When it seemed that the truck would drive into the hard darkness of the wall that stood before them as if it went into the sky, Hubert turned toward the left and rounded among the trees. Other walls stood before them. Jess had never before seen a place like this. It seemed to her that it might be a town, but there were no people there. The children began to cry and Albert screamed, "I want to go away!" Jess herself was frightened.

"Hush your fuss," Hubert said. His words were rough. "Get out of the truck," he said to her. She attended to his short angry speech; it jerked her out of her fear and dispersed a part of her dread of the place. It made her know that they, themselves and their goods, their life and their ways of being, would somehow fit into the brick walls, would make over some part of the strangeness for their own use. He had climbed from the vehicle and he walked a little way among the buildings, stalking in the broad courtyard among the flagstones and over the grass. He looked about him. Then he went toward a wing of the largest house and entered a small porch that stood out from one of the walls.

"We'll live here," he said.

She did not know how he had discovered which part of the circle of buildings, of large houses and small rooms, would shelter them. He began to carry their household goods from the truck. Jess found her lantern among her things and she made a light. When the lantern was set on a shelf she could look about the room where they would live.

There were windows opposite the door through which they had entered. Outside, the rain dripped slowly through the great gnarled trees. The rain did not trouble her. A press built into the wall beside the chimney seemed ample to hold many things. Hubert set the cooking stove before the fireplace and fixed the stovepipe into the small opening above the mantel. The children cried at the strangeness, but when the lamp was lighted and food had been cooked they cried no more. When Jess set the food on the table they had begun to live in the new place.

Hubert went away across the courtyard and his step was hollow, amplified among the walls of the building. He came back later, the sound he made enlarged as he walked nearer over the flagstones.

"It's no such place as ever I saw before!" Jess cried out.

She had begun a longer speech but she was hushed by Hubert's hostile look. They would stay here, he said. It was the Wickley place. She closed the door to shut in the space she had claimed for their living, being afraid of the great empty walls that arose outside. The beds were hastily set up and the children fell asleep clutching the familiar pillows and quilts. Her life with Hubert, together with her children and her things for housekeeping, these she gathered mentally about her to protect herself from being obliged to know and to use the large house outside her walls. She began to comfort herself with thoughts of Hubert and to court him with a fine dish of food she had carefully saved.

The morning was clear after the rain. Hubert had gone to bring the fowls from their former abode. Albert had found a sunny nook in which to play and with the second child he was busy there.

"What manner of place is this?" Jess asked herself again and again. Outside the windows toward the south were the great gnarled trees. Outside to the north was the courtyard round which were arranged the buildings, all of them built of red, weathered brick. Toward the west, joined to the small wing in which Hubert had set up their home, arose the great house. There were four rows of windows here, one row above the other.

The buildings about the court were empty. A large bell hung in the middle of the court on the top of a high pole. There was a deep well at the back of the court where the water was drawn by a bucket lifted by a winch. Jess had a great delight in the well, for it seemed to hold water sufficient to last through any drought. Not far from the well stood a large corncrib, holding only a little corn now, but ready for Hubert's filling. She went cautiously about in the strange air.

She had no names for all the buildings that lay about her. She was frightened of the things for which she had no use, as if she might be called upon to know and to use beyond her understanding. She walked toward the west beneath the great wall of the tallest house.

There were birds in the high trees and echoes among the high walls. The singing winter wren was somewhere about, and the cry of the bird was spread widely and repeated in a shadowy call again and again. Jess rounded the wall and looked cautiously at the west side. There were closed shutters at some of the windows, but some of the shutters were opened. In the middle of the great western wall there were steps of stone. They were cut evenly and laid smoothly, one above another, reaching toward a great doorway about which was spread bright glass in straight patterns at the sides, in a high fan-shape above.

Jess went cautiously up the steps, watching for Hubert to come with the fowls, delaying, looking out over the woodland and the fields. Hubert had said again and again that this would be the Wickley place, Wickwood, that they would live there, tilling the soil, renting the land. Jess saw before her, on the great left-hand door, a knocker. She lifted it and tapped heavily, listening to the sound she made, waiting.

There was no sound to answer her rap but a light echo that seemed to come from the trees. Her own hate of the place forbade her and she dared not tap again. Standing half fearfully, she waited, laying her hands on the smooth door frame, on the fluted pillars and the leading of the glass. A cord hung near her hand and, obeying the suggestion it offered, she closed her fingers about it and pulled it stiffly down. A sound cut the still air where no sound had been for so long a time that every vibration had been stilled. The tone broke the air. The first tone came in unearthly purity, but later the notes joined and overflowed one another.

She waited, not daring to touch the cord again. The stillness that followed after the peal of the bell seemed to float out from the house itself and to hush the birds. She could not think what kind of place this might be or see any use that one might make of the great doorway, of the cord, of the bell. A strange thing stood before her. Strangeness gathered to her own being until it seemed strange that she should be here, on the top of a stair of stone before a great door, waiting for Hubert to come with her hens. It was as if he might never come. As if hens might be gone from the earth.

She saw then that the doors were not locked together, that one throbbed lightly on the other when she touched it with her hand. She pushed the knob and the door spread open wide.

Inside, a great hall reached to a height that was three or four times her own stature. Tall white doors were opened into other great rooms and far back before her a stairway began. She could not comprehend the stair. It lifted, depending from the rail that spread upward like a great ribbon in the air. Her eyes followed it, her breath coming quick and hard. It rose as a light ribbon spreading toward a great window through which came the morning sun. But leaving the window in the air, it arose again and wound back, forward and up, lost from view for a space, to appear again, higher up, at a mythical distance before another great window where the sun spread a broad yellow glow. It went at last into nothingness, and the ceiling and the walls melted together in shadows.

When she had thus, in mind, ascended, her eyes closed and a faint sickness went over her, delight mingled with fear and hate. She was afraid of being called upon to know this strange ribbon of ascent that began as a stair with rail and tread and went up into unbelievable heights, step after step. She opened her eyes to look again, ready to reject the wonder as being past all belief and, therefore, having no reality.

"What place is this?" she asked, speaking in anger. Her voice rang through the empty hall, angry words, her own, crying, "What place is this?"

At one side of the floor there were grains of wheat in streaks, as if someone might have stored sacks of wheat there. Jess thought of her hens, seeing the scattered grain, and she knew that they would pick up the remaining part of it. They would hop from stone to stone, coming cautiously up the steps, and they would stretch their long necks cautiously in at the doorway, seeing the corn. They would not see the great stairway.

A light dust lay on the window ledges. A few old cobwebs hung in fragments from the ceiling. The dust, the webs, and the wheat were a link between things known and unknown, and, seeing them, she walked a little way from the hall, listening, going farther, looking into the rooms, right and left. She was angry and afraid. What she could not bring to her use she wanted to destroy. In the room to her right a large fireplace stood far at the end of a patterned floor. There were shelves set into the white wall beside the large chimney. She left this room quickly and turned toward the room at the left. Here two large rooms melted together and tall doors opened wide. There were white shapes carved beneath the windows and oblong shapes carved again on the wood of the doors, on the pillars that held the mantel. Before her a long mirror was set into a wall. In it were reflected the boughs of the trees outside against a crisscross of the window opposite.

She was confused after she had looked into the mirror, and she looked about hastily to find the door through which she had come. It was a curious, beautiful, fearful place. She wanted to destroy it. Her feet slipped too lightly on the smooth wood of the floor. There was no piece of furniture anywhere, but the spaces seemed full, as filled with their wide dimensions and the carvings on the wood. In the hall she looked again toward the stair and she stood near the doorway looking back. Then suddenly without plan, scarcely knowing that her own lips spoke, she flung out an angry cry, half screaming, "Mollie Wickley! Mollie! Where's she at?" The harsh echoes pattered and knocked among the upper walls after her own voice was done. Turning her back on the place, she went quickly out of the doorway.

In the open air she looked back toward the steps she had ascended, seeing dimly into the vista of the hall and the upward-lifting ribbon of the stair. A sadness lay heavily upon her because she could not know what people might live in the house, what shapes of women and men might fit into the doorway. She hated her sadness and she turned it to anger. She went from the west front and entered the courtyard. Hubert came soon after with the fowls and there was work to do in housing them and getting them corn.

On a cold day in January when his ewes were about to lamb, Hurbert brought them into the alrge house, driving them up the stone steps at the west front, and he prepared to stable them in the rooms there. The sheep cried and their bleating ran up the long ribbon of the stair. They were about thirty in number, and thus the wailing was incessant. Hubert and Jess went among them with lanterns. The ewes turned and drifted about among the large rooms; but as they began to bear their lambs Hubert bedded them here and there, one beneath the stairway and three others in the room to the right where the empty bookshelves spread wide beside the tall fireplace. The night came, dark and cold.

"They are a slow set," Jess said. She wanted to be done and she was out of patience with delaying sheep.

"Whoop, here! Shut fast the door!" Hubert called.

Jess was wrapped in a heavy coat and hooded in a shawl. She went among the sheep and she held a lantern high to search out each beast. If a ewe gave birth to three lambs she took one up quickly and dropped it beside a stout young beast that was giving life to but one and she thus induced it to take the second as her own. She flung out sharp commands and she brought the animals here and there. The halls were filled with the crying of the sheep. Threats came back upon her from her own voice, so that she was displeased with what she did and her displeasure made her voice more high-pitched and angry. Anger spoke again and again through the room. She wanted the lambing to be easily done, but the days had been very cold and the sheep delayed.

"It was a good place to come to lamb the sheep," she called to Hubert. "I say, a good place." She had a delight in seeing that the necessities of lambing polluted the wide halls. "A good place to lamb. . . ."

"Whoop! Bring here the old nanny as soon as you pick up the dead lamb!" Hubert was shouting above the incessant crying of the sheep.

The ewes in labor excited her anew so that she wanted to be using her strength and to be moving swiftly forward, but she had no plan beyond

Hubert's. "Whoop, rouse up the young nanny! Don't let the bitches sleep! Whoop, there!"

He was everywhere with his commands. When the task was more than half done he called to Jess that he must go to the barn for more straw for bedding. "Whoop! Shut the door tight after me. Keep the old ewe there up on her legs." He went away, carrying his lantern.

Jess fastened the outer door and she turned back into the parlors. Then she saw a dim light at the other end of the long dark space that lay before her. She saw another shape, a shrouded figure, moving far down the long way. The apparition, the Thing, seemed to be drifting forward out of the gloom, and it seemed to be coming toward her where she stood among the sheep. Jess drove the laboring mothers here and there, arranging their places and assisting their travail with her club. She would not believe that she saw anything among the sheep at the farther end of the rooms, but as she worked she glanced now and then toward the way in which she had glimpsed it. It was there or it was gone entirely. The sheep and the lambs made a great noise with their crying. Jess went to and fro, and she forgot that she had seen anything beyond the sheep far down the room in the moving dusk of white and gray which flowed in the moving light of her lantern.

All at once, looking up suddenly as she walked forward, she saw that an apparition was certainly moving there and that it was coming toward her. It carried something in its upraised hand. There was a dark covering over the head and shoulders that were sunk into the upper darkening gloom. The whole body came forward as a dark thing illuminated by a light the creature carried low at the left side. The creature or the Thing moved among the sheep. It came forward slowly and became a threatening figure, a being holding a club and a light in its hands. Jess screamed at it, a great oath flung high above the crying of the sheep. Fright had seized her and with it came a great strength to curse with her voice and to hurl forward her body.

"God curse you!" she yelled in a scream that went low in scale and cracked in her throat. "God's curse on you!" She lunged forward and lifted her lantern high to see her way among the sheep. "God's damn on you!"

The curse gave strength to her hands and to her limbs. As she hurled forward with uplifted stick the other came forward toward her, lunging and threatening. She herself moved faster. The creature's mouth was open to cry words but no sound came from it.

She dropped the lantern and flung herself upon the approaching figure, and she beat at the creature with her club while it beat at her with identical blows. Herself and the creature then were one. Anger continued, shared, and hurled against a crash of falling glass and plaster. She and the creature had beaten at the mirror from opposite sides.

The din arose above the noise of the sheep, and for an instant the beasts were quiet while the glass continued to fall. Jess stood back from the wreckage to try to understand it. Then slowly she knew that she had broken the great mirror that hung on the rear wall of the room. She took the lamp again into her hand and peered at the breakage on the floor and at the fragments that hung, cracked and crazed, at the sides of the frame.

"God's own curse on you!" She breathed her oath heavily, backing away from the dust that floated in the air.

Hubert was entering with a load of straw on his back. He had not heard the crash of glass nor had he noticed the momentary quiet of the sheep. These were soon at their bleating again, and Jess returned from the farther room where the dust of the plaster still lay on the air. Hubert poured water into deep pans he had placed here and there through the rooms. He directed Jess to make beds of the straw in each room. Their feet slipped in the wet that ran over the polished boards of the floor.

It was near midnight. Jess felt accustomed to the place now and more at ease there, she and Hubert being in possession of it. They walked about through the monstrous defilement. Hubert was muttering the count of the sheep with delight. There were two lambs beside each of the ewes but five and there were but two lambs dead and flung to the cold fireplace where they were out of the way. There were thirty-two ewes, they said, and their fingers pointed to assist and the mouths held to the sums, repeating numbers and counting profits.

Lamb by lamb, they were counted. There were two to each mother but the three in the farther room and the two under the staircase. These had but one each. "Twice thirty-two makes sixty-four," they said to assist themselves, and from this they subtracted one for each of the deficient ewes, but they became confused in this and counted all one by one. Counting with lantern and club, Jess went again through the halls, but she made thus but forty lambs, for she lost the sums and became addled among the words Hubert muttered. At last by taking one from sixty-four and then another, four times more, in the reckoning they counted themselves thirty-two ewes and fifty-nine lambs. The sheep were becoming quiet. Each lamb had nursed milk before they left it. At length they fastened the great front door with a rope tied to a nail in the door frame, and they left the sheep stabled there, being pleased with the number they had counted.

Study Guides

About a century of short story writing separates Poe's tale of the Usher family and Elizabeth Madox Roberts' story of the tenant farmer and his wife at Wickwood. Even though Miss Roberts borrowed her title from the poem quoted by Poe in "The Fall of the House of Usher" and used a setting somewhat similar to his, the two stories have marked differences in treatment and the means employed to achieve their final effect of horror. Whereas from the very beginning of his story Poe was concerned with strong impressions and the pervading terrors attached to the unhappy Ushers, Miss Roberts approaches the subject of "evil things, in robes of sorrow" in a more indirect manner. Poe begins on a sombre note of gloom and despair and foreboding; Miss Roberts' beginning is deceptively matter-of-fact. We first see Wickwood at a distance and are told of its order and solid structure—"a succession of rhomboids and squares that flowed together beneath the vague misty reds of the mass." There is no fissure apparent, no immediately recognizable symbol; the description is in part mathematical. At first glance the House of Wickley is not perceptibly the same kind of setting that we recognize immediately in the description of the House of Usher.

After reading the story carefully, we may also observe that Miss Roberts' ominiscient narrator is more reserved—and thus more subtle—in his revelation than is Poe's first-person narrator. As readers we are not as immediately affected by the surroundings and atmosphere as we are when constantly instructed by Poe's sensitive observer. (See Glossary under *point of view* for the various techniques employed to render points of view in fiction.)

But after the first few pages, the narration of "The Haunted Palace" settles in the mind and consciousness of Jess as its vantage point or angle of vision. Although told throughout from the third person, the action centers on Jess as the climax builds up. As readers we begin to view Wickwood the *place* and Wickwood the *idea* through the physical eyes and psychological state of mind of the young wife. In fact, Miss Roberts goes to considerable pains to establish the characters of Jess and Hubert in quite damning terms. Early we are told that Hubert wanted "to be free to go to fresh acres when he had exhausted a tract as he willed." He wanted "to get a power over some good land that he might drain money out of it. He was careful, moving forward through the soil, taking from it." We are also told that his wife Jess "accepted the flesh of the brood sow. Of this she ate heavily." Slowly then we learn about Wickwood from Jess, and her vision is recognized by the reader as a part of her inadequate and grasping nature. By easy stages we are prepared, knowing Jess, for the eventual ruin and "monstrous defilement" of the proud manor house. This is the subtle foreshadowing that the author manages to impart as the story unfolds. And because Miss Roberts has portrayed Jess and Hubert in such a manner that they take on the attributes of real persons, the horror of the final scene is all the more shocking. (At the literal level they are actually more convincing as people than Poe's Roderick and Madeline.) Thus the story moves from a seemingly innocent situation in which we first observe hardworking, ambitious, somewhat naive farm people to a climactic moment in which we look with terror at their acts of ruthless destruction and usurpation. By means of fiction we are led, skillfully and credibly, to a moment of unreserved belief.

The entire movement (or plot) is quite carefully charted, but let us mention briefly how effectively it is supported by one or two obvious instances of foreshadowing. Note for example the passing reference to the fairy tale in which the ogre "comes to eat up a man and eat Life itself." Note also that Jess thinks of Wickwood as a house "made for some other" and not for her. She is both unaware of and unresponsive to the history and true significance of the place, the taste which marked it, the beauty and symmetry of its architecture, its former way of life. All of these qualities and their values are beyond the narrow vision of Jess; the nearest she can come to understanding the meaning of Wickwood is through abstractions. In her consciousness—when she reflects at all—she sees only "shapes. . . . Vague forms, having not the shapes of defined bodies, but the ends of meanings. . . . " Like the Ushers, Jess is overcome by a sea of abstractions, and like her counterparts she is victimized by them until she arrives at one brief moment of self-realization which she hastily shatters to bits.

The reader should not fail to note that *House,* significantly, is capitalized in this story. As the center of the plantation, it takes on a variety of meanings as a symbol, for it represents a way of life that is in direct contrast to the life Jess and Hubert greedily embark upon as they move from one parcel of land to another. We are told, again in capitals, that when Wickwood was at its peak "Business was a Nobody then" and that "Men who came on business were let in at a side door." For Jess and Hubert, "Business comes first" and they have no scruples about stabling the ewes in the front parlors of the mansion. "It was a good place to lamb the sheep." Thus with the lambing the allegory of destruction is finally and ironically complete.

In her own way, by her own methods, and at her own pace the author has achieved her aims in this modern short story. She has created "plain folk" whom we can believe in; she has put them in a setting that is both mundane and entirely credible but also allows for the presence of supernatural forces; and finally she has convinced us through action and symbol of the terrors to be experienced in the ordinary, everyday world in which we all live.

Consider the following questions:

1. Compare the first view of Wickwood as seen through Jess's eyes with the narrator's first view of the House of Usher. Comment on the various details provided by the two authors.

2. Describe carefully the function Fannie serves in the development of the background, mood, and atmosphere of the story.

3. Many Gothic tales and a number of children's stories have for their settings a variety of haunted houses, and they tell of the ghosts that are supposed to inhabit them. List all the differences between the typical "haunted house" story and "The Haunted Palace." Write an essay in which you account, as a mature reader, for the superiority of Miss Roberts' story as serious fiction.

4. For a brief moment, Jess catches a glimpse of an "ogre" in the mirror. With her club she breaks the glass and soon returns to the business of caring for the lambs and ewes. Explain exactly what takes place in this part of the story and relate it to the ending—or what the total

meaning of the story conveys to you about Jess and Hubert and their kind. Explain also your final reaction to them. If your feelings are somewhat mixed, try to characterize your attitude in an essay that judiciously "sizes up" and explains Jess and Hubert and reveals your understanding of them as complex human beings.

JOHN UPDIKE

(1932–)

A Sense of Shelter

Snow fell against the high school all day, wet big-flaked snow that did not accumulate well. Sharpening two pencils, William looked down on a parking lot that was a blackboard in reverse, car tires had cut smooth arcs of black into the white, and wherever a school bus had backed around, it had left an autocratic signature of two *V*'s. The snow, though at moments it whirled opaquely, could not quite bleach these scars away. The temperature must be exactly 32°. The window was open a crack, and a canted pane of glass lifted outdoor air into his face, coating the cedarwood scent of pencil shavings with the transparent odor of the wet window sill. With each revolution of the handle his knuckles came within a fraction of an inch of the tilted glass, and the faint chill this proximity breathed on them sharpened his already acute sense of shelter.

The sky behind the shreads of snow was stone-colored. The murk inside the high classroom gave the air a solidity that limited the overhead radiance to its own vessels; six globes of dull incandescence floated on the top of a thin sea. The feeling the gloom gave him was not gloomy but joyous: he felt they were all sealed in, safe; the colors of cloth were dyed deeper, the sound of whispers was made more distinct, the smells of tablet paper and wet shoes and varnish and face powder pierced him with a vivid sense of possession. These were his classmates sealed in, his, the stupid as well as the clever, the plain as well as the lovely, his enemies as well as his friends, his. He felt like a king and seemed to move to his seat between the bowed heads of subjects that loved him less than he loved them. His seat was sanctioned by tradition; for twelve years he had sat at the rear of classrooms, William Young, flanked by Marsha Wyckoff and Andy Zimmerman. Once there had been two Zimmermans, but one went to work in his father's greenhouse, and in some classes—Latin and Trig—there were none, and William sat at the edge of the class as if on the lip of a cliff, and Marsha Wyckoff became Marvin Wolf or Sandra Wade, but it was always the same desk, whose surface altered from hour to hour but from whose blue-stained ink-hole his mind could extract, like a chain of magicians' handkerchiefs, a continuity of years. As a senior he was a kind of king, and as a teacher's pet another kind, a puppet king, who gathered in appointive posts and even, when the moron vote split between two football heroes, some elective ones. He was not popular, he had never had a girl, his intense friends of childhood had drifted off into teams and gangs, and in large groups—when the whole school, for instance, went in the fall to the beautiful, dung-and-cotton-candy-smelling county fair—he was always an odd man, without a seat on the bus home. But exclusion is itself a form of inclusion. He even had a nickname: Mip, because he stuttered. Taunts no longer much frightened him; he had come late into his physical inheritance, but this summer it had arrived, and he at last stood equal with his enormous, boisterous parents, and had to unbutton his shirt cuffs to get his wrists through them, and discovered he could pick up a basketball with one hand. So, his long legs blocking two aisles, he felt regal even in size and, almost trembling with happiness under the high globes of light beyond whose lunar glow invisible snowflakes were drowning on the gravel roof of his castle, believed that the long delay of unpopularity had been merely a consolidation, that he was at last strong enough to make his move. Today he would tell Mary Landis he loved her.

He had loved her ever since, a fat-faced tomboy with freckles and green eyes, she deftly stole his rubber-lined schoolbag on the walk back from second grade along Jewett Street and outran him—simply had better legs. The superior speed a boy was supposed to have failed to come; his kidneys burned with panic. In front of the grocery store next to her home she stopped and turned. She was willing to have him catch up. This humiliation on top of the rest was too much to bear. Tears broke in his throat; he spun around and ran home and threw himself on the floor of the front parlor, where his grandfather, feet twiddling, perused the newspaper and soliloquized all morning. In time the letter slot rustled, and the doorbell rang, and Mary gave his mother the schoolbag and the two of them politely exchanged whispers. Their voices had been to him, lying there on the carpet with his head wrapped in his arms, indistinguishable. Mother had always liked Mary. From when she had been a tiny girl dancing along the hedge on the end of an older sister's arm, Mother had liked her. Out of all the children that flocked, similar as pigeons, through the neighborhood, Mother's heart had reached out with claws and fastened on Mary. He never took the schoolbag to school again, had refused to touch it. He supposed it was still in the attic, still faintly smelling of sweet pink rubber.

Fixed high on the plaster like a wren clinging to a barn wall, the buzzer sounded the two-minute signal. In the middle of the classroom Mary Landis stood up, a Monitor badge pinned to her belly. Her broad red belt was buckled with a brass bow and arrow. She wore a lavender sweater with the sleeves pushed up to expose her forearms, a delicately cheap effect. Wild stories were told about her; perhaps it was merely his knowledge of these that put the hardness in her face. Her eyes seemed braced for squinting and their green was frosted. Her freckles had faded. William thought she laughed less this year; now that she was in the Secretarial Course and he in the College Preparatory, he saw her in only one class a day, this one, English. She stood a second, eclipsed at the thighs by Jack Stephens' zebra-striped shoulders, and looked back at the class with a stiff worn glance, as if she had seen the same faces too many times before. Her habit of perfect posture emphasized the angularity she had grown into. There was a nervous edge, a boxiness in her bones, that must have been waiting all along under the childish fat. Her eye sockets were deeply indented and her chin had a prim square set that seemed in the murky air tremulous and defiant. Her skirt was cut square and straight. Below the waist she was lean; the legs that had outrun him were still athletic; she starred at hockey and cheerleading. Above, she was abundant: so stacked her spine curved backwards to keep her body balanced. She turned and in switching up the aisle encountered a boy's leg thrown into her path. She coolly looked down until it withdrew. She was used to such attentions. Her pronged chest poised, Mary proceeded out the door, and someone she saw in the hall made her smile, a wide smile full of warmth and short white teeth, and love scooped at William's heart. He would tell her.

In another minute, the second bell rasped. Shuffling through the perfumed crowds to his next class, he crooned to himself in the slow, over-enunciated manner of the Negro vocalist who had brought the song back this year:

"Lah-vender blue, dilly dilly,
Lavendih gree-heen;
Eef I were king, dilly dilly,
You would: be queen."

The song gave him an exultant sliding sensation that intertwined with the pleasures of his day. He knew all the answers, he had done all the work, the teachers called upon him only to rebuke the ignorance of the others. In Trig and Soc Sci both it was this way. In gym, the fourth hour of the morning, he, who was always picked near the last, startled his side by excelling at volleyball, leaping like a madman, shouting like a bully. The ball felt light as a feather against his big bones. His hair in wet quills from the shower, he walked in the icy air to Luke's Luncheonette, where he ate three hamburgers in a booth with three juniors. There was Barry Kruppman, a tall, thyroid-eyed boy who came on the school bus from the country town of Bowsville and who was an amateur hypnotist; he told the tale of a Portland,

Oregon, businessman who under hypnosis had been taken back through sixteen reincarnations to the condition of an Egyptian concubine in the household of a high priest of Isis. There was his friend Lionel Griffin, a pudgy simp whose blond hair puffed out above his ears in two slick waxed wings. He was rumored to be a fairy, and in fact did seem most excited by the transvestite aspect of the soul's transmigration. And there was Lionel's girl Virginia, a drab little mystery who chain-smoked Herbert Tareytons and never said anything. She had sallow skin and smudged eyes and Lionel kept jabbing her and shrieking, making William wince. He would rather have sat with members of his own class, who filled the other booths, but he would have had to force himself on them. These juniors admired him and welcomed his company. He asked, "Wuh-well, was he ever a c-c-c-cockroach, like Archy?"

Kruppman's face grew intense; his furry lids dropped down over the bulge of his eyes, and when they drew back, his pupils were as small and hard as BBs. "That's the really interesting thing. There was this gap, see, between his being a knight under Charlemagne and then a sailor on a ship putting out from Macedonia—that's where Yugoslavia is now—in the time of Nero; there was this gap, when the only thing the guy would do was walk around the office snarling and growling, see, like this." Kruppman worked his blotched ferret face up into a snarl and Griffin shrieked. "He tried to bite one of the assistants and they think that for six hundred years"—the uncanny, unhealthy seriousness of his whisper hushed Griffin momentarily—"for six hundred years he just was a series of wolves. Probably in the German forests. You see, when he was in Macedonia"—his whisper barely audible—"he murdered a woman."

Griffin squealed in ecstasy and cried, "Oh, Kruppman! Kruppman, how you do go on!" and jabbed Virginia in the arm so hard a Herbert Tareyton jumped from her hand and bobbled across the Formica table. William gazed over their heads in pain.

The crowds at the soda counter had thinned so that when the door to the outside opened he saw Mary come in and hesitate there for a second where the smoke inside and the snow outside swirled together. The mixture made a kind of—Kruppman's ridiculous story had put the phrase in his head—wolf-weather, and she was just a gray shadow caught in it alone. She bought a pack of cigarettes from Luke and went out again, a kerchief around her head, the pneumatic thing above the door hissing behind her. For a long time, always in fact, she had been at the center of whatever gang was the one: in the second grade the one that walked home up Jewett Street together, and in the sixth grade the one that went bicycling as far away as the quarry and the Rentschler estate and played touch football Saturday afternoons, and in the ninth grade the one that went roller-skating at Candlebridge Park with the tenth-grade boys, and in the eleventh grade the one that held parties lasting past midnight and that on Sundays drove in caravans as far as Philadelphia and back. And all the while there had been a succession of boy friends, first Jack Stephens and Fritz March in their class and then boys a grade ahead and then Barrel Lord, who was a senior when they were sophomores and whose name was in the newspapers all football season, and then this last summer someone out of the school altogether, a man she met while working as a waitress in the city of Alton. So this year her weekends were taken up, and the party gang carried on as if she had never existed, and nobody saw her much except in school and when she stopped by in Luke's to buy a pack of cigarettes. Her silhouette against the big window had looked wan, her head hooded, her face nibbled by light, her fingers fiddling on the veined counter with her coins. He yearned to reach out, to comfort her, but he was wedged deep in the shrill booths, between the jingling guts of the pinball machine and the hillbilly joy of the jukebox. The impulse left him with a disagreeable feeling. He had loved her too long to want to pity her; it endangered the investment of worship on which he had not yet realized any return.

The two hours of the school afternoon held Latin and a study hall. In study hall, while the five people at the table with him played tic-tac-toe and sucked cough drops and yawned, he did all his homework for the next day. He prepared thirty lines of Vergil, Aeneas in the Underworld. The study hall was a huge low room in the basement of the building; its coziness crept into Tartarus. On the other side of the fudge-colored wall the circular saw in the woodworking shop whined and gasped and then whined again; it bit off pieces of wood with a rising, somehow terrorized inflection—bzzzz*zup!* He solved ten problems in trigonometry. His mind cut neatly through their knots and separated them, neat stiff squares of answer, one by one from the long but finite plank of problems that connected Plane Geometry with Solid. Lastly, as the snow on a ragged slant drifted down into the cement pits outside the steel-mullioned windows, he read a short story by Edgar Allan Poe. He closed the book softly on the pleasing sonority of its final note of horror, gazed at the red, wet, menthol-scented inner membrane of Judy Whipple's yawn, rimmed with flaking pink lipstick, and yielded his conscience to the snug sense of his work done, of the snow falling, of the warm minutes that walked through their shelter so slowly. The perforated acoustic tiling above his head seemed the lining of a long tube that would go all the way: high school merging into college, college into graduate school, graduate school into teaching at a college—section man, assistant, associate, *full* professor, possessor of a dozen languages and a thousand books, a man brilliant in his forties, wise in his fifties, renowned in his sixties, revered in his seventies, and then retired, sitting in the study lined with acoustical books until the time came for the last transition from silence to silence, and he would die, like Tennyson, with a copy of *Cymbeline* beside him on the moon-drenched bed.

After school he had to go to Room 101 and cut a sports cartoon into a stencil for the school paper. He liked the building best when it was nearly empty, when the casual residents—the rural commuters, the do-nothings, the trash—had cleared out. Then the janitors went down the halls sowing seeds of red wax and making an immaculate harvest with broad brooms, gathering all the fluff and hairpins and wrappers and powder that the animals had dropped that day. The basketball team thumped in the hollow gymnasium; the cheerleaders rehearsed behind drawn curtains on the stage. In Room 101 two empty-headed typists with stripes bleached into their hair banged away between giggles and mistakes. At her desk Mrs. Gregory, the faculty sponsor, wearily passed her pencil through misspelled news copy on tablet paper. William took the shadow box from the top of the filing cabinet and the styluses and little square plastic shading screens from their drawer and the stencil from the closet where the typed stencils hung, like fragile scarves, on hooks. B-BALLERS BOW, 57-42, was the headline. He drew a tall b-baller bowing to a stumpy pagan idol, labeled "W" for victorious Weiserton High, and traced it in the soft blue wax with the fine loop stylus. His careful breath grazed his knuckles. His eyebrows frowned while his heart bobbed happily on the giddy prattle of the typists. The shadow box was simply a black frame holding a pane of glass and lifted at one end by two legs so the light bulb, fitted in a tin tray, could slide under; it was like a primitive lean-to sheltering a fire. As he worked, his eyes smarting, he mixed himself up with the light bulb, felt himself burning under a slanting roof upon which a huge hand scratched. The glass grew hot; the danger in the job was pulling the softened wax with your damp hand, distorting or tearing the typed letters. Sometimes the center of an *o* stuck to your skin like a bit of blue confetti. But he was expert and cautious. He returned the things to their places feeling airily tall, heightened by Mrs. Gregory's appreciation, which she expressed by keeping her back turned, in effect stating that other staff members were undependable but William did not need to be watched.

In the hall outside Room 101 only the shouts of a basketball scrimmage reverberated; the chant of the cheerleaders had been silenced. Though he had done everything, he felt reluctant to leave. Neither of his parents—both worked—would be home yet, and this building was as much his home. He knew all its nooks. On the second floor of the annex, beyond the art room, there was a strange, narrow boys' lavatory that no one ever seemed to use. It was here one time that Barry Kruppman tried to hypnotize him and cure his stuttering. Kruppman's voice purred and his irises turned tiny in the bulging whites and for a moment William felt himself lean backward involuntarily, but he was distracted by the bits of bloodshot pink in the corners of these portentous eyes; the folly of giving up his will to an intellectual inferior occurred to him; he refused to let go and go under, and perhaps therefore his stuttering had continued.

The frosted window at the end of the long room cast a watery light on the green floor and made the porcelain urinals shine like slices of moon. The semi-opacity of this window gave the room's air of secrecy great density. William washed his hands with exaggerated care, enjoying the lavish amount of powdered soap provided for him in this castle. He studied his face in the mirror, making infinitesimal adjustments to attain the absolutely most flattering angle, and then put his hands below his throat to get their strong, long-fingered beauty into the picture. As he walked toward the door he sang, closing his eyes and gasping as if he were a real Negro whose entire career depended upon this recording:

"Who—told me so, dilly dilly,
Who told me soho?
Aii told myself, dilly dilly,
I told: me so."

When he emerged into the hall it was not empty: one girl walked down its varnished perspective toward him, Mary Landis, a scarf on her head and books in her arms. Her locker was up here, on the second floor of the annex. His own was in the annex basement. A tickling sensation that existed neither in the medium of sound nor of light crowded against his throat. She flipped the scarf back from her hair and in a conversational voice that carried well down the clean planes of the hall said, "Hi, Billy." The name came from way back, when they were both children, and made him feel small but brave.

"Hi. How are you?"

"Fine." Her smile broadened out from the *F* of this word.

What was so funny? Was she really, as it seemed, pleased to see him? "Du-did you just get through cheer-cheer-cheerleading?"

"Yes. Thank God. *Oh* she's so awful. She makes us do the same stupid locomotives for every cheer; I told her, no wonder nobody cheers any more."

"This is M-M-Miss Potter?" He blushed, feeling that he made an ugly face in getting past the *M*. When he got caught in the middle of a sentence the constriction was somehow worse. He admired the way words poured up her throat, distinct and petulant.

"Yes, Potbottom Potter," she said, "she's just aching for a man and takes it out on us. I wish she would get one. Honestly, Billy, I have half a mind to quit. I'll be so glad when June comes, I'll never set foot in this idiotic building again."

Her lips, pale with the lipstick worn off, crinkled bitterly. Her face, foreshortened from the height of his eyes, looked cross as a cat's. It a little shocked him that poor Miss Potter and this kind, warm school stirred her to what he had to take as actual anger; this grittiness in her was the first abrasive texture he had struck today. Couldn't she see around teachers, into their fatigue, their poverty, their fear? It had been so long since he had spoken to her, he wasn't sure how coarse she had become. "Don't quit," he brought out of his mouth at last. "It'd be n-n-n-nuh—it'd be nothing without you."

He pushed open the door at the end of the hall for her and as she passed under his arm she looked up and said, "Why, aren't you sweet?"

The stairwell, all asphalt and iron, smelled of galoshes. It felt more secret than the hall, more specially theirs; there was something magical in its shifting multiplicity of planes as they descended that lifted the spell on his tongue, so that words came as quickly as his feet pattered on the steps.

"No I mean it," he said, "you're really a beautiful cheerleader. But then you're beautiful period."

"I've skinny legs."

"Who told you that?"

"Somebody."

"Well *he* wasn't very sweet."

"No."

"Why do you hate this poor old school?"

"Now Billy. You know you don't care about this junky place any more than I do."

"I love it. It breaks my heart to hear you say you want to get out, because then I'll never see you again."

"You don't care, do you?"

"Why sure I care; you *know*"—their feet stopped; they had reached bottom, the first-floor landing, two brass-barred doors and a grimy radiator—"I've always li-loved you."

"You don't mean that."

"I do too. It's ridiculous but there it is. I wanted to tell you today and now I have."

He expected her to laugh and go out the door, but instead she showed an unforseeable willingness to discuss this awkward matter. He should have realized before this that women enjoy being talked to. "It's a very silly thing to say," she asserted tentatively.

"I don't see why," he said, fairly bold now that he couldn't seem more ridiculous, and yet picking his words with a certain strategic care. "It's not *that* silly to love somebody, I mean what the hell. Probably what's silly is not to do anything about it for umpteen years but then I never had an opportunity, I thought."

He set his books down on the radiator and she set hers down beside his. "What kind of opportunity were you waiting for?"

"Well, see, that's it; I didn't know." He wished, in a way, she would go out the door. But she had propped herself against the wall and plainly awaited more talking. "Yuh-you were such a queen and I was such a nothing and I just didn't really want to presume." It wasn't very interesting; it puzzled him that she seemed to be interested. Her face had grown quite stern, the mouth very small and thoughtful, and he made a gesture with his hands intended to release her from the bother of thinking about it; after all, it was just a disposition of his heart, nothing permanent or expensive;

perhaps it was just his mother's idea anyway. Half in impatience to close the account, he asked, "Will you marry me?"

"You don't want to marry me," she said. "You're going to go on and be a great man."

He blushed in pleasure; is this how she saw him, is this how they all saw him; as worthless now, but in time a great man? Had his hopes always been on view? He dissembled, saying, "No I'm not. But anyway, you're great now. You're so pretty, Mary."

"Oh, Billy," she said, "if you were me for just one day you'd hate it."

She said this rather blankly, watching his eyes; he wished her voice had shown more misery. In his world of closed surfaces a panel, carelessly pushed, had opened, and he hung in this openness paralyzed, unable to think what to say. Nothing he could think of quite fit the abruptly immense context. The radiator cleared its throat; its heat made, in the intimate volume just this side of the doors on whose windows the snow beat limply, a provocative snugness; he supposed he should try, and stepped forward, his hands lifting toward her shoulders. Mary sidestepped between him and the radiator and put the scarf back on. She lifted the cloth like a broad plaid halo above her head and then wrapped it around her chin and knotted it so she looked, in her red galoshes and bulky coat, like a peasant woman in a movie of Europe. With her thick hair swathed, her face seemed pale and chunky, and when she recradled the books in her arms her back bent humbly under the point of the kerchief. "It's too hot in here," she said. "I've got to wait for somebody." The disconnectedness of the two statements seemed natural in the fragmented atmosphere his stops and starts had produced. She bucked the brass bar with her shoulder and the door slammed open; he followed her into the weather.

"For the person who thinks your legs are too skinny?"

"Uh-huh." As she looked up at him a snowflake caught on the lashes of one eye. She jerkily rubbed that cheek on the shoulder of her coat and stamped a foot, splashing slush. Cold water gathered on the back of his thin shirt. He put his hands in his pockets and pressed his arms against his sides to keep from shivering.

"Thuh-then you wo-won't marry me?" His wise instinct told him the only way back was by going forward, through absurdity.

"We don't know each other," she said.

"My God," he said. "Why not? I've known you since I was two."

"What do you know about me?"

This awful seriousness of hers; he must dissolve it. "That you're not a virgin." But instead of making her laugh this made her face go dead and turned it away. Like beginning to kiss her, it was a mistake; in part, he felt grateful for his mistakes. They were like loyal friends who are nevertheless embarrassing. "What do you know about *me?*" he asked, setting himself up for a finishing insult but dreading it. He hated the stiff feel of his smile between his cheeks; glimpsed, as if the snow were a mirror, how hateful he looked.

"That you're basically very nice."

Her returning good for evil blinded him to his physical discomfort, set him burning with regret. "Listen," he said, "I did love you. Let's at least get that straight."

"You never loved anybody," she said. "You don't know what it is."

"O.K." he said. "Pardon me."

"You're excused."

"You better wait in the school," he told her. "He's-eez-eez going to be a long time."

She didn't answer and walked a little distance, toeing out in the childish Dutch way common to the women in this country, along the slack cable that divided the parking lot from the softball field. One bicycle, rusted as if it had been there for years, leaned in the rack, its fenders supporting airy crescents of white.

The warmth inside the door felt heavy. William picked up his books and ran his pencil along the black ribs of the radiator before going down the stairs to his locker in the annex basement. The shadows were thick at the foot of the steps; suddenly it felt late, he must hurry and get home. He was seized by the irrational fear that they were going to lock him in. The cloistered odors of paper, sweat, and, from the woodshop at the far end of the basement hall, sawdust no longer flattered him. The tall green double lockers appeared to study him critically through the three air slits near their tops. When he opened his locker, and put his books on his shelf, below Marvin Wolf's, and removed his coat from his hook, his self seemed to crawl into the long dark space thus made vacant, the humiliated ugly, educable self. In answer to a flick of his great hand the steel door weightlessly floated shut and through the length of his body he felt so clean and free he smiled. Between now and the happy future predicted for him he had nothing, almost literally nothing, to do.

Study Guides

Both "The Fall of the House of Usher" and "The Haunted Palace" create a powerful effect of decline and disaster. The disintegration of personality and the decay of meaningful human relationships—inevitable consequences of extreme solipsism—are dramatically and rather violently realized in both stories. John Updike in "A Sense of Shelter," exploring the same theme but using a different setting, creates quite a different total effect. Here the atmosphere is quietly understated and familiarized. Nevertheless the result is forceful in its terrifying implications.

Updike uses a realistic approach; there is no attempt at fantasy. Nor is there any effort to move from the naturalistic view to the impressionistic, which we find toward the end of Miss Roberts' story. Updike's setting is an ordinary, modern high school; the events that transpire might be repeated in countless high schools across the nation. Yet the building itself gradually takes on, in Billy's view, the atmosphere of a gloomy palace or castle. Here are deserted halls and dark, tomblike corners. But for Billy the gloom is rather pleasant, even "joyous," familiarized into typical locker rooms and half-deserted halls after classes are over.

None of the characters is very extraordinary. Billy, in fact, is rather typical: a callow, intelligent, and somewhat conceited senior. He is certainly no rare specimen like Roderick Usher. Nor is Mary a benighted clod like the farmer's wife Jess. As a person Mary is a little coarse, a bit too hard and mature for her years, brittle, sexy, and obviously nonintellectual. Yet by the time the story is finished this very familiarity of character and setting impresses us with the monstrous nature of the "real" world. Updike, like the poet Wordsworth, makes the familiar suddenly take on a surprising strangeness; our eyes are opened to a startling recognition of ourselves and the nature of our world. To create the effect he desires, Updike must make us recognize the freakishness beneath the surface of the familiar. We must admire Billy while, with sympathy and pity, we reject his folly.

Part of the success of Updike's effect is achieved through a careful choice of point of view. By using what is known technically as the limited omniscient, by focusing on the thoughts and perceptions of Billy, by allowing us to "see" through Billy's eyes, the author lets us enter the boy's world and thus provides us with an illusion of the familiar. Yet by being "omniscient," the author can also move back from Billy and give us objective and critical glimpses that are beyond the boy's perceptions. We are therefore given a kind of double vision: we respond to Billy's world as he would; we see as he would see; yet at the same time we stand apart and decry the folly of his ways. (See *Point of view* in Glossary.)

Because we respond as Billy does, we at first do not recognize the evil atmosphere which encompasses him. It seems to be the innocent air of ordinary life—promising security, comfort, and familiarity. But once we move further into the story, we find that Mary, like a bracing, rude blast of fresh air, impinges more and more on our consciousness; in contrast to Billy, she is like the chill air outside the window as it breathes on Billy's knuckles and provides a contrast to the heavy fetidness of the schoolroom. Gradually we perceive the foul atmosphere of Billy's world and find commonplace familiarity becoming almost as malignant as the oppressive atmosphere around the House of Usher.

Some of the details of setting and atmosphere deserve particular attention. First there is the snow. It is wet, "indecisive" snow, blanketing and insulating, abstracting, creating sameness, and imparting a sense of coziness and buffered security to Billy. But notice especially that the snow is indecisive—it has not yet conquered the world nor achieved its completeness. It could not quite bleach away the "scars" on its perfection—the tire marks from the school buses. This is to say that the snow has not yet been able to obliterate all traces of the "outside" world beyond the school house, Billy's castle. This outside world still intrudes—chill air on Billy's knuckles, tire marks in the snow. Like Roderick Usher at the beginning of Poe's story, Billy has not yet shut himself entirely away from the world outside himself. However, with Billy the very intrusion serves further to increase his sense of shelter. Also notice the temperature: it is exactly 32°. It is not freezing hard; yet there is no thaw. Billy is at a moment of decision, a moment of crisis when he will go either one way or another; but for the time being he is perilously balanced between two poles. Here atmosphere and setting create dramatic tension.

The school, Billy's inside world, represents mechanical routine, abstractionism, and self-flattering idealism. On the other hand, if we look carefully, we see that Mary brings before our minds a world of reality and self-knowledge. Imperfect and hard, coarse and matter-of-fact, she stands in contrast to the white abstraction outside the window. Yet Mary's world of reality and self-knowledge is characterized also by humility, love, genuine understanding, sympathy, and a tolerance which accepts human limitation with love and with continuing endurance. Witness Mary's tough manner toward, but gentle treatment of, Billy—even when he insults her; notice too her compassion, her lack of illusions, and her strength in accepting and enduring the world's flaws. Mary joins the outside world; Billy is only interested in making her queen of the abstract world where he is king.

Through the subtle implications in atmosphere and action, Updike shows the small fissures in Billy's character: he is utterly insular and uneducable. All his knowledge is self-generated and he is spinning an everlasting cocoon from his own being. He suffers the Usher sickness, and like Roderick he enjoys, before final entombment, the heightened sensations that come with acute self-awareness:

> The feeling the gloom gave him was not gloomy but joyous: he felt they were all sealed in, safe; the colors of cloth were dyed deeper, the sound of whispers was made more distinct, the smells of tablet paper and wet shoes and varnish and face powder pierced him with a vivid sense of possession. These were his classmates sealed in, his, the stupid as well as the clever, the plain as well as the lovely, his enemies as well as his friends, his.

Billy knows and loves everything that is his, and all that is his is self-generated. The source of his knowledge is made clear by his love song, the constant serenade to self:

> "Who—told me so, dilly dilly,
> Who told me soho?
> *Aii* told myself, dilly dilly,
> I told: me so."

The pathos lies in the fact that Billy, a bright high school senior, a boy who will doubtlessly be awarded the college degrees he sets as his goal, will never be really educated because he will never know or hear anything except what he tells himself. And the self, all alone, is a narrow entity; it can be contained in the space of a little tomb or hidden away in the confines of a small metal locker.

The following questions may guide your study of "A Sense of Shelter" and provide insights to its several effects.

1. The episodes concerning the stolen school bag, the lunch with the juniors, and the stenciling of a cartoon seem irrelevant at first to the central action of the story. What function do they serve and what does each episode reveal about the character of Billy and/or Mary? Are Kruppman and Griffin in any way parallels to Billy? Does Kruppman's account of a case of transmigration point to the theme of solipsism? Explain how each episode reflects the central theme.

2. Stuttering is supposed to result from and increase with extreme self-consciousness. How do the details of Billy's stuttering fit into the story? Can you discern any pattern of ebb and flow in his stuttering? What does this pattern reveal, especially when Billy is talking to Mary? What is the significance of the hypnosis experiment?

3. Billy's love scene with Mary is replete with irony. Comment on the ironic implications of Billy's thinking: "It had been so long since he had spoken to her, he wasn't sure how coarse she had become." How much sensitivity to Mary and her problem does Billy show in his attempt to kiss her and in his stating "[I know] that you're not a virgin"? What is revealed through Billy's boredom with the whole affair once he has stated his love for Mary? What is ironic about his last sentence?

4. What does the following detail contribute to the story: Billy "read a short story by Edgar Allan Poe. He closed the book softly on the pleasing sonority of its final note of horror . . ."?

5. There may be a technical violation of point of view in the crucial line ". . . his self seemed to crawl into the long dark space thus made vacant, the humiliated ugly, educable self." In context, this perception should be Billy's. Whose is it? Would Billy perceive in terms of "humiliated ugly, educable self"? What would be gained or lost if this line were omitted? If it were rephrased?

Action and Plot

Most readers are inclined to think first of the action—of what happens in a story—as soon as a title is mentioned. When they recall some form of narrative such as anecdote, parable, or tale, their first inclination is to identify the story in terms of its action—of what happened to the people involved. A drama too is a familiar kind of narrative which Aristotle insisted must have "a beginning, a middle, and an end" if it is to be a successful representation. (The beginning is the first action, which unbalances the status quo; the middle is the logical and necessary complication resulting from this act; the end is the point where equilibrium returns. The three units must be tightly linked and developed logically from first to last.) So if we as readers (or listeners) think first and almost automatically of the successive actions in a story or play, of a series of related, closely linked, and unified events which produce conflicts and even reversals, we are engaged in what seems to be the natural and time-honored response to successful fiction.

Whatever else a story finally brings us—insight into character, revelation of theme and idea, the confrontation of many kinds of problems, or perhaps merely a good laugh at ourselves—our first response is usually tied so closely to the plot that we delight in establishing firmly in our minds both the truth and validity of *how it was*. Surely this is the traditional basis of all fiction—whatever its length and particular form and its many refinements—and we may even go so far as to try to relate our knowledge of *how it was* to some symbolical or cosmological meaning beyond the level of the literal action. Thus plot orders actions so that they will finally deliver meaning.

In representative short stories plots will vary considerably in the "total action" or number of events an author will use to achieve his purpose. Whatever designation we give a piece of fiction—story, novella, novel—we will always find great variety, as the thirty stories in this collection suggest, and we are constantly reminded that there is no formula, no rule of thumb, no surefire method for plotting a good story.

But we should try to determine if the plot is logical—if one act follows another naturally and logically. Much poor fiction is characterized by preposterous and artificial inventions: events that may be beyond the realm of probability; an act that is not in keeping with the character who brings it about; a happening that is not consistent with the idea of cosmic order the story assumes at the beginning. For example, if chance is to resolve the tensions in a story, the element of chance must be established early as one of the forces at work upon the characters. This is to say that if pure coincidence is employed, it must be used to reveal that there is meaning in accident—not that tensions are resolved accidentally.

The comments following "An Imaginative Woman" will introduce several terms—defined in the Glossary—which will prove helpful in evaluating plot with regard to Hardy's story.

THOMAS HARDY

(1840–1928)

An Imaginative Woman

When William Marchmill had finished his inquiries for lodgings at the well-known watering-place of Solentsea in Upper Wessex, he returned to the hotel to find his wife. She, with the children, had rambled along the shore, and Marchmill followed in the direction indicated by the military-looking hall-porter.

"By Jove, how far you've gone! I am quite out of breath," Marchmill said, rather impatiently, when he came up with his wife, who was reading as she walked, the three children being considerably further ahead with the nurse.

Mrs. Marchmill started out of the reverie into which the book had thrown her. "Yes," she said, "you've been such a long time. I was tired of staying in that dreary hotel. But I am sorry if you have wanted me, Will?"

"Well, I have had trouble to suit myself. When you see the airy and comfortable rooms heard of, you find they are stuffy and uncomfortable. Will you come and see if what I've fixed on will do? There is not much room, I am afraid; but I can light on nothing better. The town is rather full."

The pair left the children and nurse to continue their ramble, and went back together.

In age well-balanced, in personal appearance fairly matched, and in domestic requirements conformable, in temper this couple differed, though even here they did not often clash, he being equable, if not lymphatic, and she decidedly nervous and sanguine. It was to their tastes and fancies, those smallest, greatest particulars, that no common denominator could be applied. Marchmill considered his wife's likes and inclinations somewhat silly; she considered his sordid and material. The husband's business was that of a gunmaker in a thriving city northwards, and his soul was in that business always; the lady was best characterized by that superannuated phrase of elegance "a votary of the muse." An impressionable, palpitating creature was Ella, shrinking humanely from detailed knowledge of her husband's trade whenever she reflected that everything he manufactured had for its purpose the destruction of life. She could only recover her equanimity by assuring herself that some, at least, of his weapons were sooner or later used for the extermination of horrid vermin and animals almost as cruel to their inferiors in species as human beings were to theirs.

She had never antecedently regarded this occupation of his as any objection to having him for a husband. Indeed, the necessity of getting life-leased at all cost, a cardinal virtue which all good mothers teach, kept her from thinking of it at all till she had closed with William, had passed the honeymoon, and reached the reflecting stage. Then, like a person who has stumbled upon some object in the dark, she wondered what she had got; mentally walked round it, estimated it; whether it were rare or common; contained gold, silver, or lead; were a clog or a pedestal, everything to her or nothing.

She came to some vague conclusions, and since then had kept her heart alive by pitying her proprietor's obtuseness and want of refinement, pitying herself, and letting off her delicate and ethereal emotions in imaginative occupations, day-dreams, and night-sighs, which perhaps would not much have disturbed William if he had known of them.

Her figure was small, elegant, and slight in build, tripping, or rather bounding, in movement. She was dark-eyed, and had that marvellously bright and liquid sparkle in each pupil which characterizes persons of Ella's cast of soul, and is too often a cause of heartache to the possessor's male friends, ultimately sometimes to herself. Her husband was a tall, longfeatured man, with a brown beard; he had a pondering regard; and was, it must be added, usually kind and tolerant to her. He spoke in squarely shaped sentences, and was supremely satisfied with a condition of sublunary things which made weapons a necessity.

Husband and wife walked till they had reached the house they were in search of, which stood in a terrace facing the sea, and was fronted by a small garden of wind-proof and salt-proof evergreens, stone steps leading up to the porch. It had its number in the row, but, being rather larger than the rest, was in addition sedulously distinguished as Coburg House by its landlady, though everybody else called it "Thirteen, New Parade." The spot was bright and lively now; but in winter it became necessary to place sand-bags against the door, and to stuff up the keyhole against the wind and rain, which had worn the paint so thin that the priming and knotting showed through.

The householder, who had been watching for the gentleman's return, met them in the passage, and showed the rooms. She informed them that she was a professional man's widow, left in needy circumstances by the rather sudden death of her husband, and she spoke anxiously of the conveniences of the establishment.

Mrs. Marchmill said that she liked the situation and the house; but, it being small, there would not be accommodation enough, unless she could have all the rooms.

The landlady mused with an air of disappointment. She wanted the visitors to be her tenants very badly, she said, with obvious honesty. But unfortunately two of the rooms were occupied permanently by a bachelor gentleman. He did not pay season prices, it was true; but as he kept on his apartments all the year round, and was an extremely nice and interesting young man, who gave no trouble, she did not like to turn him out for a month's "let," even at a high figure. "Perhaps, however," she added, "he might offer to go for a time."

They would not hear of this, and went back to the hotel, intending to proceed to the agent's to inquire further. Hardly had they sat down to tea when the landlady called. Her gentleman, she said, had been so obliging as to offer to give up his rooms for three or four weeks rather than drive the new-comers away.

"It is very kind, but we won't inconvenience him in that way," said the Marchmills.

"O, it won't inconvenience him, I assure you!" said the landlady eloquently. "You see, he's a different sort of young man from most—dreamy, solitary, rather melancholy—and he cares more to be here when the south-westerly gales are beating against the door, and the sea washes over the Parade, and there's not a soul in the place, than he does now in the season. He'd just as soon be where, in fact, he's going temporarily, to a little cottage on the Island opposite, for a change." She hoped therefore that they would come.

The Marchmill family accordingly took possession of the house next day, and it seemed to suit them very well. After luncheon Mr. Marchmill strolled out towards the pier, and Mrs. Marchmill, having despatched the children to their outdoor amusements on the sands, settled herself in more completely, examining this and that article, and testing the reflecting powers of the mirror in the wardrobe door.

In the small back sitting-room, which had been the young bachelor's, she found furniture of a more personal nature than in the rest. Shabby books, of correct rather than rare editions, were piled up in a queerly reserved manner in corners, as if the previous occupant had not conceived the possibility that any incoming person of the season's bringing could care to look inside them. The landlady hovered on the threshold to rectify anything that Mrs. Marchmill might not find to her satisfaction.

"I'll make this my own little room," said the latter, "because the books are here. By the way, the person who has left seems to have a good many. He won't mind my reading some of them, Mrs. Hooper, I hope?"

"O dear no, ma'am. Yes, he has a good many. You see, he is in the literary line himself somewhat. He is a poet—yes, really a poet—and he has a little income of his own, which is enough to write verses on, but not enough for cutting a figure, even if he cared to."

"A poet! O, I did not know that."

Mrs. Marchmill opened one of the books, and saw the owner's name written on the title-page. "Dear me!" she continued; "I know his name very well—Robert Trewe—of course I do; and his writings! And it is *his* rooms we have taken, and *him* we have turned out of his home?"

Ella Marchmill, sitting down alone a few minutes later, thought with interested surprise of Robert Trewe. Her own latter history will best explain that interest. Herself the only daughter of a struggling man of letters, she had during the last year or two taken to writing poems, in an endeavour to find a congenial channel in which to let flow her painfully embayed emotions, whose former limpidity and sparkle seemed departing in the stagnation caused by the routine of a practical household and the gloom of bearing children to a commonplace father. These poems, subscribed with a masculine pseudonym, had appeared in various obscure magazines, and in two cases in rather prominent ones. In the second of the latter the page which bore her effusion at the bottom, in smallish print, bore at the top, in large print, a few verses on the same subject by this very man, Robert Trewe. Both of them had, in fact, been struck by a tragic incident reported in the daily papers, and had used it simultaneously as an inspiration, the editor remarking in a note upon the coincidence, and that the excellence of both poems prompted him to give them together.

After that event Ella, otherwise "John Ivy," had watched with much attention the appearance anywhere in print of verse bearing the signature of Robert Trewe, who, with a man's unsusceptibility on the question of sex, had never once thought of passing himself off as a woman. To be sure, Mrs. Marchmill had satisfied herself with a sort of reason for doing the contrary in her case; since nobody might believe in her inspiration if they found that the sentiments came from a pushing tradesman's wife, from the mother of three children by a matter-of-fact small-arms manufacturer.

Trewe's verse contrasted with that of the rank and file or recent minor poets in being impassioned rather than ingenious, luxuriant rather than finished. Neither *symboliste* nor *décadent,* he was a pessimist in so far as that character applies to a man who looks at the worst contingencies as well as the best in the human condition. Being little attracted by excellences of form and rhythm apart from content, he sometimes, when feeling outran his artistic speed, perpetrated sonnets in the loosely rhymed Elizabethan fashion, which every right-minded reviewer said he ought not to have done.

With sad and hopeless envy Ella Marchmill had often and often scanned the rival poet's work, so much stronger as it always was than her own feeble lines. She had imitated him, and her inability to touch his level would send her into fits of despondency. Months passed away thus, till she observed from the publishers' list that Trewe had collected his fugitive pieces into a volume, which was duly issued, and was much or little praised according to chance, and had a sale quite sufficient to pay for the printing.

This step onward had suggested to John Ivy the idea of collecting her pieces also, or at any rate of making up a book of her rhymes by adding many in manuscript to the few that had seen the light, for she had been able to get no great number into print. A ruinous charge was made for costs of publication; a few reviews noticed her poor little volume; but nobody talked of it, nobody bought it, and it fell dead in a fortnight—if it had ever been alive.

The author's thoughts were diverted to another groove just then by the discovery that she was going to have a third child, and the collapse of her poetical venture had perhaps less effect upon her mind than it might have done if she had been domestically unoccupied. Her husband had paid the publisher's bill with the doctor's, and there it all had ended for the time. But, though less than a poet of her century, Ella was more than a mere multiplier of her kind, and latterly she had begun to feel the old afflatus once more. And now by an odd conjunction she found herself in the rooms of Robert Trewe.

She thoughtfully rose from her chair and searched the apartment with the interest of a fellow-tradesman. Yes, the volume of his own verse was among the rest. Though quite familiar with its contents, she read it here as if it spoke aloud to her, then called up Mrs. Hooper, the landlady, for some trivial service, and inquired again about the young man.

"Well, I'm sure you'd be interested in him, ma'am, if you could see him, only he's so shy that I don't suppose you will." Mrs. Hooper seemed nothing loth to minister to her tenant's curiosity about her predecessor. "Lived here long? Yes, nearly two years. He keeps on his rooms even when he's not here: the soft air of this place suits his chest, and he likes to be able to come back at any time. He is mostly writing or reading, and doesn't see many people, though, for the matter of that, he is such a good, kind young fellow that folks would only be too glad to be friendly with him if they knew him. You don't meet kind-hearted people every day."

"Ah, he's kind-hearted . . . and good."

"Yes; he'll oblige me in anything if I ask him. 'Mr. Trewe,' I say to him sometimes, 'you are rather out of spirits.' 'Well, I am, Mrs. Hooper,' he'll say, 'though I don't know how you should find it out.' 'Why not take a little change?' I ask. Then in a day or two he'll say that he will take a trip to Paris, or Norway, or somewhere; and I assure you he comes back all the better for it."

"Ah, indeed! His is a sensitive nature, no doubt."

"Yes. Still he's odd in some things. Once when he had finished a poem of his composition late at night he walked up and down the room rehearsing it; and the floors being so thin—jerry-built houses, you know, though I say it myself—he kept me awake up above him till I wished him further. . . . But we get on very well."

This was but the beginning of a series of conversations about the rising poet as the days went on. On one of these occasions Mrs. Hooper drew Ella's attention to what she had not noticed before: minute scribblings in pencil on the wall-paper behind the curtains at the head of the bed.

"O! let me look," said Mrs. Marchmill, unable to conceal a rush of tender curiosity as she bent her pretty face close to the wall.

"These," said Mrs. Hooper, with the manner of a woman who knew things, "are the very beginnings and first thoughts of his verses. He has tried to rub most of them out, but you can read them still. My belief is that he wakes up in the night, you know, with some rhyme in his head, and jots it down there on the wall lest he should forget it by the morning. Some of these very lines you see here I have seen afterwards in print in the magazines. Some are newer; indeed, I have not seen that one before. It must have been done only a few days ago."

"O yes! . . ."

Ella Marchmill flushed without knowing why, and suddenly wished her companion would go away, now that the information was imparted. An indescribable consciousness of personal interest rather than literary made her anxious to read the inscription alone; and she accordingly waited till she could do so, with a sense that a great store of emotion would be enjoyed in the act.

Perhaps because the sea was choppy outside the Island, Ella's husband found it much pleasanter to go sailing and steaming about without his wife, who was a bad sailor, than with her. He did not disdain to go thus alone on board the steamboats of the cheap-trippers, where there was dancing by moonlight, and where the couples would come suddenly down with a lurch into each other's arms; for, as he blandly told her, the company was too mixed for him to take her amid such scenes. Thus, while this thriving manufacturer got a great deal of change and sea-air out of his sojourn here, the life, external at least, of Ella was monotonous enough, and mainly consisted in passing a certain number of hours each day in bathing and walking up and down a stretch of shore. But the poetic impulse having again waxed strong, she was possessed by an inner flame which left her hardly conscious of what was proceeding around her.

She had read till she knew by heart Trewe's last little volume of verses, and spent a great deal of time in vainly attempting to rival some of them, till, in her failure, she burst into tears. The personal element in the magnetic attraction exercised by this circumambient, unapproachable master of hers was so much stronger than the intellectual and abstract that she could not understand it. To be sure, she was surrounded noon and night by his customary environment, which literally whispered of him to her at every moment; but he was a man she had never seen, and that all that moved her was the instinct to specialize a waiting emotion on the first fit thing that came to hand did not, of course, suggest itself to Ella.

In the natural way of passion under the too practical conditions which civilization has devised for its fruition, her husband's love for her had not survived, except in the form of fitful friendship, any more than, or even so much as, her own for him; and, being a woman of very living ardours, that required sustenance of some sort, they were beginning to feed on this chancing material, which was, indeed, of a quality far better than chance usually offers.

One day the children had been playing hide-and-seek in a closet, whence, in their excitement, they pulled out some clothing. Mrs. Hooper explained that it belonged to Mr. Trewe, and hung it up in the closet again. Possessed of her fantasy, Ella went later in the afternoon, when nobody was in that part of the house, opened the closet, unhitched one of the articles, a mackintosh, and put it on, with the water proof cap belonging to it.

"The mantle of Elijah!" she said. "Would it might inspire me to rival him, glorious genius that he is!"

Her eyes always grew wet when she thought like that, and she turned to look at herself in the glass. *His* heart had beat inside that coat, and *his* brain had worked under that hat at levels of thought she would never reach. The consciousness of her weakness beside him made her feel quite sick. Before she had got the things off her the door opened, and her husband entered the room.

"What the devil ——"

She blushed, and removed them.

"I found them in the closet here," she said, "and put them on in a freak. What have I else to do? You are always away!"

"Always away? Well . . ."

That evening she had a further talk with the landlady, who might herself have nourished a half-tender regard for the poet, so ready was she to discourse ardently about him.

"You are interested in Mr. Trewe, I know, ma'am," she said; "and he has just sent to say that he is going to call to-morrow afternoon to look up some books of his that he wants, if I'll be in, and he may select them from your room?"

"O yes!"

"You could very well meet Mr. Trewe then, if you'd like to be in the way!"

She promised with secret delight, and went to bed musing of him.

Next morning her husband observed: "I've been thinking of what you said, Ell: that I have gone about a good deal and left you without much to amuse you. Perhaps it's true. To-day, as there's not much sea, I'll take you with me on board the yacht."

For the first time in her experience of such an offer Ella was not glad. But she accepted it for the moment. The time for setting out drew near, and she went to get ready. She stood reflecting. The longing to see the poet she was now distinctly in love with overpowered all other considerations.

"I don't want to go," she said to herself. "I can't bear to be away! And I won't go."

She told her husband that she had changed her mind about wishing to sail. He was indifferent, and went his way.

For the rest of the day the house was quiet, the children having gone out upon the sands. The blinds waved in the sunshine to the soft, steady stroke of the sea beyond the wall; and the notes of the Green Silesian band, a troop of foreign gentlemen hired for the season, had drawn almost all the residents and promenaders away from the vicinity of Coburg House. A knock was audible at the door.

Mrs. Marchmill did not hear any servant go to answer it, and she became impatient. The books were in the room where she sat; but nobody came up. She rang the bell.

"There is some person waiting at the door," she said.

"O no, ma'am! He's gone long ago. I answered it," the servant replied, and Mrs. Hooper came in herself.

"So disappointing!" she said. "Mr. Trewe not coming after all!"

"But I heard him knock, I fancy!"

"No; that was somebody inquiring for lodgings who came to the wrong house. I forgot to tell you that Mr. Trewe sent a note just before lunch to say I needn't get any tea for him, as he should not require the books, and wouldn't come to select them."

Ella was miserable, and for a long time could not even re-read his mournful ballad on "Severed Lives," so aching was her erratic little heart, and so tearful her eyes. When the children came in with wet stockings, and ran up to her to tell her of their adventures, she could not feel that she cared about them half as much as usual.

. . . . .

"Mrs. Hooper, have you a photograph of—the gentleman who lived here?" She was getting to be curiously shy in mentioning his name.

"Why, yes. It's in the ornamental frame on the mantelpiece in your own bedroom, ma'am."

"No; the Royal Duke and Duchess are in that."

"Yes, so they are; but he's behind them. He belongs rightly to that frame, which I bought on purpose; but as he went away he said: 'Cover me up from those strangers that are coming, for God's sake. I don't want them staring at me, and I am sure they won't want me staring at them.' So I slipped in the Duke and Duchess temporarily in front of him, as they had no frame, and Royalties are more suitable for letting furnished than a private young man. If you take 'em out you'll see him under. Lord, ma'am, he wouldn't mind if he knew it! He didn't think the next tenant would be such an attractive lady as you, or he wouldn't have thought of hiding himself, perhaps."

"Is he handsome?" she asked timidly.

"*I* call him so. Some, perhaps, wouldn't."

"Should I?" she asked, with eagerness.

"I think you would, though some would say he's more striking than handsome; a large-eyed thoughtful fellow, you know, with a very electric flash in his eye when he looks round quickly, such as you'd expect a poet to be who doesn't get his living by it."

"How old is he?"

"Several years older than yourself, ma'am; about thirty-one or two, I think."

Ella was, as a matter of fact, a few months over thirty herself; but she did not look nearly so much. Though so immature in nature, she was entering on that tract of life in which emotional women begin to suspect that last love may be stronger than first love; and she would soon, alas, enter on the still more melancholy tract when at least the vainer ones of her sex shrink from receiving a male visitor otherwise than with their backs to the window or the blinds half down. She reflected on Mrs. Hooper's remark, and said no more about age.

Just then a telegram was brought up. It came from her husband, who had gone down the Channel as far as Budmouth with his friends in the yacht, and would not be able to get back till next day.

After her light dinner Ella idled about the shore with the children till dusk, thinking of the yet uncovered photograph in her room, with a serene sense of something ecstatic to come. For, with the subtle luxuriousness of fancy in which this young woman was an adept, on learning that her husband was to be absent that night she had refrained from incontinently rushing upstairs and opening the picture-frame, preferring to reserve the inspection till she could be alone, and a more romantic tinge be imparted to the occasion by silence, candles, solemn sea and stars outside, than was afforded by the garish afternoon sunlight.

The children had been sent to bed, and Ella soon followed, though it was not yet ten o'clock. To gratify her passionate curiosity she now made her preparations, first getting rid of superfluous garments and putting on her dressing-gown, then arranging a chair in front of the table and reading several pages of Trewe's tenderest utterances. Next she fetched the portrait-frame to the light, opened the back, took out the likeness, and set it up before her.

It was a striking countenance to look upon. The poet wore a luxuriant black moustache and imperial, and a slouched hat which shaded the forehead. The large dark eyes described by the landlady showed an unlimited capacity for misery; they looked out from beneath well-shaped brows as if they were reading the universe in the microcosm of the confronter's face, and were not altogether overjoyed at what the spectacle portended.

Ella murmured in her lowest, richest, tenderest tone: "And it's *you* who've so cruelly eclipsed me these many times!"

As she gazed long at the portrait she fell into thought, till her eyes filled with tears, and she touched the cardboard with her lips. Then she laughed with a nervous lightness, and wiped her eyes.

She thought how wicked she was, a woman having a husband and three children, to let her mind stray to a stranger in this unconscionable manner. No, he was not a stranger! She knew his thoughts and feelings as well as she knew her own; they were, in fact, the self-same thoughts and feelings as hers, which her husband distinctly lacked; perhaps luckily for himself, considering that he had to provide for family expenses.

"He's nearer my real self, he's more intimate with the real me than Will is, after all, even though I've never seen him," she said.

She laid his book and picture on the table at the bedside, and when she was reclining on the pillow she re-read those of Robert Trewe's verses which she had marked from time to time as most touching and true. Putting these aside she set up the photograph on its edge upon the coverlet, and contemplated it as she lay. Then she scanned again by the light of the candle the half-obliterated pencillings on the wall-paper beside her head. There they were—phrases, couplets, *bouts-rimés,* beginnings and middles of lines, ideas in the rough, like Shelley's scraps, and the least of them so intense, so sweet, so palpitating, that it seemed as if his very breath, warm and loving, fanned her cheeks from those walls, walls that had surrounded his head times and times as they surrounded her own now. He must often have put up his hand so—with the pencil in it. Yes, the writing was sideways, as it would be if executed by one who extended his arm thus.

These inscribed shapes of the poet's world,

> "Forms more real than living man,
> Nurslings of immortality,"

were, no doubt, the thoughts and spirit-strivings which had come to him in the dead of night, when he could let himself go and have no fear of the frost of criticism. No doubt they had often been written up hastily by the light of the moon, the rays of the lamp, in the blue-grey dawn, in full daylight perhaps never. And now her hair was dragging where his arm had lain when he secured the fugitive fancies; she was sleeping on a poet's lips, immersed in the very essence of him, permeated by his spirit as by an ether.

While she was dreaming the minutes away thus, a footstep came upon the stairs, and in a moment she heard her husband's heavy step on the landing immediately without.

"Ell, where are you?"

What possessed her she could not have described, but, with an instinctive objection to let her husband know what she had been doing, she slipped the photograph under the pillow just as he flung open the door with the air of a man who had dined not badly.

"O, I beg pardon," said William Marchmill. "Have you a headache? I am afraid I have disturbed you."

"No, I've not got a headache," said she. "How is it you've come?"

"Well, we found we could get back in very good time after all, and I didn't want to make another day of it, because of going somewhere else to-morrow."

"Shall I come down again?"

"O no. I'm as tired as a dog. I've had a good feed, and I shall turn in straight off. I want to get out at six o'clock to-morrow if I can. . . . I shan't disturb you by my getting up; it will be long before you are awake." And he came forward into the room.

While her eyes followed his movements, Ella softly pushed the photograph further out of sight.

"Sure you're not ill?" he asked, bending over her.

"No, only wicked!"

"Never mind that." And he stooped and kissed her. "I wanted to be with you to-night."

Next morning Marchmill was called at six o'clock; and in waking and yawning she heard him muttering to himself: "What the deuce is this that's been crackling under me so?" Imagining her asleep he searched round him and withdrew something. Through her helf-opened eyes she perceived it to be Mr. Trewe.

"Well, I'm damned!" her husband exclaimed.

"What, dear?" said she.

"O, you are awake? Ha! ha!"

"What *do* you mean?"

"Some bloke's photograph—a friend of our landlady's, I suppose. I wonder how it came here; whisked off the mantelpiece by accident perhaps when they were making the bed."

"I was looking at it yesterday, and it must have dropped in then."

"O, he's a friend of yours? Bless his picturesque heart!"

Ella's loyalty to the object of her admiration could not endure to hear him ridiculed. "He's a clever man!" she said, with a tremor in her gentle voice which she herself felt to be absurdly uncalled for. "He is a rising poet—the gentleman who occupied two of these rooms before we came, though I've never seen him."

"How do you know, if you've never seen him?"

"Mrs. Hooper told me when she showed me the photograph."

"O, well, I must up and be off. I shall be home rather early. Sorry I can't take you to-day, dear. Mind the children don't go getting drowned."

That day Mrs. Marchmill inquired if Mr. Trewe were likely to call at any other time.

"Yes," said Mrs. Hooper. "He's coming this day week to stay with a friend near here till you leave. He'll be sure to call."

Marchmill did return quite early in the afternoon; and, opening some letters which had arrived in his absence, declared suddenly that he and his family would have to leave a week earlier than they had expected to do—in short, in three days.

"Surely we can stay a week longer?" she pleaded. "I like it here."

"I don't. It is getting rather slow."

"Then you might leave me and the children!"

"How perverse you are, Ell! What's the use? And have to come to fetch you! No: we'll all return together; and we'll make out our time in North Wales or Brighton a little later on. Besides, you've three days longer yet."

It seemed to be her doom not to meet the man for whose rival talent she had a despairing admiration, and to whose person she was now absolutely attached. Yet she determined to make a last effort; and having gathered from her landlady that Trewe was living in a lonely spot not far from the fashionable town on the Island opposite, she crossed over in the packet from the neighbouring pier the following afternoon.

What a useless journey it was! Ella knew but vaguely where the house stood, and when she fancied she had found it, and ventured to inquire of a pedestrian if he lived there, the answer returned by the man was that he did not know. And if he did live there, how could she call upon him? Some women might have the assurance to do it, but she had not. How crazy he would think her. She might have asked him to call upon her, perhaps; but she had not the courage for that, either. She lingered mournfully about the picturesque seaside eminence till it was time to return to the town and enter the steamer for recrossing, reaching home for dinner without having been greatly missed.

At the last moment, unexpectedly enough, her husband said that he should have no objection to letting her and the children stay on till the end of the week, since she wished to do so, if she felt herself able to get home without him. She concealed the pleasure this extension of time gave her; and Marchmill went off the next morning alone.

But the week passed, and Trewe did not call.

On Saturday morning the remaining members of the Marchmill family departed from the place which had been productive of so much fervour in her. The dreary, dreary train; the sun shining in moted beams upon the hot cushions; the dusty permanent way; the mean rows of wire—these things were her accompaniment: while out of the window the deep blue sea-levels disappeared from her gaze, and with them her poet's home. Heavy-hearted, she tried to read, and wept instead.

Mr. Marchmill was in a thriving way of business, and he and his family lived in a large new house, which stood in rather extensive grounds a few miles outside the midland city wherein he carried on his trade. Ella's life was lonely here, as the suburban life is apt to be, particularly at certain seasons; and she had ample time to indulge her taste for lyric and elegiac composition. She had hardly got back when she encountered a piece by Robert Trewe in the new number of her favourite magazine, which must have been written almost immediately before her visit to Solentsea, for it contained the very couplet she had seen pencilled on the wall-paper by the bed, and Mrs. Hooper had declared to be recent. Ella could resist no longer, but seizing a pen impulsively, wrote to him as a brother-poet, using the name of John Ivy, congratulating him in her letter on his triumphant executions in metre and rhythm of thoughts that moved his soul, as compared with her own browbeaten efforts in the same pathetic trade.

To this address there came a response in a few days, little as she had dared to hope for it—a civil and brief note, in which the young poet stated that, though he was not well acquainted with Mr. Ivy's verse, he recalled the name as being one he had seen attached to some very promising pieces; that he was glad to gain Mr. Ivy's acquaintance by letter, and should certainly look with much interest for his productions in the future.

There must have been something juvenile or timid in her own epistle, as one ostensibly coming from a man, she declared to herself; for Trewe quite adopted the tone of an elder and superior in this reply. But what did it matter? He had replied; he had written to her with his own hand from that very room she knew so well, for he was now back again in his quarters.

The correspondence thus begun was continued for two months or more, Ella Marchmill sending him from time to time some that she considered to be the best of her pieces, which he very kindly accepted, though he did not say he sedulously read them, nor did he send her any of his own in return. Ella would have been more hurt at this than she was if she had not known that Trewe laboured under the impression that she was one of his own sex.

Yet the situation was unsatisfactory. A flattering little voice told her that, were he only to see her, matters would be otherwise. No doubt she would have helped on this by making a frank confession of womanhood, to begin with, if something had not happened, to her delight, to render it unnecessary. A friend of her husband's, the editor of the most important newspaper in their city and county, who was dining with them one day, observed during their conversation about the poet that his (the editor's) brother the landscape-painter was a friend of Mr. Trewe's, and that the two men were at that very moment in Wales together.

Ella was slightly acquainted with the editor's brother. The next morning down she sat and wrote, inviting him to stay at her house for a short time on his way back, and requesting him to bring with him, if practicable, his companion Mr. Trewe, whose acquaintance she was anxious to make. The answer arrived after some few days. Her correspondent and his friend Trewe would have much satisfaction in accepting her invitation on their way southward, which would be on such and such a day in the following week.

Ella was blithe and buoyant. Her scheme had succeeded; her beloved though as yet unseen one was coming. "Behold, he standeth behind our wall; he looked forth at the windows, showing himself through the lattice," she thought ecstatically. "And, lo, the winter is past, the rain is over and gone, the flowers appear on the earth, the time of the singing of birds is come, and the voice of the turtle is heard in our land."

But it was necessary to consider the details of lodging and feeding him. This she did most solicitously, and awaited the pregnant day and hour.

It was about five in the afternoon when she heard a ring at the door and the editor's brother's voice in the hall. Poetess as she was, or as she thought herself, she had not been too sublime that day to dress with infinite trouble in a fashionable robe of rich material, having a faint resemblance to the *chiton* of the Greeks, a style just then in vogue among ladies of an artistic and romantic turn, which had been obtained by Ella of her Bond Street dressmaker when she was last in London. Her visitor entered the drawing-room. She looked towards, his rear; nobody else came through the door. Where, in the name of the God of Love, was Robert Trewe?

"O, I'm sorry," said the painter, after their introductory words had been spoken. "Trewe is a curious fellow, you know, Mrs. Marchmill. He said he'd come; then he said he couldn't. He's rather dusty. We've been doing a few miles with knapsacks, you know; and he wanted to get on home."

"He—he's not coming?"

"He's not; and he asked me to make his apologies."

"When did you p-p-part from him?" she asked, her nether lip staring off quivering so much that it was like a *tremolo*-stop opened in her speech. She longed to run away from this dreadful bore and cry her eyes out.

"Just now, in the turnpike road younder there."

"What! he has actually gone past my gates?"

"Yes. When we got to them—handsome gates they are, too, the finest bit of modern wrought-iron work I have seen—when we came to them we stopped, talking there a little while, and then he wished me good-bye and went on. The truth is, he's a little bit depressed just now, and doesn't want to see anybody. He's a very good fellow, and a warm friend, but a little uncertain and gloomy sometimes; he thinks too much of things. His poetry is rather too erotic and passionate, you know, for some tastes; and he has just come in for a terrible slating from the ——*Review* that was published yesterday; he saw a copy of it at the station by accident. Perhaps you've read it?"

"No."

"So much the better. O, it is not worth thinking of; just one of those articles written to order, to please the narrow-minded set of subscribers upon whom the circulation depends. But he's upset by it. He says it is the misrepresentation that hurts him so; that, though he can stand a fair attack, he can't stand lies that he's powerless to refute and stop from spreading. That's just Trewe's weak point. He lives so much by himself that these things affect him much more than they would if he were in the bustle of fashionable or commercial life. So he wouldn't come here, making the excuse that it all looked so new and monied—if you'll pardon——"

"But—he must have known—there was sympathy here! Has he never said anything about getting letters from this address?"

"Yes, yes, he has, from John Ivy—perhaps a relative of yours, he thought, visiting here at the time?"

Did he—like Ivy, did he say?"

"Well, I don't know that he took any great interest in Ivy."

"Or in his poems?"

"Or in his poems—so far as I know, that is."

Robert Trewe took no interest in her house, in her poems, or in their writer. As soon as she could get away she went into the nursery and tried to let off her emotion by unnecessarily kissing the children, till she had a sudden sense of disgust at being reminded how plain-looking they were, like their father.

The obtuse and single-minded landscape-painter never once perceived from her conversation that it was only Trewe she wanted, and not himself. He made the best of his visit, seeming to enjoy the society of Ella's husband, who also took a great fancy to him, and showed him everywhere about the neighbourhood, neither of them noticing Ella's mood.

The painter had been gone only a day or two when, while sitting upstairs alone one morning, she glanced over the London paper just arrived, and read the following paragraph:—

SUICIDE OF A POET

Mr. Robert Trewe, who has been favourably known for some years as one of our rising lyrists, committed suicide at his lodgings at Solentsea on Saturday evening last by shooting himself in the right temple with a revolver. Readers hardly need to be reminded that Mr. Trewe has recently attracted the attention of a much wider public than had hitherto known him, by his new volume of verse, mostly of an impassioned kind, entitled "Lyrics to a Woman Unknown," which has been already favourably noticed in these pages for the extraordinary gamut of feeling it traverses, and which has been made the subject of a severe,

> if not ferocious, criticism in the —— *Review.* It is supposed, though not certainly known, that the article may have partially conduced to the sad act, as a copy of the review in question was found on his writing-table; and he has been observed to be in a somewhat depressed state of mind since the critique appeared.

Then came the report of the inquest, at which the following letter was read, it having been addressed to a friend at a distance:—

> Dear ——, —Before these lines reach your hands I shall be delivered from the inconveniences of seeing, hearing, and knowing more of the things around me. I will not trouble you by giving my reasons for the step I have taken, though I can assure you they were sound and logical. Perhaps had I been blessed with a mother, or a sister, or a female friend of another sort tenderly devoted to me, I might have thought it worth while to continue my present existence. I have long dreamt of such an unattainable creature, as you know; and she, this undiscoverable, elusive one, inspired my last volume; the imaginary woman alone, for, in spite of what has been said in some quarters, there is no real woman behind the title. She has continued to the last unrevealed, unmet, unwon. I think it desirable to mention this in order that no blame may attach to any real woman as having been the cause of my decease by cruel or cavalier treatment of me. Tell my landlady that I am sorry to have caused her this unpleasantness; but my occupancy of the rooms will soon be forgotten. There are ample funds in my name at the bank to pay all expenses.
>
> R. Trewe

Ella sat for a while as if stunned, then rushed into the adjoining chamber and flung herself upon her face on the bed.

Her grief and distraction shook her to pieces; and she lay in this frenzy of sorrow for more than an hour. Broken words came every now and then from her quivering lips: "O, if he had only known of me—known of me—me! . . O, if I had only once met him—only once; and put my hand upon his hot forehead—kissed him—let him know how I loved him—that I would have suffered shame and scorn, would have lived and died, for him! Perhaps it would have saved his dear life! . . . But no—it was not allowed! God is a jealous God; and that happiness was not for him and me!"

All possibilities were over; the meeting was stultified. Yet it was almost visible to her in her fantasy even now, though it could never be substantiated—

> "The hour which might have been, yet might not be,
> Which man's and woman's heart conceived and bore,
> Yet whereof life was barren."

. . . .

She wrote to the landlady at Solentsea in the third person, in as subdued a style as she could command, enclosing a postal order for a sovereign, and informing Mrs. Hooper that Mrs. Marchmill had seen in the papers the sad account of the poet's death, and having been, as Mrs. Hooper was aware, much interested in Mr. Trewe during her stay at Coburg House, she would be obliged if Mrs. Hooper could obtain a small portion of his hair before his coffin was closed down, and send it her as a memorial of him, as also the photograph that was in the frame.

By the return-post a letter arrived containing what had been requested. Ella wept over the portrait and secured it in her private drawer; the lock of hair she tied with white ribbon and put in her bosom, whence she drew it and kissed every now and then in some unobserved nook.

"What's the matter?" said her husband, looking up from his newspaper on one of these occasions. "Crying over something? A lock of hair? Whose is it?"

"He's dead!" she murmured.

"Who?"

"I don't want to tell you, Will, just now, unless you insist!" she said, a sob hanging heavy in her voice.

"O, all right."

"Do you mind my refusing? I will tell you some day."

"It doesn't matter in the least, of course."

He walked away whistling a few bars of no tune in particular; and when he had got down to his factory in the city the subject came into Marchmill's head again.

He, too, was aware that a suicide had taken place recently at the house they had occupied at Solentsea. Having seen the volume of poems in his wife's hand of late, and heard fragments of the landlady's conversation about Trewe when they were her tenants, he all at once said to himself, "Why of course it's he! . . . How the devil did she get to know him? What sly animals women are!"

Then he placidly dismissed the matter, and went on with his daily affairs. By this time Ella at home had come to a determination. Mrs. Hooper, in sending the hair and photograph, had informed her of the day of the funeral; and as the morning and noon wore on an overpowering wish to know where they were laying him took possession of the sympathetic woman. Caring very little now what her husband or any one else might think of her eccentricities, she wrote Marchmill a brief note, stating that she was called away for the afternoon and evening, but would return on the following morning. This she left on his desk, and having given the same information to the servants, went out of the house on foot.

When Mr. Marchmill reached home early in the afternoon the servants looked anxious. The nurse took him privately aside, and hinted that her mistress's sadness during the past few days had been such that she feared she had gone out to drown herself. Marchmill reflected. Upon the whole he thought that she had not done that. Without saying whither he was bound he also started off, telling them not to sit up for him. He drove to the railway-station, and took a ticket for Solentsea.

It was dark when he reached the place, though he had come by a fast train, and he knew that if his wife had preceded him thither it could only have been by a slower train, arriving not a great while before his own. The season at Solentsea was now past: the parade was gloomy, and the flys were few and cheap. He asked the way to the Cemetery, and soon reached it. The gate was locked, but the keeper let him in, declaring, however, that there was nobody within the precincts. Although it was not late, the autumnal darkness had now become intense; and he found some difficulty in keeping to the serpentine path which led to the quarter where, as the man had told him, the one or two interments for the day had taken place. He stepped upon the grass, and, stumbling over some pegs, stooped now and then to discern if possible a figure against the sky. He could see none; but lighting on a spot where the soil was trodden, beheld a crouching object beside a newly made grave. She heard him, and sprang up.

"Ell, how silly this is!" he said indignantly. "Running away from home—I never heard such a thing! Of course I am not jealous of this unfortunate man; but it is too ridiculous that you, a married woman with three children and a fourth coming, should go losing your head like this over a dead lover! . . . Do you know you were locked in? You might not have been able to get out all night."

She did not answer.

"I hope it didn't go far between you and him, for your own sake."

"Don't insult me, Will."

"Mind, I won't have any more of this sort of thing; do you hear?"

"Very well," she said.

He drew her arm within his own, and conducted her out of the Cemetery. It was impossible to get back that night; and not wishing to be recognized in their present sorry condition he took her to a miserable little coffee-house close to the station, whence they departed early in the morning, travelling almost without speaking, under the sense that it was one of those dreary situations occurring in married life which words could not mend, and reaching their own door at noon.

The months passed, and neither of the twain ever ventured to start a conversation upon this episode. Ella seemed to be only too frequently in a sad and listless mood, which might almost have been called pining. The time was approaching when she would have to undergo the stress of childbirth for a fourth time, and that apparently did not tend to raise her spirits.

"I don't think I shall get over it this time!" she said one day.

"Pooh! what childish foreboding! Why shouldn't it be as well now as ever?"

She shook her head. "I feel almost sure I am going to die; and I should be glad, if it were not for Nelly, and Frank, and Tiny."

"And me!"

"You'll soon find somebody to fill my place," she murmured, with a sad smile. "And you'll have a perfect right to; I assure you of that."

"Ell, you are not thinking still about that—poetical friend of yours?"

She neither admitted nor denied the charge. "I am not going to get over my illness this time," she reiterated. "Something tells me I shan't."

This view of things was rather a bad beginning, as it usually is; and, in fact, six weeks later, in the month of May, she was lying in her room, pulseless and bloodless, with hardly strength enough left to follow up one feeble breath with another, the infant for whose unnecessary life she was slowly parting with her own being fat and well. Just before her death she spoke to Marchmill softly:—

"Will, I want to confess to you the entire circumstances of that—about you know what—that time we visited Solentsea. I can't tell what possessed me—how I could forget you so, my husband! But I had got into a morbid state: I thought you had been unkind; that you had neglected me; that you weren't up to my intellectual level, while he was, and far above it. I wanted a fuller appreciator, perhaps, rather than another lover——"

She could get no further then for very exhaustion; and she went off in sudden collapse a few hours later, without having said anything more to her husband on the subject of her love for the poet. William Marchmill, in truth, like most husbands of several years' standing, was little disturbed by retrospective jealousies, and had not shown the least anxiety to press her for confessions concerning a man dead and gone beyond any power of inconveniencing him more.

But when she had been buried a couple of years it chanced one day that, in turning over some forgotten papers that he wished to destroy before his second wife entered the house, he lighted on a lock of hair in an envelope, with the photograph of the deceased poet, a date being written on the back in his late wife's hand. It was that of the time they spent at Solentsea.

Marchmill looked long and musingly at the hair and portrait, for something struck him. Fetching the little boy who had been the death of his mother, now a noisy toddler, he took him on his knee, held the lock of hair against the child's head, and set up the photograph on the table behind, so that he could closely compare the features each countenance presented. By a known but inexplicable trick of Nature there were undoubtedly strong traces of resemblance to the man Ella had never seen; the dreamy and peculiar expression of the poet's face sat, as the transmitted idea, upon the child's, and the hair was of the same hue.

"I'm damned if I didn't think so!" murmured Marchmill. "Then she *did* play me false with that fellow at the lodgings! Let me see: the dates—the second week in August . . . the third week in May. . . . Yes . . .yes. . . . Get away, you poor little brat! You are nothing to me!"

Investigation and Comment

One direct clue to Hardy's outlook as a writer of fiction can be taken from a notation in his journal for July 1881:

> The writer's problem is, how to strike the balance between the uncommon and the ordinary, so as on the one hand to give interest, on the other to give reality. In working out this problem, human nature must never be abnormal, which is introducing incredibility. The uncommonness must be in the events, not in the characters. . . . A story must be exceptional enough to justify its telling. We tale-tellers are all Ancient Mariners, and none of us is warranted in stopping Wedding Guests (in other words, the hurrying public) unless he has something more unusual to relate than the ordinary experiences of every average man and woman.

Taking Hardy at his word, we see that "An Imaginative Woman" as a story follows closely the author's idea of what fiction should attempt. His central character, the young matron Ella Marchmill, is neither abnormal nor incredible. Like many women since Eve she is impressionable, sentimental, romantic, sometimes giddy, and of course imaginative. We must certainly be honest enough to admit that as a character Ella is fairly normal, and in view of her bookish interests and "poetic" sensibilities, we can accept her responses to chance events. It is chance that initially gives her the opportunity to spend her vacation in the lodgings of a poet; her character makes it entirely possible that she would choose the poet's room and cloister herself there. This initial act begins the story and sets into motion consequent events which lead to *catastrophe*. That such a chance and such a character are possible is the premise we are asked to accept, and from this premise the plot grows in logical sequence.

What happens to Ella during the course of the story is obviously the essence of Hardy's interest. "The uncommonness," he insists, "must be in the events. . . ." So he has devised such actions and "odd conjunctions" to forward his narrative as will arrest the attention of his readers and convince them of the "persistence of the unforeseen," of the forces of "crass casualty" that operate in human affairs, and of the eventual doom that first thwarts and eventually destroys the lives of ordinary (and also imperfect) human beings. Hardy establishes chance as a universal force operating in the life of each individual. Hence we do not find incredible the many other chance occurrences at the seaside resort.

Like other writers before him, Hardy also insists, in his novel *The Mayor of Casterbridge,* that "Character is fate." Thus Ella Marchmill as a woman with individual traits must respond *characteristically* to the existing forces of chance and blind coincidence. Her eventual fate is caused by—is indeed a result of—her characteristic responses to the chain of events that she faces. Fate, then, is the confluence of character and chance.

In these terms we may see more readily what Hardy was attempting to say through characterization and a carefully structured plot. In this narrative there are no loose ends; it is as though an architect had constructed his story's edifice from a blueprint reflecting precision and strict economy. A series of actions—all consequent upon the initial act and all growing one out of the other, bringing *conflict, suspense, coincidence,* and *irony* in their wake—carries the story to its final resolution. Ella and her imaginary lover, because of Hardy's calculated interplay of character and plot, are taken to what would seem their logical and irrevocable doom.

This story further provides some rather obvious examples of how plot "works" in a narrative. Readers will find no difficulty in charting the sequence of events: the Marchmills take rooms at Solentsea that are already leased by Robert Trewe; Ella instinctively chooses to stay in Trewe's bedroom; her children discover Trewe's clothing while playing hide-and-seek and Ella dons the "mantle of Elijah"; other personal mementos of the poet are exposed; Ella visits the islands where the poet is staying but fails to see him; her husband, leaving her alone for a certain time, returns unexpectedly and, sleeping with Ella, sees the poet's picture under the pillow; Ella arranges, through the landscape painter, a meeting with Trewe; the poet does not keep the appointment and returns to Solentsea; after he commits suicide she suffers a steady decline and dies after the birth of her fourth child. These are the more significant actions that make up the structural framework of the plot and they can be summarized easily enough.

Tied in with the action are obvious moments of *suspense:* Trewe is expected to call at the lodgings for his books; thus we think Ella will meet him; her husband returns to the bedroom to find the hidden photograph; we think Trewe and Ella will finally meet when we learn the painter has accepted her invitation; we cannot predict the husband's reaction when Ella throws herself on Trewe's grave and must be taken home; we wonder what will happen when Will suspects his wife of infidelity and indeed finds her with the dead poet's photograph and lock of hair. These incidents cause us to react with varying degrees of anticipation and suspense.

The *climax* of the story comes when Trewe impulsively passes the Marchmills' house and returns to Solentsea to end his life. Up to this point in the relationship of Ella and Trewe we have followed the *rising action* and its accompanying *complication.* With Trewe's death the "lovers" are "separated"; so his final act prepares us for the swift turn of events that follow, or the *falling action* that brings the story to a close.

As is often the case, the *denouement,* or "unknotting" of the plot, carries with it a kind of final irony. The husband looks at the small child and is convinced of his wife's infidelity. This *discovery* of his, which "unknots" his relationship to his dead wife, illustrates what is usually called *dramatic irony:* a character believes one thing to be true, whereas the reader knows the truth to be something else (often the opposite). In this instance we have the contrast between Marchmill's convictions about his wife and what the reader knows to be the truth about her.

Closely related to plot is *irony of situation:* we expect one turn of events, or fulfillment, but find that the reverse, or something quite different, actually and paradoxically takes place. Part of the irony of Ella's situation arises from our knowledge that she is often very near Robert Trewe but never sees him. The reader is left to reflect on the great discrepancy between appearance and reality, fact and fancy, what is and what might have been.

Consider the following questions:

1. What incidents in the plot, other than the graveyard episode, give Marchmill grounds for suspecting infidelity? Ironically, he is tormented by his own insensibility as he suspects his wife of infidelity; yet his wife has been guilty of a greater infidelity than adultery. Explain in what way she is really unfaithful to him. Does he deserve this treatment? Is poetic justice involved?

2. Hardy carefully makes it clear that the greater part of Ella's "love" for Trewe is a longing for a kind of spiritual life denied her; a hunger for what she might have been; an expression of her inner self which she has never been able to communicate to anyone else. Does this help make credible her fantastic relationship with Trewe and her lack of will to live? Explain.

3. Write a critical essay on Hardy's handling of plot. Consider a defense of his techniques, or criticize the flaws that detract from the story's success as a credible representation of "real" life. For instance, is chance overworked?

4. Write an essay on the concepts underlying Hardy's plot and structure in this story. Consider the philosophical implications of "crass casualty" as they are reflected in both physical and "mental" action. In other words, what—according to Hardy—does action mean?

STEPHEN CRANE

(1871–1900)

The Blue Hotel

The Palace Hotel at Fort Romper was painted a light blue, a shade that is on the legs of a kind of heron, causing the bird to declare its position against any background. The Palace Hotel, then, was always screaming and howling in a way that made the dazzling winter landscape of Nebraska seem only a gray swampish hush. It stood alone on the prairie, and when the snow was falling the town two hundred yards away was not visible. But when the traveler alighted at the railway station he was obliged to pass the Palace

Published 1952 by Alfred A. Knopf, Inc. in *Stephen Crane: An Omnibus* by Robert Wooster Stallman, reprinted by permission of the publisher.

Hotel before he could come upon the company of low clapboard houses which composed Fort Romper, and it was not to be thought that any traveler could pass the Palace Hotel without looking at it. Pat Scully, the proprietor, had proved himself a master of strategy when he chose his paints. It is true that on clear days, when the great transcontinental expresses, long lines of swaying Pullmans, swept through Fort Romper, passengers were overcome at the sight, and the cult that knows the brown-reds and the subdivisions of the dark greens of the East expressed shame, pity, horror, in a laugh. But to the citizens of this prairie town and to the people who would naturally stop there, Pat Scully had performed a feat. With this opulence and splendor, these creeds, classes, egotisms, that streamed through Romper on the rails day after day, they had no color in common.

As if the displayed delights of such a blue hotel were not sufficiently enticing, it was Scully's habit to go every morning and evening to meet the leisurely trains that stopped at Romper and work his seductions upon any man that he might see wavering, gripsack in hand.

One morning, when a snow-crusted engine dragged its long string of freight cars and its one passenger coach to the station, Scully performed the marvel of catching three men. One was a shaky and quick-eyed Swede, with a great shining cheap valise; one was a tall bronzed cowboy, who was on his way to a ranch near the Dakota line; one was a little silent man from the East, who didn't look it, and didn't announce it. Scully practically made them prisoners. He was so nimble and merry and kindly that each probably felt it would be the height of brutality to try to escape. They trudged off over the creaking board sidewalks in the wake of the eager little Irishman. He wore a heavy fur cap squeezed tightly down on his head. It caused his two red ears to stick out stiffly, as if they were made of tin.

At last, Scully, elaborately, with boisterous hospitality, conducted them through the portals of the blue hotel. The room which they entered was small. It seemed to be merely a proper temple for an enormous stove, which, in the center, was humming with godlike violence. At various points on its surface the iron had become luminous and glowed yellow from the heat. Beside the stove Scully's son Johnnie was playing High-Five with an old farmer who had whiskers both gray and sandy. They were quarreling. Frequently the old farmer turned his face toward a box of sawdust—colored brown from tobacco juice—that was behind the stove, and spat with an air of great impatience and irritation. With a loud flourish of words Scully destroyed the game of cards, and bustled his son upstairs with part of the baggage of the new guests. He himself conducted them to three basins of the coldest water in the world. The cowboy and the Easterner burnished themselves fiery red with this water, until it seemed to be some kind of metal-polish. The Swede, however, merely dipped his fingers gingerly and with trepidation. It was notable that throughout this series of small ceremonies the three travelers were made to feel that Scully was very benevolent. He was conferring great favors upon them. He handed the towel from one to another with an air of philanthropic impulse.

Afterward they went to the first room, and, sitting about the stove, listened to Scully's officious clamor at his daughters, who were preparing the midday meal. They reflected in the silence of experienced men who tread carefully amid new people. Nevertheless, the old farmer, stationary, invincible in his chair near the warmest part of the stove, turned his face from the sawdust-box frequently and addressed a glowing commonplace to the strangers. Usually he was answered in short but adequate sentences by either the cowboy or the Easterner. The Swede said nothing. He seemed to be occupied in making furtive estimates of each man in the room. One might have thought that he had the sense of silly suspicion which comes to guilt. He resembled a badly frightened man.

Later, at dinner, he spoke a little, addressing his conversation entirely to Scully. He volunteered that he had come from New York, where for ten years he had worked as a tailor. These facts seemed to strike Scully as fascinating, and afterward he volunteered that he had lived at Romper for fourteen years. The Swede asked about the crops and the price of labor. He seemed barely to listen to Scully's extended replies. His eyes continued to rove from man to man.

Finally, with a laugh and a wink, he said that some of these Western communities were very dangerous; and after his statement he straightened his legs under the table, tilted his head, and laughed again, loudly. It was plain that the demonstration had no meaning to the others. They looked at him wondering and in silence.

II

As the men trooped heavily back into the front room, the two little windows presented views of a turmoiling sea of snow. The huge arms of the wind were making attempts—mighty, circular, futile—to embrace the flakes as they sped. A gate-post like a still man with a blanched face stood aghast amid this profligate fury. In a hearty voice Scully announced the presence of a blizzard. The guests of the blue hotel, lighting their pipes, assented with grunts of lazy masculine contentment. No island of the sea could be exempt in the degree of this little room with its humming stove. Johnnie, son of Scully, in a tone which defined his opinion of his ability as a card-player, challenged the old farmer of both gray and sandy whiskers to a game of High-Five. The farmer agreed with a contemptuous and bitter scoff. They sat close to the stove, and squared their knees under a wide board. The cowboy and the Easterner watched the game with interest. The Swede remained near the window, aloof, but with a countenance that showed signs of an inexplicable excitement.

The play of Johnnie and the gray-beard was suddenly ended by another quarrel. The old man arose while casting a look of heated scorn at his adversary. He slowly buttoned his coat, and then stalked with fabulous dignity from the room. In the discreet silence of all other men the Swede laughed. His laughter rang somehow childish. Men by this time had begun to look at him askance, as if they wished to inquire what ailed him.

A new game was formed jocosely. The cowboy volunteered to become the partner of Johnnie, and they all then turned to ask the Swede to throw in his lot with the little Easterner. He asked some questions about the game, and, learning that it wore many names, and that he had played it when it was under an alias, he accepted the invitation. He strode toward the men nervously, as if he expected to be assaulted. Finally, seated, he gazed from face to face and laughed shrilly. This laugh was so strange that the Easterner looked up quickly, the cowboy sat intent and with his mouth open, and Johnnie paused, holding the cards with still fingers.

Afterward there was a short silence. Then Johnnie said, "Well, let's get at it. Come on now!" They pulled their chairs forward until their knees were bunched under the board. They began to play, and their interest in the game caused the others to forget the manner of the Swede.

The cowboy was a board-whacker. Each time that he held superior cards he whanged them, one by one, with exceeding force, down upon the improvised table, and took the tricks with a glowing air of prowess and pride that sent thrills of indignation into the hearts of his opponents. A game with a board-whacker in it is sure to become intense. The countenances of the Easterner and the Swede were miserable whenever the cowboy thundered down his aces and kings, while Johnnie, his eyes gleaming with joy, chuckled and chuckled.

Because of the absorbing play none considered the strange ways of the Swede. They paid strict heed to the game. Finally, during a lull caused by a new deal, the Swede suddenly addressed Johnnie: "I suppose there have been a good many men killed in this room." The jaws of the others dropped and they looked at him.

"What in hell are you talking about?" said Johnnie.

The Swede laughed again his blatant laugh, full of a kind of false courage and defiance. "Oh, you know what I mean all right," he answered.

"I'm a liar if I do!" Johnnie protested. The card was halted, and the men stared at the Swede. Johnnie evidently felt that as the son of the proprietor, he should make a direct inquiry. "Now, what might you be drivin' at, mister?" he asked. The Swede winked at him. It was a wink full of cunning. His fingers shook on the edge of the board. "Oh, maybe you think I have been to nowheres. Maybe you think I'm a tenderfoot?"

"I don't know nothin' about you," answered Johnnie, "and I don't give a damn where you've been. All I got to say is that I don't know what you're driving at. There hain't never been nobody killed in this room."

The cowboy, who had been steadily gazing at the Swede, then spoke: "What's wrong with you, mister?"

Apparently it seemed to the Swede that he was formidably menaced. He shivered and turned white near the corners of his mouth. He sent an appealing glance in the direction of the little Easterner. During these moments he did not forget to wear his air of advanced pot-valor. "They say they don't know what I mean," he remarked mockingly to the Easterner.

The latter answered after prolonged and cautious reflection. "I don't understand you," he said, impassively.

The Swede made a movement then which announced that he thought he had encountered treachery from the only quarter where he had expected sympathy, if not help. "Oh, I see you are all against me, I see—"

The cowboy was in a state of deep stupefaction. "Say," he cried, as he tumbled the deck violently down upon the board, "say, what are you gittin' at, hey?"

The Swede sprang up with the celerity of a man escaping from a snake on the floor. "I don't want to fight!" he shouted. "I don't want to fight!"

The cowboy stretched his long legs indolently and deliberately. His hands were in his pockets. He spat into the sawdust-box. "Well, who the hell thought you did?" he inquired.

The Swede backed rapidly toward a corner of the room. His hands were out protectingly in front of his chest, but he was making an obvious struggle to control his fright. "Gentlemen," he quavered, "I suppose I am going to be killed before I can leave this house! I suppose I am going to be killed before I can leave this house!" In his eyes was the dying-swan look. Through the windows could be seen the snow turning blue in the shadow of dusk. The wind tore at the house, and some loose thing beat regularly against the clapboards like a spirit tapping.

A door opened, and Scully himself entered. He paused in surprise as he noted the tragic attitude of the Swede. Then he said, "What's the matter here?"

The Swede answered him swiftly and eagerly: "These men are going to kill me."

"Kill you!" ejaculated Scully. "Kill you! What are you talkin'?"

The Swede made the gesture of a martyr.

Scully wheeled sternly upon his son. "What is this, Johnnie?"

The lad had grown sullen. "Damned if I know," he answered. "I can't make no sense to it." He began to shuffle the cards, fluttering them together with an angry snap. "He says a good many men have been killed in this room, or something like that. And he says he's goin' to be killed here too. I don't know what ails him. He's crazy, I shouldn't wonder."

Scully then looked for explanation to the cowboy, but the cowboy simply shrugged his shoulders.

"Kill you?" said Scully again to the Swede. "Kill you? Man, you're off your nut."

"Oh, I know," burst out the Swede. "I know what will happen. Yes,

I'm crazy—yes. Yes, of course, I'm crazy—yes. But I know one thing—" There was a sort of sweat of misery and terror upon his face. "I know I won't get out of here alive."

The cowboy drew a deep breath, as if his mind was passing into the last stages of dissolution. "Well, I'm doggoned," he whispered to himself.

Scully wheeled suddenly and faced his son. "You've been troublin' this man!"

Johnnie's voice was loud with its burden of grievance. "Why, good Gawd, I ain't done nothin' to 'im."

The Swede broke in. "Gentlemen, do not disturb yourselves. I will leave this house. I will go away, because"—he accused them dramatically with his glance—"because I do not want to be killed."

Scully was furious with his son. "Will you tell me what is the matter, you young divil? What's the matter, anyhow? Speak out!"

"Blame it!" cried Johnnie in despair, "don't I tell you I don't know? He—he says we want to kill him, and that's all I know. I can't tell what ails him."

The Swede continued to repeat: "Never mind, Mr. Scully; never mind. I will leave this house. I will go away, because I do not wish to be killed. Yes, of course, I am crazy—yes. But I know one thing! I will go away. I will leave this house. Never mind, Mr. Scully; never mind. I will go away."

"You will not go 'way," said Scully. "You will not go 'way until I hear the reason of this business. If anybody has troubled you I will take care of him. This is my house. You are under my roof, and I will not allow any peaceable man to be troubled here." He cast a terrible eye upon Johnnie, the cowboy, and the Easterner.

"Never mind, Mr. Scully; never mind. I will go away. I do not wish to be killed." The Swede moved toward the door which opened upon the stairs. It was evidently his intention to go at once for his baggage.

"No, no," shouted Scully peremptorily; but the white-faced man slid by him and disappeared. "Now," said Scully severely, "what does this mane?"

Johnnie and the cowboy cried together: "Why, we didn't do nothin' to 'im!"

Scully's eyes were cold. "No," he said, "you didn't?"

Johnnie swore a deep oath. "Why, this is the wildest loon I ever see. We didn't do nothin' at all. We were jest sittin' here playin' cards, and he—"

The father suddenly spoke to the Easterner, "Mr. Blanc," he asked, "what has these boys been doin'?"

The Easterner reflected again. "I didn't see anything wrong at all," he said at last, slowly.

Scully began to howl. "But what does it mane?" He stared ferociously at his son. "I have a mind to lather you for this, me boy."

Johnnie was frantic. "Well, what have I done?" he bawled at his father.

III

"I think you are tongue-tied," said Scully finally to his son, the cowboy, and the Easterner; and at the end of this scornful sentence he left the room.

Upstairs the Swede was swiftly fastening the straps of his great valise. Once his back happened to be half turned toward the door, and, hearing a noise there, he wheeled and sprang up, uttering a loud cry. Scully's wrinkled visage showed grimly in the light of the small lamp he carried. This yellow effulgence, streaming upward, colored only his prominent features, and left his eyes, for instance, in mysterious shadow. He resembled a murderer.

"Man! man!" he exclaimed, "have you gone daffy?"

"Oh, no! Oh, no!" rejoined the other. "There are people in this world who know pretty nearly as much as you do—understand?"

For a moment they stood gazing at each other. Upon the Swede's deathly pale cheeks were two spots brightly crimson and sharply edged, as if they had been carefully painted. Scully placed the light on the table and sat himself on the edge of the bed. He spoke ruminatively. "By cracky, I never heard of such a thing in my life. It's a complete muddle. I can't, for the soul of me, think how you ever got this idea into your head." Presently he lifted his eyes and asked: "And did you sure think they were going to kill you?"

The Swede scanned the old man as if he wished to see into his mind. "I did," he said at last. He obviously suspected that this answer might precipitate an outbreak. As he pulled on a strap his whole arm shook, the elbow wavering like a bit of paper.

Scully banged his hand impressively on the footboard of the bed. "Why, man, we're goin' to have a line of ilictric street-cars in this town next spring."

" 'A line of electric street-cars,' " repeated the Swede, stupidly.

"And," said Scully, "there's a new railroad goin' to be built down from Broken Arm to here. Not to mintion the four churches and the smashin' big brick schoolhouse. Then there's the big factory, too. Why, in two years Romper'll be a met-tro-*pol*-is."

Having finished the preparation of his baggage, the Swede straightened himself. "Mr. Scully," he said, with sudden hardihood, "how much do I owe you?"

"You don't owe me anythin'," said the old man, angrily.

"Yes, I do," retorted the Swede. He took seventy-five cents from his pocket and tendered it to Scully; but the latter snapped his fingers in disdainful refusal. However, it happened that they both stood gazing in a strange fashion at three silver pieces on the Swede's open palm.

"I'll not take your money," said Scully at last. "Not after what's been goin' on here." Then a plan seemed to strike him. "Here," he cried, picking up his lamp and moving toward the door. "Here! Come with me a minute."

"No," said the Swede, in overwhelming alarm.

"Yes," urged the old man. "Come on! I want you to come and see a picter—just across the hall—in my room."

The Swede must have concluded that his hour was come. His jaw dropped and his teeth showed like a dead man's. He ultimately followed Scully across the corridor, but he had the step of one hung in chains.

Scully flashed the light high on the wall of his own chamber. There was revealed a ridiculous photograph of a little girl. She was leaning against a balustrade of gorgeous decoration, and the formidable bang to her hair was prominent. The figure was as graceful as an upright sled-stake, and, withal, it was of the hue of lead. "There," said Scully, tenderly, "that's the picter of my little girl that died. Her name was Carrie. She had the purtiest hair you ever saw! I was that fond of her, she—"

Turning then, he saw that the Swede was not contemplating the picture at all, but, instead, was keeping keen watch on the gloom in the rear.

"Look, man!" cried Scully, heartily. "That's the picter of my little gal that died. Her name was Carrie. And then here's the picter of my oldest boy, Michael. He's a lawyer in Lincoln, an' doin' well. I gave that boy a grand eddication, and I'm glad for it now. He's a fine boy. Look at 'im now. Ain't he bold as blazes, him there in Lincoln, an honored an' respicted gintleman! An honored and respicted gintleman," concluded Scully with a flourish. And, so saying, he smote the Swede jovially on the back.

The Swede faintly smiled.

"Now," said the old man, "there's only one more thing." He dropped suddenly to the floor and thrust his head beneath the bed. The Swede could hear his muffled voice. "I'd keep it under me piller if it wasn't for that boy Johnnie. Then there's the old woman— Where is it now? I never put it twice in the same place. Ah, now come out with you!"

Presently he backed clumsily from under the bed, dragging with him an old coat rolled into a bundle. "I've fetched him," he muttered. Kneeling on the floor, he unrolled the coat and extracted from its heart a large yellow-brown whisky-bottle.

His first maneuver was to hold the bottle up to the light. Reassured, apparently, that nobody had been tampering with it, he thrust it with a generous movement toward the Swede.

The weak-kneed Swede was about to eagerly clutch this element of strength, but he suddenly jerked his hand away and cast a look of horror upon Scully.

"Drink," said the old man affectionately. He had risen to his feet, and now stood facing the Swede.

There was a silence. Then again Scully said: "Drink!"

The Swede laughed wildly. He grabbed the bottle, put it to his mouth; and as his lips curled absurdly around the opening and his throat worked, he kept his glance, burning with hatred, upon the old man's face.

IV

After the departure of Scully the three men, with the cardboard still upon their knees, preserved for a long time an astounded silence. Then Johnnie said: "That's the doddangedest Swede I ever see."

"He ain't no Swede," said the cowboy, scornfully.

"Well, what is he then?" cried Johnnie. "What is he then?"

"It's my opinion," replied the cowboy deliberately, "he's some kind of a Dutchman." It was a venerable custom of the country to entitle as Swedes all light-haired men who spoke with a heavy tongue. In consequence the idea of the cowboy was not without its daring. "Yes, sir," he repeated, "It's my opinion this feller is some kind of a Dutchman."

"Well, he says he's a Swede, anyhow," muttered Johnnie, sulkily. He turned to the Easterner: "What do you think, Mr. Blanc?"

"Oh, I don't know," replied the Easterner.

"Well, what do you think makes him act that way?" asked the cowboy.

"Why, he's frightened." The Easterner knocked his pipe against a rim of the stove. "He's clear frightened out of his boots."

"What at?" cried Johnnie and the cowboy together.

The Easterner reflected over his answer.

"What at?" cried the others again.

"Oh, I don't know but it seems to me this man has been reading dime novels, and he thinks he's right out in the middle of it—the shootin' and stabbin' and all."

"But," said the cowboy, deeply scandalized, "this ain't Wyoming, ner none of them places. This is Nebrasker."

"Yes," added Johnnie, "an' why don't he wait till he gits *out West*?"

The traveled Easterner laughed. "It isn't different there even—not in these days. But he thinks he's right in the middle of hell."

Johnnie and the cowboy mused long.

"It's awful funny," remarked Johnnie at last.

"Yes," said the cowboy, "This is a queer game. I hope we don't git snowed in, because then we'd have to stand this here man bein' around with us all the time. That wouldn't be no good."

"I wish pop would throw him out," said Johnnie.

Presently they heard a loud stamping on the stairs, accompanied by ringing jokes in the voice of old Scully, and laughter, evidently from the Swede. The men around the stove stared vacantly at each other. "Gosh!" said the cowboy. The door flew open, and old Scully, flushed and anecdotal, came into the room. He was jabbering at the Swede, who followed him, laughing bravely. It was the entry of two roisterers from a banquet hall.

"Come now," said Scully sharply to the three seated men, "move up and give us a chance at the stove." The cowboy and the Easterner obediently sidled their chairs to make room for the new-comers. Johnnie, however, simply arranged himself in a more indolent attitude, and then remained motionless.

"Come! Git over, there," said Scully.

"Plenty of room on the other side of the stove," said Johnnie.

"Do you think we want to sit in the draught? roared the father.

But the Swede here interposed with a grandeur of confidence. "No, no. Let the boy sit where he likes," he cried in a bullying voice to the father.

"All right! All right!" said Scully, deferentially. The cowboy and the Easterner exchanged glances of wonder.

The five chairs were formed in a crescent about one side of the stove. The Swede began to talk; he talked arrogantly, profanely, angrily. Johnnie, the cowboy, and the Easterner maintained a morose silence, while old Scully appeared to be receptive and eager, breaking in constantly with sympathetic ejaculations.

Finally the Swede announced that he was thirsty. He moved in his chair, and said that he would go for a drink of water.

"I'll git it for you," cried Scully at once.

"No, said the Swede, contemptuously. "I'll get it for myself." He arose and stalked with the air of an owner off into the executive parts of the hotel.

As soon as the Swede was out of hearing Scully sprang to his feet and whispered intensely to the others: "Upstairs he thought I was tryin' to poison 'im."

"Say," said Johnnie, "this makes me sick. Why don't you throw 'im out in the snow?"

"Why, he's all right now," declared Scully. "It was only that he was from the East, and he thought this was a tough place. That's all. He's all right now."

The cowboy looked with admiration upon the Easterner. "You were straight," he said. "You were on to that there Dutchman."

"Well," said Johnnie to his father, "he may be all right now, but I don't see it. Other time he was scared, but now he's too fresh."

Scully's speech was always a combination of Irish brogue and idiom, Western twang and idiom, and scraps of curiously formal diction taken from the story-books and newspapers. He now hurled a strange mass of language at the head of his son. "What do I keep? What do I keep? What do I keep?" he demanded, in a voice of thunder. He slapped his knee impressively, to indicate that he himself was going to make reply, and that all should heed. "I keep a hotel," he shouted. "A hotel, do you mind? A guest under my roof has sacred privileges. He is to be intimidated by none. Not one word shall he hear that would prijudice him in favor of goin' away. I'll not have it. There's no place in this here town where they can say they iver took in a guest of mine because he was afraid to stay here." He wheeled suddenly upon the cowboy and the Easterner. "Am I right?"

"Yes, Mr. Scully," said the cowboy, "I think you're right."

"Yes, Mr. Scully," said the Easterner, "I think you're right."

V

At six-o'clock supper, the Swede fizzed like a firewheel. He sometimes seemed on the point of bursting into riotous song, and in all his madness he was encouraged by old Scully. The Easterner was encased in reserve; the cowboy sat in wide-mouthed amazement, forgetting to eat, while Johnnie wrathily demolished great plates of food. The daughters of the house, when they were obliged to replenish the biscuits, approached as warily as Indians, and, having succeeded in their purpose, fled with ill-concealed trepidation. The Swede domineered the whole feast, and he gave it the appearance of a cruel bacchanal. He seemed to have grown suddenly taller; he gazed brutally disdainful, into every face. His voice rang through the room. Once when he jabbed out harpoon-fashion with his fork to pinion a biscuit, the weapon nearly impaled the hand of the Easterner, which had been stretched quietly out for the same biscuit.

After supper, as the men filed toward the other room, the Swede smote Scully ruthlessly on the shoulder. "Well, old boy, that was a good, square meal." Johnnie looked hopefully at his father; he knew that shoulder was tender from an old fall; and, indeed, it appeared for a moment as if Scully was going to flame out over the matter, but in the end he smiled a sickly smile and remained silent. The others understood from his manner that he was admitting his responsibility for the Swede's new viewpoint.

Johnnie, however, addressed his parent in an aside. "Why don't you license somebody to kick you downstairs?" Scully scowled darkly by way of reply.

When they were gathered about the stove, the Swede insisted on another game of High-Five. Scully gently deprecated the plan at first, but the Swede turned a wolfish glare upon him. The old man subsided, and the Swede canvassed the others. In his tone there was always a great threat. The cowboy and the Easterner both remarked indifferently that they would play. Scully said that he would presently have to go to meet the 6:58 train, and so the Swede turned menacingly upon Johnnie. For a moment their glances crossed like blades, and then Johnnie smiled and said, "Yes, I'll play."

They formed a square, with the little board on their knees. The Easterner and the Swede were again partners. As the play went on, it was noticeable that the cowboy was not board-whacking as usual. Meanwhile, Scully, near the lamp, had put on his spectacles and, with an appearance curiously like an old priest, was reading a newspaper. In time he went out to meet the 6:58 train, and, despite his precautions, a gust of polar wind whirled into the room as he opened the door. Besides scattering the cards, it chilled the players to the marrow. The Swede cursed frightfully. When Scully returned, his entrance disturbed a cozy and friendly scene. The Swede again cursed. But presently they were once more intent, their heads bent forward and their hands moving swiftly. The Swede had adopted the fashion of board-whacking.

Scully took up his paper and for a long time remained immersed in matters which were extraordinarily remote from him. The lamp burned badly and once he stopped to adjust the wick. The newspaper, as he turned from page to page, rustled with a slow and comfortable sound. Then suddenly he heard three terrible words: "You are cheatin'!"

Such scenes often prove that there can be little of dramatic import in environment. Any room can present a tragic front; any room can be comic. This little den was now hideous as a torture-chamber. The new faces of the men themselves had changed it upon the instant. The Swede held a huge fist in front of Johnnie's face, while the latter looked steadily over it into the blazing orbs of his accuser. The Easterner had grown pallid; the cowboy's jaw had dropped in that expression of bovine amazement which was one of his important mannerisms. After the three words, the first sound in the room was made by Scully's paper as it floated forgotten to his feet. His spectacles had also fallen from his nose, but by a clutch he had saved them in air. His hand, grasping the spectacles, now remained poised awkwardly and near his shoulder. He stared at the card-players.

Probably the silence was while a second elapsed. Then, if the floor had been suddenly twitched out from under the men they could not have moved quicker. The five had projected themselves headlong toward a common point. It happened that Johnnie, in rising to hurl himself upon the Swede, had stumbled slightly because of his curiously instinctive care for the cards and the board. The loss of the moment allowed time for the arrival of Scully, and also allowed the cowboy time to give the Swede a great push which sent him staggering back. The men found tongue together, and hoarse shouts of rage, appeal, or fear burst from every throat. The cowboy pushed and jostled feverishly at the Swede, and the Easterner and Scully clung wildly to Johnnie; but through the smoky air, above the swaying bodies of the peace-compellers, the eyes of the two warriors ever sought each other in glances of challenge that were at once hot and steely.

Of course the board had been overturned, and now the whole company of cards was scattered over the floor, where the boots of the men trampled the fat and painted kings and queens as they gazed with their silly eyes at the war that was waging above them.

Scully's voice was dominating the yells. "Stop now! Stop, I say! Stop, now—"

Johnnie, as he struggled to burst through the rank formed by Scully and the Easterner, was crying, "Well, he says I cheated! He says I cheated! I won't allow no man to say I cheated! If he says I cheated, he's a ——!"

The cowboy was telling the Swede, "Quit now! Quit, d'ye hear—"

The screams of the Swede never ceased: "He did cheat! I saw him! I saw him—"

As for the Easterner, he was importuning in a voice that was not heeded: "Wait a moment, can't you? Oh, wait a moment. What's the good of a fight over a game of cards? Wait a moment—"

In this tumult no complete sentences were clear. "Cheat"—"Quit"—"He says"—these fragments pierced the uproar and rang out sharply. It was remarkable that, whereas Scully undoubtedly made the most noise, he was the least heard of any of the riotous band.

Then suddenly there was a great cessation. It was as if each man had paused for breath; and although the room was still lighted with the anger of men, it could be seen that there was no danger of immediate conflict, and at once Johnnie, shouldering his way forward, almost succeeded in confronting the Swede. "What did you say I cheated for? What did you say I cheated for? I don't cheat, and I won't let any man say I do!"

The Swede said, "I saw you! I saw you!"

"Well," cried Johnnie, "I'll fight any man what says I cheat!"

"No, you won't," said the cowboy. "Not here."

"Ah, be still, can't you?" said Scully, coming between them.

The quiet was sufficient to allow the Easterner's voice to be heard. He was repeating, "Oh, wait a moment, can't you? What's the good of a fight over a game of cards? Wait a moment!"

Johnnie, his red face appearing above his father's shoulder, hailed the Swede again. "Did you say I cheated?"

The Swede showed his teeth. "Yes."

"Then," said Johnnie, "we must fight."

"Yes, fight," roared the Swede. He was like a demoniac. "Yes, fight! I'll show you what kind of a man I am! I'll show you who want to fight! Maybe you think I can't fight! Maybe you think I can't! I'll show you, you skin, you card-sharp! Yes, you cheated! You cheated! You cheated!"

"Well, let's go at it, then, mister," said Johnnie, coolly.

The cowboy's brow was beaded with sweat from his efforts in intercepting all sorts of raids. He turned in despair to Scully. "What are you goin' to do now?"

A change had come over the Celtic visage of the old man. He now seemed all eagerness; his eyes glowed.

"We'll let them fight," he answered, stalwartly. "I can't put up with it any longer. I've stood this damned Swede till I'm sick. We'll let them fight."

VI

The men prepared to go out of doors. The Easterner was so nervous that he had great difficulty in getting his arms into the sleeves of his new leather coat. As the cowboy drew his fur cap down over his ears his hands trembled.

In fact, Johnnie and old Scully were the only ones who displayed no agitation. These preliminaries were conducted without words.

Scully threw open the door. "Well, come on," he said. Instantly a terrific wind caused the flame of the lamp to struggle at its wick, while a puff of black smoke sprang from the chimney-top. The stove was in mid-current of the blast, and its voice swelled to equal the roar of the storm. Some of the scarred and bedabbled cards were caught up from the floor and dashed helplessly against the farther wall. The men lowered their heads and plunged into the tempest as into a sea.

No snow was falling, but great whirls and clouds of flakes, swept up from the ground by the frantic winds, were streaming southward with the speed of bullets. The covered land was blue with the sheen of an unearthly satin, and there was no other hue save where, at the low, black railway station—which seemed incredibly distant—one light gleamed like a tiny jewel. As the men floundered into a thigh-deep drift, it was known that the Swede was bawling out something. Scully went to him, put a hand on his shoulder, and projected an ear. "What's that you say?" he shouted.

"I say," bawled the Swede again, "I won't stand much show against this gang. I know you'll all pitch on me."

Scully smote him reproachfully on the arm. "Tut, man!" he yelled. The wind tore the words from Scully's lips and scattered them far alee.

"You are all a gang of—" boomed the Swede, but the storm also seized the remainder of this sentence.

Immediately turning their backs upon the wind, the men had swung around a corner to the sheltered side of the hotel. It was the function of the little house to preserve here, amid this great devastation of snow, an irregular V-shape of heavily encrusted grass, which crackled beneath the feet. One could imagine the great drifts piled against the windward side. When the party reached the comparative peace of this spot it was found that the Swede was still bellowing.

"Oh, I know what kind of a thing this is! I know you'll all pitch on me. I can't lick you all!"

Scully turned upon him panther-fashion. "You'll not have to whip all of us. You'll have to whip my son Johnnie. An' the man what troubles you durin' that time will have me to dale with."

The arrangements were swiftly made. The two men faced each other, obedient to the harsh commands of Scully, whose face, in the subtly luminous gloom, could be seen set in the austere impersonal lines that are pictured on the countenances of the Roman veterans. The Easterner's teeth were chattering, and he was hopping up and down like a mechanical toy. The cowboy stood rock-like.

The contestants had not stripped off any clothing. Each was in his ordinary attire. Their fists were up, and they eyed each other in a calm that had the elements of leonine cruelty in it.

During this pause, the Easterner's mind, like a film, took lasting impressions of three men—the iron-nerved master of the ceremony; the Swede, pale, motionless, terrible; and Johnnie, serene yet ferocious, brutish yet heroic. The entire prelude had in it a tragedy greater than the tragedy of action, and this aspect was accentuated by the long, mellow cry of the blizzard, as it sped the tumbling and wailing flakes into the black abyss of the south.

"Now!" said Scully.

The two combatants leaped forward and crashed together like bullocks. There was heard the cushioned sound of blows, and of a curse squeezing out from between the tight teeth of one.

As for the spectactors, the Easterner's pent-up breath exploded from him with a pop of relief, absolute relief from the tension of the preliminaries. The cowboy bounded into the air with a yowl. Scully was immovable as from supreme amazement and fear at the fury of the fight which he himself had permitted and arranged.

For a time the encounter in the darkness was such a perplexity of flying arms that it presented no more detail than would a swiftly revolving wheel. Occasionally a face, as if illumined by a flash of light, would shine out, ghastly and marked with pink spots. A moment later, the men might have been known as shadows, if it were not for the involuntary utterance of oaths that came from them in whispers.

Suddenly a holocaust of warlike desire caught the cowboy, and he bolted forward with the speed of a broncho. "Go it, Johnnie! go it! Kill him! Kill him!"

Scully confronted him. "Kape back," he said; and by his glance the cowboy could tell that this man was Johnnie's father.

To the Easterner there was a monotony of unchangeable fighting that was an abomination. This confused mingling was eternal to his sense, which was concentrated in a longing for the end, the priceless end. Once the fighters lurched near him, and as he scrambled hastily backward he heard them breathe like men on the rack.

"Kill him, Johnnie! Kill him! Kill him! Kill him!" The cowboy's face was contorted like one of those agony masks in museums.

"Keep still," said Scully, icily.

Then there was a sudden loud grunt, incomplete, cut short, and Johnnie's body swung away from the Swede and fell with sickening heaviness to the grass. The cowboy was barely in time to prevent the mad Swede from flinging himself upon his prone adversary. "No, you don't," said the cowboy, interposing an arm. "Wait a second."

Scully was at his son's side. "Johnnie! Johnnie, me boy!" His voice had a quality of melancholy tenderness. "Johnnie! Can you go on with it?" He looked anxiously down into the bloody, pulpy face of his son.

There was a moment of silence, and then Johnnie answered in his ordinary voice, "Yes, I—it—yes."

Assisted by his father he struggled to his feet. "Wait a bit now till you git your wind," said the old man.

A few paces away the cowboy was lecturing the Swede. "No, you don't! Wait a second!"

The Easterner was plucking at Scully's sleeve. "Oh, this is enough," he pleaded. "This is enough! Let it go as it stands. This is enough!"

"Bill," said Scully, "git out of the road." The cowboy stepped aside. "Now." The combatants were actuated by a new caution as they advanced toward collision. They glared at each other, and then the Swede aimed a lightning blow that carried with it his entire weight. Johnnie was evidently half stupid from weakness, but he miraculously dodged, and his fist sent the over-balanced Swede sprawling.

The cowboy, Scully, and the Easterner burst into a cheer that was like a chorus of triumphant soldiery, but before its conclusion the Swede had scuffled agilely to his feet and come in berserk abandon at his foe. There was another perplexity of flying arms, and Johnnie's body again swung away and fell, even as a bundle might fall from a roof. The Swede instantly staggered to a little wind-waved tree and leaned upon it, breathing like an engine, while his savage and flame-lit eyes roamed from face to face as the men bent over Johnnie. There was a splendor of isolation in his situation at this time which the Easterner felt once when, lifting his eyes from the man on the ground, he beheld that mysterious and lonely figure, waiting.

"Are you any good yet, Johnnie?" asked Scully in a broken voice.

The son gasped and opened his eyes languidly. After a moment he answered, "No—I ain't—any good—any—more." Then, from shame and bodily ill, he began to weep, the tears furrowing down through the blood-stains on his face. "He was too—too—too heavy for me."

Scully straightened and addressed the waiting figure. "Stranger," he said, evenly, "it's all up with our side." Then his voice changed into that vibrant huskiness which is commonly the tone of the most simple and deadly announcements. "Johnnie is whipped."

Without replying, the victor moved off on the route to the front door of the hotel.

The cowboy was formulating new and unspellable blasphemies. The Easterner was startled to find that they were out in a wind that seemed to come direct from the shadowed arctic floes. He heard again the wail of the snow as it was flung to its grave in the south. He knew now that all this time the cold had been sinking into him deeper and deeper, and he wondered that he had not perished. He felt indifferent to the condition of the vanquished man.

"Johnnie, can you walk?" asked Scully.

"Did I hurt—hurt him any?" asked the son.

"Can you walk, boy? Can you walk?"

Johnnie's voice was suddenly strong. There was a robust impatience in it. "I asked you whether I hurt him any!"

"Yes, yes, Johnnie," answered the cowboy, consolingly; "he's hurt a good deal."

They raised him from the ground, and as soon as he was on his feet he went tottering off, rebuffing all attempts at assistance. When the party rounded the corner they were fairly blinded by the pelting of the snow. It burned their faces like fire. The cowboy carried Johnnie through the drift to the door. As they entered, some cards again rose from the floor and beat against the wall.

The Easterner rushed to the stove. He was so profoundly chilled that he almost dared to embrace the glowing iron. The Swede was not in the room. Johnnie sank into a chair and, folding his arms on his knees, buried his face in them. Scully, warming one foot and then the other at a rim of the stove, muttered to himself with Celtic mournfulness. The cowboy had removed his fur cap, and with a dazed and rueful air he was running one hand through his tousled locks. From overhead they could hear the creaking of boards, as the Swede tramped here and there in his room.

The sad quiet was broken by the sudden flinging open of a door that led toward the kitchen. It was instantly followed by an inrush of women. They precipitated themselves upon Johnnie amid a chorus of lamentation. Before they carried their prey off to the kitchen, there to be bathed and harangued with that mixture of sympathy and abuse which is a feat of their sex, the mother straightened herself and fixed old Scully with an eye of stern reproach. "Shame be upon you, Patrick Scully!" she cried. "Your own son, too. Shame be upon you!"

"There, now! Be quiet, now!" said the old man, weakly.

"Shame be upon you, Patrick Scully!" The girls, rallying to this slogan, sniffed disdainfully in the direction of those trembling accomplices, the cowboy and the Easterner. Presently they bore Johnnie away, and left the three men to dismal reflection.

VII

"I'd like to fight this here Dutchman myself," said the cowboy, breaking a long silence.

Scully wagged his head sadly. "No, that wouldn't do. It wouldn't be right. It wouldn't be right."

"Well, why wouldn't it?" argued the cowboy. "I don't see no harm in it."

"No," answered Scully, with mournful heroism. "It wouldn't be right. It was Johnnie's fight, and now we mustn't whip the man just because he whipped Johnnie."

"Yes, that's true enough," said the cowboy; "but—he better not get fresh with me, because I couldn't stand no more of it."

"You'll not say a word to him," commanded Scully, and even then they heard the tread of the Swede on the stairs. His entrance was made theatric. He swept the door back with a bang and swaggered to the middle of the room. No one looked at him. "Well," he cried, insolently, at Scully, "I s'pose you'll tell me now how much I owe you?"

The old man remained stolid. "You don't owe me nothin'."

"Huh!" said the Swede, "huh! Don't owe 'im nothin'."

The cowboy addressed the Swede. "Stranger, I don't see how you come to be so gay around here."

Old Scully was instantly alert. "Stop!" he shouted, holding his hand forth, fingers upward. "Bill, you shut up!"

The cowboy spat carelessly into the sawdust-box. "I didn't say a word, did I?" he asked.

"Mr. Scully," called the Swede, "how much do I owe you?" It was seen that he was attired for departure, and that he had his valise in his hand.

"You don't owe me nothin'," repeated Scully in the same imperturbable way.

"Huh!" said the Swede. "I guess you're right. I guess if it was any way at all, you'd owe me somethin'. That's what I guess." He turned to the cowboy. " 'Kill him! Kill him! Kill him!' " he mimicked, and then guffawed victoriously. " 'Kill him!' " He was convulsed with ironical humor.

But he might have been jeering the dead. The three men were immovable and silent, staring with glassy eyes at the stove.

The Swede opened the door and passed into the storm, giving one derisive glance backward at the still group.

As soon as the door was closed, Scully and the cowboy leaped to their feet and began to curse. They trampled to and fro, waving their arms and smashing into the air with their fists. "Oh, but that was a hard minute!" wailed Scully. "That was a hard minute! Him there leerin' and scoffin'! One bang at his nose was worth forty dollars to me that minute! How did you stand it, Bill?"

"How did I stand it?" cried the cowboy in a quivering voice. "How did I stand it? Oh!"

The old man burst into sudden brogue. "I'd loike to take that Swade," he wailed, "and hould 'im down on a shtone flure and bate 'im to a jelly wid a shtick!"

The cowboy groaned in sympathy. "I'd like to git him by the neck and ha-ammer him"—he brought his hand down on a chair with a noise like a pistol-shot—"hammer that there Dutchman until he couldn't tell himself from a dead coyote!"

"I'd bate 'im until he—"

"I'd show *him* some things—"

And then together they raised a yearning, fanatic cry—"Oh-o-oh! if we only could—"

"Yes!"

"Yes!"

"And then I'd—"

"O-o-oh!"

VIII

The Swede, tightly gripping his valise, tacked across the face of the storm as if he carried sails. He was following a line of little naked, gasping trees which, he knew, must mark the way of the road. His face, fresh from the pounding of Johnnie's fists, felt more pleasure than pain in the wind and the driving snow. A number of square shapes loomed upon him finally, and he knew them as the houses of the main body of the town. He found a street and made travel along it, leaning heavily upon the wind whenever, at a corner, a terrific blast caught him.

He might have been in a deserted village. We picture the world as thick with conquering and elate humanity, but here, with the bugles of the tempest pealing, it was hard to imagine a peopled earth. One viewed the existence of man then as a marvel, and conceded a glamour of wonder to these lice which were caused to cling to a whirling, fire-smitten, ice-locked, disease-stricken, space-lost bulb. The conceit of man was explained by this storm to be the very engine of life. One was a coxcomb not to die in it. However, the Swede found a saloon.

In front of it an indomitable red light was burning, and the snowflakes were made blood-color as they flew through the circumscribed territory of the lamp's shining. The Swede pushed open the door of the saloon and entered. A sanded expanse was before him, and at the end of it four men sat about a table drinking. Down one side of the room extended a radiant bar, and its guardian was leaning upon his elbows listening to the talk of the men at the table. The Swede dropped his valise upon the floor and, smiling fraternally upon the barkeeper, said, "Gimme some whisky, will you?" The man placed a bottle, a whisky-glass, and a glass of ice-thick water upon the bar. The Swede poured himself an abnormal portion of whisky and drank it in three gulps. "Pretty bad night," remarked the bartender, indifferently. He was making the pretension of blindness which is usually a distinction of his class; but it could have been seen that he was furtively studying the half-erased blood-stains on the face of the Swede. "Bad night," he said again.

"Oh, it's good enough for me," replied the Swede, hardily, as he poured himself some more whiskey. The barkeeper took his coin and maneuvered it through its reception by the highly nickeled cash-machine. A bell rang; a card labeled "20 cts." had appeared.

"No," continued the Swede, "this isn't too bad weather. It's good enough for me."

"So?" murmured the barkeeper, languidly.

The copious drams made the Swede's eyes swim, and he breathed a trifle heavier. "Yes, I like this weather. I like it. It suits me." It was apparently his design to impart a deep significance to these words.

"So?" murmured the bartender again. He turned to gaze dreamily at the scroll-like birds and bird-like scrolls which had been drawn with soap upon the mirrors in back of the bar.

"Well, I guess I'll take another drink," said the Swede, presently. "Have something?"

"No, thanks; I'm not drinkin'," answered the bartender. Afterward he asked, "How did you hurt your face?"

The Swede immediately began to boast loudly. "Why, in a fight. I thumped the soul out of a man down here at Scully's hotel."

The interest of the four men at the table was at last aroused.

"Who was it?" said one.

"Johnnie Scully," blustered the Swede. "Son of the man what runs it. He will be pretty near dead for some weeks, I can tell you. I made a nice thing of him, I did. He couldn't get up. They carried him in the house. Have a drink?"

Instantly the men in some subtle way encased themselves in reserve. "No, thanks," said one. The group was of curious formation. Two were prominent local business men; one was the district attorney; and one was a professional gambler of the kind known as "square." But a scrutiny of the group would not have enabled an observer to pick the gambler from the men of more reputable pursuits. He was, in fact, a man so delicate in manner, when among people of fair class, and so judicious in his choice of victims, that in the strictly masculine part of the town's life he had come to be explicitly trusted and admired. People called him a thoroughbred. The fear and contempt with which his craft was regarded were undoubtedly the reason why his quiet dignity shone conspicuous above the quiet dignity of men who might be merely hatters, billiard-markers, or grocery clerks. Beyond an occasional unwary traveler who came by rail, this gambler was supposed to prey solely upon reckless and senile farmers, who, when flush with good crops, drove into town in all the pride and confidence of an absolutely invulnerable stupidity. Hearing at times in circuitous fashion of the despoilment of such a farmer, the important men of Romper invariably laughed in contempt of the victim, and if they thought of the wolf at all, it was with a kind of pride at the knowledge that he would never dare think of attacking their wisdom and courage. Besides, it was popular that this gambler had a real wife and two real children in a neat cottage in a suburb, where he led an exemplary home life; and when anyone even suggested a discrepancy in his character, the crowd immediately vociferated descriptions of this virtuous family circle. Then men who led exemplary home lives, and men who did not lead exemplary home lives, all subsided in a bunch, remarking that there was nothing more to be said.

However, when a restriction was placed upon him—as, for instance, when a strong clique of members of the new Pollywog Club refused to permit him, even as a spectator, to appear in the rooms of the organization—the candor and gentleness with which he accepted the judgment disarmed many of his foes and made his friends more desperately partisan. He invariably distinguished between himself and a respectable Romper man so quickly and frankly that his manner actually appeared to be a continual broadcast compliment.

And one must not forget to declare the fundamental fact of his entire position in Romper. It is irrefutable that in all affairs outside his business, in all matters that occur eternally and commonly between man and man, this thieving card-player was so generous, so just, so moral, that, in a contest, he could have put to flight the consciences of nine tenths of the citizens of Romper.

And so it happened that he was seated in this saloon with the two prominent local merchants and the district attorney.

The Swede continued to drink raw whisky, meanwhile babbling at the barkeeper and trying to induce him to indulge in potations. "Come on. Have a drink. Come on. What—no? Well, have a little one, then. By gawd, I've whipped a man tonight, and I want to celebrate. I whipped him good, too. Gentlemen," the Swede cried to the men at the table, "have a drink?"

"Ssh!" said the barkeeper.

The group at the table, although furtively attentive, had been pretending to be deep in talk, but now a man lifted his eyes toward the Swede and said, shortly, "Thanks. We don't want any more."

At this reply the Swede ruffled out his chest like a rooster. "Well," he exploded, "it seems I can't get anybody to drink with me in this town. Seems so, don't it? Well!"

"Ssh!" said the barkeeper.

"Say," snarled the Swede, "don't you try to shut me up. I won't have it. I'm a gentleman, and I want people to drink with me. And I want 'em to drink with me now. *Now*—do you understand?" He rapped the bar with his knuckles.

Years of experience had calloused the bartender. He merely grew sulky. "I hear you," he answered.

"Well," cried the Swede, "listen hard then. See those men over there? Well, they're going to drink with me, and don't you forget it. Now you watch."

"Hi!" yelled the barkeeper, "this won't do!"

"Why won't it?" demanded the Swede. He stalked over to the table, and by chance laid his hand upon the shoulder of the gambler. "How about this?" he asked wrathfully. "I asked you to drink with me."

The gambler simply twisted his head and spoke over his shoulder. "My friend, I don't know you."

"Oh, hell!" answered the Swede, "come and have a drink."

"Now, my boy," advised the gambler, kindly, "take your hand off my shoulder and go 'way and mind your own business." He was a little, slim man, and it seemed strange to hear him use this tone of heroic patronage to the burly Swede. The other men at the table said nothing.

"What! You won't drink with me, you little dude? I'll make you, then! I'll make you!" The Swede had grasped the gambler frenziedly at the throat, and was dragging him from his chair. The other men sprang up. The barkeeper dashed around the corner of his bar. There was a great tumult, and then was seen a long blade in the hand of the gambler. It shot forward, and a human body, this citadel of virtue, wisdom, power, was pierced as easily as if it had been a melon. The Swede fell with a cry of supreme astonishment.

The prominent merchants and the district attorney must have at once tumbled out of the place backward. The bartender found himself hanging limply to the arm of a chair and gazing into the eyes of a murderer.

"Henry," said the latter, as he wiped his knife on one of the towels that hung beneath the bar rail, "you tell 'em where to find me. I'll be home, waiting for 'em." Then he vanished. A moment afterward the barkeeper was in the street dinning through the storm for help and, moreover, companionship.

The corpse of the Swede, alone in the saloon, had its eyes fixed upon a dreadful legend that dwelt atop of the cash-machine: "This registers the amount of your purchase."

IX

Months later, the cowboy was frying pork over the stove of a little ranch near the Dakota line, when there was a quick thud of hoofs outside, and presently the Easterner entered with the letters and the papers.

"Well," said the Easterner at once, "the chap that killed the Swede has got three years. Wasn't much, was it?"

"He has? Three years?" The cowboy poised his pan of pork, while he ruminated upon the news. "Three years. That ain't much."

"No. It was a light sentence," replied the Easterner as he unbuckled his spurs. "Seems there was a good deal of sympathy for him in Romper."

"If the bartender had been any good," observed the cowboy, thoughtfully, "he would have gone in and cracked that there Dutchman on the head with a bottle in the beginnin' of it and stopped all this here murderin'."

"Yes, a thousand things might have happened," said the Easterner, tartly.

The cowboy returned his pan of pork to the fire, but his philosophy continued. "It's funny, ain't it? If he hadn't said Johnnie was cheatin' he'd be alive this minute. He was an awful fool. Game played for fun, too. Not for money. I believe he was crazy."

"I feel sorry for that gambler," said the Easterner.

"Oh, so do I," said the cowboy. "He don't deserve none of it for killin' who he did."

"The Swede might not have been killed if everything had been square."

"Might not have been killed?" exclaimed the cowboy. "Everythin' square? Why, when he said that Johnnie was cheatin' and acted like such a jackass? And then in the saloon he fairly walked up to git hurt?" With these arguments the cowboy browbeat the Easterner and reduced him to rage.

"You're a fool!" cried the Easterner, viciously. "You're a bigger jackass than the Swede by a million majority. Now let me tell you one thing. Let me tell you something. Listen! Johnnie *was* cheating!"

" 'Johnnie,' " said the cowboy, blankly. There was a minute of silence, and then he said, robustly, "Why, no. The game was only for fun."

"Fun or not," said the Easterner, "Johnnie was cheating. I saw him. I know it. I saw him. And I refused to stand up and be a man. I let the Swede fight it out alone. And you—you were simply puffing around the place and wanting to fight. And then old Scully himself! We are all in it! This poor gambler isn't even a noun. He is kind of an adverb. Every sin is the result of a collaboration. We, five of us, have collaborated in the murder of this Swede. Usually there are from a dozen to forty women really involved in every murder, but in this case it seems to be only five men—you, I, Johnnie, old Scully; and that fool of an unfortunate gambler came merely as a culmination, the apex of a human movement, and gets all the punishment."

The cowboy, injured and rebellious, cried out blindly into this fog of mysterious theory: "Well, I didn't do anythin', did I?"

Study Guides

"The Blue Hotel" has many of the surface trappings of the familiar Western. Here we find the laconic cowboy, the slick gambler, the braggart gulping red-eye, the bleak prairie, and the raw frontier town. The very name Romper suggests childlike immaturity and crass, bursting vitality. Here too are the eternal card games, the knock-down, drag-out fight, the barroom killing. The story is crammed with brawling violence and exciting suspense, but unlike the brassy Western, "The Blue Hotel" is as much concerned with meaning as action. In fact, it is primarily concerned with the meaning of action. The brisk but careful plotting is merely one *modus operandi* for delivering a significant interpretation of man's relationship to fate, chance, or crass casualty. In the exploration of this relationship, Crane reveals concepts about civilization, human faults and virtues, laws of nature, and human responsibility such as excite the mature mind far more than the mere suspense and violence of overt action. In fact, the story resembles classical drama far more than it does a stereotype Western.

"The Blue Hotel" has a prologue, an epilogue, and a five-act structure. Act I ends with Scully going upstairs to join the Swede; Act II encompasses Parts III and IV; Act III takes place in Part V; Act IV depicts the fight in the storm and the Swede's departure; Act V is the scene in the barroom which ends with Part VIII. Part IX is the epilogue.

Further, as in Greek drama, the protagonist is a man not pre-eminently virtuous or evil; his misfortune results not from his vice and depravity but from some error of judgment, from a flaw in character which causes him to make a fatal miscalculation that is offensive to the laws of nature (gods, fate, cosmic order). Through poor judgment he supposes that he has complete mastery of his fate, and thus *hybris,* the great sin of overweening pride, affords him the illusion of unconquerable strength. In this self-deception he challenges fate, and the punishment of his arrogance and insolence is meted out by the *deus ex machina* (the direct hand of Fate). In Crane's story *deus ex machina* appears in the form of the Gambler, the high priest of the God of Chance.

The reader should now have the following points firmly in mind:

1. Sections I and IX constitute, respectively, a prologue and an epilogue. Each of the intervening five acts has its separate *complication, discovery* (a change from ignorance to knowledge), *reversal, climax,* and *denouement.* As an exercise, list these elements of plot in each "act."

2. Are the reversals and discoveries complete surprises or are they carefully prepared for by *foreshadowing* of character, imagery, and logical consequences of behavior? What is the function of the Swede's laugh and wink? Is it psychologically sound that a coward could turn bully? Why are you not surprised that in the fight Johnnie is defeated by the Swede and that the entire group turns against him—even Scully who before had been his champion? It is accident, more or less, that the Swede singles out the gambler for special attention, but it is no accident that the gambler reacts in the way he does. What circumstance of his character, coupled with the Swede's appearance and behavior, makes the stabbing inevitable? When do the various discoveries occur and how are they brought about? Does the reader make the discoveries before the characters? The Easterner makes two main discoveries, one about the Swede and one about himself. What are they? Pinpoint the exact moments of Johnnie's, the cowboy's, and Scully's discoveries.

With the plot firmly in mind, let us return now to the prologue. In classical drama the prologue was usually delivered by the chorus or a minor actor who served the function of introducing the chief characters, establishing the setting, and announcing the theme. In Crane's drama the prologue is delivered in the *voice* of the omniscient narrator, who, along with the Easterner, acts as a sort of chorus. The theme is announced by sounding the first of two *motifs:* the blue hotel itself. Its color, we are told, like the blue legs of a heron, causes it "to declare its position against any background." The blue, then, is its distinguishing mark, its identity, that which sets it apart from raw, encompassing nature. Thus the hotel begins to emerge as a symbol of all that is human as opposed to all that is inhuman, or all that is *supra*natural as opposed to all that is natural. Through this first motif we know that the story will deal with man against nature, the forces of human order against the forces of natural chaos.

To see how the first motif is resounded and elaborated, consider the following:

1. Upon entering the hotel, the three guests engage in a ritualistic ceremony suggestive of some sacred rite, a baptism, or a cleansing which "burnishes" them like "metal-polish." Notice, too, that Scully is described as a benevolent priest, and the three strangers are like postulants being prepared to enter the sacred "temple" and approach the presence of the "godlike" stove. Does this imagery recur elsewhere? How does the Swede react to the "baptism"? Is this significant? At intervals throughout the story, great attention is given to the stove. We are all familiar with the old-fashioned potbellied stove as the center of social communion and as a symbol of companionship, human concern, hospitality, convivial friendship. Notice each reference to the stove and especially each character's typical relation to the "god" which stands in contrast to the blizzard outside. Observe particularly the Swede's and the Easterner's responses to the stove after the fight in the storm. What else do these suggest about the nature of the hotel?

2. What other details can you discover that seem to parallel the ritualistic washing and the stove symbolism? What is the function of Scully's showing the picture of his dead child? How is this related to the brief but revealing biography of the gambler?

3. In contrast to the hospitable warmth and order of the hotel there is the cold violence and chaos of the world outside, always threatening entry and frequently intruding. When the cold blasts come through the door, what is the Swede's reaction? Are the Swede and the blast being equated? Just as violence is always threatening from the outside, so is disorder always threatening inside. What do these circumstances reveal about the hotel, its occupants, and the "blueness" of man? Does this threatening violence suggest that there is something natural to man that he finds hard to control? What brings on the climactic burst of violence in the hotel—the Swede's lack of faith and understanding, his later arrogance, Johnnie's cheating, or all these factors? What is signified when the actors leave the hotel and encounter the blizzard?

If violence and chaos, like the storm, are natural, gentleness and order must be unnatural or *supra*natural (a design or will imposed, *above* nature). Chance is chaotic—without design, without will, without order. The antithesis of chance is control—the methodizing of nature according to some set of prescribed and mutually understood rules, rituals, traditions, and conventions. Civilization, with its attendant games and arts, is nature methodized and controlled. Civilization, art, and games are therefore unnatural, even though they reflect nature. The ability to be civil, to control the forces of nature both within and without himself, is the "blue" of man that sets him apart from encompassing nature. Thus, though man is natural, he may also be *supra*natural.

The card game is a symbolic link between chaos and control, and as such it implies duality. It reflects the chaotic in that, first, in large measure it is a matter of chance, and second, it echoes the dog-eat-dog law of the jungle, being a somewhat vicarious kill-or-be-killed experience. However, as long as conventions and rules are thoroughly understood and strictly adhered to, and as long as the reflection of nature is not mistaken for the reality of nature, man's desire for violence and domination is given harmless expression. Also, though chance deals the cards, the game betokens civilization in that it permits man, by rules and conventions, to determine what fit response to casualty he may exercise through skillful control. One cannot participate in any game of civilization until one understands the particular conventions of the game; and, of course, when one cheats or breaks the rules, the game is ended and violence erupts; chaos enters to smoke up the lamp and dash the cards to the floor.

Observe the card game carefully:

1. What is revealed about each character through his typical reaction to the game? What knowledge possessed by the Easterner is revealed by his shouting: "What's the good of a fight over a game of cards!"? Which of the card players is the most civilized? Which the least? To the gambler the game is not merely one of cards; it is a means of survival, thus more a reality than a mere reflection. What are we told about his card-playing ethics? How does this information reflect the central theme? The gambler, the Easterner, and the Swede, in varying degrees, are outsiders to the particular civilization of Romper. Why? What is it about the gambler that makes him accepted in Romper? What is it that excludes him?

2. The Swede's misunderstanding of the ways of Romper and his insulting lack of faith in the natives are partially responsible for the ensuing catastrophe. Point out these misunderstandings.

The quarrels and disagreements bring us to the second motif, which is sounded with the Eastern passengers' reaction to the hotel. ". . . passengers were overcome at the sight, and the cult that knows the brown-reds and the subdivisions of the dark greens of the East expressed shame, pity, horror, in a laugh. [Remember the Swede's laugh.] But to the citizens of this prairie town and to the people who would naturally stop there, Pat Scully had performed a feat. With this opulence and splendor, these creeds, classes, egotisms, that streamed through Romper on the rails day after day, they had no color in common." Since "blue" is not the distinguishing color of civilization for the Easterners, they in great arrogance misunderstand it altogether and mistake it for a primitive vulgarity or depravity. Thus we see interwoven the theme of man's abiding conflict with "crass casualty" and the conflict of man's misunderstanding of his fellow man. This second conflict takes the pattern of West versus East.

1. But where are East and West? Where are they for the cowboy? For the Swede? Does the Easterner display the same arrogance as his fellow Easterner, the Swede? Point out all examples of East-West misunderstanding.

2. Civilization breaks down—even for the careful and understanding salesman, the phlegmatic cowboy, and the determinedly hospitable Scully—because of an insufficient concern for fellow men as individuals. Point out all examples in which individuals are abstracted into types and classes. Who is the worst offender? The least? Do abstraction and indifference explain the epilogue, Section IX, and the statement of mutual guilt and responsibility for the Swede's murder? What is the significance of the sign on the cash register?

3. Crane, like Hardy, postulates a "crass casualty" which surrounds man as a sea surrounds an island. This naturalism, derived from Darwinian theory, is the great god whose only rule states that chaos and chance shall be eternal fate and only the fittest may survive. The gods will destroy all who are not fit. The gambler, as was pointed out earlier, is a kind of counterpart to the *deus ex machina* of ancient drama; he is the hand of Fate, the instrument of Chance. As such he destroys the Swede for his *hybris*. Character also determines fate. The most fit characters and the most fit culture will survive. Who among the characters in this story are the most fit and what are the outlines of the culture that will endure?

Crane viewed the existence of man as a "marvel, and conceded a glamour of wonder to these lice which were caused to cling to a whirling, fire-smitten, ice-locked, disease-stricken, space-lost bulb." To Crane man is but a louse in relation to the terrible immensity of chaotic nature. But lice are gregarious creatures, and even in his "lousiness" and his "blueness" man can be a marvel and a wonder, and there is good reason to believe that he can survive.

J. F. POWERS

(1917–   )

Blue Island

On the day the Daviccis moved into their house, Ethel was visited by a "Welcome Wagon" hostess bearing small gifts from local merchants, but after that by nobody for three weeks, only Ralph's relatives and door-to-door salesmen. And then Mrs. Hancock came smiling. They sat on the matching green chairs which glinted with threads of what appeared to be gold. In the picture window, the overstimulated plants grew wild in pots.

Mrs. Hancock had guessed right about Ethel and Ralph, that they were newlyweds. "Am I right in thinking you're of Swedish descent, Mrs. Davicky? You, I mean?"

Ethel smiled, as if taking a compliment, and said nothing.

"I only ask because so many people in the neighborhood are. I'm not, myself," said Mrs. Hancock. She was unnaturally pink, with tinted blue hair. Her own sharp-looking teeth were transparent at the tips. "But you're so fair."

"My maiden name was Taylor," Ethel said. It was, and it wasn't—it was the name she'd got at the orphanage. Wanting a cigarette, she pushed the silver box on the coffee table toward Mrs. Hancock.

Mrs. Hancock used one of her purple claws to pry up the first cigarette from the top layer. "A good old American name like mine."

Like *what?* Ethel wanted to ask. Mrs. Hancock wasn't giving her maiden name, though.

"Is your husband in business, Mrs. Davicky?"

"Yes, he is." Ethel put the lighter—a simple column of silver, the mate to the box—to Mrs. Hancock's cigarette and then to her own.

"Not here in Blue Island?"

"No." From here on, it could be difficult. Ralph was afraid that people in the neighborhood would disapprove of his business. "In Minneapolis." The Mohawk Inn, where Ethel had worked as a waitress, was first-class—thick steaks, dark lights, an electric organ—but Ralph's other places, for which his brothers were listed as the owners, were cut-rate bars on or near Washington Avenue. "He's a distributor," Ethel said, heading her off. "Non-alcoholic beverages mostly." It was true. Ralph had taken over his family's wholesale wine business, never much in Minneapolis, and got it to pay by converting to soft drinks.

Mrs. Hancock was noticing the two paintings which, because of their size and the lowness of the ceiling, hung two feet from the floor, but she didn't comment on them. "Lovely, lovely," she said, referring to the driftwood lamp in the picture window. A faraway noise came from her stomach. She raised her voice. "But you've been lonely, haven't you? I could see it when I came in. It's this neighborhood."

"It's very nice," said Ethel quickly. Maybe Mrs. Hancock was at war with the neighbors, looking for an ally.

"I suppose you know Mrs. Nilgren," said Mrs. Hancock, nodding to the left.

"No, but I've seen her. Once she waved."

"She's nice. Tied down with children, though." Mrs. Hancock nodded to the right. "How about old Mrs. Mann?"

"I don't think anybody's there now."

"The Manns are away! California. So you don't know anybody yet?"

"No."

"I'm surprised you haven't met some of them at the Cashway."

"I never go there," Ethel said. "Ralph—that's my husband—he wants me to trade at the home-owned stores."

"Oh?" Mrs. Hancock's stomach cut loose again. "I didn't know people still felt that way." Mrs. Hancock looked down the street, in the direction of the little corner store. "Do they do much business?"

"No," said Ethel. The old couple who ran it were suspicious of her, she thought, for buying so much from them. The worst of it was that Ralph had told her to open a charge account, and she hadn't, and she never knew when he'd stop there and try to use it. There was a sign up in the store that said: In God We Trust—All Others Pay Cash.

"I'll bet that's it," Mrs. Hancock was saying. "I'm afraid people are pretty clannish around here—and the Wagners have so many friends. They live one-two-three-five houses down." Mrs. Hancock had been counting the houses across the street. "Mr. Wagner's the manager of the Cashway."

Ethel was holding her breath.

"I'm afraid so," said Mrs. Hancock.

Ethel sighed. It was Ralph's fault. She'd always wanted to trade at the Cashway.

Mrs. Hancock threw back her head, inhaling, and her eyelids, like a doll's, came down. "I'm afraid it's your move, Mrs. Davicky."

Ethel didn't feel that it was her move at all and must have shown it.

Mrs. Hancock sounded impatient. "Invite 'em in. Have 'em in for a morning coffee."

"I couldn't do that," Ethel said. "I've never been to one." She'd only read about coffees in the women's magazines to which Ralph subscribed her. "I wouldn't know how."

"Nothing to it. Rolls, coffee, and come as you are. Of course nobody really does, not really." Mrs. Hancock's stomach began again. "Oh, shut up," she said to it. "I've just come from one too many." Mrs. Hancock made a face, showing Ethel a brown mohair tongue. She laughed at Ethel. "Cheer up. It wasn't in this neighborhood."

Ethel felt better. "I'll certainly think about it," she said.

Mrs. Hancock rose, smiling, and went over to the telephone. "You'll do it right now," she said, as though being an older woman entitled her to talk that way to Ethel. "They're probably dying to get inside this lovely house."

After a moment, Ethel, who was already on her feet, having thought that Mrs. Hancock was leaving, went over and sat down to telephone. In the wall mirror she saw how she must appear to Mrs. Hancock. When the doorbell had rung, she'd been in too much of a hurry to see who it was to do anything about her lips and hair. "Will they know who I am?"

"Of course." Mrs. Hancock squatted on the white leather hassock with the phone book. "And you don't have to say I'm coming. Oh, I'll come. I'll be more than happy to. You don't need me, though. All you need is confidence."

And Mrs. Hancock was right. Ethel called eight neighbors, and six could come on Wednesday morning, which Mrs. Hancock had thought would be the best time for her. Two of the six even sounded anxious to meet Ethel, and, surprisingly, Mrs. Wagner was one of these.

"You did it all yourself," said Mrs. Hancock.

"With your help," said Ethel, feeling indebted to Mrs. Hancock, intimately so. It was as if they'd cleaned the house together.

They were saying goodbye on the front stoop when Ralph rolled into the driveway. Ordinarily at noon he parked just outside the garage, but that day he drove in—without acknowledging them in any way. "Mr. Daveechee," Ethel commented. For Mrs. Hancock, after listening to Ethel pronounce her name for all the neighbors, was still saying "Davicky."

Mrs. Hancock stayed long enough to get the idea that Ralph wasn't going to show himself. She went down the front walk saying, " 'Bye now."

While Mrs. Hancock was getting into her car, which seemed a little old for the neighborhood, Ralph came out of the garage.

Mrs. Hancock waved and nodded—which, Ethel guessed, was for Ralph's benefit, the best Mrs. Hancock could do to introduce herself at the distance. She drove off. Too late, Ralph's hand moved up to wave. He stared after Mrs. Hancock's moving car with a look that just didn't belong to him, Ethel thought, a look that she hadn't seen on his face until they moved out to Blue Island.

During lunch, Ethel tried to reproduce her conversation with Mrs. Hancock, but she couldn't tell Ralph enough. He wanted to know the neighbors' names, and she could recall the names of only three. Mrs. Wagner, one of them, was very popular in the neighborhood, and her husband . . . "You go to the Cashway then. Some of 'em sounded all right, huh?" "Ralph, they all sounded all right, real friendly. The man next door sells insurance. Mr. Nilgren."

Ethel remembered that one of the husbands was a lawyer and told Ralph that. He left the table. A few minutes later, Ethel heard him driving away.

It had been a mistake to mention the lawyer to Ralph. It had made him think of the shooting they'd had at the Bow Wow, one of the joints. There had been a mixup, and Ralph's home address had appeared in the back pages of one of the papers when the shooting was no longer news. Ethel doubted that the neighbors had seen the little item. Ralph might be right about the lawyer, though, who would probably have to keep up with everything like that.

Ralph wouldn't have worried so much about such a little thing in the old days. He was different now. It was hard to get him to smile. Ethel could remember how he would damn the Swedes for slapping higher and higher taxes on liquor and tobacco, but now, when she pointed out a letter some joker had written to the paper suggesting a tax on coffee, or when she showed him the picture of the wife of the Minnesota senator—the fearless one—christening an ore boat with a bottle of milk, which certainly should've given Ralph a laugh, he was silent.

It just made Ethel sick to see him at the windows, watching Mr. Nilgren, a sandy-haired, dim-looking man who wore plaid shirts and a red cap in the yard. Mr. Nilgren would be raking out his hedge, or wiring up the skinny little trees, or washing his car if it was Sunday morning, and there Ralph would be, behind a drape. One warm day Ethel had seen Mr. Nilgren in the yard with a golf club, and had said, "He should get some of those little balls that don't go anywhere." It had been painful to see Ralph then. She could almost *hear* him thinking. He would get some of those balls and give them to Mr. Nilgren as a present. No, it would look funny if he did. Then he got that sick look that seemed to come from wanting to do a favor for someone who might not let him do it.

A couple of days later Ethel learned that Ralph had gone to an indoor driving range to take golf lessons. He came home happy, with a club he was supposed to swing in his spare time. He'd made a friend too, another beginner. They were going to have the same schedule and be measured for clubs. During his second lesson, however, he quit. Ethel wasn't surprised, for Ralph, though strong, was awkward. She was better than he was with a hammer and nails, and he mutilated the heads of screws. He must have been badly surprised to discover he was just as bad when he went back the second time, after carrying the club around the house for three days. Ethel asked about the other beginner, and at first Ralph acted as though she'd made him up, and then he hotly rejected the word "friend," which she'd used. Finally he said, "If you ask me, that bastard's played before!"

That was just like him. At the coffee, Ethel planned to ask the women to come over soon with their husbands, but she was afraid some of the husbands wouldn't take to Ralph. Probably he could buy insurance from Mr. Nilgren. He would want to do something for the ones who weren't selling something, though—if there were any like that—and they might misunderstand Ralph. He was used to buying the drinks. He should relax and take the neighbors as they came. Or move.

She didn't know why they were there anyway. It was funny. After they were married, before they left on their honeymoon, Ralph had driven her out to Blue Island and walked her through the house. That was all there was to it. Sometimes she wondered if he'd won the house at cards. She didn't know why they were there when they could just as well be living at Minnetonka or White Bear where they could keep a launch like the one they'd hired in Florida—and where the houses were far apart and neighbors wouldn't matter so much. What were they waiting for? Some of the things they owned, she knew, were for later. They didn't need sterling for eighteen in Blue Island. And the two big pictures were definitely for later.

She didn't know what Ralph liked about his picture, which was of an Indian who looked all-in sitting on a horse that looked all-in, but he had gone to the trouble of ordering it from a regular art store. Hers was more cheerful, the palace of the Doge of Venice, Italy. Ralph hadn't wanted her to have it at first. He was really down on anything foreign. (There were never any Italian dishes on the menu at the Mohawk.) But she believed he liked her for wanting that picture, for having a weakness for things Italian, for him—and even for his father and mother whom he was always sorry to see and hadn't invited to the house. When they came anyway, with his brothers, their wives and children (and wine, which Ralph wouldn't touch), Ralph was in and out, upstairs and down, never long in the same room with them, never encouraging them to stay when they started to leave. They called him "Rock" or "Rocky," but Ralph didn't always answer to that. To one of the little boys who had followed him down into the basement, Ethel had heard him growl, "The name's Ralph"—that to a nine-year-old. His family must have noticed the change in Ralph, but they were wrong if they blamed her, just because she was a little young for him, a blonde and not a Catholic—not that Ralph went to church. In fact, she thought Ralph would be better off with his family for his friends, instead of counting so much on the neighbors. She liked Ralph's family and enjoyed having them in the house.

And if Ralph's family hadn't come around, the neighbors might even think they weren't properly married, that they had a love nest going there. Ethel didn't blame the neighbors for being suspicious of her and Ralph. Mr. Nilgren in his shirt and cap that did nothing for him, he belonged there, but not Ralph, so dark, with his dark blue suits, pearl grey hats, white jacquard shirts—and with her, with her looks and platinum hair. She tried to dress down, to look like an older woman, when she went out. The biggest thing in their favor, but it wasn't noticeable yet, was the fact that she was pregnant.

Sometimes she thought Ralph must be worrying about the baby—as she was—about the kind of life a little kid would have in a neighborhood where his father and mother didn't know anybody. There were two pre-school children at the Nilgrens'. Would they play with the Davicci kid? Ethel didn't ever want to see that sick look of Ralph's on a child of hers.

That afternoon two men in white overalls arrived from Minneapolis in a white truck and washed the windows, inside and out, including the basement and garage. Ralph had sent them. Ethel sat in the dining room and polished silver to the music of *Carmen* on records. She played whole operas when Ralph wasn't home.

In bed that night Ralph made her run through the neighbors again. Seven for sure, counting Mrs. Hancock. "Is that all?" Ethel said she was going to call the neighbor who hadn't been home. "When?" When she got the number from Mrs. Hancock. "When's that?" When Mrs. Hancock phoned, if she phoned . . . and that was where Ralph believed Ethel had really fallen down. She didn't have Mrs. Hancock's number—or address—and there wasn't a Hancock listed for Blue Island in the phone book. "How about next door?" Mrs. Nilgren was still coming. "The other side?" The Manns were still away, in California, and Ralph knew it. "They might come back. Ever think of that? You don't wanna leave them out." *Them,* he'd said, showing Ethel what was expected of her. He wanted those husbands. Ethel promised to watch for the return of the Manns. "They could come home in the night." Ethel reminded Ralph that a person in her condition needed a lot of sleep, and Ralph left her alone then.

Before Ralph was up the next morning, Ethel started to clean the house. Ralph was afraid the house-cleaning wouldn't be done right (*he* spoke of her condition) and wanted to get another crew of professionals out from Minneapolis. Ethel said it wouldn't look good. She said the neighbors expected them to do their own house-cleaning—*and window washing.* Ralph shut up.

When he came home for lunch, Ethel was able to say that Mrs. Hancock had called and that the neighbor who hadn't been home could come to the coffee. Ethel had talked to her, and she had sounded very friendly. "That's three of 'em, huh?" Ethel was tired of that one, but told him they'd *all* sounded friendly to her. "Mrs. Hancock okay?" Mrs. Hancock was okay. More than happy to be coming. Ralph asked if Ethel had got Mrs. Hancock's phone number and address. No. "Why not?" Mrs. Hancock would be there in the morning. That was why—and Ralph should get a hold on himself.

In the afternoon, after he was gone, Ethel put on one of her new conservative dresses and took the bus to Minneapolis to buy some Swedish pastry. She wanted something better than she could buy in Blue Island. In the window of the store where they'd bought Ralph's Indian, there were some little miniatures, lovely New England snow scenes. She hesited to go in when she saw the sissy clerk was on duty again. He had made Ralph sore, asking how he'd like to have the Indian framed in birch bark. The Mohawk was plastered with birch bark, and Ralph thought the sissy recognized him and was trying to be funny. "This is going into my home!" Ralph had said and ordered the gold frame costing six times as much as the Indian. However, he'd taken the sissy's advice about having a light put on it. Ethel hesitated, but she went in. In his way, the sissy was very nice, and Ethel went home with five little Old English prints. When she'd asked about the pictures in the window, the New England ones, calling them "landscapes," he'd said "snowscapes" and looked disgusted, as if they weren't what she should want.

When she got home, she hung the prints over the sofa where there was a blank space, and they looked fine in their shiny black frames. She didn't say anything to Ralph, hoping he'd notice them, but he didn't until after supper. "Hey, what is this?" he said. He bounced off the sofa, confronting her. "Ralph, they're cute!" "Not in my home!" "Ralph, they're humorous!" The clerk had called them that. But Ralph called them drunks and whores. He had Ethel feeling ashamed of herself. It was hard to believe that she could have felt they were just fat and funny and just what their living room needed, as the clerk had said. Ralph took them down. "Man or woman sell 'em to you?" Ethel, seeing what he had in mind, knew she couldn't tell him where she'd got them. She lied. "I was in Dayton's . . ." "A woman—all right, then you take 'em back!"

She was scared. Something like that was enough to make Ralph regret *marrying* her—and to remind her again that she couldn't have made him. If there had been a showdown between them, he would've learned about her first pregnancy. It would've been easy for a lawyer to find out about that. She'd listened to an old doctor who'd told her to go ahead and have it, that she'd love her little baby, who hadn't lived, but there would be a record anyway. She wasn't sorry about going to a regular hospital to have it, though it made it harder for her now, having that record. She'd done what she could for the baby. She hated to think of the whole thing, but when she did, as she did that evening, she knew she'd done her best.

It might have been a bad evening for her, with Ralph brooding on her faults, if a boy hadn't come to the door selling chances on a raffle. Ralph bought all the boy had, over five dollars' worth, and asked where he lived in the neighborhood. "I live in Minneapolis." "Huh? Whatcha doin' way out here then?" The boy said it was easier to sell chances out there. Ethel, who had been doing the dishes, returned to the sink before Ralph could see her. He went back to his *Reader's Digest,* and she slipped off to bed, early, hoping his mind would be occupied with the boy if she kept out of sight.

He came to bed after the ten o'clock news. "You awake?" Ethel, awake, but afraid he wanted to talk neighbors, moaned remotely. "If anybody comes to the door sellin' anything, make sure it's somebody local."

In the morning, Ralph checked over the silver and china laid out in the dining room and worried over the pastry. "Fresh?" Fresh! She'd put it in the deep freeze right away and it hadn't even thawed out yet. "Is *that* all?" That was all, and it was more than enough. She certainly didn't need a whole quart of whipping cream. "Want me to call up for something to go with this?" No. "Turkey or a ham? I maybe got time to go myself if I go right now." He carried on like that until ten o'clock, when she got rid of him, saying, "You wouldn't want to be the only man, Ralph."

Then she was on her own, wishing Mrs. Hancock would come early and see her through the first minutes.

But Mrs. Wagner was the first to arrive. After that, the neighbors seemed to ring the bell at regular intervals. Ethel met them at the door, hung their coats in the hall closet, returning each time to Mrs. Wagner in the kitchen. They were all very nice, but Mrs. Wagner was the nicest.

"Now let's just let everything be," she said after they'd arranged the food in the dining room. "Let's go in and meet your friends."

They found the neighbors standing before the two pictures. Ethel snapped on the spot lights. She heard little cries of pleasure all around.

"Heirlooms!"

"Is Mr. Davitchy a collector?"

"Just likes good things, huh?"

"I just love this lamp."

"I just *stare* at it when I go by."

"So do I."

Ethel, looking at her driftwood lamp, her plants, and beyond, stood in a haze of pleasure. Earlier, when she was giving her attention to Mrs. Nilgren (who was telling about the trouble "Carl" had with his trees), Ethel had seen Ralph's car cruise by, she thought, and now again, but this time there was no doubt of it. She recognized the rather old one parked in front as Mrs. Hancock's, but where was Mrs. Hancock?

"Hello, everybody!"

Mrs. Hancock had let herself in, and was hanging up her coat.

Ethel disappeared into the kitchen. She carried the coffee pot, which had been on *low,* into the dining room where they were supposed to come and help themselves. She stood by the pot, nervous, ready to pour, hoping that someone would look in and see that she was ready, but no one did.

She went to see what they were doing. They were still sitting down, listening to Mrs. Hancock. She'd had trouble with her car. That was why she was late. She saw Ethel. "I can see you want to get started," she said, rising. "So do I."

Ethel returned to the dining room and stood by the coffee pot.

Mrs. Hancock came first. "Starved," she said. She carried off her coffee, roll, and two of the little Swedish cookies, and Ethel heard her in the living room rallying the others.

They came then, quietly, and Ethel poured. When all had been served, she started another pot of coffee, and took her cup and a cookie—she wasn't hungry—into the living room.

Mrs. Hancock, sitting on the hassock, had a bottle in her hand. On the rug around her were some brushes and one copper pan. "Ladies," she was saying, "now here's something new." Noticing Ethel, Mrs. Hancock picked up the pan. "How'd you like to have this for your kitchen? Here."

Ethel crossed the room. She carried the pan back to where she'd been standing.

"This is no ordinary polish," continued Mrs. Hancock, shaking the bottle vigorously. "This is what is known as liquefied ointment. It possesses rare medicinal properties. It renews wood. It gives you a base for polishing—something to shine that simply wasn't there before. There's nothing like it on the market—not in the polish field. It's a Shipshape product, and you all know what that means." Mrs. Hancock opened the bottle and dabbed at the air. "Note the handy applicator." Snatching a cloth from her lap, she rubbed the leg of the coffee table—"remove all foreign matter first"—and dabbed at the leg with the applicator. "This does for wood what liniment does for horses. It relaxes the grain, injects new life, *soothes* the wood. Well, how do you like it?" she called over to Ethel.

Ethel glanced down at the pan, forgotten in her hand.

"Pass it around," said Mrs. Hancock.

Ethel offered the pan to Mrs. Nilgren, who was nearest.

"I've seen it, thanks."

Ethel moved to the next neighbor.

"I've seen it."

Ethel moved on. "Mrs. Wagner, have you?"

"Many times"—with a smile.

Ethel looked back where she'd been standing before she started out with the pan—and went the other way, finally stepping into the hallway. There she saw a canvas duffle bag on the side of which was embossed a pennant flying the word SHIPSHAPE. And hearing Mrs. Hancock—"And this is new, girls. Can you all see from where you're sitting?"—Ethel began to move again. She kept right on going.

Upstairs, in the bedroom, lying down, she noticed the pan in her hand. She shook it off. It hit the headboard of the bed, denting the traditional mahogany, and came to rest in the satin furrow between Ralph's pillow and hers. Oh, God! In a minute, she'd have to get up and go down to them and do *something* . . . but then she heard the coat hangers banging back empty in the closet downstairs, and the front door opening and, finally, closing. There was a moment of perfect silence in the house before her sudden sob, then another moment, before she heard someone coming, climbing the carpeted stairs.

Ethel foolishly thought it would be Mrs. Wagner, but of course it was Mrs. Hancock, after her pan.

She tiptoed into the room, adjusted the venetian blind, and seated herself lightly on the edge of the bed. "Don't think I don't know how you feel," she said. "Not that it shows yet. I wasn't *sure,* dear." She looked into Ethel's eyes, frightening her.

As though only changing positions, Ethel moved the hand that Mrs. Hancock was after.

"My ointment would fix that, restore the surface," said Mrs. Hancock, her finger searching the little wound in the headboard. She began to explain, gently—like someone with a terrible temper warming up: "When we first started having these little Shipshape parties, they didn't tell each other. They do now, oh yes, or they would if I'd let them. I'm on to them. They're just in it for the mops now. You get one, you know, for having the party in your home. It's collapsible, ideal for the small home or travel. But the truth is you let me down! Why, when you left the room the way you did, you didn't give them any choice. Why, I don't think there's one of that crowd—with the exception of May Wagner—that isn't using one of my free mops! Why, they just walked out on me!"

Ethel, closing her eyes, saw Mrs. Hancock alone, on the hassock, with her products all around her.

"It's a lot of pan for the money," Mrs. Hancock was saying now. She reached over Ethel's body for it. "You'll love your little pan," she said, fondling it.

Ethel's eyes were resisting Mrs. Hancock, but her right hand betrayed her.

"Here?" Mrs. Hancock opened a drawer, took out a purse, and handed it over saying, "Only $12.95."

Ethel found a five and a ten.

"You *do* want the ointment, don't you? The pan and the large bottle come to a little more than this, but it's not enough to worry about."

Mrs. Hancock got up, apparently to leave.

Ethel thought of something. "You do live in Blue Island, don't you?" Ralph would be sure to ask about that—if she had to tell him. And she would!

"Not any more, thank God."

Ethel nodded. She wasn't surprised.

Mrs. Hancock, at the door, peeked out—reminding Ethel of a bored visitor looking for a nurse who would tell her it was time to leave the patient. "I'll leave your ointment and mop downstairs," she said. "I just know everything's going to be all right." Then she smiled and left.

When, toward noon, Ethel heard Ralph come into the driveway, she got out of bed, straightened the spread, and concealed the pan in the closet. She went to the window and gazed down upon the crown of his pearl grey hat. He was carrying a big club of roses.

Theme and Character

The three stories in this section were chosen for study because they are closely related in *theme* and because each of the protagonists, each different from the other, clearly represents a view of life at odds with the world. All three of the stories say something significant about values sacred to an individual, and they present a trial of those values in opposition to the world. What the stories express and what the characters reflect can be equated with idea, for theme may tell us about concepts large and small, beliefs, or basic convictions. Further, theme embraces more than a mere platitude, an easy generalization about life, a pat morality, or an oversimplified statement about human nature.

More importantly, theme is an extension of experience presented through action, character, setting, and the other components of a story. It cannot be entirely isolated from these other parts, for together they all point the way to total meaning. Thus it follows that theme is *objective;* it cannot be forced on the reader except as it is embodied within the story and emerges as a result of the conflicting forces that operate within the narrative. The story is the proof of the theme—not merely an incidental illustration. The theme exists because of the story; the story does not exist because of the theme.

The commentary following "The Majesty of the Law" discusses at some length the theme in that one story. Variations of the same central idea are presented in the stories by Taylor and Faulkner. The three authors together say a great deal about a particular idea and explore in depth its implications. No significant part of the idea is omitted; thus in each story there is a seriousness of purpose toward revealing truth.

Moreover all three writers have created characters who help to represent or portray or enact a given theme and its variations. Just as there is a continuous interaction between plot and character, there is always a close relationship between character and theme. The parts are virtually inseparable: Dan is not only a character, he is also an idea, or the hint of an idea, as are Munsie and Miss Emily.

But these stories are not allegories; nor are the characters abstractions.

Stereotyped, *stock characters* appear in none of them. The characters are complex, difficult, contradictory, and above all entirely human. We know what they are from their dramatized actions, for in the art of fiction the the author does not *tell* us what they are, he *shows* us. The more we learn about them the more complex they seem and the more interesting they become. The best writers of fiction present us ultimately with the most rewarding studies in character—good, bad, noble, base, but rarely absolutely so. They are fully compounded of virtue *and* vice, wisdom *and* folly. So the range of fiction is the range of mankind's character. As readers of fiction we are assured of intimate explorations and are promised some startling discoveries about the nature of man.

FRANK O'CONNOR
(1903–)

The Majesty of the Law

Old Dan Bride was breaking brosna for the fire when he heard a step on the path. He paused, a bundle of saplings on his knee.

Dan had looked after his mother while the life was in her, and after her death no other woman had crossed his threshold. Signs on it, his house had that look. Almost everything in it he had made with his own hands in his own way. The seats of the chairs were only slices of log, rough and round and thick as the saw had left them, and with the rings still plainly visible through the grime and polish that coarse trouser-bottoms had in the course of long years imparted. Into these Dan had rammed stout knotted ash-boughs that served alike for legs and back. The deal table, bought in a shop, was an inheritance from his mother and a great pride and joy to him though it rocked whenever he touched it. On the wall, unglazed and fly-spotted, hung in mysterious isolation a Marcus Stone print, and beside the door was a calendar with a picture of a racehorse. Over the door hung a gun, old but good, and in excellent condition, and before the fire was stretched an old setter who raised his head expectantly whenever Dan rose or even stirred.

He raised it now as the steps came nearer and when Dan, laying down the bundle of saplings, cleaned his hands thoughtfully in the seat of his trousers, he gave a loud bark, but this expressed no more than a desire to show off his own watchfulness. He was half human and knew people thought he was old and past his prime.

A man's shadow fell across the oblong of dusty light thrown over the half-door before Dan looked round.

"Are you alone, Dan?" asked an apologetic voice.

"Oh, come in, come in, sergeant, come in and welcome," exclaimed the old man, hurrying on rather uncertain feet to the door which the tall policeman opened and pushed in. He stood there, half in sunlight, half in shadow, and seeing him so, you would have realized how dark the interior of the house really was. One side of his red face was turned so as to catch the light, and behind it an ash tree raised its boughs of airy green against the sky. Green fields, broken here and there by clumps of red-brown rock, flowed downhill, and beyond them, stretched all across the horizon, was the sea, flooded and almost transparent with light. The sergeant's face was fat and fresh, the old man's face, emerging from the twilight of the kitchen, had the colour of wind and sun, while the features had been so shaped by the struggle with time and the elements that they might as easily have been found impressed upon the surface of a rock.

"Begor, Dan," said the sergeant, " 'tis younger you're getting."

"Middling I am, sergeant, middling," agreed the old man in a voice which seemed to accept the remark as a compliment of which politeness would not allow him to take too much advantage. "No complaints."

"Begor, 'tis as well because no one would believe them. And the old dog doesn't look a day older."

The dog gave a low growl as though to show the sergeant that he would remember this unmannerly reference to his age, but indeed he growled every time he was mentioned, under the impression that people had nothing but ill to say of him.

"And how's yourself, sergeant?"

"Well, now, like the most of us, Dan, neither too good nor too bad. We have our own little worries, but, thanks be to God, we have our compensations."

"And the wife and family?"

"Good, praise be to God, good. They were away from me for a month, the lot of them, at the mother-in-law's place in Clare."

"In Clare, do you tell me?"

"In Clare. I had a fine quiet time."

The old man looked about him and then retired to the bedroom, from which he returned a moment later with an old shirt. With this he solemnly wiped the seat and back of the log-chair nearest the fire.

"Sit down now, sergeant. You must be tired after the journey. 'Tis a long old road. How did you come?"

"Teigue Leary gave me the lift. Wisha now, Dan, don't be putting yourself out. I won't be stopping. I promised them I'd be back inside an hour."

"What hurry is on you?" asked Dan. "Look, your foot was only on the path when I made up the fire."

"Arrah, Dan, you're not making tea for me?"

"I am not making it for you, indeed; I'm making it for myself, and I'll take it very bad of you if you won't have a cup."

"Dan, Dan, that I mightn't stir, but 'tisn't an hour since I had it at the barracks!"

"Ah, whisht, now, whisht! Whisht, will you! I have something here to give you an appetite."

The old man swung the heavy kettle onto the chain over the open fire, and the dog sat up, shaking his ears with an expression of the deepest interest. The policeman unbuttoned his tunic, opened his belt, took a pipe and a plug of tobacco from his breast pocket, and crossing his legs in an easy posture, began to cut the tobacco slowly and carefully with his pocket knife. The old man went to the dresser and took down two handsomely decorated cups, the only cups he had, which, though chipped and handleless, were used at all only on very rare occasions; for himself he preferred his tea from a basin. Happening to glance into them, he noticed that they bore signs of disuse and had collected a lot of the fine white turf-dust that always circulated in the little smoky cottage. Again he thought of the shirt, and rolling up his sleeves with a stately gesture, he wiped them inside and out till they shone. Then he bent and opened the cupboard. Inside was a quart bottle of pale liquid, obviously untouched. He removed the cork and smelt the contents, pausing for a moment in the act as though to recollect where exactly he had noticed that particular smoky smell before. Then, reassured, he stood up and poured out with a liberal hand.

"Try that now, sergeant," he said with quiet pride.

The sergeant, concealing whatever qualms he might have felt at the idea of drinking illegal whisky, looked carefully into the cup, sniffed, and glanced up at old Dan.

"It looks good," he commented.

"It should be good," replied Dan with no mock modesty.

"It tastes good too," said the sergeant.

"Ah, sha," said Dan, not wishing to praise his own hospitality in his own house, " 'tis of no great excellence."

"You'd be a good judge, I'd say," said the sergeant without irony.

"Ever since things became what they are," said Dan, carefully guarding himself against a too-direct reference to the peculiarities of the law administered by his guest, "liquor isn't what it used to be."

"I've heard that remark made before now, Dan," said the sergeant thoughtfully. "I've heard it said by men of wide experience that it used to be better in the old days."

"Liquor," said the old man, "is a thing that takes time. There was never a good job done in a hurry."

" 'Tis an art in itself."

"Just so."

"And an art takes time."

"And knowledge," added Dan with emphasis. "Every art has its secrets, and the secrets of distilling are being lost the way the old songs were lost. When I was a boy there wasn't a man in the barony but had a hundred songs in his head, but with people running here, there and everywhere, the songs were lost. . . . Ever since things became what they are," he repeated on the same guarded note, "there's so much running about the secrets are lost."

"There must have been a power of them."

"There was. Ask any man today that makes whisky do he know how to make it out of heather."

"And was it made of heather?" asked the policeman.

"It was."

"You never drank it yourself?"

"I didn't, but I knew old men that did, and they told me that no whisky that's made nowadays could compare with it."

"Musha, Dan, I think sometimes 'twas a great mistake of the law to set its hand against it."

Dan shook his head. His eyes answered for him, but it was not in nature for a man to criticize the occupation of a guest in his own home.

"Maybe so, maybe not," he said noncommittally.

"But sure, what else have the poor people?"

"Them that makes the laws have their own good reasons."

"All the same, Dan, all the same, 'tis a hard law."

The sergeant would not be outdone in generosity. Politeness required him not to yield to the old man's defence of his superiors and their mysterious ways.

"It is the secrets I'd be sorry for," said Dan, summing up. "Men die and men are born, and where one man drained another will plough, but a secret lost is lost forever."

"True," said the sergeant mournfully. "Lost forever."

Dan took his cup, rinsed it in a bucket of clear water by the door and cleaned it again with the shirt. Then he placed it carefully at the sergeant's elbow. From the dresser he took a jug of milk and a blue bag containing sugar; this he followed up with a slab of country butter and—a sure sign that he had been expecting a visitor—a round cake of homemade bread, fresh and uncut. The kettle sang and spat and the dog, shaking his ears, barked at it angrily.

"Go away, you brute!" growled Dan, kicking him out of his way.

He made the tea and filled the two cups. The sergeant cut himself a large slice of bread and buttered it thickly.

"It is just like medicines," said the old man, resuming his theme with the imperturbability of age. "Every secret there was is lost. And leave no one tell me that a doctor is as good a man as one that had the secrets of old times."

"How could he be?" asked the sergeant with his mouth full.

"The proof of that was seen when there were doctors and wise people there together."

"It wasn't to the doctors the people went, I'll engage?"

"It was not. And why?" With a sweeping gesture the old man took in the whole world outside his cabin. "Out there on the hillsides is the sure cure for every disease. Because it is written"—he tapped the table with his thumb—"it is written by the poets 'wherever you find the disease you will find the cure.' But people walk up the hills and down the hills and all they see is flowers. Flowers! As if God Almighty—honour and praise to Him!—had nothing better to do with His time than be making old flowers!"

"Things no doctor could cure the wise people cured," agreed the sergeant.

"Ah, musha, 'tis I know it," said Dan bitterly. "I know it, not in my mind but in my own four bones."

"Have you the rheumatics at you still?" the sergeant asked in a shocked tone.

"I have. Ah, if you were alive, Kitty O'Hara, or you, Nora Malley of the Glen, 'tisn't I'd be dreading the mountain wind or the sea wind; 'tisn't I'd be creeping down with my misfortunate red ticket for the blue and pink and yellow dribble-drabble of their ignorant dispensary."

"Why then indeed," said the sergeant, "I'll get you a bottle for that."

"Ah, there's no bottle ever made will cure it."

"That's where you're wrong, Dan. Don't talk now till you try it. It cured my own uncle when he was that bad he was shouting for the carpenter to cut the two legs off him with a handsaw."

"I'd give fifty pounds to get rid of it," said Dan magniloquently. "I would and five hundred."

The sergeant finished his tea in a gulp, blessed himself and struck a match which he then allowed to go out as he answered some question of the old man. He did the same with a second and third, as though titillating his appetite with delay. Finally he succeeded in getting his pipe alight and the two men pulled round their chairs, placed their toes side by side in the ashes, and in deep puffs, lively bursts of conversation, and long, long silences, enjoyed their smoke.

"I hope I'm not keeping you?" said the sergeant, as though struck by the length of his visit.

"Ah, what would you keep me from?"

"Tell me if I am. The last thing I'd like to do is waste another man's time."

"Begor, you wouldn't waste my time if you stopped all night."

"I like a little chat myself," confessed the policeman.

And again they became lost in conversation. The light grew thick and coloured and, wheeling about the kitchen before it disappeared, became tinged with gold; the kitchen itself sank into cool greyness with cold light on the cups and basins and plates of the dresser. From the ash tree a thrush began to sing. The open hearth gathered brightness till its light was a warm, even splash of crimson in the twilight.

Twilight was also descending outside when the sergeant rose to go. He fastened his belt and tunic and carefully brushed his clothes. Then he put on his cap, tilted a little to side and back.

"Well, that was a great talk," he said.

" 'Tis a pleasure," said Dan, "a real pleasure."

"And I won't forget the bottle for you."

"Heavy handling from God to you!"

"Good-bye now, Dan."

"Good-bye, sergeant, and good luck."

Dan didn't offer to accompany the sergeant beyond the door. He sat in his old place by the fire, took out his pipe once more, blew through it thoughtfully, and just as he leaned forward for a twig to kindle it, heard the steps returning. It was the sergeant. He put his head a little way over the half-door.

"Oh, Dan!" he called softly.

"Ay, sergeant?" replied Dan, looking round, but with one hand still reaching for the twig. He couldn't see the sergeant's face, only hear his voice.

"I suppose you're not thinking of paying that little fine, Dan?"

There was a brief silence. Dan pulled out the lighted twig, rose slowly and shambled towards the door, stuffing it down in the almost empty bowl of the pipe. He leaned over the half door while the sergeant with hands in the pockets of his trousers gazed rather in the direction of the laneway, yet taking in a considerable portion of the sea line.

"The way it is with me, sergeant," replied Dan unemotionally, "I am not."

"I was thinking that, Dan; I was thinking you wouldn't."

There was a long silence during which the voice of the thrush grew shriller and merrier. The sunken sun lit up rafts of purple cloud moored high above the wind.

"In a way," said the sergeant, "that was what brought me."

"I was just thinking so, sergeant, it only struck me and you going out the door."

"If 'twas only the money, Dan, I'm sure there's many would be glad to oblige you."

"I know that, sergeant. No, 'tisn't the money so much as giving that fellow the satisfaction of paying. Because he angered me, sergeant."

The sergeant made no comment on this and another long silence ensued.

"They gave me the warrant," the sergeant said at last, in a tone which dissociated him from all connection with such an unneighbourly document.

"Did they so?" exclaimed Dan, as if he was shocked by the thoughtlessness of the authorities.

"So whenever 'twould be convenient for you—"

"Well, now you mention it," said Dan, by way of throwing out a suggestion for debate, "I could go with you now."

"Ah, sha, what do you want going at this hour for?" protested the sergeant with a wave of his hand, dismissing the notion as the tone required.

"Or I could go tomorrow," added Dan, warming to the issue.

"Would it be suitable for you now?" asked the sergeant, scaling up his voice accordingly.

"But, as a matter of fact," said the old man emphatically, "the day that would be most convenient to me would be Friday after dinner, because I have some messages to do in town, and I wouldn't have the journey for nothing."

"Friday will do grand," said the sergeant with relief that this delicate matter was now practically disposed of. "If it doesn't they can damn well wait. You could walk in there yourself when it suits you and tell them I sent you."

"I'd rather have yourself there, sergeant, if it would be no inconvenience. As it is, I'd feel a bit shy."

"Why then, you needn't feel shy at all. There's a man from my own parish there, a warder; one Whelan. Ask for him; I'll tell him you're coming, and I'll guarantee when he knows you're a friend of mine he'll make you as comfortable as if you were at home."

"I'd like that fine," Dan said with profound satisfaction. "I'd like to be with friends, sergeant."

"You will be, never fear. Good-bye again now, Dan. I'll have to hurry."

"Wait now, wait till I see you to the road."

Together the two men strolled down the laneway while Dan explained how it was that he, a respectable old man, had had the grave misfortune to open the head of another old man in such a way as to require his removal to hospital, and why it was that he couldn't give the old man in question the satisfaction of paying in cash for an injury brought about through the victim's own unmannerly method of argument.

"You see, sergeant," Dan said, looking at another little cottage up the hill, "the way it is, he's there now, and he's looking at us as sure as there's a glimmer of sight in his weak, wandering, watery eyes, and nothing would give him more gratification than for me to pay. But I'll punish him. I'll lie on bare boards for him. I'll suffer for him, sergeant, so that neither he nor any of his children after him will be able to raise their heads for the shame of it."

On the following Friday he made ready his donkey and butt and set out. On his way he collected a number of neighbours who wished to bid him farewell. At the top of the hill he stopped to send them back. An old man, sitting in the sunlight, hastily made his way indoors, and a moment later the door of his cottage was quietly closed.

Having shaken all his friends by the hand, Dan lashed the old donkey, shouted: "Hup there!" and set out alone along the road to prison.

Investigation and Comment

The casual reader is inclined to dismiss some very fine stories with the statement, "They are uninteresting to me because nothing really happens." Such a reader is expressing a personal preference—for surface action or even violence—which may blind him to other rewards of fiction far more significant. In Frank O'Connor's quiet narrative the single instance of violence takes place offstage, before the story begins, when Dan Bride and his adversary quarrel bitterly and come to blows. But this altercation is not dramatized as a central incident in the story, even through it is the immediate cause of the interview between Dan and the police sergeant at the center of the stage.

The tone of the story, like the action, can be characterized as muted. Even the characters' voices, recreated in the rhythms of the Irish idiom, are musical and concordant. If we were watching the interview between Dan and the police sergeant beyond earshot, we would be hard pressed to devise a story about the visit. It would seem to us that a friendly, rather routine chat is taking place between two Irish villagers; nothing happens except that they meet, drink tea, and part amicably. Therefore we must conclude that what is not overtly said, but what is implied—what is not acted, but what is suggested—is highly important. We are dealing with *understatement* and thus must look closely at the implications in small actions, in barely perceptible gestures, in images that reveal character, in the seemingly trivial and random patterns of behavior that objectively imply the theme lying solidly below the story's surface. The title of a story should also be scrutinized carefully since it often focuses our attention on some particular facet of the action. Here we know that the story will be about the majesty of the law, but we do not know what law, or in what way the law is majestic.

The first details appear in the description of Dan's house. Almost every item in it is his own handiwork. His furnishings are rough, simple, but strong and serviceable. They are a reflection of Dan himself: he is "seasoned," dependable, plain. Among his household furnishings are a few heirlooms and a few items that would pass for art. "The deal table, bought in a shop, was an inheritance from his mother and a great pride and joy to him though it rocked whenever he touched it." In contrast to Dan's rough handmade chairs, the table is shoddy and unsteady; even so, Dan treasures it, chiefly because it is sacred to the memory of his mother, but also because it is no doubt more "artistic" than his own coarser efforts. It is clear that Dan is characterized, up to this point, by three main qualities: he is individualistic and independent; he takes care of his own wants and needs, he looks after his own responsibilities. Second, he has a keen sense of order and propriety; he respects those things that his forbears valued. Third, Dan preserves what has value from both the past and the present. That these details are not accidental, but are part of a pattern, is confirmed by the introduction of the china cups (used only on very rare occasions), which Dan wipes with great care; by his manner in serving the whiskey (a product requiring patience, skill, and time); and by his comments about the lost arts of the distiller, ballad singers, and herbalists.

We soon observe that these same attitudes are typical of the sergeant. Both men show a sense of proper behavior toward a fellow man. Their meeting is marked by politeness and is smoothed by their mutual respect for the other's comfort, ease, and individual opinions. Both exercise great care and demonstrate great skill in adhering to the forms, laws, and codes of civil conduct. Both men, but Dan in particular, are artists in their human relationships, and as we learn from their conversation, an art takes a long time, great knowledge, and a secret awareness.

Notice, for example, their greeting. One claims he is "middling"; the other is "neither too good nor too bad." This is ritualistic, formalized politeness, because for one to say that he is in top condition or that he is in a bad state would be either to brag or to complain; and that would be ill-mannered. Dan in the role of host is extremely solicitous of his guest's comfort. With great care he dusts the seat his guest is to sit in; he lays before him his very best fare. From his meager store Dan uses his best china, proffers his untouched whiskey, provides tea, butter, and fresh-baked bread. Dan, who disapproves of liquor laws, is careful to defend law; the agent of the law, knowing Dan's opinion, attacks the lawmakers. For Dan "it was not in nature for a man to criticize the occupation of a guest in his own home."

The whole story can be regarded as a dramatization of a polite way of performing an unpleasant task. Though we do not know this until the end of the story, we see that the entire visit has been successfully conducted as a ritual of form and manners, that it signifies the true respect of one man for another. Dan has known all along that the sergeant would come; but for the sake of politeness, Dan pretends that this is a surprise social call. The sergeant, too, pretends that this is merely a friendly visit. He even pretends to have forgotten that there is a warrant to deliver. For the sake of each other's integrity, they ignore the unpleasant purpose of the visit: the removal of Dan to jail.

By now, through the accumulation of carefully chosen details and repeated patterns of action, the theme of the story is brought into focus. We have seen dramatized two "artists" engaged in the art of observing laws. We also see that, however simple and rustic, the law is indeed majestic, deriving its majesty from the great respect one individual has for another. We are also made aware that there are two kinds of law. One is written, abstracted, set down in statute books, and is made manifest by the warrant, the sergeant, and the legal action taken by Dan's adversary. This law is impersonal. It is removed from the concrete, particular human situation; further, it is a law that, in practice, causes the individual to turn over his own responsibility to the state. The second kind of law is unwritten. It is concrete instead of abstract. It can be called manners, mutual respect, the concern of one man for another. Each individual executes the law himself and does not relegate it to a third person. These are laws that confront one individual with another: Dan and the sergeant and the neighbor, rather than defendant and plaintiff, or party of the first part and party of the second.

This second kind of relationship is clear when we consider the following conversation between Dan and the Sergeant:

> "Ever since things became what they are," said Dan, carefully guarding himself against a too-direct reference to the peculiarities of the law administered by his guest, "liquor isn't what it used to be."
>
> "I've heard that remark made before now, Dan," said the sergeant thoughtfully. "I've heard it said by men of wide experience that it used to be better in the old days."
>
> "Liquor," said the old man, "is a thing that takes time. There was never a good job done in a hurry."
>
> " 'Tis an art in itself."
>
> "Just so."
>
> "And an art takes time."
>
> "And knowledge," added Dan with emphasis. "Every art has its secrets, and the secrets of distilling are being lost the way the old songs were lost. When I was a boy there wasn't a man in the barony but had a hundred songs in his head, but with people running here, there, and everywhere, the songs were lost. . . . Ever since things became what they are," he repeated on the same guarded note, "there's so much running about the secrets are lost."

It is here apparent that the two kinds of law—the concrete and the abstract, the positive and the negative, the traditional and the statutory—are often in conflict and contradiction. The distilling of liquor is illegal; yet the instrument of statutory law, the sergeant, does not hesitate to agree that something valuable has been lost because of the abstract law.

As readers in a world where "there's so much running about the secrets are lost," we are surprised that an arresting officer and a law offender could be so civil to each other, that they could take the time to observe a certain ritual of respect and kindness. We are shocked into an uncomfortable awareness that we have almost lost a secret; we have sacrificed individual human relationships to the dehumanized and impersonal forces in modern life. We see that the laws by which we live are "hard" laws, as Dan says. They are hard in every sense of the word: inflexible, unbending, devoid of feeling, harsh, frozen.

By this time we have reached the crux of the story; the conflict has been clearly outlined in its several complex tensions. The over-all or enveloping conflict is between the concrete and the abstract, between the individual and the mass, between assuming self-responsibility and surrendering it to institutions. (Almost all the common meanings of *civil*, with the many connotations the word brings to mind, can be applied to this story. The word *civil* has its roots in *civilis*, from the Latin *civis*, meaning citizen.) On one side is Dan who represents the traditional, the individual, and personal intercourse between men—the old "lost" art of human conduct. In the middle is the sergeant, who knows he must enforce the abstract laws although he has not yet lost a humane respect for the individual. At the other end is the old man, Dan's adversary, who represents the purely abstract, the statutory law, or the "new" impersonal code of human conduct.

Here then is the dilemma. If one abides by statutory laws, he may violate human responsibility, human justice, and the sacred integrity of the individual. Yet if he abides only by the laws of personal integrity he may be denying the very principle of law, declaring himself for anarchy, laying the foundation for chaos, demanding that each individual operate as an absolute law unto himself. Either alternative brings ruin and barbarity of one sort or another. Therefore the story has brought us to a point of tension that has far-reaching consequences.

But the story does not leave us here—the theme is not yet fully enacted. The denouement—when Dan agrees to go to prison rather than pay his fine—comes as something of a mild surprise, even though we have been made aware earlier of Dan's strong sense of personal duty, his keen respect for order and law, and his regard for the values of the past. Going to prison (instead of paying the fine) is the only move he could make that would be consistent with his nature and his values. Dan is willing to suffer physically, as the old man has suffered physically. "But I'll punish him, I'll lie on bare boards for him. I'll suffer for him, sergeant, so that neither he nor any of his children after him will be able to raise their heads for the shame of it." The shame of it is that the old man, as well as all his neighbors, knows that injustice has been answered with sacrifice, and that by not accepting his own responsibility—through denying the unwritten laws of human respect, and then attempting to bring in abstract justice as a recompense and ally for concrete human failings—the old man proves himself a coward and barbarian. He has forgotten the secret meaning of all law.

The beginning of the resolution comes with Dan's statement: "Wherever you find the disease you will find the cure." The disease in the larger sense is abstractionism. The real cure for society, the story suggests, is to be found in the secrets of the past, in friendly, man-to-man respect, in direct responsibility.

As in all good fiction, the theme in this story is not easily extracted from the narrative that relates it or the characters who enact it. Nevertheless, the following statement indicates at least in a brief way what the story is about.

> Man, a free agent, makes laws for himself and his society to the best of his logical ability. But because man is human and given to both weakness and rashness, he is not always able to live up to and abide by the ideals of law to

> which he gives consent. Some men (like Dan) are aware of their shortcomings and are willing to bow, like good citizens, to the "majesty" of the ideal they have agreed upon in their society, even when the ideal, in a particular instance, is not altogether just. Some men (like the sergeant) when charged with administering the law are so aware of the central human conflict between the concrete and the abstract that they are willing to temper justice with mercy and civility and make the punishment a convenience, as it were, to suit the character of the offender. Men who lose sight of their own responsibility, or of the humanity of a fellow man, lose the basis upon which the structure of civilization is built. At the same time those men who do not respect social contracts, even when they seem unjust, are also reverting to barbarity.

If there is to be real civility, we will do well to understand Dan's "ditching" metaphor and all it implies: "Men die and men are born, and where one man drained another will plough, but a secret lost is lost forever."

PETER TAYLOR

(1917–   )

What You Hear From 'Em?

Sometimes people misunderstood Aunt Munsie's question, but she wouldn't bother to clarify it. She might repeat it two or three times, in order to drown out some fool answer she was getting from some fool white woman, or man, either. "What you hear from 'em?" she would ask. And, then, louder and louder: "What you hear from 'em?" *What you hear from 'em?"* She was so deaf that anyone whom she thoroughly drowned out only laughed and said Aunt Munsie had got so deaf she couldn't hear it thunder.

It was, of course, only the most utterly fool answers that ever received Aunt Munsie's drowning-out treatment. She was, for a number of years at least, willing to listen to those who mistook her "'em" to mean any and all of the Dr. Tolliver children. And for more years than that she was willing to listen to those who thought she wanted just *any* news of her two favorites among the Tolliver children—Thad and Will. But later on she stopped putting the question to all insensitive and frivolous souls who didn't understand that what she was interested in hearing—and *all* she was interested in

Reprinted by permission of the author.

hearing—was when Mr. Thad Tolliver and Mr. Will Tolliver were going to pack up their families and come back to Thornton for good.

They had always promised her to come back—to come back sure enough, once and for all. On separate occasions, both Thad and Will had actually given her their word. She had not seen them together for ten years, but each of them had made visits to Thornton now and then with his own family. She would see a big car stopping in front of her house on a Sunday afternoon and see either Will or Thad with his wife and children piling out into the dusty street—it was nearly always summer when they came—and then see them filing across the street, jumping the ditch, and unlatching the gate to her yard. She always met them in that pen of a yard, but long before they had jumped the ditch she was clapping her hands and calling out "Hai-ee! Hai-ee, now! Look-a-here! Whee! Whee! Look-a-here!" She had got so blind that she was never sure whether it was Mr. Thad or Mr. Will until she had her arms around his waist. They had always looked a good deal alike, and their city clothes made them look even more alike nowadays. Aunt Munsie's eyes were so bad, besides being so full of moisture on those occasions, that she really recognized them by their girth. Will had grown a regular wash pot of a stomach and Thad was still thin as a rail. They would sit on her porch for twenty or thirty minutes—whichever one it was and his family—and then they would be gone again.

Aunt Munsie would never try to detain them—not seriously. Those short little old visits didn't mean a thing to her. He—Thad or Will—would lean against the banister rail and tell her how well his children were doing in school or college, and she would make each child in turn come and sit beside her on the swing for a minute and receive a hug around the waist or shoulders. They were timid with her, not seeing her any more than they did, but she could tell from their big Tolliver smiles that they liked her to hug them and make over them. Usually, she would lead them all out to her back yard and show them her pigs and dogs and chickens. (She always had at least one frizzly chicken to show the children.) They would traipse through her house to the back yard and then traipse through again to the front porch. It would be time for them to go when they came back, and Aunt Munsie would look up at *him*—Mr. Thad or Mr. Will (she had begun calling them "Mr." the day they married)—and say, "Now, look-a-here. When you comin' back?"

Both Thad and Will knew what she meant, of course, and whichever it was would tell her he was making definite plans to wind up his business and that he was going to buy a certain piece of property, "a mile north of town" or "on the old River Road," and build a jim-dandy house there. He would say, too, how good Aunt Munsie's own house was looking, and his wife would say how grand the zinnias and cannas looked in the yard. (The yard was all flowers—not a blade of grass, and the ground packed hard in little paths between the flower beds.) The visit was almost over then. There remained only the exchange of presents. One of the children would hand Aunt Munsie a paper bag containing a pint of whisky or a carton of cigarettes. Aunt Munsie would go to her back porch or to the pit in the yard and get a fern or a wandering Jew, potted in a rusty lard bucket, and make Mrs. Thad or Mrs. Will take it along. Then the visit was over, and they would leave. From the porch Aunt Munsie would wave good-by with one hand and lay the other hand, trembling slightly, on the banister rail. And sometimes her departing guests, looking back from the yard, would observe that the banisters themselves were trembling under her hand—so insecurely were those knobby banisters attached to the knobby porch pillars. Often as not Thad or Will, observing this, would remind his wife that Aunt Munsie's porch banisters and pillars had come off a porch of the house where he had grown up. (Their father, Dr. Tolliver, had been one of the first to widen his porches and remove the gingerbread from his house.) The children and their mother would wave to Aunt Munsie from the street. Their father would close the gate, resting his hand a moment on its familiar wrought-iron frame, and wave to her before he jumped the ditch. If the children had not gone too far ahead, he might even draw their attention to the iron fence which, with its iron gate, had been around the yard at the Tolliver place till Dr. Tolliver took it down and set out a hedge, just a few weeks before he died.

But such paltry little visits meant nothing to Aunt Munsie. No more did the letters that came with "her things" at Christmas. She was supposed to get her daughter, Lucrecie, who lived next door, to read the letters, but in late years she had taken to putting them away unopened, and some of the presents, too. All she wanted to hear from *them* was when they were coming back for good, and she had learned that the Christmas letters never told her that. On her daily route with her slop wagon through the Square, up Jackson Street, and down Jefferson, there were only four or five houses left where she asked her question. These were houses where the amount of pig slop was not worth stopping for, houses where one old maid, or maybe two, lived, or a widow with one old bachelor son who had never amounted to anything and ate no more than a woman. And so—in the summertime, anyway—she took to calling out at the top of her lungs, when she approached the house of one of the elect, "What you hear from 'em?" Sometimes a Miss Patty or a Miss Lucille or a Mr. Ralph would get up out of a porch chair and come down the brick walk to converse with Aunt Munsie. Or sometimes one of them would just lean out over the shrubbery planted around the porch and call, "Not a thing, Munsie. Not a thing lately."

She would shake her head and call back, "Naw. Naw. Not a thing. Nobody don't hear from 'em. Too busy, they be."

Aunt Munsie's skin was the color of a faded tow sack. She was hardly four feet tall. She was generally believed to be totally bald, and on her head she always wore a white dust cap with an elastic band. She wore an apron, too, while making her rounds with her slop wagon. Even when the weather got bad and she tied a wool scarf about her head and wore an overcoat, she put on an apron over the coat. Her hands and feet were delicately small, which made the old-timers sure she was of Guinea stock that had come to Tennessee out of South Carolina. What most touched the hearts of old ladies on Jackson and Jefferson Streets were her little feet. The sight of her feet "took them back to the old days," they said, because Aunt Munsie still wore flat-heeled, high button shoes. Where ever did Munsie find such shoes any more?

She walked down the street, down the very center of the street, with a spry step, and she was continually turning her head from side to side, as though looking at the old houses and trees for the first time. If her sight was as bad as she sometimes let on it was, she probably recognized the houses only by their roof lines against the Thornton sky. Since this was nearly thirty years ago, most of the big Victorian and ante-bellum houses were still standing, though with their lovely gingerbread work beginning to go. (It went first from houses where there was someone, like Dr. Tolliver, with a special eye for style and for keeping up with the times.) The streets hadn't yet been broadened—or only Nashville Street had—and the maples and elms met above the streets. In the autumn, their leaves covered the high banks and filled the deep ditches on either side. The dark macadam surfacing itself was barely wide enough for two automobiles to pass. Aunt Munsie, pulling her slop wagon, which was a long, low, four-wheeled vehicle about the size and shape of a coffin, paraded down the center of the street without any regard for, if with any awareness of, the traffic problems she sometimes made. Seizing the wagon's heavy, sawed-off-looking tongue, she hauled it after her with a series of impatient jerks, just as though that tongue were the arm of some very stubborn, overgrown white child she had to nurse in her old age. Strangers in town or trifling high-school boys would blow their horns at her, but she was never known to so much as glance over her shoulder at the sound of a horn. Now and then a pedestrian on the sidewalk would call out to the driver of an automobile, "She's so deaf she can't hear it thunder."

It wouldn't have occurred to anyone in Thornton—not in those days—that something ought to be done about Aunt Munsie and her wagon for the sake of the public good. In those days, everyone had equal rights on the streets of Thornton. A vehicle was a vehicle, and a person was a person, each with the right to move as slowly as he pleased and to stop where and as often as he pleased. In the Thornton mind, there was no imaginary line down the middle of the street, and, indeed, no one there at that time had heard of drawing a real line on *any* street. It was merely out of politeness that you made room for others to pass. Nobody would have blown a horn at an old colored woman with her slop wagon—nobody but some Yankee stranger or a trifling high-school boy or maybe old Mr. Ralph Hadley in a special fit of temper. When citizens of Thornton were in a particular hurry and got caught behind Aunt Munsie, they leaned out their car windows and shouted: "Aunt Munsie, can you make a little room?" And Aunt Munsie didn't fail to hear *them*. She would holler, "Hai-ee, now! Whee! Look-a-here!" and jerk her wagon to one side. As they passed her, she would wave her little hand and grin a toothless, pink-gummed grin.

Yet, without any concern for the public good, Aunt Munsie's friends and connections among the white women began to worry more and more about the danger of her being run down by an automobile. They talked among themselves and they talked to her about it. They wanted her to give up collecting slop, now she had got so blind and deaf. "Pshaw," said Aunt Munsie, closing her eyes contemptuously. "Not me." She meant by that that no one would dare run into her or her wagon. Sometimes when she crossed the Square on a busy Saturday morning or on a first Monday, she would hold up one hand with the palm turned outward and stop all traffic until she was safely across and in the alley beside the hotel.

Thornton wasn't even then what it had been before the Great World War. In every other house there was a stranger or a mill hand who had moved up from Factory Town. Some of the biggest old places stood empty, the way Dr. Tolliver's had until it burned. They stood empty not because nobody wanted to rent them or buy them but because the heirs who had gone off somewhere making money could never be got to part with "the home place." The story was that Thad Tolliver nearly went crazy when he heard their old house had burned, and wanted to sue the town, and even said he was going to help get the Republicans into office. Yet Thad had hardly put foot in the house since the day his daddy died. It was said the Tolliver house had caught fire from the Major Pettigru house, which had burned two nights before. And no doubt it had. Sparks could have smoldered in that roof of rotten shingles for a long time before bursting into flame. Some even said the Pettigru house might have caught from the Johnston house, which had burned earlier that same fall. But Thad knew and Will knew and everybody knew the town wasn't to blame, and knew there was no firebug. Why, those old houses stood there empty year after year, and in the fall the leaves fell from the trees and settled around the porches and stoops, and who was there to rake the leaves? Maybe it was a good thing those houses burned, and maybe it would have been as well if some of the houses that still had people in them burned, too. There were houses in Thornton the heirs had never left that looked far worse than the Tolliver or the Pettigru or the Johnston house ever had. The people who lived in them were the ones who gave Aunt Munsie the biggest fool answers to her question, the people whom she soon quit asking her question of or even passing the time of day with, except when she couldn't help it, out of politeness. For, truly, to Aunt Munsie there were things under the sun worse than going off and getting rich in Nashville or in Memphis or even in Washington, D.C. It was a subject she and her daughter Lucrecie sometimes mouthed at each other about across their back fence.

Lucrecie was shiftless, and she liked shiftless white people like the ones who didn't have the ambition to leave Thornton. She thought their shiftlessness showed they were *quality*. "Quality?" Aunt Munsie would echo, her voice full of sarcasm. "Whee! Hai-ee! You talk like *you* was *my* mammy, Crecie. Well, if there be quality, there be quality *and* quality. There's quality and there's *has-been* quality, Crecie." There was no end to that argument Aunt Munsie had with Crecie, and it wasn't at all important to Aunt Munsie. The people who still lived in those houses—the ones she called has-been quality—meant little more to her than the mill hands, or the strangers from up North who ran the Piggly Wiggly, the five-and-ten-cent store, and the roller-skating rink.

There was this to be said, though, for the has-been quality: They knew *who* Aunt Munsie was, and in a limited, literal way they understood what she said. But those *others*—why, they thought Aunt Munsie a beggar, and she knew they did. They spoke of her as Old What You Have for Mom, because that's what they thought she was saying when she called out, "What you hear from 'em?" Their ears were not attuned to that soft "r" she put in "from" or the elision that made "from 'em" sound to them like "for Mom." Many's the time Aunt Munsie had seen or sensed the presence of one of those *other* people, watching from next door, when Miss Florence Lovell, say, came down her front walk and handed her a little parcel of scraps across the ditch. Aunt Munsie knew what they thought of her—how they laughed at her and felt sorry for her and despised her all at once. But, like the has-been quality, they didn't matter, never had, never would. Not ever.

Oh, they mattered in a way to Lucrecie. Lucrecie thought about them and talked about them a lot. She called them "white trash" and even "radical Republicans." It made Aunt Munsie grin to hear Crecie go on, because she knew Crecie got all her notions from her own has-been-quality people. And so it didn't matter, except that Aunt Munsie knew that Crecie truly had all sorts of good sense and had only been carried away and spoiled by such folks as she had worked for, such folks as had really raised Crecie from the time she was big enough to run errands for them, fifty years back. In her heart, Aunt Munsie knew that even Lucrecie didn't matter to her the way a daughter might. It was because while Aunt Munsie had been raising a family of white children, a different sort of white people from hers had been raising her own child, Crecie. Sometimes, if Aunt Munsie was in her chicken yard or out in her little patch of cotton when Mr. Thad or Mr. Will arrived, Crecie would come out to the fence and say, "Mama, some of your chillun's out front."

Miss Florence Lovell and Miss Patty Bean, and especially Miss Lucille Satterfield, were all the time after Aunt Munsie to give up collecting slop. "You're going to get run over by one of those crazy drivers, Munsie," they said. Miss Lucille was the widow of old Judge Satterfield. "If the Judge were alive, Munsie," she said, "I'd make him find a way to stop you. But the men down at the courthouse don't listen to the women in this town any more. Not since we got the vote. And I think they'd be most too scared of you to do what I want them to do." Aunt Munsie wouldn't listen to any of that. She knew that if Miss Lucille had come out there to her gate, she must have *something* she was going to say about Mr. Thad or Mr. Will. Miss Lucille had two brothers and a son of her own who were lawyers in Memphis, and who lived in style down there and kept Lucille in style here in Thornton. Memphis was where Thad Tolliver had his Ford and Lincoln agency, and so Miss Lucille always had news about Thad, and indirectly about Will, too.

"Is they doin' any good? What you hear from 'em?" Aunt Munsie asked Miss Lucille one afternoon in early spring. She had come along just when Miss Lucille was out picking some of the jonquils that grew in profusion on the steep bank between the sidewalk and the ditch in front of her house.

"Mr. Thad and his folks will be up one day in April, Munsie," Miss Lucille said in her pleasantly hoarse voice. "I understand Mr. Will and his crowd may come for Easter Sunday."

"One day, and gone again!" said Aunt Munsie.

"We always try to get them to stay at least one night, but they're busy folks, Munsie."

"When they comin' back sure enough, Miss Lucille?"

"Goodness knows, Munsie. Goodness knows. Goodness knows when any of them are coming back to stay." Miss Lucille took three quick little steps down the bank and hopped lightly across the ditch. "They're prospering so, Munsie," she said, throwing her chin up and smiling proudly. This fragile lady, this daughter, wife, sister, mother of lawyers (and, of course, the darling of all their hearts), stood there in the street with her pretty little feet and shapely ankles close together, and holding a handful of jonquils before her as if it were her bridal bouquet. "They're *all* prospering so, Munsie. Mine *and* yours. You ought to go down to Memphis to see them now and then, the way I do. Or go up to Nashville to see Mr. Will. I understand he's got an even finer establishment than Thad. They've done well, Munsie—yours *and* mine —and we can be proud of them. You owe it to yourself to go and see how well they're fixed. They're rich men by our standards in Thornton, and they're going farther—*all* of them."

Aunt Munsie dropped the tongue of her wagon noisily on the pavement. "What I want to go see 'em for?" she said angrily and with a lowering brow. Then she stooped and, picking up the wagon tongue again, she wheeled her vehicle toward the middle of the street, to get by Miss Lucille, and started off toward the Square. As she turned out into the street, the brakes of a car, as so often, screeched behind her. Presently everyone in the neighborhood could hear Mr. Ralph Hadley tooting the insignificant little horn on his mama's coupé and shouting at Aunt Munsie in his own tooty voice, above the sound of the horn. Aunt Munsie pulled over, making just enough room to let poor old Mr. Ralph get by but without once looking back at him. Then, before Mr. Ralph could get his car started again, Miss Lucille was running along beside Aunt Munsie, saying, "Munsie, you be careful! You're going to meet your death on the streets of Thornton, Tennessee!"

"Let 'em," said Aunt Munsie.

Miss Lucille didn't know whether Munsie meant "Let 'em run over me; I don't care" or meant "Let 'em just dare!" Miss Lucille soon turned back, without Aunt Munsie's ever looking at her. And when Mr. Ralph Hadley did get his motor started, and sailed past in his mama's coupé, Aunt Munsie didn't give him a look, either. Nor did Mr. Ralph bother to turn his face to look at Aunt Munsie. He was on his way to the drugstore, to pick up his mama's prescriptions, and he was too entirely put out, peeved, and upset to endure even the briefest exchange with that ugly, uppity old Munsie of the Tollivers.

Aunt Munsie continued to tug her slop wagon on toward the Square. There was a more animated expression on her face than usual, and every so often her lips would move rapidly and emphatically over a phrase or sentence. Why should she go to Memphis and Nashville and see how rich they were? No matter how rich they were, what difference did it make; they didn't own any land, did they? Or at least none in Cameron County. She had heard the old Doctor tell them—tell his boys and tell his girls, and tell the old lady, too, in her day—that nobody was rich who didn't own land, and nobody stayed rich who didn't see after his land firsthand. But of course Aunt Munsie had herself mocked the old Doctor to his face for going on about land so much. She knew it was only something he had heard his own daddy go on about. She would say right to his face that she hadn't ever seen *him* behind a plow. And was there ever anybody more scared of a mule than Dr. Tolliver was? Mules or horses, either? Aunt Munsie had heard him say that the happiest day of his life was the day he first learned that the horseless carriage was a reality.

No, it was not really to own land that Thad and Will ought to come back to Thornton. It was more that if they were going to be rich, they ought to come home, where their granddaddy had owned land and where their money counted for something. How could they ever be rich anywhere else? They could have a lot of money in the bank and a fine house, that was all—like that mill manager from Chi. The mill manager could have a yard full of big cars and a stucco house as big as you like, but who would ever take him for rich? Aunt Munsie would sometimes say all these things to Crecie, or something as nearly like them as she could find words for. Crecie might nod her head in agreement or she might be in a mood to say being rich wasn't any good for anybody and didn't matter, and that you could live on just being quality better than on being rich in Thornton. "Quality's better than land or better than money in the bank here," Crecie would say.

Aunt Munsie would sneer at her and say, "It never were."

Lucrecie could talk all she wanted about the old times! Aunt Munsie knew too much about what they were like, for both the richest white folks and the blackest field hands. Nothing about the old times was as good as these days, and there were going to be better times yet when Mr. Thad and Mr. Will Tolliver came back. Everybody lived easier now than they used to, and were better off. She could never be got to reminisce about her childhood in slavery, or her life with her husband, or even about those halcyon days after the old Mizziz had died and Aunt Munsie's word had become law in the Tolliver household. Without being able to book-read or even to make numbers, she had finished raising the whole pack of towheaded Tollivers just as the Mizziz would have wanted it done. The Doctor told her that she *had* to—he didn't ever once think about getting another wife, or taking in some cousin, not after his "Molly darling"—and Aunt Munsie *did*. But, as Crecie said, when a time was past in her mama's life, it seemed to be gone and done with in her head, too.

Lucrecie would say frankly she thought her mama was "hard about people and things in the world." She talked about her mama not only to the Blalocks, for whom she had worked all her life, but to anybody else who gave her an opening. It wasn't just about her mama, though, that she would talk to anybody. She liked to talk, and she talked about Aunt Munsie not in any ugly, resentful way but as she would about when the sheep-rains would begin or where the fire was last night. (Crecie was twice the size of her mama, and black the way her old daddy had been, and loud and good-natured the way he was—or at least the way Aunt Munsie wasn't. You wouldn't have known they were mother and daughter, and not many of the young people in town did realize it. Only by accident did they live next door to each other; Mr. Thad and Mr. Will had bought Munsie her house, and Crecie had heired hers from her second husband.) *That* was how she talked about her mama—as she would have about any lonely, eccentric, harmless neighbor. "I may be dead wrong, but I think Mama's kind of hardhearted," she would say. "Mama's a good old soul, I reckon, but when something's past, it's gone and done with for Mama. She don't think about day before yestiddy—yestiddy, either. I don't know, maybe that's the way to be. Maybe that's why the old soul's gonna outlive us all." Then, obviously thinking about what a picture of health she herself was at sixty, Crecie would toss her head about and laugh so loud you might hear her all the way to the fair grounds.

Crecie, however, knew her mama was not honest-to-God mean and hadn't ever been mean to the Tolliver children, the way the Blalocks liked to make out she had. All the Tolliver children but Mr. Thad and Mr. Will had quarreled with her for good by the time they were grown, but they had quarreled with the old Doctor, too (and as if they were the only ones who shook off their old folks this day and time). When Crecie talked about her mama, she didn't spare her anything, but she was fair to her, too. And it was in no hateful or disloyal spirit that she took part in the conspiracy that finally got Aunt Munsie and her slop wagon off the streets of Thornton. Crecie would have done the same for any neighbor. She had small part enough, actually, in that conspiracy. Her part was merely to break the news to Aunt Munsie that there was now a law against keeping pigs within the city limits. It was a small part but one that no one else quite dared to take.

"They ain't no such law!" Aunt Munsie roared back at Crecie. She was slopping her pigs when Crecie came to the fence and told her about the law. It had seemed the most appropriate time to Lucrecie. "They ain't never been such a law, Crecie," Aunt Munsie said. "Every house on Jackson and Jefferson used to keep pigs."

"It's a brand-new law, Mama."

Aunt Munsie finished bailing out the last of the slop from her wagon. It was just before twilight. The last, weak rays of the sun colored the clouds behind the mock orange tree in Crecie's yard. When Aunt Munsie turned around from the sty, she pretended that that little bit of light in the clouds hurt her eyes, and turned away her head. And when Lucrecie said that everybody had until the first of the year to get rid of their pigs, Aunt Munsie was in a spell of deafness. She headed out toward the crib to get some corn for the chickens. She was trying to think whether anybody else inside the town still kept pigs. Herb Mallory did—two doors beyond Crecie. Then Aunt Munsie remembered Herb didn't pay town taxes. The town line ran between him and Shad Willis.

That was sometime in June, and before July came, Aunt Munsie knew all there was worth knowing about the conspiracy. Mr. Thad and Mr. Will had each been in town for a day during the spring. They and their families had been to her house and sat on the porch; the children had gone back to look at her half-grown collie dog and the two hounds, at the old sow and her farrow of new pigs, and at the frizzliest frizzly chicken Aunt Munsie had ever had. And on those visits to Thornton, Mr. Thad and Mr. Will had also made their usual round among their distant kin and close friends. Everywhere they went, they had heard of the near-accidents Aunt Munsie was causing with her slop wagon and the real danger there was of her being run over. Miss Lucille Satterfield and Miss Patty Bean had both been to the mayor's office and also to see Judge Lawrence to try to get Aunt Munsie "ruled" off the streets, but the men in the courthouse and in the mayor's office didn't listen to the women in Thornton any more. And so either Mr. Thad or Mr. Will—how would which one of them it was matter to Munsie?—had been prevailed upon to stop by Mayor Lunt's office, and in a few second's time had set the wheels of conspiracy in motion. Soon a general inquiry had been made in the town as to how many citizens still kept pigs. Only two property owners besides Aunt Munsie had been found to have pigs on their premises, and they, being men, had been docile and reasonable enough to sell what they had on hand to Mr. Will or Mr. Thad Tolliver. Immediately afterward—within a matter of weeks, that is—a town ordinance had been passed forbidding the possession of swine within the corporate limits of Thornton. Aunt Munsie had got the story bit by bit from Miss Florence and Miss Patty and Miss Lucille and others, including the constable himself, whom she did not hesitate to stop right in the middle of the Square on a Saturday noon. Whether it was Mr. Thad or Mr. Will who had been prevailed upon by the ladies she never ferreted out, but that was only because she did not wish to do so.

The constable's word was the last word for her. The constable said yes, it was the law, and he admitted yes, he had sold his own pigs—for the constable was one of those two reasonable souls—to Mr. Thad or Mr. Will. He didn't say which of them it was, or if he did, Aunt Munsie didn't bother to remember it. And after her interview with the constable, Aunt Munsie never again exchanged words with any human being about the ordinance against pigs. That afternoon, she took a fishing pole from under her house and drove the old sow and the nine shoats down to Herb Mallory's, on the outside of town. They were his, she said, if he wanted them, and he could pay her at killing time.

It was literally true that Aunt Munsie never again exchanged words with anyone about the ordinance against pigs or about the conspiracy she had discovered against herself. But her daughter Lucrecie had a tale to tell about what Aunt Munsie did that afternoon after she had seen the constable and before she drove the pigs over to Herb Mallory's. It was mostly a tale of what Aunt Munsie said to her pigs and to her dogs and her chickens.

Crecie was in her own back yard washing her hair when her mama came down the rickety porch steps and into the yard next door. Crecie had her head in the pot of suds, and so she couldn't look up, but she knew by the way Mama flew down the steps that there was trouble. "She come down them steps like she was wasp-nest bit, or like some youngon who's got hisself wasp-nest bit—and her all of eighty, I reckon!" Then, as Crecie told it, her mama scurried around in the yard for a minute or so like she thought Judgment was about to catch up with her, and pretty soon she commenced slamming at something. Crecie wrapped a towel about her soapy head, squatted low, and edged over toward the plank fence. She peered between the planks and saw what her mama was up to. Since there never had been a gate to the fence around the pigsty, Mama had taken the wood ax and was knocking a hole in it. But directly, just after Crecie had taken her place by the plank fence, her mama had left off her slamming at the sty and turned about so quickly and so exactly toward Crecie that Crecie thought the poor, blind old soul had managed to spy her squatting there. Right away, though, Crecie realized it was not *her* that Mama was staring at. She saw that all Aunt Munsie's chickens and those three dogs of hers had come up behind her, and were all clucking and whining to know why she didn't stop that infernal racket and put out some feed for them.

Crecie's mama set one hand on her hip and rested the ax on the ground. "Just look at yuh!" she said, and then she let the chickens and the dogs—and the pigs, too—have it. She told them what a miserable bunch of creatures they were, and asked them what right they had to always be looking for handouts from her. She sounded like the boss-man who's caught all his pickets laying off before sundown, and she sounded, too, like the preacher giving his sinners Hail Columbia at camp meeting. Finally, shouting at the top of her voice and swinging the ax wide and broad above their heads, she sent the dogs howling under the house and the chickens scattering in every direction. "Now, g'wine! G'wine widja!" she shouted after them. Only the collie pup, of the three dogs, didn't scamper to the farthest corner underneath the house. He stopped under the porch steps, and not two seconds later he was poking his long head out again and showing the whites of his doleful brown eyes. Crecie's mama took a step toward him and then she halted. "You want to know what's the commotion about? I reckoned you would," she said with profound contempt, as though the collie were a more reasonable soul than the other animals, and as though there were nothing she held in such thorough disrespect as reason. "I tell you what the commotion's about," she said. "They *ain't* comin' back. They ain't never comin' back. They ain't never had no notion of comin' back." She turned her head to one side, and the only explanation Crecie could find for her mama's next words was that that collie pup did look so much like Miss Lucille Satterfield.

"Why don't I go down to Memphis or up to Nashville and see 'em sometime, like *you* does?" Aunt Munsie asked the collie. "I tell you why. Becaze I ain't nothin' to 'em in Memphis, and they ain't nothin' to me in Nashville. *You* can go!" she said, advancing and shaking the big ax at the dog. "A collie dog's a collie dog anywhar. But Aunt Munsie, she's just their Aunt Munsie here in Thornton. I got mind enough to see *that*." The collie slowly pulled his head back under the steps, and Aunt Munsie watched for a minute to see if he would show himself again. When he didn't, she went and jerked the fishing pole out from under the house and headed toward the pigsty. Crecie remained squatting beside the fence until her mama and the pigs were out in the street and on their way to Herb Mallory's.

That was the end of Aunt Munsie's keeping pigs and the end of her daily rounds with her slop wagon, but it was not the end of Aunt Munsie. She lived on for nearly twenty years after that, till long after Lucrecie had been put away, in fine style, by the Blalocks. Ever afterward, though, Aunt Munsie seemed different to people. They said she softened, and everybody said it was a change for the better. She would take paper money from under her carpet, or out of the chinks in her walls, and buy things for up at the church, or buy her own whisky when she got sick, intead of making somebody bring her a nip. On the Square she would laugh and holler with the white folks the way they liked her to and the way Crecie and all the other old-timers did, and she even took to tying a bandanna about her head—took to talking old-nigger foolishness, too, about the Bell Witch, and claiming she remembered the day General N. B. Forrest rode into town and saved all the cotton from the Yankees at the depot. When Mr. Will and Mr. Thad came to see her with their families, she got so she would reminisce with them about their daddy and tease them about all the silly little things they had done when they were growing up: "Mr. Thad—him still in kilts, too—he says, 'Aunt Munsie, reach down in yo' stockin' and git me a copper cent. I want some store candy.' " She told them about how Miss Yola Ewing, the sewing woman, heard her threatening to bust Will's back wide open when he broke the lamp chimney, and how Miss Yola went to the Doctor and told him he ought to run Aunt Munsie off. Then Aunt Munsie and the Doctor had had a big laugh about it out in the kitchen, and Miss Yola must have eavesdropped on them, because she left without finishing the girls' Easter dresses.

Indeed, these visits from Mr. Thad and Mr. Will continued as long as Aunt Munsie lived, but she never asked them any more about when they were sure enough coming back. And the children, though she hugged them more than ever—and, toward the last, there were the children's children to be hugged—never again set foot in her back yard. Aunt Munsie lived on for nearly twenty years, and when they finally buried her, they put on her tombstone that she was aged one hundred years, though nobody knew how old she was. There was no record of when she was born. All anyone knew was that in her last years she had said she was a girl helping about the big house when freedom came. That would have made her probably about twelve years old in 1865, according to her statements and depictions. But all agreed that in her extreme old age Aunt Munsie, like other old darkies, was not very reliable about dates and such things. Her spirit softened, even her voice lost some of the rasping quality that it had always had, and in general she became not very reliable about facts.

Study Guides

Both "The Majesty of the Law" and "What You Hear from 'Em?" are concerned with the losses that are inevitable when one pattern of life dissolves and another begins to emerge. Both O'Connor and Taylor are careful to dramatize the unwritten "laws" of abiding civility and to assess and clarify, through an ordered presentation of experience, the "constants" of civilization in a changing and mutable world. If the reader is not alert, he is likely to oversimplify the conflicts explored in Taylor's story. He may say either "Nothing much happens" or "An old eccentric, living in the past, finally comes to reason, adopts modern ways, and is much the better for the change." Such oversimplification does violence to a subtle story.

One way to understand the tensions in "What You Hear from 'Em?" is to consider its *focus*. From the first to the last sentence, Aunt Munsie is the center of action and the object of commentary—whether the action is presented directly or recounted by other characters in the story. Even when the commentary springs directly from Munsie herself, from the narrator, or from the townspeople of Thornton, the focus is always on Munsie. Thus we are permitted to view her from several perspectives; we see her through many eyes and know many opinions about her character and actions. This complex focusing permits us to become aware of the judgments held by various observers in Thornton, and because of their views, her character begins to stand in bold relief against the world.

It is obvious that Thornton is made up of three elements: Crecie's "Quality," Munsie's "Elect," and finally the "Others." One task is to determine as precisely as possible what each of these classes thinks of Munsie and what she thinks of them. In this connection: What standards for evaluation provide the bases of judgment for each class? The Quality and the Elect have attitudes toward Munsie that are far more complex than the attitudes of the Others. Can you explain why? Does the fallacy of oversimplification operate in the judgment of the Others? To the degree that people *know* Munsie does their attitude toward her increase in complexity? What does this suggest about constant and abiding human values? Like Dan in "The Majesty of the Law," Munsie, for the most part, is a strong, highly respected member of her society, though many respect her without consciously knowing why. What human qualities in Munsie command their respect? Though venerated, she is not as well understood by her society as is Dan. Why? What class understands her least? What details transmit this knowledge to the reader?

In varying degrees most of the community thinks of Munsie as an eccentric. One may conclude, therefore, that she represents still another "class." Or more precisely, she belongs to no class but rather to the "realm of complete individuals," since her values are no longer held by anyone but herself—even though for years she earnestly believes they exist in Will and Thad and some of the Elect.

Also crucial to a full appreciation of this story is a clear conception of what Munsie's values actually are. In fact, the reader must have an understanding even greater than that of any one character or even the narrator himself. Toward achieving this understanding, consider the following details and what they imply:

1. Munsie's preserving the iron gate and gingerbread banister from Dr. Tolliver's house.
2. The nature of her deafness and blindness.
3. The ditch—perhaps suggestive of a moat—around her house; the "inner-sanctum" quality of her back yard, once open to the children and later closed to them.

4. The ritualistic visits and exchanges of presents. (Why does Munsie stop opening the presents and reading the letters?)
5. Munsie's condemnation of Crecie's idea of Quality?
6. The significance of the following passage: "In those days, everyone had equal rights on the streets of Thornton. A vehicle was a vehicle, and a person was a person, each with the right to move as slowly as he pleased and to stop where and as often as he pleased. In the Thornton mind, there was no imaginary line down the middle of the street, and, indeed, no one there at that time had heard of drawing a real line on any street. It was merely out of politeness that you made room for others to pass."
7. Munsie's meaning in the following: "No, it was not really to own land that Thad and Will ought to come back to Thornton. It was more that if they were going to be rich, they ought to come home, where their granddaddy had owned land and where their money counted for something. How could they ever be rich anywhere else?"
8. The empty houses of Thornton. Is Munsie sentimental about these houses or about anything else in Thornton? To answer this question, consider Thad's reaction to the burning of the old home place. Are Thad and Will completely honest about their feelings or are they deceiving themselves about their true standards? What does Munsie, before her great change, have to say about "the good old days"? If Munsie is not sentimental, how may her view be characterized? What does she think of reason, which is the opposite of *sentimentality* and sometimes even denies genuine and proper emotion?

It would be a dangerous oversimplification to say that Munsie "lives in the past," even though, before her transformation, she does not altogether live in the present. Actually she has no place to live: the past, she knows, is irrevocably gone; the present is intolerable to an individual with her "set" values. In order to live in the present she would be required to forego, deny, and even betray her sacred integrity, the very meaning of her existence. Thus Munsie has decided to live only in the future: she has somehow to keep faith that the future will preserve and reaffirm the best from the past. (Note that she is not interested in preserving the past merely for its own sake.) She must have faith that her "chillun" will return to Thornton if life there is to be vital and continuous, for it is the children to whom the values of civilization are transmitted. If this cannot be the case, then she too must break faith—and she does so as the story ends. Thad and Will as the Elect, holders of the sacred trust, the children of Thornton, do not return, have never intended to return. Thus Munsie's long-time, abiding faith has been betrayed.

Ironically, the boys think they are acting in her best interest, even when they must resort to underhandedness. Why do they not offer to buy Munsie's pigs? Why do they not go to her personally? Why, like Dan's enemy, do they resort to statutory law? Why do they attempt to hide their "conspiracy" from her? They take it upon themselves to legislate her life, and the very legislation, which, like Dan, she accepts, strips her of individuality, self-responsibility, and independence. Thus Munsie abandons faith. (The reader would do well to ask himself at this point about the characteristics of faith. Under what conditions can confidence be called faith? Is it based on reason? Upon what is it based? If faith disintegrates when all evidence denies its feasibility, can it still be called faith?)

Having lost her confidence in the future, Munsie perpetrates a betrayal greater even than that of Thad and Will. (She never again admits them to her backyard, for instance.) She also betrays herself. This renunciation and the betrayal that follows are reported by Crecie. This is the climax of the story—the point, in terms of action, when Munsie drives away her pigs and dogs, her charges, her responsibilities. She repudiates them and sends them scattering with "Now, g'wine! G'wine widja!" Look at this scene carefully. Her charges come to her expecting the former individual love and attention. What do they get? Why does she sound like a preacher berating "sinners"? What or who is being equated with the dogs in this scene? Consider the rather stark realization Munsie faces when she says: ". . . I ain't nothin' to 'em in Memphis, and they ain't nothin' to me in Nashville. . . . A collie dog's a collie dog anywhar. But Aunt Munsie, she's just their Aunt Munsie here in Thornton."

After the climax, the denouement follows rapidly. Aunt Munsie's transformation from a human being, from a defender of the faith, from a person of courage and integrity to a mere stereotype, to one of Crecie and Miss Lucille's inferior kind, is shockingly swift. She begins to tell lies. She puts on the bandanna—a ripe symbol of the stereotyped, good-natured, loud-mouthed, lovable but irresponsible "Mammy." Unlike Dan, Munsie fails to keep faith with her values in the struggle with change. He acts proudly; Munsie declines sadly—without dignity or integrity. Her story approaches tragedy and becomes, finally, a kind of elegy for the softening and decline of the human spirit, the passing of values sacred to the community of humankind.

WILLIAM FAULKNER

(1897–1962)

A Rose for Emily

I

When Miss Emily Grierson died, our whole town went to her funeral: the men through a sort of respectful affection for a fallen monument, the women mostly out of curiosity to see the inside of her house, which no one save an old manservant—a combined gardener and cook—had seen in at least ten years.

It was a big, squarish frame house that had once been white, decorated with cupolas and spires and scrolled balconies in the heavily lightsome style of the seventies, set on what had once been our most select street. But garages and cotton gins had encroached and obliterated even the august names of that neighborhood; only Miss Emily's house was left, lifting its stubborn and coquettish decay above the cotton wagons and the gasoline pumps—an eyesore among eyesores. And now Miss Emily had gone to join the representatives of those august names where they lay in the cedar-bemused cemetery among the ranked and anonymous graves of Union and Confederate soldiers who fell at the battle of Jefferson.

Alive, Miss Emily had been a tradition, a duty, and a care; a sort of hereditary obligation upon the town, dating from that day in 1894 when Colonel Sartoris, the mayor—he who fathered the edict that no Negro woman should appear on the streets without an apron—remitted her taxes, the dispensation dating from the death of her father on into perpetuity. Not that Miss Emily would have accepted charity. Colonel Sartoris invented an involved tale to the effect that Miss Emily's father had loaned money to the town, which the town, as a matter of business, preferred this way of repaying. Only a man of Colonel Sartoris' generation and thought could have invented it, and only a woman could have believed it.

When the next generation, with its more modern ideas, became mayors and aldermen, this arrangement created some little dissatisfaction. On the first of the year they mailed her a tax notice. February came, and there was no reply. They wrote her a formal letter, asking her to call at the sheriff's office at her convenience. A week later the mayor wrote her himself, offering to call or to send his car for her, and received in reply a note on paper of an archaic shape, in a thin, flowing calligraphy in faded ink, to the effect that she no longer went out at all. The tax notice was also enclosed, without comment.

They called a special meeting of the Board of Aldermen. A deputation waited upon her, knocked at the door through which no visitor had passed since she ceased giving china-painting lessons eight or ten years earlier. They were admitted by the old Negro into a dim hall from which a stairway mounted into still more shadow. It smelled of dust and disuse—a close, dank smell. The Negro led them into the parlor. It was furnished in heavy, leather-covered furniture. When the Negro opened the blinds of one window, a faint dust rose sluggishly about their thighs, spinning with slow motes in the single sun-ray. On a tarnished gilt easel before the fireplace stood a crayon portrait of Miss Emily's father.

They rose when she entered—a small, fat woman in black, with a thin gold chain descending to her waist and vanishing into her belt, leaning on an ebony cane with a tarnished gold head. Her skeleton was small and spare; perhaps that was why what would have been merely plumpness in another was obesity in her. She looked bloated, like a body long submerged in motionless water, and of that pallid hue. Her eyes, lost in the fatty ridges of her face, looked like two small pieces of coal pressed into a lump of dough as they moved from one face to another while the visitors stated their errand.

She did not ask them to sit. She just stood in the door and listened quietly until the spokesman came to a stumbling halt. Then they could hear the invisible watch ticking at the end of the gold chain.

Her voice was dry and cold. "I have no taxes in Jefferson. Colonel Sartoris explained it to me. Perhaps one of you can gain access to the city records and satisfy yourselves."

"But we have. We are the city authorities, Miss Emily. Didn't you get a notice from the sheriff, signed by him?"

"I received a paper, yes," Miss Emily said. "Perhaps he considers himself the sheriff. . . . I have no taxes in Jefferson."

"But there is nothing on the books to show that, you see. We must go by the—"

"See Colonel Sartoris. I have no taxes in Jefferson."

"But, Miss Emily—"

"See Colonel Sartoris." (Colonel Sartoris had been dead almost ten years.) "I have no taxes in Jefferson. Tobe!" The Negro appeared. "Show these gentlemen out."

II

So she vanquished them, horse and foot, just as she had vanquished their fathers thirty years before about the smell. That was two years after her father's death and a short time after her sweetheart—the one we believed would marry her—had deserted her. After her father's death she went out very little; after her sweetheart went away, people hardly saw her at all. A few of the ladies had the temerity to call, but were not received, and the only sign of life about the place was the Negro man—a young man then—going in and out with a market basket.

"Just as if a man—any man—could keep a kitchen properly," the ladies said; so they were not surprised when the smell developed. It was another link between the gross, teeming world and the high and mighty Griersons.

A neighbor, a woman, complained to the mayor, Judge Stevens, eighty years old.

"But what will you have me do about it, madam?" he said.

"Why, send her word to stop it," the woman said. "Isn't there a law?"

"I'm sure that won't be necessary," Judge Stevens said. "It's probably just a snake or a rat that nigger of hers killed in the yard. I'll speak to him about it."

The next day he received two more complaints, one from a man who came in diffident deprecation. "We really must do something about it, Judge. I'd be the last one in the world to bother Miss Emily, but we've got to do something." That night the Board of Aldermen met—three graybeards and one younger man, a member of the rising generation.

"It's simple enough," he said. "Send her word to have her place cleaned up. Give her a certain time to do it in, and if she don't . . ."

"Dammit, sir," Judge Stevens said, "will you accuse a lady to her face of smelling bad?"

So the next night, after midnight, four men crossed Miss Emily's lawn and slunk about the house like burglars, sniffing along the base of the brickwork and at the cellar openings while one of them performed a regular sowing motion with his hand out of a sack slung from his shoulder. They broke open the cellar door and sprinkled lime there, and in all the outbuildings. As they recrossed the lawn, a window that had been dark was lighted and Miss Emily sat in it, the light behind her, and her upright torso motionless as that of an idol. They crept quietly across the lawn and into the shadow of the locusts that lined the street. After a week or two the smell went away.

That was when people had begun to feel really sorry for her. People in our town, remembering how old lady Wyatt, her great-aunt, had gone completely crazy at last, believed that the Griersons held themselves a little too high for what they really were. None of the young men were quite good enough for Miss Emily and such. We had long thought of them as a tableau; Miss Emily a slender figure in white in the background, her father a spraddled silhouette in the foreground, his back to her and clutching a horsewhip, the two of them framed by the back-flung front door. So when she got to be thirty and was still single, we were not pleased exactly, but vindicated; even with insanity in the family she wouldn't have turned down all of her chances if they had really materialized.

When her father died, it got about that the house was all that was left to her; and in a way, people were glad. At last they could pity Miss Emily. Being left alone, and a pauper, she had become humanized. Now she too would know the old thrill and the old despair of a penny more or less.

The day after his death all the ladies prepared to call at the house and offer condolence and aid, as is our custom. Miss Emily met them at the door, dressed as usual and with no trace of grief on her face. She told them that her father was not dead. She did that for three days, with the ministers calling on her, and the doctors, trying to persuade her to let them dispose of the body. Just as they were about to resort to law and force, she broke down, and they buried her father quickly.

We did not say she was crazy then. We believed she had to do that. We remembered all the young men her father had driven away, and we knew that with nothing left, she would have to cling to that which had robbed her, as people will.

III

She was sick for a long time. When we saw here again, her hair was cut short, making her look like a girl, with a vague resemblance to those angels in colored church windows—sort of tragic and serene.

The town had just let the contracts for paving the sidewalks, and in the summer after her father's death they began to work. The construction company came with niggers and mules and machinery, and a foreman named Homer Barron, a Yankee—a big, dark, ready man, with a big voice and eyes lighter than his face. The little boys would follow in groups to hear him cuss the niggers, and the niggers singing in time to the rise and fall of picks. Pretty soon he knew everybody in town. Whenever you heard a lot of laughing anywhere about the square, Homer Barron would be in the center of the group. Presently we began to see him and Miss Emily on Sunday afternoons driving in the yellow-wheeled buggy and the matched team of bays from the livery stable.

At first we were glad that Miss Emily would have an interest, because the ladies all said, "Of course a Grierson would not think seriously of a Northerner, a day laborer." But there were still others, older people, who said that even grief could not cause a real lady to forget *noblesse oblige*—without calling it *noblesse oblige*. They just said, "Poor Emily. Her kinsfolk should come to her." She had some kin in Alabama; but years ago her father had fallen out with them over the estate of old lady Wyatt, the crazy woman, and there was no communication between the two families. They had not even been represented at the funeral.

And as soon as the old people said, "Poor Emily," the whispering began. "Do you suppose it's really so?" they said to one another. "Of course it is. What else could . . ." This behind their hands; rustling of craned silk and satin behind jalousies closed upon the sun of Sunday afternoon as the thin, swift clop-clop-clop of the matched team passed: "Poor Emily."

She carried her head high enough—even when we believed that she was fallen. It was as if she demanded more than ever the recognition of her dignity as the last Grierson; as if it had wanted that touch of earthiness to reaffirm her imperviousness. Like when she bought the rat poison, the arsenic. That was over a year after they had begun to say "Poor Emily," and while the two female cousins were visiting her.

"I want some poison," she said to the druggist. She was over thirty then, still a slight woman, though thinner than usual, with cold, haughty black eyes in a face the flesh of which was strained across the temples and about the eyesockets as you imagine a lighthouse-keeper's face ought to look. "I want some poison," she said.

"Yes, Miss Emily. What kind? For rats and such? I'd recom—"

"I want the best you have. I don't care what kind."

The druggist named several. "They'll kill anything up to an elephant. But what you want is—"

"Arsenic," Miss Emily said. "Is that a good one?"

"Is . . . arsenic? Yes ma'am. But what you want—"

"I want arsenic."

The druggist looked down at her. She looked back at him, erect, her face like a strained flag. "Why, of course," the druggist said. "If that's what you want. But the law requires you to tell what you are going to use it for."

Miss Emily just stared at him, her head tilted back in order to look him eye for eye, until he looked away and went and got the arsenic and wrapped it up. The Negro delivery boy brought her the package; the druggist didn't come back. When she opened the package at home there was written on the box, under the skull and bones: "For rats."

IV

So the next day we all said, "She will kill herself"; and we said it would be the best thing. When she had first begun to be seen with Homer Barron, we had said, "She will marry him." Then we said, "She will persuade him yet," because Homer himself had remarked—he liked men, and it was known that he drank with the younger men in the Elk's Club—that he was not a marrying man. Later we said, "Poor Emily," behind the jalousies as they passed on Sunday afternoon in the glittering buggy, Miss Emily with her head high and Homer Barron with his hat cocked and a cigar in his teeth, reins and whip in a yellow glove.

Then some of the ladies began to say that it was a disgrace to the town and a bad example to the young people. The men did not want to interfere, but at last the ladies forced the Baptist minister—Miss Emily's people were Episcopal—to call upon her. He would never divulge what happened during that interview, but he refused to go back again. The next Sunday they again drove about the streets, and the following day the minister's wife wrote to Miss Emily's relations in Alabama.

So she had blood-kin under her roof again and we sat back to watch developments. At first nothing happened. Then we were sure that they were to be married. We learned that Miss Emily had been to the jeweler's and ordered a man's toilet set in silver, with the letters H.B. on each piece. Two days later we learned that she had bought a complete outfit of men's clothing, including a nightshirt, and we said, "They are married." We were really glad. We were glad because the two female cousins were even more Grierson than Miss Emily had ever been.

So we were not surprised when Homer Barron—the streets had been finished some time since—was gone. We were a little disappointed that there was not a public blowing-off, but we believed that he had gone on to prepare for Miss Emily's coming, or to give her a chance to get rid of the cousins. (By that time it was a cabal, and we were all Miss Emily's allies to help circumvent the cousins.) Sure enough, after another week they departed. And, as we had expected all along, within three days Homer Barron was back in town. A neighbor saw the Negro man admit him at the kitchen door at dusk one evening.

And that was the last we saw of Homer Barron. And of Miss Emily for some time. The Negro man went in and out with the market basket, but the front door remained closed. Now and then we would see her at a window for a moment, as the men did that night when they sprinkled the lime, but for almost six months she did not appear on the streets. Then we knew that this was to be expected too; as if that quality of her father which had thwarted her woman's life so many times had been too virulent and too furious to die.

When we next saw Miss Emily, she had grown fat and her hair was turning gray. During the next few years it grew grayer and grayer until it attained an even pepper-and-salt iron-gray, when it ceased turning. Up to the day of her death at seventy-four it was still that vigorous iron-gray, like the hair of an active man.

From that time on her front door remained closed, save for a period of six or seven years, when she was about forty, during which she gave lessons in china-painting. She fitted up a studio in one of the downstairs rooms, where the daughters and granddaughters of Colonel Sartoris' contemporaries were sent to her with the same regularity and in the same spirit that they were sent on Sundays with a twenty-five cent piece for the collection plate. Meanwhile her taxes had been remitted.

Then the newer generation became the backbone and the spirit of the town, and the painting pupils grew up and fell away and did not send their children to her with boxes of color and tedious brushes and pictures cut from the ladies' magazines. The front door closed upon the last one and remained closed for good. When the town got free postal delivery Miss Emily alone refused to let them fasten the metal numbers above her door and attach a mailbox to it. She would not listen to them.

Daily, monthly, yearly we watched the Negro grow grayer and more stooped, going in and out with the market basket. Each December we sent her a tax notice, which would be returned by the post office a week later, unclaimed. Now and then we would see her in one of the downstairs windows—she had evidently shut up the top floor of the house—like the carven torso of an idol in a niche, looking or not looking at us, we could never tell which. Thus she passed from generation to generation—dear, inescapable, impervious, tranquil, and perverse.

And so she died. Fell ill in the house filled with dust and shadows, with only a doddering Negro man to wait on her. We did not even know she was sick; we had long since given up trying to get any information from the Negro. He talked to no one, probably not even to her, for his voice had grown harsh and rusty, as if from disuse.

She died in one of the downstairs rooms, in a heavy walnut bed with a curtain, her gray head propped on a pillow yellow and moldy with age and lack of sunlight.

V

The Negro met the first of the ladies at the front door and let them in, with their hushed, sibilant voices and their quick, curious glances, and then he disappeared. He walked right through the house and out the back and was not seen again.

The two female cousins came at once. They held the funeral on the second day, with the town coming to look at Miss Emily beneath a mass of bought flowers, with the crayon face of her father musing profoundly above the bier and the ladies sibilant and macabre; and the very old men—some in their brushed Confederate uniforms—on the porch and the lawn, talking of Miss Emily as if she had been a contemporary of theirs, believing that they had danced with her and courted her perhaps, confusing time with its mathematical progression, as the old do, to whom all the past is not a diminishing road, but, instead, a huge meadow which no winter ever quite touches, divided from them now by the narrow bottleneck of the most recent decade of years.

Already we knew that there was one room in that region above stairs which no one had seen in forty years, and which would have to be forced. They waited until Miss Emily was decently in the ground before they opened it.

The violence of breaking down the door seemed to fill this room with pervading dust. A thin, acrid pall as of the tomb seemed to lie everywhere upon this room decked and furnished as for a bridal: upon the valance curtains of faded rose color, upon the rose-shaded lights, upon the dressing table, upon the delicate array of crystal and the man's toilet things backed with tarnished silver, silver so tarnished that the monogram was obscured. Among them lay a collar and tie, as if they had just been removed, which, lifted, left upon the surface a pale crescent in the dust. Upon a chair hung the suit, carefully folded; beneath it the two mute shoes and the discarded socks.

The man himself lay in the bed.

For a long while we just stood there, looking down at the profound and fleshless grin. The body had apparently once lain in the attitude of an embrace, but now the long sleep that outlasts love, that conquers even the grimace of love, had cuckolded him. What was left of him, rotted beneath what was left of the nightshirt, had become inextricable from the bed in which he lay; and upon him and upon the pillow beside him lay that even coating of the patient and biding dust.

Then we noticed that in the second pillow was the indentation of a head. One of us lifted something from it, and leaning forward, that faint and invisible dust dry and acrid in the nostrils, we saw a long strand of iron-gray hair.

Symbol, Theme, and Epiphany

Looking back at sections one and two, we note that the stories there, along with those by Taylor and Faulkner in section three, can be classified as "tragedies of waste": a character of courage and virtue is destroyed through some fatal flaw in judgment or understanding; a potentially ideal relationship is ruined; high expectations and dreams fall into chaos and become nightmares. Thus the conditions under which man lives are frequently harsh; order is forever crumbling as he strives, often nobly and bravely, to create "form" or construct "meaning" for himself; the end may be complete and total defeat. But other stories in this text are clearly stories of victory. "The Majesty of the Law," for instance, ends on a positive note of quiet triumph. Perhaps "The Blue Hotel" makes a promise of victory through the Easterner's awareness of complicity and the merging of "East" and "West." We may even find the beginnings of victory in Mrs. Davicci's recognition of error and in her husband's club of roses. Although the forces of dissolution are strong, victory is nevertheless possible.

Writers of merit are concerned with both themes, with what *is* and what *might be;* in searching for a total awareness of man's condition, they explore the far-reaching possibilities of finding the ideal. Moreover, in section four each story is concerned with how a character achieves awareness—how he comes to recognize disorder and limitation as well as order and possibility. And in each of these stories the protagonist achieves some kind of significant victory.

The arrival at awareness is often called *epiphany*; as a term it connotes thematically what discovery signifies in plot. Epiphany derives from the celebration commemorating the Magi's discovery of Christ, or the first revelation of Christ (Ultimate Truth) to man. When used as a literary term, epiphany means a character's discovery of some highly significant truth about himself, about the nature of the world, or about his relationship to universal truth. Thus the three stories in this section all share the common theme of discovery: conscious awareness emerges from heretofore uncomprehended and disordered experience.

Just as Miranda in "The Grave" discovers the symbolic meaning of a coffin screw head, so the reader's awareness of total meaning in a story often depends upon his recognition and understanding of *symbol.* This literary device is a means of compressing a great deal of meaning in a brief space and is employed in both poetry and prose to allude to "larger" meanings.

A symbol is, first of all, a concrete object or a specific character or action. Literally it is only itself: a particular thing or a specific act. But it is more than that: it is also a state, condition, idea; and it may evoke a profusion of ideas. For example, a rose is a rose; but by traditional and/or particular reference in a story, a rose may be, separately or all at once, freshness, ideal perfection, purity, ephemeral beauty, transience. A symbol is thus a kind of metaphor in which similarities between an object and an idea suggest an equation of the two. The very fact that a rose is short-lived, that it is pleasing in color, shape, texture, and aroma, that in contrast it appears among ugly thorns, that its value is increased by its rarity and short life—all these suggest its innate capacity for becoming a symbol. The rose for Emily in the title of Faulkner's story is a rose, but perhaps it is also short-lived beauty, transience, and withered decay.

Whether or not a rose used as an image in a story is also a symbol in the story must be determined by the context in which it appears. It may be both, for images "rise" to symbolic connotations. But *all images are not symbols,* and a reader errs when he "forces" images to function as symbols. The context will suggest whether similarities between object and idea are present, whether the first points to the second. If a story deals with the traditional themes of *ubi sunt* or *carpe diem* and a rose is mentioned in varying contexts, or if it figures prominently in some significant action, then the reader is usually justified in assuming that the rose is symbolic. But the context should never be warped or twisted to conform to the reader's preconceived idea of a rose's extended meaning. By repeated patterns of action, pointed juxtaposition, and allusion to other well-known symbols, the context permits an image to expand legitimately into symbol.

The context will also determine to what degree the meaning is to be extended. It will define the limits of expansion. Because Faulkner's story is about the decline and perversion of values, we are perhaps justified in thinking of the rose in his title as a symbol of the purity of absolute idealism that has withered in a world of perpetual change; the rose may even represent fragile perfection fading in time. On the other hand, the context in this story supports no interpretation of the rose as a symbol of dewy youthfulness and fresh vitality.

In the three epiphany stories that follow, symbols are used in a variety of ways to deliver theme. Readers will observe that "The Grave" relies heavily on *foreshadowing* and *emergent symbol;* in "A Summer's Reading" only one dominant symbol emerges: the act of reading one hundred books is equated with personal and public honor; on the other hand "When the Light Gets Green" employs much highly complex symbolism, with imagery and color as the prime symbols of the recurring cycles of destruction, change, and growth.

KATHERINE ANNE PORTER

(*1894–*)

The Grave

The grandfather, dead for more than thirty years, had been twice disturbed in his long repose by the constancy and possessiveness of his widow. She removed his bones first to Louisiana and then to Texas as if she had set out to find her own burial place, knowing well she would never return to the places she had left. In Texas she set up a small cemetery in a corner of her first farm, and as the family connection grew, and oddments of relations came over from Kentucky to settle, it contained at last about twenty graves. After the grandmother's death, part of her land was to be sold for the benefit of certain of her children, and the cemetery happened to lie in the part set aside for sale. It was necessary to take up the bodies and bury them again in the family plot in the big new public cemetery, where the grandmother had been buried. At last her husband was to lie beside her for eternity, as she had planned.

The family cemetery had been a pleasant small neglected garden of tangled rose bushes and ragged cedar trees and cypress, the simple flat stones rising out of uncropped sweet-smelling wild grass. The graves were lying open and empty one burning day when Miranda and her brother Paul, who often went together to hunt rabbits and doves, propped their twenty-two Winchester rifles carefully against the rail fence, climbed over and explored among the graves. She was nine years old and he was twelve.

They peered into the pits all shaped alike with such purposeful accuracy, and looking at each other with pleased adventurous eyes, they said in solemn tones: "These were graves!" trying by words to shape a special, suitable emotion in their minds, but they felt nothing except an agreeable thrill of wonder: they were seeing a new sight, doing something they had not done before. In them both there was also a small disappointment at the entire commonplaceness of the actual spectacle. Even if it had once contained a coffin for years upon years, when the coffin was gone a grave was just a hole in the ground. Miranda leaped into the pit that had held her grandfather's bones. Scratching around aimlessly and pleasurably as any young animal, she scooped up a lump of earth and weighed it in her palm. It had a pleasantly sweet, corrupt smell, being mixed with cedar needles and small leaves, and as the crumbs fell apart, she saw a silver dove no larger than a hazel nut, with spread wings and a neat fan-shaped tail. The breast had a deep round hollow in it. Turning it up to the fierce sunlight, she saw that the inside of the hollow was cut in little whorls. She scrambled out, over the pile of loose earth that had fallen back into one end of the grave, calling to Paul that she had found something, he must guess what. . . . His head appeared smiling over the rim of another grave. He waved a closed hand at her. "I've got something too!" They ran to compare treasures, making a game of it, so many guesses each, all wrong, and a final showdown with opened palms. Paul had found a thin wide gold ring carved with intricate flowers and leaves. Miranda was smitten at sight of the ring and wished to have it. Paul seemed more impressed by the dove. They made a trade, with some little bickering. After he had got the dove in his hand, Paul said, "Don't you know what this is? This is a screw head for a *coffin!* . . . I'll bet nobody else in the world has one like this!"

Miranda glanced at it without covetousness. She had the gold ring on her thumb; it fitted perfectly. "Maybe we ought to go now," she said, "maybe one of the niggers'll see us and tell somebody." They knew the land had been sold, the cemetery was no longer theirs, and they felt like trespassers. They climbed back over the fence, slung their rifles loosely under their arms—they had been shooting at targets with various kinds of firearms since they were seven years old—and set out to look for the rabbits and doves or whatever small game might happen along. On these expeditions Miranda always followed at Paul's heels along the path, obeying instructions about handling her gun when going through fences; learning how to stand it up properly so it would not slip and fire unexpectedly; how to wait her time for a shot and not just bang away in the air without looking, spoiling shots for Paul, who really could hit things if given a chance. Now and then, in her excitement at seeing birds whizz up suddenly before her face, or a rabbit leap across her very toes, she lost her head, and almost without sighting she flung her rifle up and pulled the trigger. She hardly ever hit any sort of mark. She had no proper sense of hunting at all. Her brother would be often completely disgusted with her. "You don't care whether you get your bird or not," he said. "That's no way to hunt." Miranda could not understand his indignation. She had seen him smash his hat and yell with fury when he had missed his aim. "What I like about shooting," said Miranda, with exasperating inconsequence, "is pulling the trigger and hearing the noise."

"Then, by golly," said Paul, "whyn't you go back to the range and shoot at bulls-eyes?"

"I'd just as soon," said Miranda, "only like this, we walk around more."

"Well, you just stay behind and stop spoiling my shots," said Paul, who, when he made a kill, wanted to be certain he had made it. Miranda, who alone brought down a bird once in twenty rounds, always claimed as her own any game they got when they fired at the same moment. It was tiresome and unfair and her brother was sick of it.

"Now, the first dove we see, or the first rabbit, is mine," he told her. "And the next will be yours. Remember that and don't get smarty."

"What about snakes?" asked Miranda idly. "Can I have the first snake?"

Waving her thumb gently and watching her gold ring glitter, Miranda lost interest in shooting. She was wearing her summer roughing outfit: dark blue overalls, a light blue shirt, a hired-man's straw hat, and thick brown sandals. Her brother had the same outfit except his was a sober hickory-nut color. Ordinarily Miranda preferred her overalls to any other dress, though it was making rather a scandal in the countryside, for the year was 1903, and in the back country the law of female decorum had teeth in it. Her father had been criticized for letting his girls dress like boys and go careering around astride barebacked horses. Big sister Maria, the really independent and fearless one, in spite of her rather affected ways, rode at a dead run with only a rope knotted around her horse's nose. It was said the motherless family was running down, with the Grandmother no longer there to hold it together. It was known that she had discriminated against her son Harry in her will, and that he was in straits about money. Some of his old neighbors reflected with vicious satisfaction that now he would probably not be so stiffnecked, nor have any more high-stepping horses either. Miranda knew this, though she could not say how. She had met along the road old women of the kind who smoked corn-cob pipes, who had treated her grandmother with most sincere respect. They slanted their gummy old eyes sideways at the granddaughter and said, "Ain't you ashamed of yoself, Missy? It's aginst the Scriptures to dress like that. Whut yo Pappy thinkin about?" Miranda, with her powerful social sense, which was like a fine set of antennae radiating from every pore of her skin, would feel ashamed because she knew well it was rude and ill-bred to shock anybody, even bad-tempered old crones, though she had faith in her father's judgment and was perfectly comfortable in the clothes. Her father had said, "They're just what you need, and they'll save your dresses for school. . . ." This sounded quite simple and natural to her. She had been brought up in rigorous economy. Wastefulness was vulgar. It was also a sin. These were truths; she had heard them repeated many times and never once disputed.

Now the ring, shining with the serene purity of fine gold on her rather grubby thumb, turned her feelings against her overalls and sockless feet, toes sticking through the thick brown leather straps. She wanted to go back to the farmhouse, take a good cold bath, dust herself with plenty of Maria's violet talcum powder—provided Maria was not present to object, of course—put on the thinnest, most becoming dress she owned, with a big sash, and sit in a wicker chair under the trees . . . These things were not all she wanted, of course; she had vague stirrings of desire for luxury and a grand way of living which could not take precise form in her imagination but were founded on family legend of past wealth and leisure. These immediate comforts were what she could have, and she wanted them at once. She lagged rather far behind Paul, and once she thought of just turning back without a word and going home. She stopped, thinking that Paul would never do that to her, and so she would have to tell him. When a rabbit leaped, she let Paul have it without dispute. He killed it with one shot.

When she came up with him, he was already kneeling, examining the wound, the rabbit trailing from his hands. "Right through the head," he said complacently, as if he had aimed for it. He took out his sharp, competent bowie knife and started to skin the body. He did it very cleanly and quickly. Uncle Jimbilly knew how to prepare the skins so that Miranda always had fur coats for her dolls, for though she never cared much for her dolls she liked seeing them in fur coats. The children knelt facing each other over the dead animal. Miranda watched admiringly while her brother stripped the skin away as if he were taking off a glove. The flayed flesh emerged dark scarlet, sleek, firm; Miranda with thumb and finger felt the long fine muscles with the silvery flat strips binding them to the joints. Brother lifted the oddly bloated belly. "Look," he said, in a low amazed voice. "It was going to have young ones."

Very carefully he slit the thin flesh from the center ribs to the flanks, and a scarlet bag appeared. He slit again and pulled the bag open, and there lay a bundle of tiny rabbits, each wrapped in a thin scarlet veil. The brother pulled these off and there they were, dark gray, their wet down lying in minute even ripples, like a baby's head just washed, their unbelievably small delicate ears folded close, their little blind faces almost featureless.

Miranda said, "Oh, I want to *see,*" under her breath. She looked and looked—excited but not frightened, for she was accustomed to the sight of animals killed in hunting—filled with pity and astonishment and a kind of shocked delight in the wonderful little creatures for their own sakes, they were so pretty. She touched one of them ever so carefully, "Ah, there's blood running over them," she said and began to tremble without knowing why. Yet she wanted most deeply to see and to know. Having seen, she felt at once as if she had known all along. The very memory of her former ignorance faded, she had always known just this. No one had ever told her anything outright, she had been rather unobservant of the animal life around her because she was so accustomed to animals. They seemed simply disorderly and unaccountably rude in their habits, but altogether natural and not very interesting. Her brother had spoken as if he had known about everything all along. He may have seen all this before. He had never said a word to her, but she knew now a part at least of what he knew. She understood a little of the secret, formless intuitions in her own mind and body, which had been clearing up, taking form, so gradually and so steadily she had not realized that she was learning what she had to know. Paul said cautiously, as if he were talking about something forbidden: "They were just about ready to be born." His voice dropped on the last word. "I know," said Miranda, "like kittens. I know, like babies." She was quietly and terribly agitated, standing again with her rifle under her arm, looking down at the bloody heap. "I don't want the skin," she said, "I won't have it." Paul buried the young rabbits again in their mother's body, wrapped the skin around her, carried her to a clump of sage bushes, and hid her away. He came out again at once and said to Miranda, with an eager friendliness, a confidential tone quite unusual in him, as if he were taking her into an important secret on equal terms: "Listen now. Now you listen to me, and don't ever forget. Don't you ever tell a living soul that you saw this. Don't tell a soul. Don't tell Dad because I'll get into trouble. He'll say I'm leading you into things you ought not to do. He's always saying that. So now don't you go and forget and blab out sometime the way you're always doing. . . . Now, that's a secret. Don't you tell."

Miranda never told, she did not even wish to tell anybody. She thought about the whole worrisome affair with confused unhappiness for a few days. Then it sank quietly into her mind and was heaped over by accumulated thousands of impressions, for nearly twenty years. One day she was picking her path among the puddles and crushed refuse of a market street in a strange city of a strange country, when without warning, plain and clear in its true colors as if she looked through a frame upon a scene that had not stirred nor changed since the moment it happened, the episode of that far-off day leaped from its burial place before her mind's eye. She was so reasonlessly horrified she halted suddenly staring, the scene before her eyes dimmed by the vision back of them. An Indian vendor had held up before her a tray of dyed sugar sweets, in the shapes of all kinds of small creatures: birds, baby chicks, baby rabbits, lambs, baby pigs. They were in gay colors and smelled of vanilla, maybe. . . . It was a very hot day and the smell in the market, with its piles of raw flesh and wilting flowers, was like the mingled sweetness and corruption she had smelled that other day in the empty cemetery at home: the day she had remembered always until now vaguely as the time she and her brother had found treasure in the opened graves. Instantly upon this thought the dreadful vision faded, and she saw clearly her brother, whose childhood face she had forgotten, standing again in the blazing sunshine, again twelve years old, a pleased sober smile in his eyes, turning the silver dove over and over in his hands.

Investigation and Comment

Through the discoveries of nine-year-old Miranda, Katherine Anne Porter points out the destructive forces in the natural world and the entrapment of man in "old mortality." Before the story closes, she unveils the aesthetics by which man may live if he is to confront decay and waste in his world and transform mere existence into the art of living. This seems a big order for a very short work of fiction, but let us look closely at how Miss Porter achieves her purpose.

Though Miranda is the central character and the dramatized action does not begin until she finds the screw head from the coffin, the story opens with an account of the life and burial of Miranda's grandparents. If this preliminary exposition is not irrelevant, as it might seem at first, then the enveloping action must point to some larger "idea" to which Miranda's experience as a child is related. The story must obviously be concerned with something bigger and more encompassing than Miranda herself. It is about a preadolescent child, but the theme explores, among other things, the persistence of the past and its values. So the opening paragraph suggests a theme that examines the proper role of the past (the grave) among the living.

The title itself is revealing. The grave supplies the central image, calls forth further related images, provides part of the setting for the literal action, and comes into vivid focus in the closing passage. Because of this recurring emphasis, we may infer that the grave is to function as a symbol that gathers into one image a cluster of separate but allied meanings. The enveloping action first hints that the grave is tradition —the remains from the past which the present holds sacred. The children's grandmother, now in the grave too, is part of tradition, and she is characterized by "constancy and possessiveness." She is faithful to what remains of the past and carries it with her since it is her particular possession, part of her treasured values. The grandmother, having once preserved, and now having entered the grave, signifies that tradition is not only something transmitted from the past; it is also something that must be sacred to an individual. It must be private but also communal. It is precious as long as it holds what is personally significant, but otherwise it is hollow and meaningless (". . . when the coffin was gone a grave was just a hole in the ground").

The grave holds not only the past—or all that remains of it. It also contains something of great value. Both Paul and Miranda find "treasure in the opened grave," though Miranda does not completely recognize the true value of her treasure until she is an adult. Further, each living person is the grave of those whom they keep in memory; the memory contains what remains of the past, of all persons who existed yesterday. Therefore each individual is, in effect, a grave. Further, he is the grave for himself, since all that remains of the "you" that was yesterday is contained in the "you" that exists at this moment and will not exist in the next. The adult is the grave of the youth; the adolescent is the grave of the child. These meanings of the grave as the central symbol are made clearer as the story develops. Note for example: "Paul *buried* the young rabbits again in their mother's body"; memory was *"heaped over* by accumulated thousands of impressions"; "that far-off day leaped from its *burial place* before her mind's eye." [Italics added.]

The grave is equated, first, with the *living* past, memory, a great treasure, a tradition that is both collective and personal. But also compressed in the grave image is a second equation: since the past betokens decay, since memory is but the mental record of dead times, since tradition is merely the collective and codified memory of bygone experience—the grave becomes the equivalent of decay, waste, and mortality. This twofold meaning, as Miss Porter presents it, is no "contrariness" on the part of the author. The ambiguity, instead of representing confusion, is actually a concise refinement, for the profound reality of life that she explores is everything her symbol encompasses. A full or total view is never arrived at with simplified abstractions. The world *is* complex, contradictory, paradoxical, mixed. One idea is forever merging with another. One aspect of the grave merges and blends with the other, so that the author's symbol reflects a full cognizance of the *ambiguity* and *paradox* inherent in the human condition.

It is this very paradoxical nature of life that Paul and Miranda, in their innocence, are breathless to explore when they venture into the grave. As children taking their first steps toward epiphany, they are like young animals—and animals have no real sense of death, tragedy, or aesthetics. These sensibilities come with maturity and human perception. The two young innocents on the edge of the grave are about to become aware of the human predicament and, eventually, the proper role of man in the world.

The two treasures they find in the grave extend the theme significantly. Miranda discovers the ornamental screw head and swaps it for the ring found by Paul. Their individual preferences reveal much about each child's character and degree of awareness. Paul prefers the screw head, which is both pleasing to the eye *and* practical. His immediate recognition of its function, in combination with its ornamental quality, indicates that his sense of aesthetics has developed to such a point that he appreciates the sensual appeal of form as well as the function of that form. Miranda on the other hand prefers the ring. It is beautiful, as is the dove, but it serves no practical purpose immediately perceivable to her. She admires its glitter; it stirs longings for sensual refinement (cleanliness, a fancy dress, bath powder, rocking-chair leisure). There are "stirrings of desire for luxury and a grand way of living which could not take precise form in her imagination." As yet, Miranda's aesthetic sense is almost entirely superficial. She does not yet "see" clearly that a true aesthetic also appreciates function—the practical application of a pleasing form. She is not as advanced in her awareness as Paul is; so the two children provide a telling contrast. However, the ring stirs additional longings in

Miranda which at first she only faintly recognizes. With the ring on her thumb, she loses interest in shooting—a very unladylike pastime—and becomes aware of her untidiness, her grubby thumb, her boylike behavior, and her shocking overalls. In her desire for luxury there is also a desire for the feminine graces of orderliness and propriety. Stirring in her is the first consciousness of her proper "function"—to be a girl, to fulfill herself in her proper role. Thus the ring suggests to her instinctively a kind of order she has not yet known.

As a *traditional symbol* the ring further suggests perfection, wholeness, unending cycles of life, opposites bound into unity. The reader, if not Miranda, recognizes these implications in the image of the ring and watches their effect on the child. As a symbol of order the ring is used as traditional symbol: it acquires its meaning, in part, from sources *outside* the frame of the story. As a symbol of sensuality and luxury the ring becomes an *emergent symbol*: its meaning is acquired from *within* the framework of the story and is applicable only to the particular context from which it emerges.

The dove has long been a traditional symbol of the Holy Ghost, of peace, of divine inspiration, or even of Christ (Divinity functioning as man). But these traditional meanings of the dove are perhaps not sufficiently supported by the context for us to insist upon such an interpretation in this story. Hence, as symbol the dove is almost entirely emergent; its meaning (the combining of form and function into a thing of beauty) is applicable only in this particular story.

The implied contrast between the ring and the dove, between Paul and Miranda in their degree of aesthetic development, is given additional elaboration in the hunting episode. Miranda is but little concerned with the "art" of hunting, though she is being patiently instructed by Paul who hunts like a skillful artist. The hunting-as-art metaphor is an apt one here. There are rules that must not be violated, conventions that must be observed, and ideals that must be pursued. (Paul wants to make every shot count and wants to bring down the prey "right through the head.") There must be precision, control, order, and, above all, strict observance of the law of economy. There must be no wild shots, no lost motion, no mere banging away; all should be "sharp, competent," finished off "cleanly and quickly." In contrast, Miranda "just bangs away without looking," spoils shots, fires out of turn, wastes bullets. All she cares about is "pulling the trigger and hearing the noise," and her only interest in the game is the wasteful luxury of seeing fur coats on her dolls, about which she actually cares little. Miranda's hunting reflects her disorder and irresponsible wastefulness. Her aesthetics are imperfect because she fails to observe the prime law of economy. These details tie the theme of aesthetic awareness to that of waste.

Despite this inclination toward disorder and wanton destruction, Miranda does have a powerful social sense which makes her aware that "wastefulness was vulgar . . . and also a sin." Her budding aesthetic sense recognizes the principle of economy even though she has not practiced it. She knows that waste—even though it is the law of nature—should not be the law of man. Waste is a sin, and only man can sin. She knows that needless offense to convention is also wasteful, for in offending convention she is preventing an understanding between men. In disregarding tradition she would be guilty of ignoring centuries of wisdom which man has painfully garnered from experience. Convention itself is an economical way of establishing understanding among members of society. Through convention, "content" is given a form that is readily perceivable.

In reality Miranda is a promising, rather sensitive little girl, but in relation to her conventional society, she *appears* improper, unladylike, coarse, savage. Some of her family share the same wanton traits which the grandmother, as the embodiment of strict economy and order, has disdained. (It is a significant fact that the grandmother discriminated against her son Harry because she knew he was given to wasteful living and would not wisely conserve his inheritance.) Miranda, "though she could not say how," knows her clothes and her behavior are reprehensible even though they are "practical." She comes to recognize that in spite of their utilitarian function, her overalls are in truth wasteful because they promote misunderstanding. She is beginning to learn a lesson in aesthetics: form must be understood, and it must be proper to the content. Overalls in her society are not understood and hence they belie her "womanliness." Art, whether concerned with living or hunting, must put form and function in balance. Miranda's native sensitivity—"antennae radiating from every pore of her skin"—makes her ashamed of her present disorder because she is beginning to learn that to be "rude and ill-bred" is also wasteful. Both tradition and intuition reveal to her these principles inherent in the art of living.

We see that the epiphany which Miranda is to experience is carefully prepared for. What a character becomes at the end of the story must be the result of tendencies present from the beginning. The ultimate discovery Miranda makes is therefore no surprise because we see that she is prepared, by instinct and training, to receive the final revelation. The seeds of perception have been dormant in her from the beginning and are clearly marked by these details: she is sensitive to trespassing on others' property, to deserting Paul without telling him, to the disorder and confusion among the farm animals, to Paul's adept skill in dressing the rabbit.

When the secret of life is exposed in the rabbit, when the grave is opened and the treasure found, in a breathless desire for clarification she exclaims, "Oh, I want to *see*." She wants to see (know) the secrets (the buried truth, the hidden mystery, the miracle) that will make the formless disorder of life meaningful. She is filled with "shocked delight" at the marvel of new life; with pity and astonishment she reflects that it is so easily and quickly destroyed. She stands in awe at the knowledge that willful waste is a condition of life, and she becomes a kind of depository for this knowledge as the rabbits are reburied in their mother's body. At last she learns respect for the sacred nature of life. She trembles at the grandeur of Nature's cycle of destruction and creation. She and Paul are shocked at the profanity of their wanton killing; yet they come to accept waste as a necessary condition of existence: the old must be wasted to produce the new; the blood of the mother must bathe the young to give them life. "The very memory of her former ignorance faded, she had always known just this." With the epiphany, the veil is lifted.

Of course, what Miranda comes "to see and to know" is not just the fact of procreation—her natural function as woman. It is not this knowledge which shocks either her or Paul. Their obvious feeling of guilt does not spring from this; nor is this the "secret" which Paul, now accepting her as an initiate, asks her to keep. Like the Easterner in "The Blue Hotel," they both recognize their involvement in sinful destruction (the wanton killing of the rabbits), which to some degree is an unavoidable condition of living. They accept the natural cycle of death and rebirth and their own responsibility in that continuous cycle. They know further that waste is to be involved in destruction without also being engaged in rebirth and regeneration. Blood spilled in Death is redeemed only by blood sacrificed to Life. They recognize sin as participation in the destruction of life without fighting for its preservation. Miranda now recognizes Paul's secret: the unavoidable involvement in destruction. She feels revulsion: "I don't want the skin," she said, "I won't have it."

But Miranda's epiphany is not yet complete, not yet framed "plain and clear in its true colors." She knows the first half of Paul's secret, what *natural* life is, but she has not yet formulated the aesthetics—the rules, traditions, principles—of converting natural life into the art of *human* life. The knowledge that she has achieved must be buried ("heaped over by accumulated thousands of impressions") and must gradually become part of her personal tradition which the past self delivers to the future. Paradoxically the secret treasure of the past is entombed in the living grave of the present. In a world rank with corruption, raw flesh, and wilting flowers, the true aesthetic rises from its grave, as the resurrected Christ (Truth) rose to appear to the watchers at the tomb. Now the epiphany is complete; the second part of Paul's secret emerges; the dreadful vision of sin and waste fades. Paul appears sober and smiling—sober with acceptance, but smiling with the assurance that man need not participate in willful waste as long as he practices the antithesis of nature: the redeeming art of creative preservation. Beauty and function are thus united in the silver dove, which becomes Miranda's symbolic treasure from the grave.

The following are suggestions for exercises:

1. Compare the significance of the card "game" in "The Blue Hotel" and the hunting "game" in "The Grave."
2. Compare and contrast coming of age in "The Grave" and in "Her First Ball"; in "A Summer's Reading" and "I Want to Know Why"; in "The Grave" and "When the Light Gets Green."
3. Discuss the values of youth and age, or the romantic versus the realistic view of life, as dramatized in "Her First Ball," "Youth," or "When the Light Gets Green."

BERNARD MALAMUD

(*1914–*)

A Summer's Reading

George Stoyonovich was a neighborhood boy who had quit high school on an impulse when he was sixteen, run out of patience, and though he was ashamed everytime he went looking for a job, when people asked him if he had finished and he had to say no, he never went back to school. This summer was a hard time for jobs and he had none. Having so much time on his hands, George thought of going to summer school, but the kids in his classes would be too young. He also considered registering in a night high school, only he didn't like the idea of the teachers always telling him what to do. He felt they had not respected him. The result was he stayed off the streets and in his room most of the day. He was close to twenty and had needs with the neighborhood girls, but no money to spend, and he couldn't get more than an occasional few cents because his father was poor, and his sister Sophie, who resembled George, a tall bony girl of twenty-three, earned very little and what she had she kept for herself. Their mother was dead, and Sophie had to take care of the house.

Very early in the morning George's father got up to go to work in a fish market. Sophie left at about eight for her long ride in the subway to a cafeteria in the Bronx. George had his coffee by himself, then hung around in the house. When the house, a five-room railroad flat above a butcher store, got on his nerves he cleaned it up—mopped the floors with a wet mop and put things away. But most of the time he sat in his room. In the afternoons he listened to the ball game. Otherwise he had a couple of old copies of the *World Almanac* he had bought long ago, and he liked to read in them and also the magazines and newspapers that Sophie brought home, that had been left on the tables in the cafeteria. They were mostly picture magazines about movie stars and sports figures, also usually the *News* and *Mirror*. Sophie herself read whatever fell into her hands, although she sometimes read good books.

She once asked George what he did in his room all day and he said he read a lot too.

"Of what besides what I bring home? Do you ever read any worthwhile books?"

"Some," George answered, although he really didn't. He had tried to read a book or two that Sophie had in the house but found he was in no mood for them. Lately he couldn't stand made-up stories, they got on his nerves. He wished he had some hobby to work at—as a kid he was good in carpentry, but where could he work at it? Sometimes during the day he went for walks, but mostly he did his walking after the hot sun had gone down and it was cooler in the streets.

In the evening after supper George left the house and wandered in the neighborhood. During the sultry days some of the storekeepers and their wives sat in chairs on the thick, broken sidewalks in front of their shops, fanning themselves, and George walked past them and the guys hanging out on the candy store corner. A couple of them he had known his whole life, but nobody recognized each other. He had no place special to go, but generally, saving it till the last, he left the neighborhood and walked for blocks till he came to a darkly lit little park with benches and trees and an iron railing, giving it a feeling of privacy. He sat on a bench here, watching the leafy trees and the flowers blooming on the inside of the railing, thinking of a better life for himself. He thought of the jobs he had had since he had quit school—delivery boy, stock clerk, runner, lately working in a factory—and he was dissatisfied with all of them. He felt he would someday like to have a good job and live in a private house with a porch, on a street with trees. He wanted to have some dough in his pocket to buy things with, and a girl to go with, so as not to be so lonely, especially on Saturday nights. He wanted people to like and respect him. He thought about these things often but mostly when he was alone at night. Around midnight he got up and drifted back to his hot and stony neighborhood.

One time while on his walk George met Mr. Cattanzara coming home very late from work. He wondered if he was drunk but then could tell he wasn't. Mr. Cattanzara, a stocky, bald-headed man who worked in a change booth on an IRT station, lived on the next block after George's, above a shoe repair store. Nights, during the hot weather, he sat on his stoop in an undershirt, reading the *New York Times* in the light of the shoemaker's window. He read it from the first page to the last, then went up to sleep. And all the time he was reading the paper, his wife, a fat woman with a white face, leaned out of the window, gazing into the street, her thick white arms folded under her loose breast, on the window ledge.

Once in a while Mr. Cattanzara came home drunk, but it was a quiet drunk. He never made any trouble, only walked stiffly up the street and slowly climbed the stairs into the hall. Though drunk, he looked the same as always, except for his tight walk, the quietness, and that his eyes were wet. George liked Mr. Cattanzara because he remembered him giving him nickels to buy lemon ice with when he was a squirt. Mr. Cattanzara was a different type than those in the neighborhood. He asked different questions than the others when he met you, and he seemed to know what went on in all the newspapers. He read them, as his fat sick wife watched from the window.

"What are you doing with yourself this summer, George?" Mr. Cattanzara asked. "I see you walkin' around at nights."

George felt embarrassed. "I like to walk."

"What are you doin' in the day now?"

"Nothing much just right now. I'm waiting for a job." Since it shamed him to admit he wasn't working, George said, "I'm staying home—but I'm reading a lot to pick up my education."

Mr. Cattanzara looked interested. He mopped his hot face with a red handkerchief.

"What are you readin'?"

George hesitated, then said, "I got a list of books in the library once, and now I'm gonna read them this summer." He felt strange and a little unhappy saying this, but he wanted Mr. Cattanzara to respect him.

"How many books are there on it?"

"I never counted them. Maybe around a hundred."

Mr. Cattanzara whistled through his teeth.

"I figure if I did that," George went on earnestly, "it would help me in my education. I don't mean the kind they give you in high school. I want to know different things than they learn there, if you know what I mean."

The change maker nodded. "Still and all, one hundred books is a pretty big load for one summer."

"It might take longer."

"After you're finished with some, maybe you and I can shoot the breeze about them?" said Mr. Cattanzara.

"When I'm finished," George answered.

Mr. Cattanzara went home and George continued on his walk. After that, though he had the urge to, George did nothing different from usual. He still took his walks at night, ending up in the little park. But one evening the shoemaker on the next block stopped George to say he was a good boy, and George figured that Mr. Cattanzara had told him all about the books he was reading. From the shoemaker it must have gone down the street, because George saw a couple of people smiling kindly at him, though nobody spoke to him personally. He felt a little better around the neighborhood and liked it more, though not so much he would want to live in it forever. He had never exactly disliked the people in it, yet he had never liked them very much either. It was the fault of the neighborhood. To his surprise, George found out that his father and Sophie knew about his reading too. His father was too shy to say anything about it—he was never much of a talker in his whole life—but Sophie was softer to George, and she showed him in other ways she was proud of him.

As the summer went on George felt in a good mood about things. He cleaned the house every day, as a favor to Sophie, and he enjoyed the ball games more. Sophie gave him a buck a week allowance, and though it still wasn't enough and he had to use it carefully, it was a helluva lot better than just having two bits now and then. What he bought with the money—cigarettes mostly, an occasional beer or movie ticket—he got a big kick out of. Life wasn't so bad if you knew how to appreciate it. Occasionally he bought a paperback book from the newsstand, but he never got around to reading it, though he was glad to have a couple of books in his room. But he read thoroughly Sophie's magazines and newspapers. And at night was the most enjoyable time, because when he passed the storekeepers sitting outside their stores, he could tell they regarded him highly. He walked erect, and though he did not say much to them, or they to him, he could feel approval on all sides. A couple of nights he felt so good that he skipped the park at the end of the evening. He just wandered in the neighborhood, where people had known him from the time he was a kid playing punchball whenever there was a game of it going; he wandered there, then came home and got undressed for bed, feeling fine.

For a few weeks he had talked only once with Mr. Cattanzara, and though the change maker had said nothing more about the books, asked no questions, his silence made George a little uneasy. For a while George didn't pass in front of Mr. Cattanzara's house anymore, until one night, forgetting himself, he approached it from a different direction than he usually did when he did. It was already past midnight. The street, except for one or two people, was deserted, and George was surprised when he saw Mr. Cattanzara still reading his newspaper by the light of the street lamp overhead. His impulse was to stop at the stoop and talk to him. He wasn't sure what he wanted to say, though he felt the words would come when he began to talk; but the more he thought about it, the more the idea scared him, and he decided he'd better not. He even considered beating it home by another street, but he was too near Mr. Cattanzara, and the change maker might see him as he ran, and get annoyed. So George unobtrusively crossed the street, trying to make it seem as if he had to look in a store window on the other side, which he did, and then went on, uncomfortable at what he was doing. He feared Mr. Cattanzara would glance up from his paper and call him a dirty rat for walking on the other side of the street, but all he did was sit there, sweating through his undershirt, his bald head shining in the dim light as he read his *Times,* and upstairs his fat wife leaned out of the window, seeming to read the paper along with him. George thought she would spy him and yell out to Mr. Cattanzara, but she never moved her eyes off her husband.

George made up his mind to stay away from the change maker until he had got some of his softback books read, but when he started them and saw they were mostly story books, he lost his interest and didn't bother to finish them. He lost his interest in reading other things too. Sophie's magazines and newspapers went unread. She saw them piling up on a chair in his room and asked why he was no longer looking at them, and George told her it was because of all the other reading he had to do. Sophie said she had guessed that was it. So for most of the day, George had the radio on, turning to music when he was sick of the human voice. He kept the house fairly neat, and Sophie said nothing on the days when he neglected it. She was still kind and gave him his extra buck, though things weren't so good for him as they had been before.

But they were good enough, considering. Also his night walks invariably picked him up, no matter how bad the day was. Then one night George saw Mr. Cattanzara coming down the street toward him. George was about to turn and run but he recognized from Mr. Cattanzara's walk that he was drunk, and if so, probably he would not even bother to notice him. So George kept on walking straight ahead until he came abreast of Mr. Cattanzara and though he felt wound up enough to pop into the sky, he was not surprised when Mr. Cattanzara passed him without a word, walking slowly, his face and body stiff. George drew a breath in relief at his narrow escape, when he heard his name called, and there stood Mr. Cattanzara at his elbow, smelling like the inside of a beer barrel. His eyes were sad as he gazed at George, and George felt so intensely uncomfortable he was tempted to shove the drunk aside and continue on his walk.

But he couldn't act that way to him, and, besides, Mr. Cattanzara took a nickel out of his pants pocket and handed it to him.

"Go buy yourself a lemon ice, Georgie."

"It's not that time anymore, Mr. Cattanzara," George said, "I am a big guy now."

"No, you ain't," said Mr. Cattanzara, to which George made no reply he could think of.

"How are all your books comin' along now?" Mr. Cattanzara asked. Though he tried to stand steady, he swayed a little.

"Fine, I guess," said George, feeling the red crawling up his face.

"You ain't sure?" The change maker smiled slyly, a way George had never seen him smile.

"Sure I'm sure. They're fine."

Though his head swayed in little arcs, Mr. Cattanzara's eyes were steady. He had small blue eyes which could hurt if you looked at them too long.

"George," he said, "name me one book on that list that you read this summer, and I will drink to your health."

"I don't want anybody drinking to me."

"Name me one so I can ask you a question on it. Who can tell, if it's a good book maybe I might wanna read it myself."

George knew he looked passable on the outside, but inside he was crumbling apart.

Unable to reply, he shut his eyes, but when—years later—he opened them, he saw that Mr. Cattanzara had, out of pity, gone away, but in his ears he still heard the words he had said when he left: "George, don't do what I did."

The next night he was afraid to leave his room, and though Sophie argued with him he wouldn't open the door.

"What are you doing in there?" she asked.

"Nothing."

"Aren't you reading?"

"No."

She was silent a minute, then asked, "Where do you keep the books you read? I never see any in your room outside of a few cheap trashy ones."

He wouldn't tell her.

"In that case you're not worth a buck of my hard-earned money. Why should I break my back for you? Go on out, you bum, and get a job."

He stayed in his room for almost a week, except to sneak into the kitchen when nobody was home. Sophie railed at him, then begged him to come out, and his old father wept, but George wouldn't budge, though the weather was terrible and his small room stifling. He found it very hard to breathe, each breath was like drawing a flame into his lungs.

One night, unable to stand the heat anymore, he burst into the street at one A.M., a shadow of himself. He hoped to sneak to the park without being seen, but there were people all over the block, wilted and listless, waiting for a breeze. George lowered his eyes and walked, in disgrace, away from them, but before long he discovered they were still friendly to him. He figured Mr. Cattanzara hadn't told on him. Maybe when he woke up out of his drunk the next morning, he had forgotten all about meeting George. George felt his confidence slowly come back to him.

That same night a man on a street corner asked him if it was true that he had finished reading so many books, and George admitted he had. The man said it was a wonderful thing for a boy his age to read so much.

"Yeah," George said, but he felt relieved. He hoped nobody would mention the books anymore, and when, after a couple of days, he accidentally met Mr. Cattanzara again, *he* didn't, though George had the idea he was the one who had started the rumor that he had finished all the books.

One evening in the fall, George ran out of his house to the library, where he hadn't been in years. There were books all over the place, wherever he looked, and though he was struggling to control an inward trembling, he easily counted off a hundred, then sat down at a table to read.

Study Guides

In "A Summer's Reading" various pressures urge George to an epiphany. Some of these forces are individual and are centered in George; some are at work in the society around him. He attempts to deceive both himself and the society. Almost by accident, it would seem, he is highly successful in fooling one; but he is eventually a dismal failure in deceiving the other—himself.

1. George practices a technique of self-deception perhaps familiar at one time or another to every youth struggling toward maturity. What are his means of hiding the truth from himself? The following details give clues: He "had quit high school on an impulse . . . run out of patience." "This summer was a hard time for jobs." He "thought of going to summer school, but the kids in his classes would be too young." "He didn't like the idea of the teachers always telling him what to do. He felt they had not respected him." "I'm staying home—but I'm reading a lot to pick up my education." "He had never exactly disliked the people in it [the neighborhood], yet he had never liked them very much either. It was the fault of the neighborhood."

2. It is obvious that George is evasive, undisciplined, and self-indulgent. He thinks good things should come to him with little or no effort. It is also obvious that in spite of himself George is highly sensitive to the people around him and, above all, is immensely proud. Point out the details which reflect these traits of character. What is the significance of his pattern of housecleaning? Of walking? Of listening to the radio? Of reading newspapers, magazines, and the *World Almanac?* How does the content which distinguishes these publications relate to George? He likes picture magazines about movie stars but not "made-up stories." What is ironic about his taste and what does the irony reveal about George? What do his lies, particularly to Mr. Cattanzara and to his sister, reveal about him?

3. George fancies himself isolated from his society and largely disengaged from its values; yet he wants his neighbors to respect him and is ashamed when he does not measure up to their standards for a worthy citizen. Mr. Cattanzara and his sister Sophie are the two people he most respects. Why? What are their standards for judging a good citizen? What does this suggest about George's real values, the ones he is too lazy to pursue? Are Sophie and Mr. Cattanzara's standards traditional to the neighborhood? Tradition is one of the forces propelling George toward epiphany. Does he, consciously or unconsciously, share in that tradition? How do you know? Finally, by telling a lie, he gets the neighborhood's respect which he seeks. Is it entirely an accident that the lie about self-education comes so readily to his lips?

4. Mr. Cattanzara may be seen as parallel to George in some ways. What tendencies in George's character and in his behavior constitute a parallel to Mr. Cattanzara's quiet, escapist drinking? His assiduous read-

ing of the *New York Times?* What is the significance of Mrs. Cattanzara's eternal watching from her window? What did Mr. Cattanzara mean when he said "George, don't do what I did"? What did Mr. Cattanzara "do"? Do his perpetual newspaper reading, occasional drunkenness, and purely mechanical job suggest the path he took?

5. George knows Mr. Cattanzara is no longer deceived about the summer's reading when he insults him with the nickel for lemon ice. George is frightened that Mr. Cattanzara will tell and thus shame him in the eyes of the whole community. Yet Mr. Cattanzara lies and tells the neighbors that George has finished his reading. Can you suggest why Mr. Cattanzara does this? Does it demonstrate faith? Understanding and sympathy? Magnanimity? Because of the combined falsehoods of George and Mr. Cattanzara, George gains even greater respect from his society, but in the process he loses something more important: self-respect. His epiphany comes when he fully recognizes that public honor without self-respect is meaningless; and when the agitation brought on by this realization reaches its climax, he rushes to the library to do the act—read a hundred books—that would return to him his private honor. Is this action a total surprise? What part did the example of Mr. Cattanzara's faith and magnanimity play in George's regeneration? Would his final act have had the same meaning if Mr. Cattanzara had told the world George was a "no-good bum" and a despicable pretender?

ROBERT PENN WARREN

(1905–)

When the Light Gets Green

My grandfather had a long white beard and sat under the cedar tree. The beard, as a matter of fact, was not very long and not white, only gray, but when I was a child and was away from him at school during the winter, I would think of him, not seeing him in my mind's eye, and say: He has a long white beard. Therefore, it was a shock to me, on the first morning back home, to watch him lean over the dresser toward the wavy green mirror, which in his always shadowy room reflected things like deep water riffled by a little wind, and clip his gray beard to a point. It is gray and pointed, I would say then, remembering what I had thought before.

He turned his face to the green wavy glass, first one side and then the other in quarter profile, and lifted the long shears, which trembled a little, to cut the beard. His face being turned like that, with his good nose and pointed gray beard, he looked like General Robert E. Lee, without any white horse to ride. My grandfather had been a soldier, too, but now he wore blue-jean pants and when he leaned over like that toward the mirror, I couldn't help but notice how small his hips and backsides were. Only they weren't just small, they were shrunken. I noticed how the blue jeans hung loose from his suspenders and loose off his legs and down around his shoes. And in the morning when I noticed all this about his legs and backsides, I felt a tight feeling in my stomach like when you walk behind a woman and see the high heel of her shoe is worn and twisted and jerks her ankle every time she takes a step.

Always before my grandfather had finished clipping his beard, my Uncle Kirby came to the door and beat on it for breakfast. "I'll be down in just a minute, thank you, sir," my grandfather said. My uncle called him Mr. Barden. "Mr. Barden, breakfast is ready." It was because my Uncle Kirby was not my real uncle, having married my Aunt Lucy, who lived with my grandfather. Then my grandfather put on a black vest and put his gold watch and chain in the vest and picked up his cob pipe from the dresser top, and he and I went down to breakfast, after Uncle Kirby was already downstairs.

When he came into the dining room, Aunt Lucy was sitting at the foot of the table with the iron coffee pot on a plate beside her. She said, "Good morning, Papa."

"Good morning, Lucy," he said, and sat down at the head of the table, taking one more big puff off his pipe before laying it beside his plate.

"You've brought that old pipe down to breakfast again," my aunt said, while she poured the bright-looking coffee into the cups.

"Don't it stink," he always said.

My uncle never talked at breakfast, but when my grandfather said that, my uncle always opened his lips to grin like a dog panting, and showed his hooked teeth. His teeth were yellow because he chewed tobacco, which my grandfather didn't do, although his beard was yellow around the mouth from smoking. Aunt Lucy didn't like my uncle to chew, that was the whole trouble. So she rode my grandfather for bringing his pipe down, all in fun at first before she got serious about it. But he always brought it down just the same, and said to her, "Don't it stink."

After we ate, my uncle got up and said, "I got to get going," and went out through the kitchen where the cook was knocking and sloshing around. If it had rained right and was a good tobacco-setting season, my grandfather went off with me down to the stable to get his mare, for he had to see the setting. We saddled up the mare and went across the lot, where limestone bunched out of the ground and cedar trees and blue grass grew out of the split rock. A branch of cold water with minnows in it went through the lot between rocks and under the cedar trees; it was where I used to play before I got big enough to go to the river with the niggers to swim.

My grandfather rode across the lot and over the rise back of the house. He sat up pretty straight for an old man, holding the bridle in his left hand, and in his right hand a long hickory tobacco stick whittled down to make a walking cane. I walked behind him and watched the big straw hat he wore waggle a little above his narrow neck, or how he held the stick in the middle, firm and straight up like something carried in a parade, or how smooth and slow the muscles in the mare's flanks worked as she put each hoof down in the ground, going up hill. Sassafras bushes and blackberry bushes grew thick along the lane over the rise. In summer, tufts of hay would catch and hang on the dry bushes and showed that the hay wagons had been that way; but when we went that way in setting time, just after breakfast, the blackberry blooms were hardly gone, only a few rusty patches of white left, and the sassafras leaves showed still wet with dew or maybe the rain.

From the rise we could look back on the house. The shingles were black with damp, and the whitewash grayish, except in spots where the sun already struck it and it was drying. The tops of the cedar trees, too, were below us, very dark green and quiet. When we crossed the rise, there were the fields going down toward the river, all checked off and ready for setting, very even, only for the gullies where brush was piled to stop the washing. The fields were reddish from the wet, not yet steaming. Across them, the green woods and the sycamores showing white far off told where the river was.

The hands were standing at the edge of the field under the trees when we got there. The little niggers were filling their baskets with the wet plants to drop, and I got me a basket and filled it. My Uncle Kirby gave me fifty cents for dropping plants, but he didn't give the little niggers that much, I remember. The hands and women stood around waiting a minute, watching Uncle Kirby, who always fumed around, waving his dibble, his blue shirt already sticking to his arms with sweat. "Get the lead out," he said. The little niggers filled faster, grinning with their teeth at him. "Goddam, get the lead out!" My grandfather sat on his mare under the trees, still holding the walking cane, and said, "Why don't you start 'em, sir?"

Then, all of a sudden, they all moved out into the field, scattering out down the rows, the droppers first, and after a minute the setters, who lurched along, never straightening up, down the rows toward the river. I walked down my row, separating out the plants and dopping them at the hills, while it got hotter and the ground steamed. The sun broke out now and then, making my shadow on the ground, then the cloud would come again, and I could see its shadow drifting at me on the red field.

My grandfather rode very slow along the edge of the field to watch the setting, or stayed still under the trees. After a while, maybe about ten o'clock, he would leave and go home. I could see him riding the mare up the rise and then go over the rise; or if I was working the other way toward the river, when I turned round at the end, the lane would be empty and nothing on top the rise, with the cloudy, blue-gray sky low behind it.

The tobacco was all he cared about, now we didn't have any horses that were any real good. He had some silver cups, only one real silver one though, that his horses won at fairs, but all that was before I was born. The real silver one, the one he kept on his dresser and kept string and old minnie balls and pins and things in, had *1859* on it because his horse won it then before the War, when he was a young man. Uncle Kirby said horses were foolishness, and Grandfather said, yes, he reckoned horses were foolishness, all right. So what he cared about now was the tobacco. One time he was a tobacco-buyer for three years, but after he bought a lot of tobacco and had it in his sheds, the sheds burned up on him. He didn't have enough insurance to do any good and he was a ruined man. After that all his children, he had all girls and his money was gone, said about him, "Papa's just visionary, he tried to be a tobacco-buyer but he's too visionary and not practical." But he always said, "All tobacco-buyers are sons-of-bitches, and three years is enough of a man's life for him to be a son-of-a-bitch, I reckon." Now he was old, the corn could get the rust or the hay get rained on for all he cared, it was Uncle Kirby's worry, but all summer, off and on, he had to go down to the tobacco field to watch them sucker or plow or worm, and sometimes he pulled a few suckers himself. And when a cloud would blow up black in summer, he got nervous as a cat, not knowing whether it was the rain they needed or maybe a hail storm coming that would cut the tobacco up bad.

Mornings he didn't go down to the field, he went out under the cedar tree where his chair was. Most of the time he took a book with him along with his pipe, for he was an inveterate reader. His being an inveterate reader was one of the things made his children say he was visionary. He read a lot until his eyes went bad the summer before he had his stroke, then after that, I read to him some, but not as much as I ought. He used to read out loud some from Macaulay's *History of England* or Gibbon's *Decline and Fall,* about Flodden Field or about how the Janizaries took Constantinople amid great slaughter and how the Turk surveyed the carnage and quoted from the Persian poet about the lizard keeping the courts of the mighty. My grandfather knew some poetry, too, and he said it to himself when he didn't have anything else to do. I lay on my back on the ground, feeling the grass cool and tickly on the back of my neck, and looked upside down into the cedar tree where the limbs were tangled and black-green like big hairy fern fronds with the sky blue all around, while he said some poetry. Like the "Isles of Greece, the Isles of Greece, where burning Sappho loved and sung." Or like "Roll on, thou deep and dark blue ocean, roll."

But he never read poetry, he just said what he already knew. He only read history and *Napoleon and His Marshals,* having been a soldier and fought in the War himself. He rode off and joined the cavalry, but he never told me whether he took the horse that won the real silver cup or not. He was with Forrest before Forrest was a general. He said Forrest was a great general, and if they had done what Forrest wanted and cleaned the country ahead of the Yankees, like the Russians beat Napoleon, they'd whipped the Yankees sure. He told me about Fort Donelson, how they fought in the winter woods, and how they got away with Forrest at night, splashing through the cold water. And how the dead men looked in the river bottoms in winter, and I lay on my back on the grass, looking up in the thick cedar limbs, and thought how it was to be dead.

After Shiloh was fought and they pushed the Yankees down in the river, my grandfather was a captain, for he raised a cavalry company of his own out of West Tennessee. He was a captain, but he never got promoted after the War; when I was a little boy everybody still called him Captain Barden, though they called lots of other people in our section Colonel and Major. One time I said to him: "Grandpa, did you ever kill any Yankees?" He said: "God-a-Mighty, how do I know?" So, being little, I thought he was just a captain because he never killed anybody, and I was ashamed. He talked about how they took Fort Pillow, and the drunk niggers under the bluff. And one time he said niggers couldn't stand a charge or stand the cold steel, so I thought maybe he killed some of them. But then I thought, Niggers don't count, maybe.

He only talked much in the morning. Almost every afternoon right after dinner, he went to sleep in his chair, with his hands curled up in his lap, one of them holding the pipe that still sent up a little smoke in the shadow, and his head propped back on the tree trunk. His mouth hung open, and under the hairs of his mustache, all yellow with nicotine, you could see his black teeth and his lips that were wet and pink like a baby's. Usually I remember him that way, asleep.

I remember him that way, or else trampling up and down the front porch, nervous as a cat, while a cloud blew up and the trees began to rustle. He tapped his walking cane on the boards and whistled through his teeth with his breath and kept looking off at the sky where the cloud and sometimes the lightning was. Then of a sudden it came, and if it was rain he used to go up to his room and lie down; but if it came hail on the tobacco, he stayed on the front porch, not trampling any more, and watched the hail rattle off the roof and bounce soft on the grass. "God-a-Mighty," he always said, "bigger'n minnie balls," even when it wasn't so big.

In 1914, just before the war began, it was a hot summer with the tobacco mighty good but needing rain. And when the dry spell broke and a cloud blew up, my grandfather came out on the front porch, watching it like that. It was mighty still, with lightning way off, so far you couldn't hardly hear the thunder. Then the leaves began to ruffle like they do when the light gets green, and my grandfather said to me, "Son, it's gonna hail." And he stood still. Down in the pasture, that far off, you could see the cattle bunching up and the white horse charging across the pasture, looking bright, for the sun was shining bright before the cloud struck it all at once. "It's gonna hail," my grandfather said. It was dark, with jagged lightning and the thunder high and steady. And there the hail was.

He just turned around and went in the house. I watched the hail bouncing, then I heard a noise and my aunt yelled. I ran back in the dining room where the noise was, and my grandfather was lying on the floor with the old silver pitcher he dropped and a broken glass. We tried to drag him, but he was too heavy; then my Uncle Kirby came up wet from the stable and we carried my grandfather upstairs and put him on his bed. My aunt tried to call the doctor even if the lightning might hit the telephone. I stayed back in the dining room and picked up the broken glass and the pitcher and wiped up the floor with a rag. After a while Dr. Blake came from town; then he went away.

When Dr. Blake was gone, I went upstairs to see my grandfather. I shut the door and went in his room, which was almost dark, like always, and quiet because the hail didn't beat on the roof any more. He was lying on his back in the featherbed, with a sheet pulled up over him, lying there in the dark. He had his hands curled loose on his stomach, like when he went to sleep in his chair holding the pipe. I sat on a split-bottom chair by the bed and looked at him: he had his eyes shut and his mouth hung loose, but you couldn't hear his breathing. Then I quit looking at him and looked round the room, my eyes getting used to the shadow. I could see his pants on the floor, and the silver cup on the dresser by the mirror, which was green and wavy like water.

When he said something, I almost jumped out of my skin, hearing his voice like that. He said, "Son, I'm gonna die." I tried to say something, but I couldn't. And he waited, then he said, "I'm on borrowed time, it's time to die." I said, "No!" so sudden and loud I jumped. He waited a long time and said, "It's time to die. Nobody loves me." I tried to say, "Grandpa, I love you." And then I did say it all right, feeling like it hadn't been me said it, and knowing all of a sudden it was a lie, because I didn't feel anything. He just lay there; and I went downstairs.

It was sunshiny in the yard, the clouds gone, but the grass was wet. I walked down toward the gate, rubbing my bare feet over the slick cold grass. A hen was in the yard and she kept trying to peck up a piece of hail, like a fool chicken will do after it hails; but every time she pecked, it bounced away from her over the green grass. I leaned against the gate, noticing the ground on one side the posts, close up, was still dry and dusty. I wondered if the tobacco was cut up bad, because Uncle Kirby had gone to see. And while I looked through the gate down across the pasture where everything in the sun was green and shiny with wet and the cattle grazed, I thought about my grandfather, not feeling anything. But I said out loud anyway, "Grandpa, I love you."

My grandfather lived four more years. The year after his stroke they sold the farm and moved away, so I didn't stay with them any more. My grandfather died in 1918, just before the news came that my Uncle Kirby was killed in France, and my aunt had to go to work in a store. I got the letter about my grandfather, who died of flu, but I thought about four years back, and it didn't matter much.

Allusion, Allegory, and Myth

In our introduction we suggested suitable criteria for judging and evaluating the stories in this collection. We mentioned that a story which attempts to convey a great deal to the reader—to embody a large view of man or the universe within the limits imposed by short fiction—would probably command greater critical acclaim, all things being equal, than a story which is clearly limited in scope and application.

The two stories in this section—"Youth" and "A Worn Path"—are about journeys of one kind or another. Yet in each narrative the meaning transcends the literal level of the journey, so that the episodes, taken together, stand for some broad experience applicable to mankind. This is another way of saying that the skillful ordering of literal experience may suggest both a comment on and an interpretation of life. The experience of a journey may even provide a solution to the difficulty of viewing life in its totality. After being confronted with a maze of contradictions, setbacks, deceptions, and half-truths, a character may reach the end of a journey and find some ultimate, unchanging truth. He may arrive at some universal scheme which becomes acceptable to his idea of himself in relation to nature, God, destiny, or whatever powers are greater than himself. In this view a short story becomes one part of a giant metaphor: Life *is* a short story with far-reaching implications. By the same token, life is an allegory which relates man's movements through space and in time. Action itself is invariably symbolical in this scheme of universals.

A strict allegory employs a kind of master symbolism by which separate objects or acts usually assume their meaning by reference to the master plan or the whole construct. Thus a journey can be a master symbol of life, and if each event that makes up the journey is equated with specific aspects of life, then the journey is allegorical. For example, a wayfarer meets a resplendent damsel along the road; she offers him wealth, which he eagerly accepts, and then she turns him into a swine. This simple incident can be equated with man's temptation in life to succumb to greed.

Very closely related to allegory are *parable* and *myth*. All three of these types of fiction attempt to express maximum meaning through compression and a calculated use of symbols. Of the three, myth is the most ambitious, for it often embodies and unifies in one construct three or four distinct frames of reference in order to reveal several "levels" of truth.

Although generalizations about various techniques in fiction may prove hazardous, allegory, parable, and myth are often characterized by rather meager plots, simplified or "flat" characters, elements of the supernatural or fantastic, and a generous use of allusion. In fact, allusion is rather like a handmaiden to allegory. By alluding to other actions, narratives, people, or ideas, a writer may furnish hints and parallels that not only enrich his literal narrative but point the way to an understanding of his story's larger meaning. It is through references to things beyond the literal bounds of the story, whether they are real or fictitious, that he imparts a broader meaning to the story itself. Allusion helps us to understand relevant associations; we connect the symbol with the idea, and we see correspondences that may be almost limitless in what they ultimately suggest to us.

JOSEPH CONRAD

(1857–1924)

Youth

This could have occurred nowhere but in England, where men and sea interpenetrate, so to speak—the sea entering into the life of most men, and the men knowing something or everything about the sea, in the way of amusement, of travel, or of bread-winning.

We were sitting round a mahogany table that reflected the bottle, the claret glasses, and our faces as we leaned on our elbows. There was a director of companies, an accountant, a lawyer, Marlow, and myself. The director had been a *Conway* boy, the accountant had served four years at sea, the lawyer—a fine crusted Tory, High Churchman, the best of old fellows, the soul of honor—had been chief officer in the P. & O. service in the good old days when mail-boats were square-rigged at least on two masts, and used to come down the China Sea before a fair monsoon with stun'-sails set alow and aloft. We all began life in the merchant service. Between the five of us there was the strong bond of the sea, and also the fellowship of the craft, which no amount of enthusiasm for yachting, cruising, and so on can give, since one is only the amusement of life and the other is life itself.

Marlow (at least I think that is how he spelt his name) told the story, or rather the chronicle, of a voyage:

"Yes, I have seen a little of the Eastern seas; but what I remember best is my first voyage there. You fellows know there are those voyages that seem ordered for the illustration of life, that might stand for a symbol of existence. You fight, work, sweat, nearly kill yourself, sometimes do kill yourself, trying to accomplish something—and you can't. Not from any fault of yours. You simply can do nothing, neither great nor little—not a thing in the world—not even marry an old maid, or get a wretched 600-ton cargo of coal to its port of destination.

"It was altogether a memorable affair. It was my first voyage to the East, and my first voyage as second mate; it was also my skipper's first command. You'll admit it was time. He was sixty if a day; a little man, with a broad, not very straight back, with bowed shoulders and one leg more bandy than the other, he had that queer twisted-about appearance you see so often in men who work in the fields. He had a nutcracker face—chin and nose trying to come together over a sunken mouth—and it was framed in iron-gray fluffy hair, that looked like a chin strap of cotton-wool sprinkled with coal dust. And he had blue eyes in that old face of his, which were amazingly like a boy's, with that candid expression some quite common men preserve to the end of their days by a rare internal gift of simplicity of heart and rectitude of soul. What induced him to accept me was a wonder. I had come out of a crack Australian clipper, where I had been third officer, and he seemed to have a prejudice against crack clippers as aristocratic and high-toned. He said to me, 'You know, in this ship you will have to work.' I said I had to work in every ship I had ever been in. 'Ah, but this is different, and you gentlemen out of them big ships; . . . but there! I dare say you will do. Join tomorrow.'

"I joined tomorrow. It was twenty-two years ago; and I was just twenty. How time passes! It was one of the happiest days of my life. Fancy! Second mate for the first time—a really responsible officer! I wouldn't have thrown up my new billet for a fortune. The mate looked me over carefully. He was also an old chap, but of another stamp. He had a Roman nose, a snow-white, long beard, and his name was Mahon, but he insisted that it should be pronounced Mann. He was well connected; yet there was something wrong with his luck, and he had never got on.

"As to the captain, he had been for years in coasters, then in the Mediterranean, and last in the West Indian trade. He had never been round the Capes. He could just write a kind of sketchy hand, and didn't care for writing at all. Both were thorough good seamen of course, and between those two old chaps I felt like a small boy between two grandfathers.

"The ship also was old. Her name was the *Judea*. Queer name, isn't it? She belonged to a man Wilmer, Wilcox—some name like that; but he has been bankrupt and dead these twenty years or more, and his name don't matter. She had been laid up in Shadwell basin for ever so long. You can imagine her state. She was all rust, dust, grime—soot aloft, dirt on deck. To me it was like coming out of a palace into a ruined cottage. She was about 400 tons, had a primitive windlass, wooden latches on the doors, not a bit of brass about her, and a big square stern. There was on it, below her name in big letters, a lot of scroll work, with the gilt off, and some sort of a coat of arms, with the motto 'Do or Die' underneath. I remember it took my fancy immensely. There was a touch of romance in it, something that made me love the old thing—something that appealed to my youth!

"We left London in ballast—sand ballast—to load a cargo of coal in a northern port for Bankok. Bankok! I thrilled. I had been six years at sea, but had only seen Melbourne and Sydney, very good places, charming places in their way—but Bankok!

"We worked out of the Thames under canvas, with a North Sea pilot on board. His name was Jermyn, and he dodged all day long about the galley drying his handkerchief before the stove. Apparently he never slept. He was a dismal man, with a perpetual tear sparkling at the end of his nose, who either had been in trouble, or was in trouble, or expected to be in trouble—couldn't be happy unless something went wrong. He mistrusted my youth, my common sense, and my seamanship, and made a point of showing it in a hundred little ways. I dare say he was right. It seems to me I knew very little then, and I know not much more now; but I cherish a hate for that Jermyn to this day.

"We were a week working up as far as Yarmouth Roads, and then we got into a gale—the famous October gale of twenty-two years ago. It was wind, lightning, sleet, snow, and a terrific sea. We were flying light, and you may imagine how bad it was when I tell you we had smashed bulwarks and a flooded deck. On the second night she shifted her ballast into the lee bow, and by that time we had been blown off somewhere on the Dogger Bank. There was nothing for it but go below with shovels and try to right her, and there we were in that vast hold, gloomy like a cavern, the tallow dips stuck and flickering on the beams, the gale howling above, the ship tossing about like mad on her side; there we all were, Jermyn, the captain, everyone, hardly able to keep our feet, engaged on that gravedigger's work, and trying to toss shovelfuls of wet sand up to windward. At every tumble of the ship you could see vaguely in the dim light men falling down with a great flourish of shovels. One of the ship's boys (we had two), impressed by the weirdness of the scene, wept as if his heart would break. We could hear him blubbering somewhere in the shadows.

"On the third day the gale died out, and by-and-by a north-country tug picked us up. We took sixteen days in all to get from London to the Tyne! When we got into dock we had lost our turn for loading, and they hauled us off to a tier where we remained for a month. Mrs. Beard (the captain's name was Beard) came from Colchester to see the old man. She lived on board. The crew of runners had left, and there remained only the officers, one boy, and the steward, a mulatto who answered to the name of Abraham. Mrs. Beard was an old woman, with a face all wrinkled and ruddy like a winter apple, and the figure of a young girl. She caught sight of me once, sewing on a button, and insisted on having my shirts to repair. This was something different from the captains' wives I had known on board crack clippers. When I brought her the shirts, she said: 'And the socks? They want mending, I am sure, and John's—Captain Beard's—things are all in order now. I would be glad of something to do.' Bless the old woman. She overhauled my outfit for me, and meantime I read for the first time 'Sartor Resartus' and Burnaby's 'Ride to Khiva.' I didn't understand much of the first then; but I remember I preferred the soldier to the philosopher at the time; a preference which life has only confirmed. One was a man, and the other was either more—or less. However, they are both dead, and Mrs. Beard is dead, and youth, strength, genius, thoughts, achievements, simple hearts—all die. . . . No matter.

"They loaded us at last. We shipped a crew. Eight able seamen and two boys. We hauled off one evening to the buoys at the dock-gates, ready to go out, and with a fair prospect of beginning the voyage next day. Mrs. Beard was to start for home by a late train. When the ship was fast we went to tea. We sat rather silent through the meal—Mahon, the old couple, and I. I finished first, and slipped away for a smoke, my cabin being in a deckhouse just against the poop. It was high water, blowing fresh with a drizzle; the double dock-gates were opened, and the steam colliers were going in and out in the darkness with their lights burning bright, a great plashing of propellers, rattling of winches, and a lot of hailing on the pier-heads. I watched the procession of headlights gliding high and of green lights gliding low in the night, when suddenly a red gleam flashed at me, vanished, came into view again, and remained. The fore-end of a steamer loomed up close. I shouted down the cabin, 'Come up, quick!' and then heard a startled voice saying afar in the dark, 'Stop her, sir.' A bell jingled. Another voice cried warningly, 'We are going right into that bark, sir.' The answer to this was a gruff 'All right,' and the next thing was a heavy crash as the steamer struck a glancing blow with the bluff of her bow about our fore-rigging. There was a moment of confusion, yelling, and running about. Steam roared. Then somebody was heard saying, 'All clear, sir.' . . . 'Are you all right?' asked the gruff voice. I had jumped forward to see the damage, and hailed back, 'I think so.' 'Easy astern,' said the gruff voice. A bell jingled. 'What steamer is that?' screamed Mahon. By that time she was no more to us than a bulky shadow maneuvering a little way off. They shouted at us some name—a woman's name, Miranda or Melissa—or some such thing. 'This means another month in this beastly hole,' said Mahon to me, as we peered with lamps about the splintered bulwarks and broken braces. 'But where's the captain?'

"We had not heard or seen anything of him all that time. We went aft to look. A doleful voice arose hailing somewhere in the middle of the dock, '*Judea* ahoy!' . . . How the devil did he get there? . . . 'Hallo!' we shouted. 'I am adrift in our boat without oars,' he cried. A belated waterman offered his services, and Mahon struck a bargain with him for half-a-crown to tow our skipper alongside; but it was Mrs. Beard that came up the ladder first. They had been floating about the dock in that mizzly cold rain for nearly an hour. I was never so surprised in my life.

"It appears that when he heard my shout 'Come up,' he understood at once what was the matter, caught up his wife, ran on deck, and across, and down into our boat, which was fast to the ladder. Not bad for a sixty-year-old. Just imagine that old fellow saving heroically in his arms that old woman—the woman of his life. He set her down on a thwart, and was ready to climb back on board when the painter came adrift somehow, and away they went together. Of course in the confusion we did not hear him shouting. He looked abashed. She said cheerfully, 'I suppose it does not matter my losing the train now?' 'No, Jenny—you go below and get warm,' he growled. Then to us: 'A sailor has no business with a wife—I say. There I was, out of the ship. Well, no harm done this time. Let's go and look at what that fool of a steamer smashed.'

"It wasn't much, but it delayed us three weeks. At the end of that time, the captain being engaged with his agents, I carried Mrs. Beard's bag to the railway station and put her all comfy into a third-class carriage. She lowered the window to say, 'You are a good young man. If you see John—Captain Beard—without his muffler at night, just remind him from me to keep his throat well wrapped up.' 'Certainly, Mrs. Beard,' I said. 'You are a good young man; I noticed how attentive you are to John—to Captain—' The train pulled out suddenly; I took my cap off to the old woman: never saw her again. . . . Pass the bottle.

"We went to sea next day. When we made that start for Bankok we had been already three months out of London. We had expected to be a fortnight or so—at the outside.

"It was January, and the weather was beautiful—the beautiful sunny winter weather that has more charm than in the summertime, because it is unexpected, and crisp, and you know it won't, it can't, last long. It's like a windfall, like a godsend, like an unexpected piece of luck.

"It lasted all down the North Sea, all down Channel; and it lasted till we were three hundred miles or so to the westward of the Lizards: then the wind went round to the sou'west and began to pipe up. In two days it blew a gale. The *Judea*, hove to, wallowed on the Atlantic like an old candlebox. It blew day after day: it blew with spite, without interval, without mercy, without rest. The world was nothing but an immensity of great foaming waves rushing at us, under a sky low enough to touch with the hand and dirty like a smoked ceiling. In the stormy space surrounding us there was as much flying spray as air. Day after day and night after night there was nothing round the ship but the howl of the wind, the tumult of the sea, the noise of water pouring over her deck. There was no rest for her and no rest for us. She tossed, she pitched, she stood on her head, she sat on her tail, she rolled, she groaned, and we had to hold on while on deck and cling to our bunks when below, in a constant effort of body and worry of mind.

"One night Mahon spoke through the small window of my berth. It opened right into my very bed, and I was lying there sleepless, in my boots, feeling as though I had not slept for years, and could not if I tried. He said excitedly—

" 'You got the sounding-rod in here, Marlow? I can't get the pumps to suck. By God it's no child's play.'

"I gave him the sounding-rod and lay down again, trying to think of various things—but I thought only of the pumps. When I came on deck they were still at it, and my watch relieved at the pumps. By the light of the lantern brought on deck to examine the sounding-rod I caught a glimpse of their weary, serious faces. We pumped all the four hours. We pumped all night, all day, all the week—watch and watch. She was working herself loose, and leaked badly—not enough to drown us at once, but enough to kill us with the work at the pumps. And while we pumped the ship was going from us piecemeal: the bulwarks went, the stanchions were torn out, the ventilators smashed, the cabin door burst in. There was not a dry spot in the ship. She was being gutted bit by bit. The longboat changed, as if by magic, into matchwood where she stood in her gripes. I had lashed her myself, and was rather proud of my handiwork, which had withstood so long the malice of the sea. And we pumped. And there was no break in the weather. The sea was white like a sheet of foam, like a caldron of boiling milk; there was not a break in the clouds, no—not the size of a man's hand—no, not for so much as ten seconds. There was for us no sky, there were for us no stars, no sun, no universe—nothing but angry clouds and an infuriated sea. We pumped watch and watch, for dear life; and it seemed to last for months, for years, for all eternity, as though we had been dead and gone to a hell for sailors. We forgot the day of the week, the name of the month, what year it was, and whether we had ever been ashore. The sails blew away, she lay broadside on under a weather-cloth, the ocean poured over her, and we did not care. We turned those handles, and had the eyes of idiots. As soon as we had crawled on deck I used to take a round turn with a rope about the men, the pumps, and the mainmast, and we turned, we turned incessantly, with the water to our waists, to our necks, over our heads. It was all one. We had forgotten how it felt to be dry.

"And there was somewhere in me the thought: By Jove! this is the deuce of an adventure—something you read about; and it is my first voyage as second mate—and I am only twenty—and here I am lasting it out as well as any of these men, and keeping my chaps up to the mark. I was pleased. I would not have given up the experience for worlds. I had moments of exultation. Whenever the old dismantled craft pitched heavily with her counter high in the air, she seemed to me to throw up, like an appeal, like a defiance, like a cry to the clouds without mercy, the words written on her stern: '*Judea,* London. Do or Die.'

"O youth! The strength of it, the faith of it, the imagination of it! To me she was not an old rattletrap carting about the world a lot of coal for a freight—to me she was the endeavor, the test, the trial of life. I think of her with pleasure, with affection, with regret—as you would think of someone dead you have loved. I shall never forget her. . . . Pass the bottle.

"One night when, tied to the mast, as I explained, we were pumping on, deafened with the wind, and without spirit enough in us to wish ourselves dead, a heavy sea crashed aboard and swept clean over us. As soon as I got my breath I shouted, as in duty bound, 'Keep on, boys!' when suddenly I felt something hard floating on deck strike the calf of my leg. I made a grab at it and missed. It was so dark we could not see each other's faces within a foot—you understand.

"After that thump the ship kept quiet for a while, and the thing, whatever it was, struck my leg again. This time I caught it—and it was a saucepan. At first, being stupid with fatigue and thinking of nothing but the pumps, I did not understand what I had in my hand. Suddenly it dawned upon me, and I shouted, 'Boys, the house on deck is gone. Leave this, and let's look for the cook.'

"There was a deckhouse forward, which contained the galley, the cook's berth, and the quarters of the crew. As we had expected for days to see it swept away, the hands had been ordered to sleep in the cabin—the only safe place in the ship. The steward, Abraham, however, persisted in clinging to his berth, stupidly, like a mule—from sheer fright I believe, like an animal that won't leave a stable falling in an earthquake. So we went to look for him. It was chancing death, since once out of our lashings we were as exposed as if on a raft. But we went. The house was shattered as if a shell had exploded inside. Most of it had gone overboard—stove, men's quarters, and their property, all was gone; but two posts, holding a portion of the bulkhead to which Abraham's bunk was attached, remained as if by a miracle. We groped in the ruins and came upon this, and there he was, sitting in his bunk, surrounded by foam and wreckage, jabbering cheerfully to himself. He was out of his mind; completely and for ever mad, with this sudden shock coming upon the fag-end of his endurance. We snatched him up, lugged him aft, and pitched him head-first down the cabin companion. You understand there was no time to carry him down with infinite precautions and wait to see how he got on. Those below would pick him up at the bottom of the stairs all right. We were in a hurry to go back to the pumps. That business could not wait. A bad leak is an inhuman thing.

"One would think that the sole purpose of that fiendish gale had been to make a lunatic of that poor devil of a mulatto. It eased before morning, and next day the sky cleared, and as the sea went down the leak took up. When it came to bending a fresh set of sails the crew demanded to put back—and really there was nothing else to do. Boats gone, decks swept clean, cabin gutted, men without a stitch but what they stood in, stores spoiled, ship strained. We put her head for home, and—would you believe it? The wind came east right in our teeth. It blew fresh, it blew continuously. We had to beat up every inch of the way, but she did not leak so badly, the water keeping comparatively smooth. Two hours' pumping in every four is no joke—but it kept her afloat as far as Falmouth.

"The good people there live on casualties of the sea, and no doubt were glad to see us. A hungry crowd of shipwrights sharpened their chisels at the sight of that carcass of a ship. And, by Jove! they had pretty pickings off us before they were done. I fancy the owner was already in a tight place. There were delays. Then it was decided to take part of the cargo out and calk her topsides. This was done, the repairs finished, cargo reshipped; a new crew came on board, and we went out—for Bankok. At the end of a week we were back again. The crew said they weren't going to Bankok—a hundred and fifty days' passage—in a something hooker that wanted pumping eight hours out of the twenty-four; and the nautical papers inserted again the little paragraph: '*Judea*. Bark. Tyne to Bankok; coals; put back to Falmouth leaky and with crew refusing duty.'

"There were more delays—more tinkering. The owner came down for a day, and said she was as right as a little fiddle. Poor old Captain Beard looked like the ghost of a Geordie skipper—through the worry and humiliation of it. Remember he was sixty, and it was his first command. Mahon said it was a foolish business, and would end badly. I loved the ship more than ever, and wanted awfully to get to Bankok. To Bankok! Magic name, blessed name. Mesopotamia wasn't a patch on it. Remember I was twenty, and it was my first second mate's billet, and the East was waiting for me.

"We went out and anchored in the outer roads with a fresh crew—the third. She leaked worse than ever. It was as if those confounded shipwrights had actually made a hole in her. This time we did not even go outside. The crew simply refused to man the windlass.

"They towed us back to the inner harbor, and we became a fixture, a feature, an institution of the place. People pointed us out to visitors as 'That 'ere bark that's going to Bankok—has been here six months—put back three times.' On holidays the small boys pulling about in boats would hail, '*Judea*, ahoy!' and if a head showed above the rail shouted, 'Where you bound to? —Bankok?' and jeered. We were only three on board. The poor old skipper mooned in the cabin. Mahon undertook the cooking, and unexpectedly developed all a Frenchman's genius for preparing nice little messes. I looked languidly after the rigging. We became citizens of Falmouth. Every shopkeeper knew us. At the barber's or tobacconist's they asked familiarly, 'Do you think you will ever get to Bankok?' Meantime the owner, the underwriters, and the charterers squabbled amongst themselves in London, and our pay went on. . . . Pass the bottle.

"It was horrid. Morally it was worse than pumping for life. It seemed as though we had been forgotten by the world, belonged to nobody, would get nowhere; it seemed that, as if bewitched, we would have to live for ever and ever in that inner harbor, a derision and a byword to generations of longshore loafers and dishonest boatmen. I obtained three months' pay and a five days' leave, and made a rush for London. It took me a day to get there and pretty well another to come back—but three months' pay went all the same. I don't know what I did with it. I went to a music hall, I believe, lunched, dined, and supped in a swell place in Regent Street, and was back to time, with nothing but a complete set of Byron's works and a new railway rug to show for three months' work. The boatman who pulled me off to the ship said: 'Hallo! I thought you had left the old thing. *She* will never get to Bankok.' 'That's all *you* know about it,' I said scornfully—but I didn't like that prophecy at all.

"Suddenly a man, some kind of agent to somebody, appeared with full powers. He had grog blossoms all over his face, an indomitable energy, and was a jolly soul. We leaped into life again. A hulk came alongside, took our cargo, and then we went into dry dock to get our copper stripped. No wonder she leaked. The poor thing, strained beyond endurance by the gale, had, as if in disgust, spat out all the oakum of her lower seams. She was recalked, new coppered, and made as tight as a bottle. We went back to the hulk and reshipped our cargo.

"Then on a fine moonlight night, all the rats left the ship.

"We had been infested with them. They had destroyed our sails, consumed more stores than the crew, affably shared our beds and our dangers, and now, when the ship was made seaworthy, concluded to clear out. I called Mahon to enjoy the spectacle. Rat after rat appeared on our rail, took a last look over his shoulder, and leaped with a hollow thud into the empty hulk. We tried to count them, but soon lost the tale. Mahon said: 'Well, well! don't talk to me about the intelligence of rats. They ought to have left before, when we had that narrow squeak from foundering. There you have the proof how silly is the superstition about them. They leave a good ship for an old rotten hulk, where there is nothing to eat, too, the fools! . . . I don't believe they know what is safe or what is good for them, any more than you or I.'

"And after some more talk we agreed that the wisdom of rats had been grossly overrated, being in fact no greater than that of men.

"The story of the ship was known, by this, all up the Channel from Land's End to the Forelands, and we could get no crew on the south coast. They sent us one all complete from Liverpool, and we left once more—for Bankok.

"We had fair breezes, smooth water right into the tropics, and the old

Judea lumbered along in the sunshine. When she went eight knots everything cracked aloft, and we tied our caps to our heads; but mostly she strolled on at the rate of three miles an hour. What could you expect? She was tired—that old ship. Her youth was where mine is—where yours is—you fellows who listen to this yarn; and what friend would throw your years and your weariness in your face? We didn't grumble at her. To us aft, at least, it seemed as though we had been born in her, reared in her, had lived in her for ages, had never known any other ship. I would just as soon have abused the old village church at home for not being a cathedral.

"And for me there was also my youth to make me patient. There was all the East before me, and all life, and the thought that I had been tried in that ship and had come out pretty well. And I thought of men of old who, centuries ago, went that road in ships that sailed no better, to the land of palms, and spices, and yellow sands, and of brown nations ruled by kings more cruel than Nero the Roman and more splendid than Solomon the Jew. The old bark lumbered on, heavy with her age and the burden of her cargo, while I lived the life of youth in ignorance and hope. She lumbered on through an interminable procession of days; and the fresh gilding flashed back at the setting sun, seemed to cry out over the darkening sea the words painted on her stern, '*Judea*, London. Do or Die.'

"Then we entered the Indian Ocean and steered northerly for Java Head. The winds were light. Weeks slipped by. She crawled on, do or die, and people at home began to think of posting us as overdue.

"One Saturday evening, I being off duty, the men asked me to give them an extra bucket of water or so—for washing clothes. As I did not wish to screw on the fresh-water pump so late, I went forward whistling, and with a key in my hand to unlock the forepeak scuttle, intending to serve the water out of a spare tank we kept there.

"The smell down below was as unexpected as it was frightful. One would have thought hundreds of paraffin lamps had been flaring and smoking in that hole for days. I was glad to get out. The man with me coughed and said, 'Funny smell, sir.' I answered negligently, 'It's good for the health, they say,' and walked aft.

"The first thing I did was to put my head down the square of the midship ventilator. As I lifted the lid a visible breath, something like a thin fog, a puff of faint haze, rose from the opening. The ascending air was hot, and had a heavy, sooty, paraffiny smell. I gave one sniff, and put down the lid gently. It was no use choking myself. The cargo was on fire.

"Next day she began to smoke in earnest. You see it was to be expected, for though the coal was of a safe kind, that cargo had been so handled, so broken up with handling, that it looked more like smithy coal than anything else. Then it had been wetted—more than once. It rained all the time we were taking it back from the hulk, and now with this long passage it got heated, and there was another case of spontaneous combustion.

"The captain called us into the cabin. He had a chart spread on the table, and looked unhappy. He said, 'The coast of West Australia is near, but I mean to proceed to our destination. It is the hurricane month too; but we will just keep her head for Bankok, and fight the fire. No more putting back anywhere, if we all get roasted. We will try first to stifle this 'ere damned combustion by want of air.'

"We tried. We battened down everything, and still she smoked. The smoke kept coming out through imperceptible crevices; it forced itself through bulkheads and covers; it oozed here and there and everywhere in slender threads, in an invisible film, in an incomprehensible manner. It made its way into the cabin, into the forecastle; it poisoned the sheltered places on the deck; it could be sniffed as high as the mainyard. It was clear that if the smoke came out the air came in. This was disheartening. This combustion refused to be stifled.

"We resolved to try water, and took the hatches off. Enormous volumes of smoke, whitish, yellowish, thick, greasy, misty, choking, ascended as high as the trucks. All hands cleared out aft. Then the poisonous cloud blew away, and we went back to work in a smoke that was no thicker now than that of an ordinary factory chimney.

"We rigged the force pump, got the hose along, and by-and-by it burst. Well, it was as old as the ship—a prehistoric hose, and past repair. Then we pumped with the feeble head-pump, drew water with buckets, and in this way managed in time to pour lots of Indian Ocean into the main hatch. The bright stream flashed in sunshine, fell into a layer of white crawling smoke, and vanished on the black surface of coal. Steam ascended mingling with the smoke. We poured salt water as into a barrel without a bottom. It was our fate to pump in that ship, to pump out of her, to pump into her; and after keeping water out of her to save ourselves from being drowned, we frantically poured water into her to save ourselves from being burnt.

"And she crawled on, do or die, in the serene weather. The sky was a miracle of purity, a miracle of azure. The sea was polished, was blue, was pellucid, was sparkling like a precious stone, extending on all sides, all round to the horizon—as if the whole terrestrial globe had been one jewel, one colossal sapphire, a single gem fashioned into a planet. And on the luster of the great calm waters the *Judea* glided imperceptibly, enveloped in languid and unclean vapors, in a lazy cloud that drifted to leeward, light and slow: a pestiferous cloud defiling the splendor of sea and sky.

"All this time of course we saw no fire. The cargo smoldered at the bottom somewhere. Once Mahon, as we were working side by side, said to me with a queer smile: 'Now, if she only would spring a tidy leak—like that time when we first left the Channel—it would put a stopper on this fire. Wouldn't it?' I remarked irrelevantly, 'Do you remember the rats?'

"We fought the fire and sailed the ship too as carefully as though nothing had been the matter. The steward cooked and attended on us.

Of the other twelve men, eight worked while four rested. Everyone took his turn, captain included. There was equality, and if not exactly fraternity, then a deal of good feeling. Sometimes a man, as he dashed a bucketful of water down the hatchway, would yell out, 'Hurrah for Bankok!' and the rest laughed. But generally we were taciturn and serious—and thirsty. Oh! how thirsty! And we had to be careful with the water. Strict allowance. The ship smoked, the sun blazed. . . . Pass the bottle.

"We tried everything. We even made an attempt to dig down to the fire. No good, of course. No man could remain more than a minute below. Mahon, who went first, fainted there, and the man who went to fetch him out did likewise. We lugged them out on deck. Then I leaped down to show how easily it could be done. They had learned wisdom by that time, and contended themselves by fishing for me with a chain-hook tied to a broom handle, I believe. I did not offer to go and fetch up my shovel, which was left down below.

"Things began to look bad. We put the longboat into the water. The second boat was ready to swing out. We had also another, a fourteen-foot thing, on davits aft, where it was quite safe.

"Then behold, the smoke suddenly decreased. We redoubled our efforts to flood the bottom of the ship. In two days there was no smoke at all. Everybody was on the broad grin. This was on a Friday. On Saturday no work, but sailing the ship of course was done. The men washed their clothes and their faces for the first time in a fortnight, and had a special dinner given them. They spoke of spontaneous combustion with contempt, and implied *they* were the boys to put out combustions. Somehow we all felt as though we each had inherited a large fortune. But a beastly smell of burning hung about the ship. Captain Beard had hollow eyes and sunken cheeks. I had never noticed so much before how twisted and bowed he was. He and Mahon prowled soberly about hatches and ventilators, sniffing. It struck me suddenly poor Mahon was a very, very old chap. As to me, I was as pleased and proud as though I had helped to win a great naval battle. O! Youth!

"The night was fine. In the morning a homeward-bound ship passed us hull down—the first we had seen for months; but we were nearing the land at last, Java Head being about 190 miles off, and nearly due north.

"Next day it was my watch on deck from eight to twelve. At breakfast the captain observed, 'It's wonderful how that smell hangs about the cabin.' About ten, the mate being on the poop, I stepped down on the main deck for a moment. The carpenter's bench stood abaft the main-mast: I leaned about it sucking at my pipe, and the carpenter, a young chap, came to talk to me. He remarked, 'I think we have done very well, haven't we?' and then I perceived with annoyance the fool was trying to tilt the bench. I said curtly, 'Don't, Chips,' and immediately became aware of a queer sensation, of an absurd delusion—I seemed somehow to be in the air. I heard all round me like a pent-up breath released—as if a thousand giants simultaneously had said Phoo!—and felt a dull concussion which made my ribs ache suddenly. No doubt about it—I was in the air, and my body was describing a short parabola. But short as it was, I had the time to think several thoughts in, as far as I can remember, the following order: "This can't be the carpenter—What is it?—Some accident—Submarine volcano?—Coals, gas!—By Jove! we are being blown up—Everybody's dead—I am falling into the afterhatch—I see fire in it.'

"The coal dust suspended in the air of the hold had glowed dull red at the moment of the explosion. In the twinkling of an eye, in an infinitesimal fraction of a second since the first tilt of the bench, I was sprawling full length on the cargo. I picked myself up and scrambled out. It was quick like a rebound. The deck was a wilderness of smashed timber, lying crosswise like trees in a wood after a hurricane; an immense curtain of soiled rags waved gently before me—it was the mainsail blown to strips. I thought, The masts will be toppling over directly; and to get out of the way bolted on all fours towards the poop-ladder. The first person I saw was Mahon, with eyes like saucers, his mouth open, and the long white hair standing on end round his head like a silver halo. He was just about to go down when the sight of the main deck stirring, heaving up, and changing into splinters before his eyes, petrified him on the top step. I stared at him in unbelief, and he stared at me with a queer kind of shocked curiosity. I did not know that I had no hair, no eyebrows, no eyelashes, that my young mustache was burnt off, that my face was black, one cheek laid open, my nose cut, and my chin bleeding. I had lost my cap, one of my slippers, and my shirt was torn to rags. Of all this I was not aware. I was amazed to see the ship still afloat, the poop-deck whole—and, most of all, to see anybody alive. Also the peace of the sky and the serenity of the sea were distinctly surprising. I suppose I expected to see them convulsed with horror. . . . Pass the bottle.

"There was a voice hailing the ship from somewhere—in the air, in the sky—I couldn't tell. Presently I saw the captain—and he was mad. He asked me eagerly, 'Where's the cabin-table?' and to hear such a question was a frightful shock. I had just been blown up, you understand, and vibrated with that experience—I wasn't quite sure whether I was alive. Mahon began to stamp with both feet and yelled at him, 'Good God! don't you see the deck's blown out of her?' I found my voice, and stammered out as if conscious of some gross neglect of duty, 'I don't know where the cabin-table is.' It was like an absurd dream.

"Do you know what he wanted next? Well, he wanted to trim the yards. Very placidly, and as if lost in thought, he insisted on having the foreyard squared. 'I don't know if there's anybody alive,' said Mahon, almost tearfully. 'Surely,' he said, gently, 'there will be enough left to square the foreyard.'

"The old chap, it seems, was in his own berth, winding up the chronometers, when the shock sent him spinning. Immediately it occurred to him—as he said afterwards—that the ship had struck something, and he ran out into the cabin. There, he saw, the cabin-table had vanished somewhere. The deck being blown up, it had fallen down into the lazarette of course. Where we had our breakfast that morning he saw only a great hole in the floor. This appeared to him so awfully mysterious, and impressed him so immensely, that what he saw and heard after he got on deck were mere trifles in comparison. And, mark, he noticed directly the wheel deserted and his bark off her course—and his only thought was to get that miserable, stripped, undecked, smoldering shell of a ship back again with her head pointing at her port of destination. Bankok! That's what he was after. I tell you this quiet, bowed, bandy-legged, almost deformed little man was immense in the singleness of his idea and in his placid ignorance of our agitation. He motioned us forward with a commanding gesture, and went to take the wheel himself.

"Yes; that was the first thing we did—trim the yards of that wreck! No one was killed, or even disabled, but everyone was more or less hurt. You should have seen them! Some were in rags, with black faces, like coal-heavers, like sweeps, and had bullet heads that seemed closely cropped, but were in fact singed to the skin. Others, of the watch below, awakened by being shot out from their collapsing bunks, shivered incessantly, and kept on groaning even as we went about our work. But they all worked. That crew of Liverpool hard cases had in them the right stuff. It's my experience they always have. It is the sea that gives it—the vastness, the loneliness surrounding their dark stolid souls. Ah! Well! we stumbled, we crept, we fell, we barked our shins on the wreckage, we hauled. The masts stood, but we did not know how much they might be charred down below. It was nearly calm, but a long swell ran from the west and made her roll. They might go at any moment. We looked at them with apprehension. One could not foresee which way they would fall.

"Then we retreated aft and looked about us. The deck was a tangle of planks on edge, of planks on end, of splinters, of ruined woodwork. The masts rose from that chaos like big trees above a matted undergrowth. The interstices of that mass of wreckage were full of something whitish, sluggish, stirring—of something that was like a greasy fog. The smoke of the invisible fire was coming up again, was trailing, like a poisonous thick mist in some valley choked with dead wood. Already lazy wisps were beginning to curl upwards amongst the mass of splinters. Here and there a piece of timber, stuck upright, resembled a post. Half of a fife-rail had been shot through the foresail, and the sky made a patch of glorious blue in the ignobly soiled canvas. A portion of several boards holding together had fallen across the rail, and one end protruded overboard, like a gangway leading upon nothing, like a gangway leading over the deep sea, leading to death—as if inviting us to walk the plank at once and be done with our ridiculous troubles. And still the air, the sky—a ghost, something invisible was hailing the ship.

"Someone had the sense to look over, and there was the helmsman, who had impulsively jumped overboard, anxious to come back. He yelled and swam lustily like a merman, keeping up with the ship. We threw him a rope, and presently he stood amongst us streaming with water and very crestfallen. The captain had surrendered the wheel, and apart, elbow on rail and chin in hand, gazed at the sea wistfully. We asked ourselves, What next? I thought, Now, this is something like. This is great. I wonder what will happen. O youth!

"Suddenly Mahon sighted a steamer far astern. Captain Beard said, 'We may do something with her yet.' We hoisted two flags, which said in the international language of the sea, 'On fire. Want immediate assistance.' The steamer grew bigger rapidly, and by-and-by spoke with two flags on her foremast, 'I am coming to your assistance.'

"In half an hour she was abreast, to windward, within hail, and rolling slightly, with her engines stopped. We lost our composure, and yelled all together with excitement, 'We've been blown up.' A man in a white helmet, on the bridge, cried, 'Yes! All right! all right!' and he nodded his head, and smiled, and made soothing motions with his hand as though at a lot of frightened children. One of the boats dropped in the water, and walked towards us upon the sea with her long oars. Four Calashes pulled a swinging stroke. This was my first sight of Malay seamen. I've known them since, but what struck me then was their unconcern: they came alongside, and even the bowman standing up and holding to our main-chains with the boat-hook did not deign to lift his head for a glance. I thought people who had been blown up deserved more attention.

"A little man, dry like a chip and agile like a monkey, clambered up. It was the mate of the steamer. He gave one look, and cried, 'O boys—you had better quit.'

"We were silent. He talked apart with the captain for a time—seemed to argue with him. Then they went away together to the steamer.

"When our skipper came back we learned that the steamer was the *Sommerville,* Captain Nash, from West Australia to Singapore via Batavia with mails, and that the agreement was she should tow us to Anjer or Batavia, if possible, where we could extinguish the fire by scuttling, and then proceed on our voyage—to Bankok! The old man seemed excited. 'We will do it yet,' he said to Mahon, fiercely. He shook his fist at the sky. Nobody else said a word.

"At noon the steamer began to tow. She went ahead slim and high, and what was left of the *Judea* followed at the end of seventy fathom of tow-rope—followed her swiftly like a cloud of smoke with mastheads protruding above. We went aloft to furl the sails. We coughed on the yards, and were careful about the bunts. Do you see the lot of us there, putting a neat furl on the sails of that ship doomed to arrive nowhere? There was not a man who didn't think that at any moment the masts would topple over. From aloft we could not see the ship for smoke, and they worked carefully, passing the gaskets with even turns. 'Harbor furl—aloft there!' cried Mahon from below.

"You understand this? I don't think one of those chaps expected to get down in the usual way. When we did I heard them saying to each other, 'Well, I thought we would come down overboard, in a lump—sticks and all—blame me if I didn't.' 'That's what I was thinking to myself,' would answer wearily another battered and bandaged scarecrow. And, mind, these were men without the drilled-in habit of obedience. To an onlooker they would be a lot of profane scallywags without a redeeming point. What made them do it—what made them obey me when I, thinking consciously how fine it was, made them drop the bunt of the foresail twice to try and do it better? What? They had no professional reputation—no examples, no praise. It wasn't a sense of duty; they all knew well enough how to shirk, and laze, and dodge—when they had a mind to it—and mostly they had. Was it the two pounds ten a month that sent them there? They didn't think their pay half good enough. No; it was something in them, something inborn and subtle and everlasting. I don't say positively that the crew of a French or German merchantman wouldn't have done it, but I doubt whether it would have been done in the same way. There was a completeness in it, something solid like a principle, and masterful like an instinct—a disclosure of something secret—of that hidden something, that gift, of good or evil that makes racial difference, that shapes the fate of nations.

"It was that night at ten that, for the first time since we had been fighting it, we saw the fire. The speed of the towing had fanned the smoldering destruction. A blue gleam appeared forward, shining below the wreck of the deck. It wavered in patches, it seemed to stir and creep like the light of a glowworm. I saw it first, and told Mahon. 'Then the game's up,' he said. 'We had better stop this towing, or she will burst out suddenly fore and aft before we can clear out.' We set up a yell; rang bells to attract their attention; they towed on. At last Mahon and I had to crawl forward and cut the rope with an ax. There was no time to cast off the lashings. Red tongues could be seen licking the wilderness of splinters under our feet as we made our way back to the poop.

"Of course they very soon found out in the steamer that the rope was gone. She gave a loud blast of her whistle, her lights were seen sweeping in a wide circle, she came up ranging close alongside, and stopped. We were all in a tight group on the poop looking at her. Every man had saved a little bundle or a bag. Suddenly a conical flame with a twisted top shot up forward and threw upon the black sea a circle of light, with the two vessels side by side and heaving gently in its center. Captain Beard had been sitting on the gratings still and mute for hours, but now he rose slowly and advanced in front of us, to the mizzen-shrouds. Captain Nash hailed: 'Come along! Look sharp. I have mail bags on board. I will take you and your boats to Singapore.'

" 'Thank you! No!' said our skipper. 'We must see the last of the ship.'

" 'I can't stand by any longer,' shouted the other. 'Mails—you know.'

" 'Ay! ay! We are all right.'

" 'Very well! I'll report you in Singapore. . . . Good-by!'

"He waved his hand. Our men dropped their bundles quietly. The steamer moved ahead, and passing out of the circle of light, vanished at once from our sight, dazzled by the fire which burned fiercely. And then I knew that I would see the East first as commander of a small boat. I thought it fine; and the fidelity to the old ship was fine. We should see the last of her. Oh the glamour of youth! Oh the fire of it, more dazzling than the flames of the burning ship, throwing a magic light on the wide earth, leaping audaciously to the sky, presently to be quenched by time, more cruel, more pitiless, more bitter than the sea—and like the flames of the burning ship surrounded by an impenetrable night.

"The old man warned us in his gentle and inflexible way that it was part of our duty to save for the underwriters as much as we could of the ship's gear. Accordingly we went to work aft, while she blazed forward to give us plenty of light. We lugged out a lot of rubbish. What didn't we save? An old barometer fixed with an absurd quantity of screws nearly cost me my life: a sudden rush of smoke came upon me, and I just got away in time. There were various stores, bolts of canvas, coils of rope; the poop looked like a marine bazaar, and the boats were lumbered to the gunwales. One would have thought the old man wanted to take as much as he could of his first command with him. He was very, very quiet, but off his balance evidently. Would you believe it? He wanted to take a length of old stream-cable and a kedge-anchor with him in the longboat. We said, 'Ay, ay, sir,' deferentially, and on the quiet let the thing slip overboard. The heavy medicine chest went that way, two bags of green coffee, tins of paint—fancy, paint!—a whole lot of things. Then I was ordered with two hands into the boats to make a stowage and get them ready against the time it would be proper for us to leave the ship.

"We put everything straight, stepped the longboat's mast for our skipper, who was to take charge of her, and I was not sorry to sit down for a moment. My face felt raw, every limb ached as if broken, I was aware of all my ribs, and would have sworn to a twist in the backbone. The boats, fast astern, lay in a deep shadow, and all around I could see the circle of the sea lighted by the fire. A gigantic flame arose forward straight and clear.

It flared fierce, with noises like the whir of wings, with rumbles as of thunder. There were cracks, detonations, and from the cone of flame the sparks flew upwards, as man is born to trouble, to leaky ships, and to ships that burn.

"What bothered me was that the ship, lying broadside to the swell and to such wind as there was—a mere breath—the boats would not keep astern where they were safe, but persisted, in a pig-headed way boats have, in getting under the counter and then swinging alongside. They were knocking about dangerously and coming near the flame, while the ship rolled on them, and, of course, there was always the danger of the masts going over the side at any moment. I and my two boak-keepers kept them off as best we could with oars and boat-hooks; but to be constantly at it became exasperating, since there was no reason why we should not leave at once. We could not see those on board, nor could we imagine what caused the delay. The boat-keepers were swearing feebly, and I had not only my share of the work, but also had to keep at it two men who showed a constant inclination to lay themselves down and let things slide.

"At last I hailed 'On deck there,' and someone looked over. 'We're ready here,' I said. The head disappeared, and very soon popped up again. 'The captain says, All right, sir, and to keep the boats well clear of the ship.'

"Half an hour passed. Suddenly there was a frightful racket, rattle, clanking of chain, hiss of water, and millions of sparks flew up into the shivering column of smoke that stood leaning slightly above the ship. The catheads had burned away, and the two red-hot anchors had gone to the bottom, tearing out after them two hundred fathom of red-hot chain. The ship trembled, the mass of flame swayed as if ready to collapse, and the fore top-gallant-mast fell. It darted down like an arrow of fire, shot under, and instantly leaping up within an oar's-length of the boats, floated quietly, very black on the luminous sea. I hailed the deck again. After some time a man in an unexpectedly cheerful but also muffled tone, as though he had been trying to speak with his mouth shut, informed me, 'Coming directly, sir,' and vanished. For a long time I heard nothing but the whir and roar of the fire. There were also whistling sounds. The boats jumped, tugged at the painters, ran at each other playfully, knocked their sides together, or, do what we would, swung in a bunch against the ship's side. I couldn't stand it any longer, and swarming up a rope, clambered aboard over the stern.

"It was as bright as day. Coming up like this, the sheet of fire facing me was a terrifying sight, and the heat seemed hardly bearable at first. On a settee cushion dragged out of the cabin, Captain Beard, with his legs drawn up and one arm under his head, slept with the light playing on him. Do you know what the rest were busy about? They were sitting on deck right aft, round an open case, eating bread and cheese and drinking bottled stout.

"On the background of flames twisting in fierce tongues above their heads they seemed at home like salamanders, and looked like a band of desperate pirates. The fire sparkled in the whites of their eyes, gleamed on patches of white skin seen through the torn shirts. Each had the marks as of a battle about him—bandaged heads, tied-up arms, a strip of dirty rag round a knee—and each man had a bottle between his legs and a chunk of cheese in his hand. Mahon got up. With his handsome and disreputable head, his hooked profile, his long white beard, and with an uncorked bottle in his hand, he resembled one of those reckless sea-robbers of old making merry amidst violence and disaster. 'The last meal on board,' he explained solemnly. 'We had nothing to eat all day, and it was no use leaving all this.' He flourished the bottle and indicated the sleeping skipper. 'He said he couldn't swallow anything, so I got him to lie down,' he went on; and as I stared, 'I don't know whether you are aware, young fellow, the man had no sleep to speak of for days—and there will be dam' little sleep in the boats.' 'There will be no boats by-and-by if you fool about much longer,' I said, indignantly. I walked up to the skipper and shook him by the shoulder. At last he opened his eyes, but did not move. 'Time to leave her, sir,' I said, quietly.

"He got up painfully, looked at the flames, at the sea sparkling round the ship, and black, black as ink farther away; he looked at the stars shining dim through a thin veil of smoke in a sky black, black as Erebus.

" 'Youngest first,' he said.

"And the ordinary seaman, wiping his mouth with the back of his hand, got up, clambered over the taffrail, and vanished. Others followed. One, on the point of going over, stopped short to drain his bottle, and with a great swing of his arm flung it at the fire. 'Take this!' he cried.

"The skipper lingered disconsolately, and we left him to commune alone for awhile with his first command. Then I went up again and brought him away at last. It was time. The ironwork on the poop was hot to the touch.

"Then the painter of the longboat was cut, and the three boats, tied together, drifted clear of the ship. It was just sixteen hours after the explosion when we abandoned her. Mahon had charge of the second boat, and I had the smallest—the 14-foot thing. The longboat would have taken the lot of us; but the skipper said we must save as much property as we could—for the underwriters—and so I got my first command. I had two men with me, a bag of biscuits, a few tins of meat, and a breaker of water. I was ordered to keep close to the longboat, that in case of bad weather we might be taken into her.

"And do you know what I thought? I thought I would part company as soon as I could. I wanted to have my first command all to myself. I wasn't going to sail in a squadron if there were a chance for independent cruising. I would make land by myself. I would beat the other boats. Youth! All youth! The silly, charming, beautiful youth.

"But we did not make a start at once. We must see the last of the ship. And so the boats drifted about that night, heaving and setting on the swell. The men dozed, waked, sighed, groaned. I looked at the burning ship.

"Between the darkness of earth and heaven she was burning fiercely upon a disc of purple sea shot by the blood-red play of gleams; upon a disc of water glittering and sinister. A high, clear flame, an immense and lonely flame, ascended from the ocean, and from its summit the black smoke poured continuously at the sky. She burned furiously, mournful and imposing like a funeral pile kindled in the night, surrounded by the sea, watched over by the stars. A magnificent death had come like a grace, like a gift, like a reward to that old ship at the end of her laborious days. The surrender of her weary ghost to the keeping of stars and sea was stirring like the sight of a glorious triumph. The masts fell just before daybreak, and for a moment there was a burst and turmoil of sparks that seemed to fill with flying fire the night patient and watchful, the vast night lying silent upon the sea. At daylight she was only a charred shell, floating still under a cloud of smoke and bearing a glowing mass of coal within.

"Then the oars were got out, and the boats forming in a line moved round her remains as if in procession—the longboat leading. As we pulled across her stern a slim dart of fire shot out viciously at us, and suddenly she went down, head first, in a great hiss of steam. The unconsumed stern was the last to sink; but the paint had gone, had cracked, had peeled off, and there were no letters, there was no word, no stubborn device that was like her soul, to flash at the rising sun her creed and her name.

"We made our way north. A breeze sprang up, and about noon all the boats came together for the last time. I had no mast or sail in mine, but I made a mast out of a spare oar and hoisted a boat-awning for a sail, with a boathook for a yard. She was certainly overmasted, but I had the satisfaction of knowing that with the wind aft I could beat the other two. I had to wait for them. Then we all had a look at the captain's chart, and, after a sociable meal of hard bread and water, got our last instructions. These were simple: steer north, and keep together as much as possible. 'Be careful with that jury rig, Marlow,' said the captain; and Mahon, as I sailed proudly past his boat, wrinkled his curved nose and hailed, 'You will sail that ship of yours under water if you don't look out, young fellow.' He was a malicious old man—and may the deep sea where he sleeps now rock him gently, rock him tenderly to the end of time!

"Before sunset a thick rain-squall passed over the two boats, which were far astern, and that was the last I saw of them for a time. Next day I sat steering my cockle-shell—my first command—with nothing but water and sky around me. I did sight in the afternoon the upper sails of a ship far away, but said nothing, and my men did not notice her. You see I was afraid she might be homeward bound, and I had no mind to turn back from the portals of the East. I was steering for Java—another blessed name—like Bankok, you know. I steered many days.

"I need not tell you what it is to be knocking about in an open boat. I remember nights and days of calm when we pulled, we pulled, and the boat seemed to stand still, as if bewitched within the circle of the sea horizon. I remember the heat, the deluge of rain-squalls that kept us baling for dear life (but filled our water cask), and I remember sixteen hours on end with a mouth dry as a cinder and a steering-oar over the stern to keep my first command head on to a breaking sea. I did not know how good a man I was till then. I remember the drawn faces, the dejected figures of my two men, and I remember my youth and the feeling that will never come back any more—the feeling that I could last for ever, outlast the sea, the earth, and all men; the deceitful feeling that lures us on to joys, to perils, to love, to vain effort—to death; the triumphant conviction of strength, the heat of life in the handful of dust, the glow in the heart that with every year grows dim, grows cold, grows small, and expires—and expires, too soon, too soon—before life itself.

"And this is how I see the East. I have seen its secret places and have looked into its very soul; but now I see it always from a small boat, a high outline of mountains, blue and afar in the morning; like faint mist at noon; a jagged wall of purple at sunset. I have the feel of the oar in my hand, the vision of a scorching blue sea in my eyes. And I see a bay, a wide bay, smooth as glass and polished like ice, shimmering in the dark. A red light burns far off upon the gloom of the land, and the night is soft and warm. We drag at the oars with aching arms, and suddenly a puff of wind, a puff faint and tepid and laden with strange odors of blossoms, of aromatic wood, comes out of the still night—the first sigh of the East on my face. That I can never forget. It was impalpable and enslaving, like a charm, like a whispered promise of mysterious delight.

"We had been pulling this finishing spell for eleven hours. Two pulled, and he whose turn it was to rest sat at the tiller. We had made out the red light in that bay and steered for it, guessing it must mark some small coasting port. We passed two vessels, outlandish and high-sterned, sleeping at anchor, and, approaching the light, now very dim, ran the boat's nose against the end of a jutting wharf. We were blind with fatigue. My men dropped the oars and fell off the thwarts as if dead. I made fast to a pile. A current rippled softly. The scented obscurity of the shore was grouped into vast masses, a density of colossal clumps of vegetation, probably—mute and fantastic shapes. And at their foot the semicircle of a beach gleamed faintly, like an illusion. There was not a light, not a stir, not a sound. The mysterious East faced me, perfumed like a flower, silent like death, dark like a grave.

"And I sat weary beyond expression, exulting like a conqueror, sleepless and entranced as if before a profound, a fateful enigma.

"A splashing of oars, a measured dip reverberating on the level of water, intensified by the silence of the shore into loud claps, made me jump up. A boat, a European boat, was coming in. I invoked the name of the dead; I hailed: *Judea* ahoy! A thin shout answered.

"It was the captain. I had beaten the flagship by three hours, and I was glad to hear the old man's voice again, tremulous and tired. 'Is it you, Marlow?' 'Mind the end of that jetty, sir,' I cried.

"He approached cautiously, and brought up with the deep-sea lead-line which we had saved—for the underwriters. I eased my painter and fell alongside. He sat, a broken figure at the stern, wet with dew, his hands clasped in his lap. His men were asleep already. 'I had a terrible time of it,' he murmured. 'Mahon is behind—not very far.' We conversed in whispers, in low whispers, as if afraid to wake up the land. Guns, thunder, earthquakes would not have awakened the men just then.

"Looking around as we talked, I saw away at sea a bright light traveling in the night. 'There's a steamer passing the bay,' I said. She was not passing, she was entering, and she even came close and anchored. 'I wish,' said the old man, 'you would find out whether she is English. Perhaps they could give us a passage somewhere.' He seemed nervously anxious. So by dint of punching and kicking I started one of my men into a state of somnambulism, and giving him an oar, took another and pulled towards the lights of the steamer.

"There was a murmur of voices in her, metallic hollow clangs of the engine room, footsteps on the deck. Her ports shone, round like dilated eyes. Shapes moved about, and there was a shadowy man high up on the bridge. He heard my oars.

"And then, before I could open my lips, the East spoke to me, but it was in a Western voice. A torrent of words was poured into the enigmatical, the fateful silence; outlandish, angry words, mixed with words and even whole sentences of good English, less strange but even more surprising. The voice swore and cursed violently; it riddled the solemn peace of the bay by a volley of abuse. It began by calling me Pig, and from that went crescendo into unmentionable adjectives—in English. The man up there raged aloud in two languages, and with a sincerity in his fury that almost convinced me I had, in some way, sinned against the harmony of the universe. I could hardly see him, but began to think he would work himself into a fit.

"Suddenly he ceased, and I could hear him snorting and blowing like a porpoise. I said—

" 'What steamer is this, pray?'

" 'Eh? What's this? And who are you?'

" 'Castaway crew of an English bark burnt at sea. We came here tonight. I am the second mate. The captain is in the longboat, and wishes to know if you would give us a passage somewhere.'

" 'Oh, my goodness! I say. . . . This is the *Celestial* from Singapore on her return trip. I'll arrange with your captain in the morning . . . and . . . I say . . . did you hear me just now?'

" 'I should think the whole bay heard you.'

" 'I thought you were a shore boat. Now, look here—this infernal lazy scoundrel of a caretaker has gone to sleep again—curse him. The light is out, and I nearly ran foul of the end of this damned jetty. This is the third time he plays me this trick. Now, I ask you, can anybody stand this kind of thing? It's enough to drive a man out of his mind. I'll report him. . . . I'll get the Assistant Resident to give him the sack, by . . . See—there's no light. It's out, isn't it? I take you to witness the light's out. There should be a light, you know. A red light on the—'

" 'There was a light,' I said, mildly.

' "But it's out, man! What's the use of talking like this? You can see for yourself it's out—don't you? If you had to take a valuable steamer along this God-forsaken coast you would want a light too. I'll kick him from end to end of his miserable wharf. You'll see if I don't. I will—'

" 'So I may tell my captain you'll take us?' I broke in.

" 'Yes, I'll take you. Good night,' he said, brusquely.

"I pulled back, made fast again to the jetty, and then went to sleep at last. I had faced the silence of the East. I had heard some of its languages. But when I opened my eyes again the silence was as complete as though it had never been broken. I was lying in a flood of light, and the sky had never looked so far, so high, before. I opened my eyes and lay without moving.

"And then I saw the men of the East—they were looking at me. The whole length of the jetty was full of people. I saw brown, bronze, yellow faces, the black eyes, the glitter, the color of an Eastern crowd. And all these beings stared without a murmur, without a sigh, without a movement. They stared down at the boats, at the sleeping men who at night had come to them from the sea. Nothing moved. The fronds of palms stood still against the sky. Not a branch stirred along the shore, and the brown roofs of hidden houses peeped through the green foliage, through the big leaves that hung shining and still like leaves forged of heavy metal. This was the East of the ancient navigators, so old, so mysterious, resplendent and somber, living and unchanged, full of danger and promise. And these were the men. I sat up suddenly. A wave of movement passed through the crowd from end to end, passed along the heads, swayed the bodies, ran along the jetty like a ripple on the water, like a breath of wind on a field—and all was still again. I see it now—the wide sweep of the bay, the glittering sands, the wealth of green infinite and varied, the sea blue like the sea of a dream, the crowd of attentive faces, the blaze of vivid color—the water reflecting it all, the curve of the shore, the jetty, the high-sterned outlandish craft floating still, and the three boats with tired men from the West sleeping unconscious of the land and the people and of the violence of sunshine. They slept thrown across the thwarts, curled on bottom-boards, in the careless attitudes of death. The head of the old skipper, leaning back in the stern of the longboat, had fallen on his breast, and he looked as though he would never wake. Farther out old Mahon's face was upturned to the sky, with the long white beard spread out on his breast, as though he had been shot where he sat at the tiller; and a man, all in a heap in the bow of the boat, slept with both arms embracing the stem-head and with his cheek laid on the gunwale. The East looked at them without a sound.

"I have known its fascinations since: I have seen the mysterious shores, the still water, the lands of brown nations, where a stealthy Nemesis lies in wait, pursues, overtakes so many of the conquering race, who are proud of their wisdom, of their knowledge, of their strength. But for me all the East is contained in that vision of my youth. It is all in that moment when I opened my young eyes on it. I came upon it from a tussle with the sea—and I was young—and I saw it looking at me. And this is all that is left of it! Only a moment; a moment of strength, of romance, of glamour—of youth! . . . A flick of sunshine upon a strange shore, the time to remember, the time for a sigh, and—good-by!—Night—Good-by . . . !"

He drank.

"Ah! The good old time—the good old time. Youth and the sea. Glamour and the sea! The good, strong sea, the salt, bitter sea, that could whisper to you and roar at you and knock your breath out of you."

He drank again.

"By all that's wonderful, it is the sea, I believe, the sea itself—or is it youth alone? Who can tell? But you here—you all had something out of life: money, love—whatever one gets on shore—and, tell me, wasn't that the best time, that time when we were young at sea; young and had nothing, on the sea that gives nothing, except hard knocks—and sometimes a chance to feel your strength—that only—what you all regret?"

And we all nodded at him: the man of finance, the man of accounts, the man of law, we all nodded at him over the polished table that like a still sheet of brown water reflected our faces, lined, wrinkled; our faces marked by toil, by deceptions, by success, by love; our weary eyes looking still, looking always, looking anxiously for something out of life, that while it is expected is already gone—has passed unseen, in a sigh, in a flash—together with the youth, with the strength, with the romance of illusions.

Study Guides

The theme of Conrad's "Youth" is indicated by the title and the recurrent pattern of such exclamations as: "O youth!"—"Youth! All youth! The silly, charming, beautiful youth." This theme, ironically enough, is examined from the perspective of an experienced, middle-aged man. At intervals Marlow interrupts the narrative to lament the passing of a kind of glory from the earth. These interruptions finally make the theme explicit:

> ". . . I remember my youth and the feeling that will never come back any more—the feeling that I could last for ever, outlast the sea, the earth, and all men; the deceitful feeling that lures us on to joys, to perils, to love, to vain effort—to death; the triumphant conviction of strength, the heat of life in the handful of dust, the glow in the heart that with every year grows dim, grows cold, grows small, and expires—and expires, too soon, too soon—before life itself."

At the end of the story the theme is restated by the first-person narrator to give strength to Marlow's reflections and to confirm his judgment:

> . . . we all nodded at him over the polished table that like a still sheet of brown water reflected our faces, lined, wrinkled; our faces marked by toil, by deceptions, by success, by love; our weary eyes looking still, looking always, looking anxiously for something out of life, that while it is expected is already gone—has passed unseen, in a sigh, in a flash—together with the youth, with the strength, with the romance of illusions.

The story, then, is about youth and the romance of illusions, but it is not simply the tedious reminiscence of an aging sailor. Marlow himself remarks, ". . . there are those voyages that seem ordered for the illustration of life, that might stand for a symbol of existence." The voyage equals life—the trial, the challenge, the test that man must undergo if he is to live, if he is to learn his capacities and limitations, to prove himself worthy of manhood, to know what is ideal and what is real.

1. Work out the significant parallels in the voyage-is-life metaphor. What is the significance of the false starts of the *Judea?* Of the pilot Jermyn and the mockers at Falmouth? Of the ship's motto "Do or Die"? Of the numerous accidents such as the shifting of the ballast, the collision, the spontaneous combustion?

Several allusions contribute to the significance of this voyage-is-life metaphor. One complex of these—the names *Judea,* Beard, Jermyn, and Abraham—refers to people and events in the Old Testament. The name *Judea,* for instance, brings to mind the Exodus of the Jews, the trials and tribulations of their journey to the Promised Land. Since the children of the old kingdom of Judah were the strongest of the tribes of Israel, there is a further suggestion that those who stay with the *Judea* are not only chosen people but the strongest of the elect. This possible allusion gives additional emphasis to Marlow's remarks about the superiority of the crew with their "hidden something, that gift, of good or evil that makes racial difference, that shapes the fate of nations." If *Judea* alludes to the Exodus of the Jews, then the name Beard may be supposed to suggest Moses, the bearded leader of the Israelites. Like Moses, Beard does not reach the Promised Land. The pilot Jermyn suggests the prophet Jeremiah, author of Lamentations, the severe critic of the present and prophesier of future calamity. Traditional biblical interpretation equates Abraham with faith because of his willingness to obey without question

God's command to sacrifice his son Isaac. The cook Abraham certainly possesses this blind faith.

These allusions are all grouped at the beginning of the story and serve to characterize the nature of the voyage. Obviously, they are not meant to occupy the center of the reader's attention. They serve rather to provide a subtle emphasis, an almost subliminal underscoring of the theme of the story. They also give additional evidence of the unusual quality of the voyage, of its fitness to be an allegory of life itself. Moreover, they provide a slightly ironic comment since Beard, Jermyn, and Abraham do not at first glance seem to have the heroic stature of prophets and patriarchs.

2. Consider the following questions: What does young Marlow's hatred of the "true prophet" Jermyn suggest about man's real condition and youth's reaction to it? What is the significance of the madness of the cook? Is faith a kind of madness? What allusions, if any, are made by the other names in the story: Mahon, Miranda or Melissa, *Sommerville, Celestial?* Does the context support your views?

The voyage then has the Promised Land as its goal. And, according to the logic of the allegory, it must be concluded that the pursuit of the ideal must be a prime condition of life. To the young Marlow, this ideal is the East, the never-before-seen land of mystery. He endures the misfortunes and overcomes the hardships of the voyage almost cheerfully because of his objective. The full significance of the voyage, however, cannot be understood from the point of view of the younger Marlow. The teller of the story, the older, more cautious man that the young Marlow becomes, must also be taken into account. For him, years after the ill-fated voyage, it is the experience itself that he calls ideal. For him, the allusions to biblical lore are ironic. For him, the voyage contains much that is faintly ridiculous. Yet he sees in the actions and enthusiasms of youth a greater ideal than the young sailor to Bangkok could realize. The folly and glory of refurling a sail on a mast almost toppling into the sea are fully apparent to him.

3. Consider the following questions: Is the ideal found in the pursuit or in the attainment? If an ideal is ever attained, is it still ideal? Is the ideal an illusion? If Bangkok or "The East" instead of the voyage itself is interpreted as the ultimate ideal and if the East is death, what are the philosophical implications? Can death be the realization of an ideal?

Thus interwoven with Conrad's allegory of the cruel struggles of life is a view that allows man to glean glory from it. This view is equated with youth, which becomes a symbol of a state, a condition, a total reaction to living. We know that Conrad does not mean youth to be merely a reckoning of years. The captain is as youthful in spirit as Marlow—look at his heroic action, his romantic gesture of saving his wife, his eagerness to assume his first command. We are told that his eyes are "amazingly like a boy's, with that candid expression some quite common men preserve to the end of their days by a rare internal gift of simplicity of heart and rectitude of soul." In contrast, the five at the table have outlived youth. They pass the bottle, hoping to put artificial fire into middle age. They sail over a still, brown pool of a table instead of the wild, magnificent sea. They realize now in retrospect that life is an expending, a whole-hearted giving of youth.

4. Explain how the two narrators who provide the complex, "envelope" point of view lend objectivity to Conrad's story. What is gained by having the story told by Marlow instead of the voice which speaks at the beginning and end? What would be lost if Marlow's "O youth!" were uttered by the narrator who begins the story? Would the objectivity of the story be destroyed if youth were not shown to be, in part, pure romantic illusion?

EUDORA WELTY

(1909–)

A Worn Path

It was December—a bright frozen day in the early morning. Far out in the country there was an old Negro woman with her head tied in a red rag, coming along a path through the pinewoods. Her name was Phoenix Jackson. She was very old and small and she walked slowly in the dark pine shadows, moving a little from side to side in her steps, with the balanced heaviness and lightness of a pendulum in a grandfather clock. She carried a thin, small cane made from an umbrella, and with this she kept tapping the frozen earth in front of her. This made a grave and persistent noise in the still air, that seemed meditative, like the chirping of a solitary little bird.

She wore a dark striped dress reaching down to her shoetops, and an equally long apron of bleached sugar sacks, with a full pocket; all neat and tidy, but every time she took a step she might have fallen over her shoelaces, which dragged from her unlaced shoes. She looked straight ahead. Her eyes were blue with age. Her skin had a pattern all its own of numberless branching wrinkles and as though a whole little tree stood in the middle of her forehead, but a golden color ran underneath, and the two knobs of her cheeks were illuminated by a yellow burning under the dark. Under the red rag her hair came down on her neck in the frailest of ringlets, still black, and with an odor like copper.

Now and then there was a quivering in the thicket. Old Phoenix said, "Out of my way, all you foxes, owls, beetles, jack rabbits, coons, and wild animals! . . . Keep out from under these feet, little bobwhites. . . . Keep the big wild hogs out of my path. Don't let none of those come running my direction. I got a long way." Under her small black-freckled hand her cane, limber as a buggy whip, would switch at the brush as if to rouse up any hiding things.

On she went. The woods were deep and still. The sun made the pine needles almost too bright to look at, up where the wind rocked. The cones dropped as light as feathers. Down in the hollow was the mourning dove—it was not too late for him.

The path ran up a hill. "Seem like there is chains about my feet, time I get this far," she said, in the voice of argument old people keep to use with themselves. "Something always take a hold on this hill—pleads I should stay."

After she got to the top she turned and gave a full, severe look behind her where she had come. "Up through pines," she said at length. "Now down through oaks."

Her eyes opened their widest and she started down gently. But before she got to the bottom of the hill a bush caught her dress.

Her fingers were busy and intent, but her skirts were full and long, so that before she could pull them free in one place they were caught in another. It was not possible to allow the dress to tear. "I in the thorny bush," she said. "Thorns, you doing your appointed work. Never want to let folks past—no sir. Old eyes thought you was a pretty little *green* bush."

Finally, trembling all over, she stood free, and after a moment dared to stoop for her cane.

"Sun so high!" she cried, leaning back and looking, while the thick tears went over her eyes. "The time getting all gone here."

At the foot of this hill was a place where a log was laid across the creek.

"Now comes the trial," said Phoenix.

Putting her right foot out, she mounted the log and shut her eyes. Lifting her skirt, leveling her cane fiercely before her, like a festival figure in some parade, she began to march across. Then she opened her eyes and she was safe on the other side.

"I wasn't as old as I thought," she said.

But she sat down to rest. She spread her skirts on the bank around her and folded her hands over her knees. Up above her was a tree in a pearly cloud of mistletoe. She did not dare to close her eyes, and when a little boy brought her a little plate with a slice of marble-cake on it she spoke to him. "That would be acceptable," she said. But when she went to take it there was just her own hand in the air.

So she left that tree, and had to go through a barbed-wire fence. There she had to creep and crawl, spreading her knees and stretching her fingers like a baby trying to climb the steps. But she talked loudly to herself: she could not let her dress be torn now, so late in the day, and she could not pay for having her arm or her leg sawed off if she got caught fast where she was.

At last she was safe through the fence and risen up out in the clearing. Big dead trees, like black men with one arm, were standing in the purple stalks of the withered cotton field. There sat a buzzard.

"Who you watching?"

In the furrow she made her way along.

"Glad this not the season for bulls," she said, looking sideways, "and the good Lord made his snakes to curl up and sleep in the winter. A pleasure I don't see no two-headed snake coming around that tree, where it come once. It took a while to get by him, back in the summer."

She passed through the old cotton and went into a field of dead corn. It whispered and shook, and was taller than her head. "Through the maze now," she said, for there was no path.

Then there was something tall, black, and skinny there, moving before her.

At first she took it for a man. It could have been a man dancing in the field. But she stood still and listened, and it did not make a sound. It was as silent as a ghost.

"Ghost," she said sharply, "who be you the ghost of? For I have heard of nary death close by."

But there was no answer, only the ragged dancing in the wind.

She shut her eyes, reached out her hand, and touched a sleeve. She found a coat and inside that an emptiness, cold as ice.

"You scarecrow," she said. Her face lighted. "I ought to be shut up for good," she said with laughter. "My senses is gone. I too old. I the oldest people I ever know. Dance, old scarecrow," she said, "while I dancing with you."

She kicked her foot over the furrow, and with mouth drawn down shook her head once or twice in a little strutting way. Some husks blew down and whirled in streamers about her skirts.

Then she went on, parting her way from side to side with the cane, through the whispering field. At last she came to the end, to a wagon track, where the silver grass blew between the red ruts. The quail were walking around like pullets, seeming all dainty and unseen.

"Walk pretty," she said. "This the easy place. This the easy going."

She followed the track, swaying through the quiet bare fields, through the little strings of trees silver in their dead leaves, past cabins silver from weather, with the doors and windows boarded shut, all like old women under a spell stitting there. "I walking in their sleep," she said, nodding her head vigorously.

In a ravine she went where a spring was silently flowing through a hollow log. Old Phoenix bent and drank. "Sweetgum makes the water sweet," she said, and drank more. "Nobody knows who made this well, for it was here when I was born."

The track crossed a swampy part where the moss hung as white as lace from every limb. "Sleep on, alligators, and blow your bubbles." Then the track went into the road.

Deep, deep the road went down between the high green-colored banks. Overhead the live-oaks met, and it was as dark as a cave.

A black dog with a lolling tongue came up out of the weeds by the ditch. She was meditating, and not ready, and when he came at her she only hit him a little with her cane. Over she went in the ditch, like a little puff of milk-weed.

Down there, her senses drifted away. A dream visited her, and she reached her hand up, but nothing reached down and gave her a pull. So she lay there and presently went to talking. "Old woman," she said to herself, "that black dog come up out of the weeds to stall you off, and now there he sitting on his fine tail, smiling at you."

A white man finally came along and found her—a hunter, a young man, with his dog on a chain.

"Well, Granny!" he laughed. "What are you doing there?"

"Lying on my back like a June-bug waiting to be turned over, mister," she said, reaching up her hand.

He lifted her up, gave her a swing in the air, and set her down, "Anything broken, Granny?"

"No sir, them old dead weeds is springy enough," said Phoenix, when she had got her breath. "I thank you for your trouble."

"Where do you live, Granny?" he asked, while the two dogs were growling at each other.

"Away back yonder, sir, behind the ridge. You can't even see it from here."

"On your way home?"

"No, sir, I going to town."

"Why, that's too far! That's as far as I walk when I come out myself, and I get something for my trouble." He patted the stuffed bag he carried, and there hung down a little closed claw. It was one of the bobwhites, with its beak hooked bitterly to show it was dead. "Now you go on home, Granny!"

"I bound to go to town, mister," said Phoenix. "The time come around."

He gave another laugh, filling the whole landscape. "I know you colored people! Wouldn't miss going to town to see Santa Claus!"

But something held Old Phoenix very still. The deep lines in her face went into a fierce and different radiation. Without warning she had seen with her own eyes a flashing nickel fall out of the man's pocket on to the ground.

"How old are you, Granny?" he was saying.

"There is no telling, mister," she said, "no telling."

Then she gave a little cry and clapped her hands, and said, "Git on away from here, dog! Look! Look at that dog!" She laughed as if in admiration. "He ain't scared of nobody. He a big black dog." She whispered, "Sick him!"

"Watch me get rid of that cur," said the man. "Sick him, Pete! Sick him!"

Phoenix heard the dogs fighting and heard the man running and throwing sticks. She even heard a gunshot. But she was slowly bending forward by that time, further and further forward, the lids stretched down over her eyes, as if she were doing this in her sleep. Her chin was lowered almost to her knees. The yellow palm of her hand came out from the fold of her apron. Her fingers slid down and along the ground under the piece of money with the grace and care they would have in lifting an egg from under a sitting hen. Then she slowly straightened up, she stood erect, and the nickel was in her apron pocket. A bird flew by. Her lips moved. "God watching me the whole time. I come to stealing."

The man came back, and his own dog panted about them. "Well, I scared him off that time," he said, and then he laughed and lifted his gun and pointed it at Phoenix.

She stood straight and faced him.

"Doesn't the gun scare you?" he said, still pointing it.

"No, sir, I seen plenty go off closer by, in my day, and for less than what I done," she said, holding utterly still.

He smiled, and shouldered the gun. "Well, Granny," he said, "you must be a hundred years old, and scared of nothing. I'd give you a dime if I had any money with me. But you take my advice and stay home, and nothing will happen to you."

"I bound to go on my way, mister," said Phoenix. She inclined her head in the red rag. Then they went in different directions, but she could hear the gun shooting again and again over the hill.

She walked on. The shadows hung from the oak trees to the road like curtains. Then she smelled wood-smoke, and smelled the river, and she saw a steeple and the cabins on their steep steps. Dozens of little black children whirled around her. There ahead was Natchez shining. Bells were ringing. She walked on.

In the paved city it was Christmas time. There were red and green electric lights strung and crisscrossed everywhere, and all turned on in the daytime. Old Phoenix would have been lost if she had not distrusted her eyesight and depended on her feet to know where to take her.

She paused quietly on the sidewalk, where people were passing by. A lady came along in the crowd, carrying an armful of red-, green-, and silver-wrapped presents; she gave off perfume like the red roses in hot summer, and Phoenix stopped her.

"Please, missy, will you lace up my shoe?" She held up her foot.

"What do you want, Grandma?"

"See my shoe," said Phoenix. "Do all right for out in the country, but wouldn't look right to go in a big building."

"Stand still then, Grandma," said the lady. She put her packages down carefully on the sidewalk beside her and laced and tied both shoes tightly.

"Can't lace 'em with a cane," said Phoenix. "Thank you, missy. I doesn't mind asking a nice lady to tie up my shoe when I gets out on the street."

Moving slowly and from side to side, she went into the stone building and into a tower of steps, where she walked up and around and around until her feet knew to stop.

She entered a door, and there she saw nailed up on the wall the document that had been stamped with the gold seal and framed in the gold frame which matched the dream that was hung up in her head.

"Here I be," she said. There was a fixed and ceremonial stiffness over her body.

"A charity case, I suppose," said an attendant who sat at the desk before her.

But Phoenix only looked above her head. There was sweat on her face; the wrinkles shone like a bright net.

"Speak up, Grandma," the woman said. "What's your name? We must have your history, you know. Have you been here before? What seems to be the trouble with you?"

Old Phoenix only gave a twitch to her face as if a fly were bothering her.

"Are you deaf?" cried the attendant.

But then the nurse came in.

"Oh, that's just old Aunt Phoenix," she said. "She doesn't come for herself—she has a little grandson. She makes these trips just as regular as clockwork. She lives away back off the Old Natchez Trace." She bent down. "Well, Aunt Phoenix, why don't you just take a seat? We won't keep you standing after your long trip." She pointed.

The old woman sat down, bolt upright in the chair.

"Now, how is the boy?" asked the nurse.

Old Phoenix did not speak.

"I said, how is the boy?"

But Phoenix only waited and stared straight ahead, her face very solemn and withdrawn into rigidity.

"Is his throat any better?" asked the nurse. "Aunt Phoenix, don't you hear me? Is your grandson's throat any better since the last time you came for the medicine?"

With her hand on her knees, the old woman waited, silent, erect and motionless, just as if she were in armor.

"You mustn't take up our time this way, Aunt Phoenix," the nurse said. "Tell us quickly about your grandson, and get it over. He isn't dead, is he?"

At last there came a flicker and then a flame of comprehension across her face, and she spoke.

"My grandson. It was my memory had left me. There I sat and forgot why I made my long trip."

"Forgot?" The nurse frowned. "After you came so far?"

Then Phoenix was like an old woman begging a dignified forgiveness for waking up frightened in the night. "I never did go to school—I was too old at the Surrender," she said in a soft voice. "I'm an old woman without an education. It was my memory fail me. My little grandson, he is just the same, and I forgot it in the coming."

"Throat never heals, does it?" said the nurse, speaking in a loud, sure voice to Old Phoenix. By now she had a card with something written on it, a little list. "Yes. Swallowed lye. When was it—January—two—three years ago—"

Phoenix spoke unasked now. "No, missy, he not dead, he just the same. Every little while his throat begin to close up again, and he not able to swallow. He not get his breath. He not able to help himself. So the time come around, and I go on another trip for the soothing medicine."

"All right. The doctor said as long as you came to get it you could have it," said the nurse. "But it's an obstinate case."

"My little grandson, he sit up there in the house all wrapped up, waiting by himself," Phoenix went on. "We is the only two left in the world. He suffer and it don't seem to put him back at all. He got a sweet look. He going to last. He wear a little patch quilt and peep out, holding his mouth open like a little bird. I remembers so plain now. I not going to forget him again, no, the whole enduring time. I could tell him from all the others in creation."

"All right." The nurse was trying to hush her now. She brought her a bottle of medicine. "Charity," she said, making a check mark in a book.

Old Phoenix held the bottle close to her eyes and then carefully put it into her pocket.

"I thank you," she said.

"It's Christmas time, Grandma," said the attendant. "Could I give you a few pennies out of my purse?"

"Five pennies is a nickel," said Phoenix stiffly.

"Here's a nickel," said the attendant.

Phoenix rose carefully and held out her hand. She received the nickel and then fished the other nickel out of her pocket and laid it beside the new one. She stared at her palm closely, with her head on one side.

Then she gave a tap with her cane on the floor.

"This is what come to me to do," she said. "I going to the store and buy my child a little windmill they sells, made out of paper. He going to find it hard to believe there such a thing in the world. I'll march myself back where he waiting, holding it straight up in this hand."

She lifted her free hand, gave a little nod, turned round, and walked out of the doctor's office. Then her slow step began on the stairs, going down.

Study Guides

The author of "A Worn Path" refuses to state her "whole intention," to use Edmund Spenser's phrase, as directly as Conrad does in "Youth." Although she recreates a journey along a worn path from the backhills of Mississippi to the city of Natchez, she does not make a blunt statement explaining the "dark conceit" or larger significance of the old woman's slow and painful progress. The allegorical and symbolical frame of reference is implied instead of stated, suggested rather than insisted upon.

Like other stories with this same *structure,* the account of Old Phoenix relates a series of incidents along the road. Only enough surface tensions to keep us reading are created by the obstacles which hinder the progress of the journey. At first glance, these incidents seem quite trivial: Phoenix gets her skirt caught in a briar bush, has a daydream while sitting under a tree full of mistletoe, meets a black dog, chats with a quail hunter, steals a nickel, and so forth. The scene with the hunter can be considered a minor climax. The major climax comes at the doctor's office when she forgets what she came for. The denouement occurs when she resolves never to forget again and decides to buy a windmill to take to her grandson.

In addition to the rather sparse plot development, we see that the characters in "A Worn Path" are drawn with an economy suggestive of *myth,* for the author has developed them only enough to create a shadow of verisimilitude. Although these are hardly stock characters (whose actions can be easily predicted), they are not complex individuals in any realistic sense. As is proper, Phoenix is the most fully developed character; but our interest in her is not as an individual but as a type. She is a simple, superstitious, aged Negro with a great deal of fortitude, instinctive slyness, and a fine sense of humor. Her character is implied more than it is dramatized explicitly. Our interest derives from the character she symbolizes. Indeed, it is only when we become aware of the symbolical and mythical nature of the story that either plot or character fully excites us.

We are first made aware of the momentous implications in the story by the author's subtle use of allusion. She tells us that Phoenix was "just as if she were in armor"; she marched "like a festival figure in some parade." These and other passing references suggest journeys famous in literature, and they give us license to recall these journeys: the mythical knight in shining armor in quest of the Holy Grail; the pilgrim wending his way toward the Holy Shrine; the journey of the Magi toward Bethlehem to seek the infant Christ.

Appropriate to her time and place, Phoenix encounters the same trials, deceptions, and terrors that plagued Ulysses in his wanderings and caused the knights-errant from King Arthur's Court to quake and falter. As in the epic romances, devilish agents of evil stay her progress and cast a magic spell: "Seem like there is chains about my feet, time I get this far. . . . Something always take a hold on this hill." Moreover, Phoenix is the victim of wicked deception: "Thorns, you doing your appointed work . . . Old eyes thought you was a pretty little *green* bush."

1. Explore the events in Phoenix's journey that parallel typical episodes from heroic literature (the epic and the romance). On her journey does she encounter "dragons," fantastic monsters, tests of faith, dreary forests, a wasteland, and enchanted areas? Can you find a counterpart of a trip to the underworld? Of Cerberus? The wayfaring knight often has a "vision," sometimes sent to tempt him, to divert him from his purpose. The visions are often in the form of false miracles. If Phoenix's purpose is to seek, unselfishly and unerringly, medicine for her grandson, what is the nature of the temptation in the two tormenting visions that disappear into thin air? These visions are false miracles, yet they are perhaps reflections of the one true Christian miracle. Comment on this last statement. Phoenix, humanly, finally submits to temptation—she steals a nickel. What is implied about the nature of temptation and "sin" in the circumstances of this episode? Phoenix immediately expects deserved punishment for her "sin." Why doesn't she get it? What is the significance of the bag of dead birds the hunter carries? What is peculiar about a phoenix? What, in the Christian tradition, are the conditions through which man may arise from the dead? Part of these conditions depend on certain acts of the individual. Does Phoenix perform these acts? Part also depends on Grace—a pure gift, something unearned and unearnable by man, hence a gift of charity. Do these conditions explain why the hunter does not, symbolically, add another bird to his bag?

2. In spite of her one deviation into error, Phoenix meets all the trials and tests of the traditional pilgrim's faith. Through one episode after another she moves forward toward "the shining city," which we can equate with the New Jerusalem of the Red Cross Knight. We are justified, by the context, in thinking of her as a person with simple, blind faith: we see her put her right foot on the perilous footlog and close her eyes to march across. "Then she opened her eyes and she was safe on the other side." Faith guides her to the city: "Old Phoenix would have been lost if she had not distrusted her eyesight and depended on her feet to know where to take her."

Since there are several references to birds and a number of bird images in this story, we come to associate them specifically with Phoenix herself. We are told that she is "walking pretty" with the quail, making a noise "like the chirping of a solitary little bird," instructing the bobwhites to take care lest she step on them. (Notice too the description of her grandson.) This sort of imagery—in a context where frail birds face constant danger—strongly suggests two famous passages from the New Testament:

> No man can serve two masters: for either he will hate the one, and love the other; or else he will hold to the one, and despise the other. Ye cannot serve God and mammon.
>
> Therefore I say unto you, Take no thought for your life, what ye shall eat, or what ye shall drink; nor yet for your body, what ye shall put on. Is not the life more than meat, and the body more than raiment?

> Behold the fowls of the air: for they sow not, neither do they reap, nor gather into barns, yet your heavenly Father feedeth them. Are you not much better than they? [Matt. 6:24-26]

> And I say unto you my friends, Be not afraid of them that kill the body, and after that have no more that they can do.
> But I will forewarn you whom ye shall fear: Fear him, which after he hath killed hath power to cast into hell, yea, I say unto you, Fear him.
> Are not five sparrows sold for two farthings, and not one of them is forgotten before God?
> But even the very hairs of your head are all numbered. Fear not therefore: ye are of more value than many sparrows. [Luke 12:4-7]

Do these passages help clarify the ambiguous episode involving the hunter? Do they explain why Phoenix has no fear when the gun is pointed at her? As soon as she steals the nickel, a bird flies by and immediately Phoenix says: "God watching me the whole time." Does the appearance of the bird at this point have any significance? "To watch" means to keep under surveillance as well as to guard, to protect, to keep from harm. Which of the meanings does Phoenix employ in this statement? Are both meanings implied?

3. Like all redeemed Christians, Phoenix achieves salvation not because she deserves it but because she makes a selfless quest for someone else (her grandson), and because all Christians, through Grace, are "charity cases," as the nurse in the doctor's office implies near the end of the story. Examine closely the episode in the city. What is significant about the time of year? the woman in the street who ties Phoenix's shoes? What is suggested by "the document that had been stamped with the gold seal and framed in the gold frame which matched the dream that was hung up in her head"? The "medicine" Phoenix seeks may be more than literal. It may correspond to Grace, the redeeming sacrificial Blood of Christ, or the Holy Grail in Christian doctrine and the medieval quest. Explore the significant implications in the "medicine" analogy. The medicine soothes but does not absolutely cure the "obstinate case." What may the "obstinate case" suggest about the nature of the human condition? Could it possibly be an analogy to the concept of Original Sin? What, perhaps, is signified by the fact that the medicine must be sought repeatedly over a "worn" path? A well-known Biblical statement says: "And I say unto you, Ask, and it shall be given you; seek, and ye shall find; knock, and it shall be opened unto you." What reported statement by the doctor can be taken as an allusion to this verse from Luke 11:9?

4. With the money acquired on her trip, Phoenix wants to buy a paper windmill for her grandson; she remarks: "He going to find it hard to believe there such a thing in the world." The windmill may be regarded here rather like a miracle. In both fable and myth, fantastic and miraculous elements often appear. Discuss the nature of this miracle. Visualize a windmill such as Phoenix wants to buy. What does its silhouette suggest? Does the context support interpreting the windmill as a symbolic cross which Phoenix carries, "holding it straight up in this hand"?

With the medicine and the windmill in hand, Phoenix returns to her grandson. Having once forgotten, like most human beings, the purpose of her life's journey, she swears she will never forget again—the whole *enduring* time. Perhaps the denouement of the story alludes to a statement following another famous parable: "Verily I say unto you, Inasmuch as ye did it not to one of the least of these, ye did it not to me." Explain how this allusion interrelates with the Christmas setting, the woman with Christmas packages and the hunter with a bag, the nurse, and the grandson.

5. Stories that suggest myth are capable of diverse interpretations because their narrative pattern is often archetypal. Thus this story need not necessarily be interpreted in the light of Christian concepts. It may simply portray the search for an ideal, for salvation, or for redemption from the wastefulness of life. It may even be read as a myth that recounts the cycle of nature and the regeneration of the new from the old. Discuss possible non-Christian interpretations which the context of the story may support.

6. Consider "My Kinsman, Major Molineux" in terms of myth and investigate the journey in that story as symbol.

Fantasy, Ambiguity, and Credibility

We have already observed that although fiction provides us with an insight into reality, the aims of fiction are not a presentation of literal fact. Fiction is interested in another kind of truth; it may present the impossible, as well as the possible, for fiction is the "fact" delivered through imagination. It is, to use Henry James's phrase, an ordering and presentation of "a direct impression of life." An impression is not necessarily a fact, although it may very well be an insight.

How an author presents this "direct impression" and reveals the "imaginative fact" to his reader may be chiefly a matter of technique. In its approach a story may develop along the lines of realism, impressionism, or even pure *fantasy.* In any case, literal fact that can be documented is irrelevant in a literary scale of values. What is important is the larger or more encompassing truth imaginative literature can reveal. So in studying fiction we must accept a paradox: fact is not necessarily truth; the unreal may be a means by which we perceive reality.

Perhaps nowhere is the literary paradox more clearly apparent than in those examples of fiction which arrive at truth through fantasy. In using this technique an author asks us to accept, momentarily, what is not true in order to "get at" or "unveil" the mysteries of truth. In these terms we think of fantasy as a fictional technique that employs the irrational and the improbable to bring truth closer to hand.

For example, we often attempt to explain a complex idea by beginning with "If we imagine that. . . ." Then we devise or create some kind of hypothetical analogy, which itself is a kind of fantasy. We know from the beginning that the imagined assumption is not real and cannot be proved by rational methods; yet this fanciful approach may be the best and most economical means we have of expressing and clarifying a difficult concept or complex belief. Through the method of analogy we invent a fiction in order to present a truth that otherwise might remain obstinately beyond our powers of expression. Throughout the history of literature authors have turned to fantasy to explore the truth behind fact and phenomenon; they may confront us with the weird, fantastic, or supernatural in order to make the real world more understandable and far more meaningful.

Even though an analogy (or a story) may begin with "Let us imagine," we, having granted this first basic assumption, demand that a logical progression should follow. Whatever else happens beyond the first premise must be credible, must be a logical outgrowth of the fanciful condition created in the original suspension of disbelief. The rule established by the first premise, even though in itself it is an impossibility, must not be violated. This is to say that an imaginative or fictional world may dictate its own rules of operation; but having once defined them, it is no more free to suspend them than we are to dispense with the law of gravity. For instance, "The Rocking-Horse Winner" makes only one fantastic assumption: by putting himself into a trance by mechanical means which exhaust his physical and conscious powers, man may achieve psychic and intuitive powers that can predict the outcome of future events. Once this premise is granted, nothing occurs in the Lawrence story which is not completely credible.

Ambiguity, though not restricted to stories of the fantastic, is often one of their characteristics; it is indeed one of the qualities that clearly justifies the use of fantasy. The three stories in the following section provide excellent examples of literary ambiguity. This method of presentation allows the reader alternate meanings—more than one interpretation, perhaps several related impressions or insights at the same time. Although ambiguity is obviously undesirable at the level of literal fact, it is a legitimate means of enrichment in stories and poetry. With several choices before him, the reader may become aware of them all without having to choose one in preference to another. The author may drive us two ways—which is what ambiguity means literally—and when he exerts complete control over the language and structure of his story, he gives us a double view and perhaps several combined images of reality. The particular example in this section is "My Kinsman, Major Molineux."

MILDRED HAUN

(1911–   )

Barshia's Horse He Made, It Flew

"So tired. So tired," he said. Always Barshia said that. And I guess it did tire him to keep his foot going up and down. All the time. But that's all he ever did save just piddle with fancy things. Pretty fancy things. And when he stretched out in bed at night, that foot kept a-going. Even in his sleep, it went. I told Amy if ever that foot stopped going I would know Barshia was dead. His heart would stop before his foot did.

Sometimes I lost patience with him. If he would have moved the rest of his body some. I ought to have had more pity on him. But I didn't understand at first—not till Dona Fawver told me that about Teelie—I didn't. You see, Barshia was Ad's oldest boy by his first old woman. I thought he was just lazy or crazy one. I didn't know which. Or maybe both.

Barshia could take up more room than anybody I ever seed too. He would set there by the window with his legs all sprawled out. And that foot a-going. When I was sweeping I would try my best to get him to move. But, mind you, he wouldn't even move a smidgin. Not to save my soul, he wouldn't. And he wouldn't say anything about why he wouldn't. He would just look at me. Like he could run through me. Or squall out at me to bring him everwhat he had need for.

He didn't talk much—just set there. Sometimes he would tell me or Amy one that he wanted a drink of water. Amy was a youngon then and seemed like Barshia kept her trotting all the time, bringing something to him. We always went out and got him water when he asked for it. Sometimes I went and got him a drink on my own accord. He always took it—just swallowed it down. Sometimes after he took a drink, he would say that he was tired. Always he was tired. No matter what. He looked like he was stuck to that chair. But we could get him to come to the table nearly every meal. We learned we had to call him a long time beforehands. If we waited till dinner was on the table he wouldn't come at all. Ad would make me or Amy one fetch his victuals to him. Ad never named anything to me about it—ne'er a word. I don't know whether he thought what Dona did or not. I just don't know. If I recollected to call Barshia before the sun got on the porch at all, he would get there by the time it got three planks in on the floor. He was pretty dauncy about his eating too. If we didn't have everything to suit him, he swelt up like a sycamore ball in wet weather. And he would throw a plate at me every time he got mad when he was at the table. Ad would take it up and side with Barshia.

It was at the table he done most of his talking. He would set there after he got through eating and tell about the big things he had done and the big things he was going to keep on doing. Always making his words keep time with his foot patting. He was a-going to get him a fine big brood sow. That he was. And he was a-going to have the finest hogs of anybody in the whole country. He would raise him some turkeys too. Big bunches of turkeys like he had heard about. Like other folkses had. He could make money, he said—a heap of money off a big bunch of fat red turkeys. Red turkeys with white wings. He could hear them gobbling. He liked to hear them gobble. He was going to take that money and make him a fine big house to live in. It was all in his mind's eye. He was going to make a heap of good furniture to put in it too. Pretty furniture like Grandpa used to make.

But the house never did get built. Barshia would set there without moving anything save his right foot. From daylight till dark it went up and down. It made just enough noise to get on my nerves and aggravate the life out of me. Even after Dona told me that—even if I did have pity on him—it still wore on me.

He wouldn't allow me nor Amy neither one to sing around the house. Every time we started to sing he would tell us to shut up. Said we sounded like a buzzard trying to sing. Then he would show us how. When Amy was three year old she could sing right well. But Barshia fussed so much she soon got so she didn't even try. And Barshia could play the fiddle. He was good at playing and singing anything. Them things he made up hisself and sung, I thought were good.

I couldn't hardly spin or weave or do anything around where he was. But I had to. I would put a dip of snuff in my mouth and go on and thole it the best I could. Sometimes I wished he would lose the use of that right leg. That was before I knowed. Having him forever patting the floor was enough to run a hog wild. And just seeing him setting there with his legs all sprawled out. All sprawled out and one foot a-going up and down, pickety peck—no matter what a body was trying to do.

Womenfolks didn't like to come here much because he set there no matter what nor who. None ever come save Teelie Edes. Teelie come to cut his hair for him and to get him to help her make some things. I didn't think it strange for her to come—not till Dona told me what she was.

In the summertime he set right there by the window. All summer long he just set there. That is the most coolest spot a body can find in the summertime. I never have seen a day when there wasn't a breeze blowing through there. Of course Barshia set right in the window and knocked the breeze off everybody else. Sprawled out in the only chair on the place that set good. That big one he made one day. The one I had such a time getting the willows for. The one he said he dreampt the pattern of.

When cold weather come on he would tell me to move his chair up in front of the fireplace. He would sprawl out there in the same way all winter long. There wasn't room for anybody else to get around save just at the sides. Every time anybody set down he would rare about them killing time. "Setting here hain't buying the baby a new dress nor paying for the one it's got," he would say. And he would keep on patting his foot. Whether he was piddling with anything or not.

Sometimes though he wanted us to pop popcorn for him, and we did. We never could pop it to suit him much. He said he just liked to see the white balls go up and down. It did seem like they went up and down just like his foot—fell right into the time. He made us crack walnuts and pick out the kernels for him. One time he got so mad at Amy because she didn't get the boy's britches out whole that he grabbed the hammer and hit her on the head with it. He knocked the breath plumb out of her. That was before she was yet four year old. I thought he had kilt her and it near scared the daylights out of me. Barshia didn't do a thing but set there and grin like a 'possum all the time I was working with her. Amy has still got the scar on her face. None of us ever told the truth about the scar. We always just said she bumped into the crib door over there.

Barshia said he liked to watch the blaze and see the sparks fly up. Sparks like the color of his hair. It was right pretty. And Barshia thought it was pretty—he was stuck on himself. Sometimes the smoke would puff out in the room and he would say, "Look at it. It comes right toward me. Smoke always follows beauty." I guess he was right pretty. But just setting there all day. Even when he was making anything. Then stretching out in bed at night. He laid so still you never could have told whether he was dead or alive if it hadn't been for that foot. It kept going.

Ad said Barshia was the thinkin'est boy in the world. And he could think. I know that too. He took it by spells. He could think of more pretty chairs and tables to be made out of willows and green hickories. But he never would budge out of his chair to get the things to make what he wanted. He always sent me out to get the kind of wood he needed. Of course, I did all the hard work in making them too—always looking to be hit over the head any minute. And Amy toted pegs and things that Barshia would call for. It's a wonder me and her are still alive. We made some mighty pretty tables and they come in right handy too. He fixed them hearts and horseshoes and things between the table legs.

When anybody come in, me and Amy always quit working on the things. Of course no womenfolks hardly ever come save Teelie. And sometimes Dona. Barshia would tell Teelie he was making them chairs and things while it was bad weather and there wasn't much he could do outside. Teelie always bragged about him making them so pretty. And she would get him to show her how. Said she liked to do things like that too.

I couldn't help but notice some things Teelie did. Even before Dona told me about her. Of course, I didn't think anything at the time. But I just noted. She watched his foot like a hawk. Her head would go up and down to keep time with it. And her eyes would sparkle like a toad's eyes. She looked like it done her good. I took note of it. I never did name it to anybody else. How her eyes looked, you know, that witchy stare.

Barshia could make nearly anything we needed that way. But we had to let him do it when the notion struck him. Nigh every time we asked him he would say he was too tired. "So tired," he would say. Or he would say he was busy right then. "As busy as a tick in a tar bucket," he would say. He made that washstand there. Hewed it out with his hands. And cut out that place there in the shape of a rooster. Then filled the place in with red cedar. It is a handy old washstand. And that red rooster setting up there on the drawer. Any kind of bird or varmint he could carve out of wood. Made walking sticks and carved all kinds of heads on the handle ends of them.

And them monkeys. He made them for all the girls that asked him to. He would make things like that for girls. And chains made out of little fine twigs, all lapped around and fancied up. He would do that, but he wouldn't talk to a girl hardly at all. Of course, none of them wanted him to. Teelie was the only woman I ever saw him talk to much. He would talk to her. And sing for her. She said she liked to hear him sing. He would sing the songs he made up hisself. Teelie would keep time and watch his foot.

I wish Dona had told me sooner. For a long while after I married Ad I thought Barshia mighty queer. Right from the first I took note of it. For a long time I wanted to ask somebody about it. But I never could bring myself to name it to Teelie. For Teelie was counted queer too. But one day Dona Fawver come and spent the day with us. She helped me get dinner. And I named something about Teelie a-coming to see Barshia and cutting his hair for him. Dona asked me if I ever feared Teelie. Some folks talked, she said, about what Teelie did—things a witch would do.

Then she lit in on Barshia. I didn't see any link between them. But she switched from one to tother. I was glad to hear anything I could. I wish she had talked before. She told me about how Barshia's ma had raised him up to think he was something on a stick, and how she had learnt him to think he was too pretty to work. That was the reason he had got so he didn't want to move. He had got used to setting there and having other folks wait on him like he was a king.

That was the reason he was so everlasting hateful and always poking fun at other folks. His ma had learnt him to think he was better than anybody else. I guess that is the reason he always made fun of me and Amy when we tried to sing. He was always throwing it up to Amy about being so ugly she had to whip her face before she could go to sleep. Every little thing she did he would call her as awkward as a blind buzzard. From the time she was big enough to know what he meant he fussed at her that way.

And Barshia was always talking about his red hair. Everybody said they thought he was right pretty. Pretty as a speckled pup, some said. He did look all right. But I never could think about that. Not with that foot a-going. Up and down.

He was fat as a mud ball, you know. Never did anything to sweat the fat off. Just setting there. His skin, it was white as a strawberry blossom. Some folks said he looked like he had the hant bleach. He was afeared a little dirt would get on him. Always hollering for me or Amy to bring some water and wash his face for him. It seemed like a blue million times a day we washed him. He wanted us to keep him clean as a pin—shirts and everything. And he was foreverlasting fussing about us not keeping the house clean.

The house got to leaking like a sifter. There wasn't a place in it where it didn't leak. Not a spot big enough to keep a bed in. Every time I said anything about splitting the boards to patch it with, Barshia would argue there wasn't any use because it wouldn't be but a short while till he would have us a new house put up. He said he had it in mind to build a fine one. Ad, he acted like he thought it was so. He would talk about it. Barshia said he had it all planned out in his mind and he was going to cut the logs as soon as he got rested. He said he was tired, so tired, he said, from working all the summer long, and he needed a little rest before he started in on something like that. That is what he said in the fall. Every time me or Amy either one spoke a word he would tell us to shut up because we were bothering his thinking about the new house. And that foot.

Dona kept on telling me things by the littles. Every time I would see her. She knowed Ad's first old woman well, and had seen all the youngons grow up. Said Barshia hadn't always been like he was now. But said he was wild as a buck when he was younger. Said when he was born he didn't weigh but two pound. And said Marthy—Marthy was the name of Ad's first old woman—said Marthy like to have died when Barshia come. He was the first youngon, and she wasn't quite fourteen year old yet. Said Ad had kicked and cussed her about so much it wasn't any wonder she had a hard time. He wouldn't go after Marthy's ma to help get Barshia born, Ad wouldn't. Just went after Teelie Edes. That is all he would do. Said he wasn't going to have Marthy's ma around him. Claimed it was easier for Teelie to come anyhow—all her youngons being dead, and her living over there in that old place by herself. That was before I started being Granny-woman so much.

It was on the last night of April Barshia was born. A rainy, sloppy night, Dona said. She heard somebody pass by her house on horseback a little before midnight and she just allowed it was Ad. Said she had a feeling everything wasn't going off all right, and something told her she ought to go. So she got up out of bed and went right over there.

Said it was a good thing she did too. For it was a long span of time before Ad got back. He come by himself and walking. Ad said Teelie thought there wouldn't be any use in coming till nigh daylight, because a woman never was ready when she thought she was. Teelie sent word for Marthy to lay still and she would be there in plenty of time. So Ad left Old Maud for her to ride when she got ready to come and he footed it on back. Dona said, sure enough, along a short span after chicken crow, Teelie come riding up to the porch on Old Maud. They got Barshia born about the crack of day. Dona said she was scared to death. Marthy laid there for twenty-one days just as black in the face as a Melungeon. Folks thought she would die, sure as the Lord. But Teelie waited on her, and she got all right.

Barshia growed off all right too, Dona said. Teelie brought her cow over there and left it so Ad and Marthy could have milk to feed him on. You see, they had to raise Barshia on a bottle because Marthy didn't give any milk. She laid there them twenty-one days without knowing she had a baby. Ad went and got one of them old blowzy Goolen girls to do the work while

Marthy was in bed. And then he slept with her all the time. Right there in the room where Marthy was. Dona said he took Marthy's chickens to the store and sold them to get that old huzzy clothes.

Dona said Teelie was mighty good to Marthy. She helped out a lot. She just about stood on the edge of Marthy's grave and kept Marthy pushed out. She went every day. She set and stared at that Goolen girl till the girl got scared and upped and went home. The old Goolen girl caught up Old Maud and went riding her off. Left word that she would turn the horse loose when she got home and let her come on back by herself. But before she got out of sight of the house Old Maud got scared at something and throwed her off. Teelie said right then she always liked Old Maud and that made her like her better.

When Barshia was a youngon, folks told Marthy he couldn't live. Everybody save Teelie. And Teelie always said he would live longer than Marthy. Teelie tried to get Marthy not to give in to him so much. Told her it was going to be the ruination of him. Of course Marthy never paid any attention to Teelie. Nobody did.

Marthy never did make Barshia mind anything she said. He just run the whole place. Dona said he was so tiny when he was a baby that Marthy had to nurse him on a pillow to know she had anything in her lap. She worried all the time about how she was going to live without him when he died. Even after he got to be a great big hulk of a boy she worried about him. But Dona said she believed Teelie got mad at Barshia the day she told him not to kill that toad frog and he went on and did it anyhow. He was three year old then. And Teelie was still letting her cow stay over there. Out there in the yard, right in front of Teelie, Barshia killed a toad frog. The cow started giving bloody milk, of course, and got so bad they had to kill her. Marthy's ma give them another cow.

Dona said Barshia was worst when he was about fifteen year old. That was when he went to running after whores. The same ones Ad run after—only he was worse than Ad. He spent everything he could get his hands on. Of course he couldn't get his hands on much. He borrowed every cent he could from everybody that would loan him anything. Sometimes he would come in drunk and beat Marthy like whipping a cow. Ad would take up for him. Always, Dona said. Ad would say he was the best youngon he had.

Barshia and Ad got together and sold off Marthy's last chicken, and the last cow. There wasn't anything a body could say to Barshia that would do him any good. When a body tried to tell him anything he would get mad and cuss a blue streak. Nigh everybody was afeared of him. Nigh everybody save Teelie. She would talk right straight to him sometimes.

Dona said folks give him the name of being one that would fight a circle saw. Everybody looked on him as having sense enough too, if he would just use it. He could tell other folks how to do anything. But even back then he never would do anything himself. He never walked anywhere either. Always rode Old Maud. Everybody talked about it being a shame the way he run that horse. Teelie would stand and stare at him every time she seed him running her that way. He made Maud come and stick her head out the door for him to put the bridle on her. He would beat her and try to make her get down on her knees for him to get on. Teelie always said he tried to make Old Maud have more sense than he had.

Every time he got on Old Maud he would just lay the lash to her. The more she run the more he whipped her. He wore a spur on his right heel, and kept that foot going up and down all the time to spur Old Maud. His foot went up and down, rolling that spur wheel into Old Maud's side. He would take boys on behind him. Sometimes as many as four would ride her. Along nigh Christmas time he got some firecrackers and would light them and lay them between Old Maud's ears. She was always afeared of loud noises.

But finally, one day, he run her all the way from home to Del Rio, and she dropped over dead—right in front of the store porch. Barshia burnt dried grass under her after she was dead, trying to make her get up. Teelie was there that day with a basket of eggs and she told him not to burn that grass under Maud. But he went right on, and set his foot up on her to stick that spur in her. Dona said she had heard several folks name it about how Teelie watched Barshia's foot as it went up and down sticking the spur into Old Maud's side.

Dona said she never had named it to another living soul, but she seed Teelie pull off her dress one time and there was a brown spot on her left breast in the shape of a frog. That is always a sure witch sign. I don't know. But if Teelie ever dies I am going to help lay her out. I want to know for sure. But Marthy got Bob Gollahon to take his team of mules and drag Old Maud in home. She skinned her and kept the hide for a keepsake. She kept it propped up in the stable. And when Ad moved over here he brought it along with him.

After that, Barshia managed somehow to get another horse. Bought it on credit. He run it all the time, till Delley Sample had to take the horse back because Barshia never did pay for it. Then Barshia tried to make Marthy borrow enough money to buy him another horse. And he tried to borrow other folks' horses to ride places. But, of course, nobody would let him have one. He throwed it up to Marthy that she didn't try to get things for him. But said someday he would have a horse finer than anybody in the country and they would all want to borrow hisn.

Dona said that was the way he did up till he was seventeen years old. Carried on that way for nigh three years, you see. Then when he didn't have anything to spend it got so nobody would have anything to do with him. There wasn't much left for him to do save to stay at home. Marthy never would so much as let him turn over his hands to do a solitary thing. She never would let him set his feet on the ground in wet weather for fear it would hurt him.

All Marthy could talk about was how pretty Barshia was. She wanted him right there in the room to do the talking no matter who come. She would brag about him saying such funny things. Dona said everybody did think he was plumb pretty back then before he sprung out and got so fat. Red hair with a big wave in it, blue eyes. That fair skin, white as a lily. And his teeth too. I guess I would have thought him pretty if I could have ever looked at anything save that pattety foot. Me and Amy catered to him like Marthy had done, and washed his face every time he told us to. He always had us wash his hair in egg. That made it curly and shiny, he said. I reckon it did. Something did. He said hair needed working just like plants did, so he made us scratch his head for him every day. Me or Amy one.

But Dona said it was caused from the way Marthy let him do—that pride and laziness was. That foot—it didn't go up and down. Not till Teelie saw him kill Old Maud. She said Teelie liked Old Maud. And, more than that, Barshia killed that toad frog. I don't know. I never have named it to anybody else. Me and Dona talks. Maybe too much.

For the most part I let Barshia alone and didn't pay any more attention to his fussing than to a little dust in the sunshine. But right there toward the last—for them last two weeks. It all come about so fast and yet so slow. He was setting there one day, stone-still, you know, save for his right foot. It hadn't been going up and down any faster—just the same. All the morning he set there like his mind was galavanting away off somewhere. A little while before dinner he told Amy to fetch him the Bible book. That's how it all started. He said he could understand the Bible better than a preacher could. He could too. But when he told what he had been reading about, he always fixed it up and told it to suit his own mind. He didn't ever tell a thing like it was in the Bible. Never.

Soon that evening Teelie come. Before we got dinner over. I was glad to have her come. Her and Barshia made things together, and me and Army got to rest from being bossed about and dogging for him. For a short span, we did. That evening—it was a pretty evening—the sun and robins and everything. Everything just budding out. Teelie was cutting Barshia's hair for him again. She said she liked to cut that hair. I took note that she put some in her apron pocket.

Barshia started telling her them stories he had been reading in the Bible. Told her some of them were good stories—the one about Jesus Christ himself. How he was buried by some trashy folks, you know. And how, after they stuck him down into the grave, he riz up and up and up—plumb up to Heaven. Teelie, she said she didn't believe them tales much. She believed they were something somebody made up on the Lord. So she told some that she liked better. Teelie had a good memory and she knowed lots of things. She clipped the hair and he patted his foot and she nodded her head and talked. Clip-clip, pat-pat, you know. I set and took it all in—all I could.

Teelie told the tale about the man that made the flying horse—the same old tale. The one Ma used to tell to me. How he flew right past his slow-pokey brothers, into the rich girl's window—and won the pretty fair lady. And a pot of gold too, of course. Always they won money with the girl. The same old story. But Teelie, she put more to it. She knowed a man—Old Bogus Snyder was his name. A man that might nigh made a flying horse. But died before he got it done. She said she never did see the horse but she had seen Bogus.

Barshia, he just set there. He blinked and blinked like a toad frog in a hail storm. Teelie watched his foot, and kept her head going up and down with it. Up and down. That owlish grin on her face. Barshia seemed not to want to speak e'er a word. She didn't try to get him to.

She stayed till late that evening. Said there was something she wanted Barshia to help her make. They worked on it. But I could see Barshia's mind wasn't so much on what he was doing. She wanted him to cut her the shape of a horse out of cedar. Said she wanted something pretty to set on her center table. He helped her all that evening, making it. It was right pretty too, I thought. Before she started she asked me to loan her some beeswax. Said she needed some. Amy went and got it for her—a right smart dab. She asked Barshia if it was soft enough to work into anything. He took it in his hands and squez it. She nodded her head up and down with his foot. That was to get him to touch the wax, I guess. I guess it was.

But that night we couldn't get Barshia to go to bed at all. He said he was going to set up and think. Think and plan, you know. Ad said about the new house, he guessed. But I didn't think it was any house. Barshia set all the next morning. Set and moved that foot up and down. Every time I looked at him I thought I could see the picture of a horse in his eyes. I guess I just thought that because I had a hankering. A while before dinner he hollered for Amy to come there. Right then I knowed what was up. Or thought I did. And that was what it was.

Me and Amy went up on Sals King Mountain and I cut the things that evening. The kind of little saplings and things he told us to. We toted them up to the woodpile. He said he was going to bow out some little limbs like ribs and make a sort of frame of a horse, and then stretch Old Maud's hide over it. That is what he did. He clumb up on top of the fruit-drying kiln. Said he could have a good start from up there.

Me and Amy worked on that horse. Amy toted things and run after things till I feared she would stop growing. We took Barshia's cussings and beatings. He would hit us with everwhat he had in his hands when he got mad because we didn't do things to suit him. We had two 'possum hides there that Barshia took to make the wings out of. Fixed them, you know, sort of like a kite. So the air could suck up under them. I sort of thought it a crazy stunt. But then I had seen so much. I never was quite sure what to think. A body never knows, you know, with folks like that, just what might happen. It did, of course.

Ad, he didn't say a word while Barshia was working on it. Didn't give it much heed. Nobody didn't pass through here during them two weeks. So just Barshia and me and Amy knowed much about it. We worked and worked. Me or Amy one had to be right there on the ground to take things up the ladder to him. Always we had to be there—one of us. To take him things. To help him saw and hammer and nail and cut and measure and measure. We never did know when he was going into one of them mad fits and knock us off. He never stopped that foot. He set up there in that chair and kept his foot going up and down. When I was nailing I would fall into the time he kept with that right foot——pit-pat, bang-bang, crack-crack. And sawing with the handsaw, pit-pat, push-pull, see-saw. Teelie she come and helped sometimes. She nodded her head with his foot and grinned—like an owl. That grin.

Till finally he got it made. It looked queer. Bent willow limbs for ribs. Hickory legs with knots for knees. But it did look like a horse's bones. And a pedal on its right side. A pedal so that when it worked up and down the wings would flop-flop, you know, up and down. And that would make the horse fly through the air.

Ad, he still didn't pay it any heed. Just me and Army. We seed it all. Rainy days we worked right on. Then he sent us to the barn to bring Old Maud's skin. We unripped it down the belly where it was sewed. We clawed the straw stuffing out. I hated to. I thought of Marthy—how she would feel—and somehow, of Teelie too.

Teelie, she come that very evening—just as we got the hide stretched over the frame. That stiff dry hide. But it fit all right. Barshia could measure things—just with his eyes. He was good. At that, he was. It looked right well. We sewed the hide back together down the throat and down the belly. Twine strings through them gashes in Old Maud. Teelie, she grinned when we split a place in the hide for that pedal to stick out. And them kite-like wings. Horsehide and 'possum hide. 'Possumhide wings. It looked all right. Barshia made me pull out the top riddle in the kiln. It slanted down. And lift the horse out on it. I did. I feared it might slide off if the wind should blow or if anything jarred it.

Barshia set there and looked at it. Teelie watched his foot and her head went up and down with it. She took hold of the pedal—moved it just a smidgin and the wings begun to move too.

The next day—it was Sunday—Ad and the boys went galavanting off somewhere. I don't know where. Me and the girls were by ourselves with Barshia. And even Amy wasn't big enough to help much. She was company though, and generally I was pacified when she was with me. But that day

I felt different—somehow, I did. A little wren flew through the house that morning. I looked at Amy and she looked back at me.

All that morning Barshia kept us busy. His foot kept on—up and down. He talked to the time of it. He was going to Heaven, he said. Going to fly to Heaven. God was calling him home, and he sung "To See the Shining Angels," and "Don't You Want to Go?"

The primping he did. We nearly wore our legs off waiting on him. Made us wash and scrub him up good, head and all. In that soap that we made and scented up with horse-mint leaves. Said he wanted to be clean when first the angels seed him. Said he would marry one of them. One with yellow curls. He liked yellow hair, he said. Next to red it was the prettiest. His own hair did look pretty that morning. Plumb pretty—like a star, or like the sun almost. It shined and was so fluffy.

He cleaned his teeth and had Amy clean his teeth and had me clean his teeth. Till he wore out all the beggar-louse-root toothbrushes Amy had. He told her to go get some more. But it was so early in the spring. They weren't big enough yet. I told him so. "Borrow some," he said. "Go, borrow some for me. From Teelie. She keeps them all the time. Enough for the whole country." Amy went. It was a right fur piece for a youngon to go.

It was after midday when she got back. I had done took Barshia's dinner to him. She give him the toothbrushes and he started cleaning his teeth again. Rubbed them up and down as his foot went up and down.

Me and Amy set down to eat. She looked at me. I looked at her. And then she talked. Like youngons will, you know. About what Teelie had in them shelves where she kept her toothbrushes. Thorns and leaves and everything. Said that little wooden horse Barshia whittled out was laying on the floor. A little beeswax man was fastened on to it. A man made out of old, dirty-looking beeswax. His head was broke off and laying there, made out of clean-looking, new beeswax, the head, with hair stuck on it—Barshia's hair. A thorn was stuck through the man's right foot, Amy said. Said she took note of it. I looked at her. I don't reckon she was old enough to know. But she did look like she was thinking about something strange.

After dinner, Barshia set there in his chair for a short while. Me and Amy set there in the chair looking at one another and at his foot. It went up and down till I thought I couldn't thole it any longer—e'er a bit longer. I felt pity for him too. But somehow, I got to thinking good of Teelie. I hadn't before.

Barshia got up and went to the door. He turned around. In the door, he turned around. Said for us to tell Ad and them where he had gone. He was tired of this old world, he said. And he was tired of living and working. Said he wanted to go some place where he wouldn't have to even think.

All along I had halfway thought that it wouldn't happen. That maybe he was just talking to hear his head roar. That was what Ad had said. When I seed him in the door I knowed he wasn't just talking. Standing there in the door, bearing his whole weight on his left foot, I knowed he wasn't. That right foot still going up and down. I had pity for him. In a way. And yet. Then he went out.

I watched out the little window door. I could see from there. I told Amy not to look. He clumb up the ladder. I had made it out of poles so I could get to the top riddle easy. He clumb up the ladder slow. Like a caterpillar climbing. Every time he set his right foot on the poles of that ladder, his toes went up and down. I set there and looked. He got to the top.

I saw it all. He got on Old Maud. That is what me and Amy had been calling it. He got on and tied his left foot to Old Maud's side. Pulled the string through the holes he had made in her. He fastened on his spur—the same old spur. That thing. Them sharp points in the wheel. He started working the pedal up and down.

Them 'possum-hide wings, they begun to flop. Sure enough they could flop. Up and down. Old Maud, she begun to move. Just sliding a little, I thought. But she got her front feet to the edge. I held my breath. He kept working the pedal, you know. It looked like Old Maud went straight up. Up into the air. And them wings a-flopping. "Amy, it is going up. It is," I yelled. I shut my eyes. I opened them again.

I saw it going down. The wings still flopping. But going down. Head foremost down. Down to the ground on its head. His head too, I guess. I didn't look at him. I didn't want to see it all. "Amy, he's kilt," I said. "Ad ought to have knowed."

Amy went twirling around like a leaf in a whirlwind. I did too. We got to him. He was laying there with his head all bent down under his chest. Old Maud's was too. The sticks in her neck were broke. I didn't look at Barshia's head so much. I looked at his foot. "He hain't kilt," I said. We untied him from Old Maud. Him and Old Maud.

Barshia was heavy. You know how fat he was. I couldn't tote him in. He didn't say a word. Not e'er a word, he didn't. Amy helped all she could and we managed to drag him to the house and get him in. I didn't listen to see if he was breathing. I watched that foot. Up and down. Just like Old Maud, I thought. We stretched him out on the bed. I saw his neck was limber. Limber as a dish clout. "I'll splinter it up," I said. But something told me there wasn't any use. Not in that.

I took a-hold of his neck and watched his foot. Always that. His head rolled over a little. He looked at me. "I won't be so tired. So tired," he said. Keeping time.

I stood and watched him—like one dog watching another die. He laid there like common—stone-still save for that foot. Then it stopped.

Study Guides

Rare is the critic who would argue that this tale of Barshia and his flying horse fails to qualify as a modern short story. The development in plot, characterization, and theme has the technical competence that we have already observed in other stories. At the same time it is well to point out that this is also a fantasy which incorporates many of the characteristics of the ancient tale from oral tradition. The unlikely chance that a horse may fly—but somehow does—obviously fired the imagination of the Greeks: the persistent story of Pegasus proves it. Many centuries after the first flight of Pegasus, Chaucer wrote about a "hors of bras" in "The Squire's Tale" and explained to his readers how to ride horseback into space. So from Icarus in Crete to the witches of Salem, we know that man has tried to soar beyond his terrestrial bounds. We know too that cows, by the good authority of Mother Goose, have been jumping over the moon for longer than any astronaut can remember.

Miss Haun has here adapted some of the rich materials of folk literature for a modern short story; in bringing the fantasy up to date she has reminded us again that the incredible can somehow appear real and quite credible when presented by a gifted storyteller. Like Coleridge before her and the traditional bard or "maker" before him, she has calculated the reader's inclination toward a "willing suspension of disbelief" which induces the mythical world of "poetic faith." We can come to believe as the narrator believes if his views of the world grow naturally and logically out of the given premises of character, time, and place. If the narrator is made to seem real, if the story has verisimilitude beyond its stated premise, we are led to accept the narrator's account of events which are otherwise fantastic. In this story the granny-woman follows closely the tale-and-ballad tradition from which all "literary" art has developed.

The narrator speaks simply and naturally in the mountain dialect of Cocke County, Tennessee. Her phrases are peppered and spiced with folk metaphors and pithy proverbs. As a midwife she comes by the facts of life firsthand; she voices the folk customs of the region, including long-held beliefs and superstitions; gradually she comes to believe in the witchcraft of Teelie Edes and thus accounts for the hex that caused Barshia's right foot to move up and down, up and down, after Teelie saw him kill the frog and ride Old Maud to her death. Barshia cannot stop his cursed foot or calm the terrible tick that came with the hex. A spell is upon him; he *must* indulge in dreams, figments, and conspiracies with a witch. The granny-woman "senses" the inevitability of his fate when she learns from Amy about the effigy at Teelie's house—the beeswax figure with a thorn stuck in its foot and the severed head at its side. She is certain of Barshia's doom after the wren flies through the house and foretells his death. All the "signs" are "sure."

As troublesome to her as Barshia is, the granny-woman maintains a generous sympathy for him and patiently puts up with his contrary ways. Perhaps her sympathy, compounded with pity, is universal in what it implies: the man who dares to be different in the pursuit of his vision, who throws defiance at the laws of nature, ventures into space, and reaches out beyond the limits of his grasp is watched with awe and a certain admiration. He does not belong to the race of ordinary men; there is a terrifying mark on him—a twitching foot, a glittering eye, the "hant bleach" on his face. So Barshia is at once a rascal, an artist, and a kind of fallen hero. And so was Satan. Barshia wants to fly to Heaven "To See the Shining Angels." His foot yearns to put the spur to his Pegasus, and his ingenuity starts him for one brief moment on his way. "Amy, it is going up. It is," the granny-woman cries. And the foot keeps moving even after the breath of life vanishes and Barshia "laid there like common." Even so, we should not forget that, however briefly, "the horse he made, it flew."

This tale of one man's pride and vaunting ego—however remote in setting and incredible in terms of the literal world—is nevertheless worth the telling. It commands our attention in the same way that we respond to myth: we learn to see the hard truths of the real world through fantasy and illusion and perhaps a bit of literary witchcraft.

The following are suggestions for further study:

1. Consider Barshia as a type of Romantic artist who sees visions beyond the realm of the mundane world; he is "strange" and somewhat Satanic; he dreams impossibilities; he is hagridden with egotism. Like Coleridge's Ancient Mariner and Keats's Knight-at-arms in "La Belle Dame Sans Merci," the artist is cursed with a vision he cannot forget. Explore the character of Barshia in these terms. Cite the details that would lend support to such an interpretation. What would Teelie represent in this view? How is the Pegasus myth related? Is the Daedalus-Icarus tale suggested? What relationship of the artist to his art is inferred by Barshia's horse's flight? By its falling?

2. Can the events in the story be explained "scientifically"—by psychology and logical reason? Is Barshia's final act a logical development of those character traits given him from the first? How much of Teelie's witchery is merely the power of suggestion working on a susceptible and neurotic mind? Can the horse's flying be explained by physics? If the story has a scientific explanation, how does Teelie fit into the action?

3. Compare and contrast the "scientific" and the "supernatural" elements of this story with those of "The Rocking-Horse Winner." If Barshia's creativity may be called the working of intuition, how are the themes of the two stories similar? Why are both of the protagonists exhausted and finally ruined? How responsible is each for his own destruction?

4. Make a study of the folk beliefs, superstitions, and figures of speech in this story. How do they contribute to the total meaning?

D. H. LAWRENCE

(1885–1930)

The Rocking-Horse Winner

There was a woman who was beautiful, who started with all the advantages, yet she had no luck. She married for love, and the love turned to dust. She had bonny children, yet she felt they had been thrust upon her, and she could not love them. They looked at her coldly, as if they were finding fault with her. And hurriedly she felt she must cover up some fault in herself. Yet what it was that she must cover up she never knew. Nevertheless, when her children were present, she always felt the centre of her heart go hard. This troubled her, and in her manner she was all the more gentle and anxious for her children, as if she loved them very much. Only she herself knew that at the centre of her heart was a hard little place that could not feel love, no, not for anybody. Everybody else said of her: "She is such a good mother. She adores her children." Only she herself, and her children themselves, knew it was not so. They read it in each other's eyes.

There were a boy and two little girls. They lived in a pleasant house, with a garden, and they had discreet servants, and felt themselves superior to anyone in the neighbourhood.

Although they lived in style, they felt always an anxiety in the house. There was never enough money. The mother had a small income, and the father had a small income, but not nearly enough for the social position which they had to keep up. The father went into town to some office. But though he had good prospects, these prospects never materialized. There was always the grinding sense of the shortage of money, though the style was always kept up.

At last the mother said: "I will see if I can't make something." But she did not know where to begin. She racked her brains, and tried this thing and the other, but could not find anything successful. The failure made deep lines come into her face. Her children were growing up, they would have to go to school. There must be more money, there must be more money. The father, who was always very handsome and expensive in his tastes, seemed as if he never would be able to do anything worth doing. And the mother, who had a great belief in herself, did not succeed any better, and her tastes were just as expensive.

And so the house came to be haunted by the unspoken phrase: There must be more money! There must be more money! The children could hear it all the time, though nobody said it aloud. They heard it at Christmas, when the expensive and splendid toys filled the nursery. Behind the shining modern rocking horse, behind the smart doll's-house, a voice would start whispering: "There must be more money! There must be more money!" And the children would stop playing, to listen for a moment. They would look into each other's eyes, to see if they had all heard. And each one saw in the eyes of the other two that they too had heard. "There must be more money! There must be more money!"

It came whispering from the springs of the still-swaying rocking horse, and even the horse, bending his wooden, champing head, heard it. The big doll, sitting so pink and smirking in her new pram, could hear it quite plainly, and seemed to be smirking all the more self-consciously because of it. The foolish puppy, too, that took the place of the Teddy bear, he was looking so extraordinarily foolish for no other reason but that he heard the secret whisper all over the house: "There must be more money!"

Yet nobody ever said it aloud. The whisper was everywhere, and therefore no one spoke it. Just as no one ever says: "We are breathing!" in spite of the fact that breath is coming and going all the time.

"Mother," said the boy Paul one day, "why don't we keep a car of our own? Why do we always use uncle's, or else a taxi?"

"Because we're the poor members of the family," said the mother.

"But why are we, mother?"

"Well—I suppose," she said slowly and bitterly, "it's because your father has no luck."

The boy was silent for some time.

"Is luck money, mother?" he asked, rather timidly.

"No, Paul. Not quite. It's what causes you to have money."

"Oh!" said Paul vaguely. "I thought when Uncle Oscar said filthy lucker, it meant money."

"Filthy lucre does mean money," said the mother. "But it's lucre, not luck."

"Oh!" said the boy. "Then what is luck, mother?"

"It's what causes you to have money. If you're lucky you have money. That's why it's better to be born lucky than rich. If you're rich, you may lose your money. But if you're lucky, you will always get more money."

"Oh! Will you? And is father not lucky?"

"Very unlucky, I should say," she said bitterly.

The boy watched her with unsure eyes.

"Why?" he asked.

"I don't know. Nobody ever knows why one person is lucky and another unlucky."

"Don't they? Nobody at all? Does nobody know?"

"Perhaps God. But He never tells."

"He ought to, then. And aren't you lucky either, mother?"

"I can't be, if I married an unlucky husband."

"But by yourself, aren't you?"

"I used to think I was, before I married. Now I think I am very unlucky indeed."

"Why?"

"Well—never mind! Perhaps I'm not really," she said.

The child looked at her, to see if she meant it. But he saw, by the lines of her mouth, that she was only trying to hide something from him.

"Well, anyhow," he said stoutly, "I'm a lucky person."

"Why?" said his mother, with a sudden laugh.

He stared at her. He didn't even know why he had said it.

"God told me," he asserted, brazening it out.

"I hope He did, dear!" she said, again with a laugh, but rather bitter.

"He did, mother!"

"Excellent!" said the mother, using one of her husband's exclamations.

The boy saw she did not believe him; or, rather, that she paid no attention to his assertion. This angered him somewhat, and made him want to compel her attention.

He went off by himself, vaguely, in a childish way, seeking for the clue to "luck." Absorbed, taking no heed of other people, he went about with a sort of stealth, seeking inwardly for luck. He wanted luck, he wanted it, he wanted it. When the two girls were playing dolls in the nursery, he would sit on his big rocking horse, charging madly into space, with a frenzy that made the little girls peer at him uneasily. Wildly the horse careered, the waving dark hair of the boy tossed, his eyes had a strange glare in them. The little girls dared not speak to him.

When he had ridden to the end of his mad little journey, he climbed down and stood in front of his rocking horse, staring fixedly into its lowered face. Its red mouth was slightly open, its big eye was wide and glassy-bright.

"Now!" he would silently command the snorting steed. "Now, take me to where there is luck! Now take me!"

And he would slash the horse on the neck with the little whip he had asked Uncle Oscar for. He knew the horse could take him to where there was luck, if only he forced it. So he would mount again, and start on his furious ride, hoping at last to get there. He knew he could get there.

"You'll break your horse, Paul!" said the nurse.

"He's always riding like that! I wish he'd leave off!" said his elder sister Joan.

But he only glared down on them in silence. Nurse gave him up. She could make nothing of him. Anyhow he was growing beyond her.

One day his mother and his Uncle Oscar came in when he was on one of his furious rides. He did not speak to them.

"Hallo, you young jockey! Riding a winner?" said his uncle.

"Aren't you growing too big for a rocking horse? You're not a very little boy any longer, you know," said his mother.

But Paul only gave a blue glare from his big, rather close-set eyes. He would speak to nobody when he was in full tilt. His mother watched him with an anxious expression on her face.

At last he suddenly stopped forcing his horse into the mechanical gallop, and slid down.

"Well, I got there!" he announced fiercely, his blue eyes still flaring, and his sturdy long legs straddling apart.

"Where did you get to?" asked his mother.

"Where I wanted to go," he flared back at her.

"That's right, son!" said Uncle Oscar. "Don't you stop till you get there. What's the horse's name?"

"He doesn't have a name," said the boy.

"Gets on without all right?" asked the uncle.

"Well, he has different names. He was called Sansovino last week."

"Sansovino, eh? Won the Ascot. How did you know his name?"

"He always talks about horse races with Bassett," said Joan.

The uncle was delighted to find that his small nephew was posted with all the racing news. Bassett, the young gardener, who had been wounded in the left foot in the war and had got his present job through Oscar Cresswell, whose batman he had been, was a perfect blade of the "turf." He lived in the racing events, and the small boy lived with him.

Oscar Cresswell got it all from Bassett.

"Master Paul comes and asks me, so I can't do more than tell him, sir," said Bassett, his face terribly serious, as if he were speaking of religious matters.

"And does he ever put anything on a horse he fancies?"

"Well—I don't want to give him away—he's a young sport, a fine sport, sir. Would you mind asking him yourself? He sort of takes a pleasure in it, and perhaps he'd feel I was giving him away, sir, if you don't mind."

Bassett was serious as a church.

The uncle went back to his nephew, and took him off for a ride in the car.

"Say, Paul, old man, do you ever put anything on a horse?" the uncle asked.

The boy watched the handsome man closely.

"Why, do you think I oughtn't to?" he parried.

"Not a bit of it! I thought perhaps you might give me a tip for the Lincoln."

The car sped on into the country, going down to Uncle Oscar's place in Hampshire.

"Honour bright?" said the nephew.

"Honour bright, son!" said the uncle.

"Well, then, Daffodil."

"Daffodil! I doubt it, sonny. What about Mirza?"

"I only know the winner," said the boy. "That's Daffodil."

"Daffodil, eh?"

There was a pause. Daffodil was an obscure horse comparatively.

"Uncle!"

"Yes, son?"

"You won't let it go any further, will you? I promised Bassett."

"Bassett be damned, old man! What's he got to do with it?"

"We're partners. We've been partners from the first. Uncle, he lent me my first five shillings, which I lost. I promised him, honour bright, it was only between me and him; only you gave me that ten-shilling note I started winning with, so I thought you were lucky. You won't let it go any further, will you?"

The boy gazed at his uncle from those big, hot, blue eyes, set rather close together. The uncle stirred and laughed uneasily.

"Right you are, son! I'll keep your tip private. Daffodil, eh? How much are you putting on him?"

"All except twenty pounds," said the boy. "I keep that in reserve."

The uncle thought it a good joke.

"You keep twenty pounds in reserve, do you, you young romancer? What are you betting, then?"

"I'm betting three hundred," said the boy gravely. "But it's between you and me, Uncle Oscar! Honour bright?"

The uncle burst into a roar of laughter.

"It's between you and me all right, you young Nat Gould," he said, laughing. "But where's your three hundred?"

"Bassett keeps it for me. We're partners."

"You are, are you! And what is Bassett putting on Daffodil?"

"He won't go quite as high as I do, I expect. Perhaps he'll go a hundred and fifty."

"What, pennies?" laughed the uncle.

"Pounds," said the child, with a surprised look at his uncle. "Bassett keeps a bigger reserve than I do."

Between wonder and amusement Uncle Oscar was silent. He pursued the matter no further, but he determined to take his nephew with him to the Lincoln races.

"Now, son," he said, "I'm putting twenty on Mirza, and I'll put five for you on any horse you fancy. What's your pick?"

"Daffodil, uncle."

"No, not the fiver on Daffodil!"

"I should if it was my own fiver," said the child.

"Good! Good! Right you are! A fiver for me and a fiver for you on Daffodil."

The child had never been to a race meeting before, and his eyes were blue fire. He pursed his mouth tight, and watched. A Frenchman just in front had put his money on Lancelot. Wild with excitement, he flayed his arms up and down, yelling "Lancelot! Lancelot!" in his French accent.

Daffodil came in first, Lancelot second, Mirza third. The child, flushed and with eyes blazing, was curiously serene. His uncle brought him four five-pound notes, four to one.

"What am I to do with these?" he cried, waving them before the boy's eyes.

"I suppose we'll talk to Bassett," said the boy. "I expect I have fifteen hundred now; and twenty in reserve; and this twenty."

His uncle studied him for some moments.

"Look here, son!" he said. "You're not serious about Bassett and that fifteen hundred, are you?"

"Yes, I am. But it's between you and me, uncle. Honour bright!"

"Honour bright all right, son! But I must talk to Bassett."

"If you'd like to be a partner, uncle, with Bassett and me, we could all be partners. Only, you'd have to promise, honour bright, uncle, not to let it go beyond us three. Bassett and I are lucky, and you must be lucky, because it was your ten shillings I started winning with. . . ."

Uncle Oscar took both Bassett and Paul into Richmond Park for an afternoon, and there they talked.

"It's like this, you see, sir," Bassett said. "Master Paul would get me talking about racing events, spinning yarns, you know, sir. And he was always keen on knowing if I'd made or if I'd lost. It's about a year since, now, that I put five shillings on Blush of Dawn for him—and we lost. Then the luck turned, with that ten shillings he had from you, that we put on Singhalese. And since that time, it's been pretty steady, all things considering. What do you say, Master Paul?"

"We're all right when we're sure," said Paul. "It's when we're not quite sure that we go down."

"Oh, but we're careful then," said Bassett.

"But when are you sure?" smiled Uncle Oscar.

"It's Master Paul, sir," said Bassett, in a secret, religious voice. "It's as if he had it from heaven. Like Daffodil, now, for the Lincoln. That was as sure as eggs."

"Did you put anything on Daffodil?" asked Oscar Cresswell.

"Yes, sir, I made my bit."

"And my nephew?"

Bassett was obstinately silent, looking at Paul.

"I made twelve hundred, didn't I, Bassett? I told uncle I was putting three hundred on Daffodil."

"That's right," said Bassett, nodding.

"But where's the money?" asked the uncle.

"I keep it safe locked up, sir. Master Paul he can have it any minute he likes to ask for it."

"What, fifteen hundred pounds?"

"And twenty! and forty, that is, with the twenty he made on the course."

"It's amazing!" said the uncle.

"If Master Paul offers you to be partners, sir, I would, if I were you; if you'll excuse me," said Bassett.

Oscar Cresswell thought about it.

"I'll see the money," he said.

They drove home again, and sure enough, Bassett came round to the garden-house with fifteen hundred pounds in notes. The twenty pounds reserve was left with Joe Glee, in the Turf Commission deposit.

"You see, it's all right, uncle, when I'm sure! Then we go strong, for all we're worth. Don't we, Bassett?"

"We do that, Master Paul."

"And when are you sure?" said the uncle, laughing.

"Oh, well, sometimes I'm absolutely sure, like about Daffodil," said the boy; "and sometimes I have an idea; and sometimes I haven't even an idea, have I, Bassett? Then we're careful, because we mostly go down."

"You do, do you! And when you're sure, like about Daffodil, what makes you sure, sonny?"

"Oh, well, I don't know," said the boy uneasily. "I'm sure, you know, uncle; that's all."

"It's as if he had it from heaven, sir," Bassett reiterated.

"I should say so!" said the uncle.

But he became a partner. And when the Leger was coming on, Paul was "sure" about Lively Spark, which was a quite inconsiderable horse. The boy insisted on putting a thousand on the horse, Bassett went for five hundred, and Oscar Cresswell two hundred. Lively Spark came in first, and the betting had been ten to one against him. Paul had made ten thousand.

"You see," he said, "I was absolutely sure of him."

Even Oscar Cresswell had cleared two thousand.

"Look here, son," he said, "this sort of thing makes me nervous."

"It needn't, uncle! Perhaps I shan't be sure again for a long time."

"But what are you going to do with your money?" asked the uncle.

"Of course," said the boy, "I started it for mother. She said she had no luck, because father is unlucky, so I thought if I was lucky, it might stop whispering."

"What might stop whispering?"

"Our house. I hate our house for whispering."

"What does it whisper?"

"Why—why"—the boy fidgeted—"why, I don't know. But it's always short of money, you know, uncle."

"I know it, son, I know it."

"You know people send mother writs, don't you, uncle?"

"I'm afraid I do," said the uncle.

"And then the house whispers, like people laughing at you behind your back. It's awful, that is! I thought if I was lucky. . . ."

"You might stop it," added the uncle.

The boy watched him with big blue eyes that had an uncanny cold fire in them, and he said never a word.

"Well, then!" said the uncle. "What are we doing?"

"I shouldn't like mother to know I was lucky," said the boy.

"Why not, son?"

"She'd stop me."

"I don't think she would."

"Oh!"—and the boy writhed in an odd way—"I don't want her to know, uncle."

"All right, son! We'll manage it without her knowing."

They managed it very easily. Paul, at the other's suggestion, handed over five thousand pounds to his uncle, who deposited it with the family lawyer, who was then to inform Paul's mother that a relative had put five thousand pounds into his hands, which sum was to be paid out a thousand pounds at a time, on the mother's birthday, for the next five years.

"So she'll have a birthday present of a thousand pounds for five successive years," said Uncle Oscar. "I hope it won't make it all the harder for her later."

Paul's mother had her birthday in November. The house had been "whispering" worse than ever lately, and, even in spite of his luck, Paul could not bear up against it. He was very anxious to see the effect of the birthday letter, telling his mother about the thousand pounds.

When there were no visitors, Paul now took his meals with his parents, as he was beyond the nursery control. His mother went into town nearly every day. She had discovered that she had an odd knack of sketching furs and dress materials, so she worked secretly in the studio of a friend who was the chief "artist" for the leading drapers. She drew the figures of ladies in furs and ladies in silk and sequins for the newspaper advertisements. This young woman artist earned several thousand pounds a year, but Paul's mother only made several hundreds, and she was again dissatisfied. She so wanted to be first in something, and she did not succeed, even in making sketches for drapery advertisements.

She was down to breakfast on the morning of her birthday. Paul watched her face as she read her letters. He knew the lawyer's letter. As his mother read it, her face hardened and became more expressionless. Then a cold, determined look came on her mouth. She hid the letter under the pile of others, and said not a word about it.

"Didn't you have anything nice in the post for your birthday, mother?" said Paul.

"Quite moderately nice," she said, her voice cold and absent.

She went away to town without saying more.

But in the afternoon Uncle Oscar appeared. He said Paul's mother had had a long interview with the lawyer, asking if the whole five thousand could be advanced at once, as she was in debt.

"What do you think, uncle?" said the boy.

"I leave it to you, son."

"Oh, let her have it, then! We can get some more with the other," said the boy.

"A bird in the hand is worth two in the bush, laddie!" said Uncle Oscar.

"But I'm sure to know for the Grand National; or the Lincolnshire; or else the Derby. I'm sure to know for one of them," said Paul.

So Uncle Oscar signed the agreement, and Paul's mother touched the whole five thousand. Then something very curious happened. The voices in the house suddenly went mad, like a chorus of frogs on a spring evening. There were certain new furnishings, and Paul had a tutor. He was really going to Eton, his father's school, in the following autumn. There were flowers in the winter, and a blossoming of the luxury Paul's mother had been used to. And yet the voices in the house, behind the sprays of mimosa and almond blossom, and from under the piles of iridescent cushions, simply trilled and screamed in a sort of ecstasy: "There must be more money! Oh-h-, there must be more money. Oh, now, now-w! Now-w-w—there must be more money!—more than ever! More than ever!"

It frightened Paul terribly. He studied away at his Latin and Greek with his tutors. But his intense hours were spent with Bassett. The Grand National had gone by: he had not "known," and had lost a hundred pounds. Summer was at hand. He was in agony for the Lincoln. But even for the Lincoln he didn't "know" and he lost fifty pounds. He became wild-eyed and strange, as if something were going to explode in him.

"Let it alone, son! Don't you bother about it!" urged Uncle Oscar. But it was as if the boy couldn't really hear what his uncle was saying.

"I've got to know for the Derby! I've got to know for the Derby!" the child reiterated, his big blue eyes blazing with a sort of madness.

His mother noticed how overwrought he was.

"You'd better go to the seaside. Wouldn't you like to go now to the seaside, instead of waiting? I think you'd better," she said, looking down at him anxiously, her heart curiously heavy because of him.

But the child lifted his uncanny blue eyes.

"I couldn't possibly go before the Derby, mother!" he said. "I couldn't possibly!"

"Why not?" she said, her voice becoming heavy when she was opposed. "Why not? You can still go from the seaside to see the Derby with your Uncle Oscar, if that's what you wish. No need for you to wait here. Besides, I think you care too much about these races. It's a bad sign. My family has been a gambling family, and you won't know till you grow up how much damage it has done. But it has done damage. I shall have to send Bassett away, and ask Uncle Oscar not to talk racing to you, unless you promise to be reasonable about it; go away to the seaside and forget it. You're all nerves!"

"I'll do what you like, mother, so long as you don't send me away till after the Derby," the boy said.

"Send you away from where? Just from this house?"

"Yes," he said, gazing at her.

"Why, you curious child, what makes you care about this house so much, suddenly? I never knew you loved it."

He gazed at her without speaking. He had a secret within a secret, something he had not divulged, even to Bassett or to his Uncle Oscar.

But his mother, after standing undecided and a little bit sullen for some moments, said:

"Very well, then! Don't go to the seaside till after the Derby, if you don't wish it. But promise me you won't let your nerves go to pieces. Promise you won't think so much about horse racing and events, as you call them!"

"Oh, no," said the boy casually. "I won't think much about them, mother. You needn't worry. I wouldn't worry, mother, if I were you."

"If you were me and I were you," said his mother, "I wonder what we should do!"

"But you know you needn't worry, mother, don't you?" the boy repeated.

"I should be awfully glad to know it," she said wearily.

"Oh, well, you can, you know. I mean, you ought to know you needn't worry," he insisted.

"Ought I? Then I'll see about it," she said.

Paul's secret of secrets was his wooden horse, that which had no name. Since he was emancipated from a nurse and a nursery-governess, he had had his rocking horse removed to his own bedroom at the top of the house.

"Surely, you're too big for a rocking horse!" his mother had remonstrated.

"Well, you see, mother, till I can have a real horse, I like to have some sort of animal about," had been his quaint answer.

"Do you feel he keeps you company?" she laughed.

"Oh, yes! He's very good, he always keeps me company, when I'm there," said Paul.

So the horse, rather shabby, stood in an arrested prance in the boy's bedroom.

The Derby was drawing near, and the boy grew more and more tense. He hardly heard what was spoken to him, he was very frail, and his eyes were really uncanny. His mother had sudden seizures of uneasiness about him. Sometimes, for half-an-hour, she would feel a sudden anxiety about him that was almost anguish. She wanted to rush to him at once, and know he was safe.

Two nights before the Derby, she was at a big party in town, when one of her rushes of anxiety about her boy, her first-born, gripped her heart till she could hardly speak. She fought with the feeling, might and main, for she believed in common sense. But it was too strong. She had to leave the dance and go downstairs to telephone to the country. The children's nursery-governess was terribly surprised and startled at being rung up in the night.

"Are the children all right, Miss Wilmot?"

"Oh, yes, they are quite all right."

"Master Paul? Is he all right?"

"He went to bed as right as a trivet. Shall I run up and look at him?"

"No," said Paul's mother reluctantly. "No! Don't trouble. It's all right. Don't sit up. We shall be home fairly soon." She did not want her son's privacy intruded upon.

"Very good," said the governess.

It was about one o'clock when Paul's mother and father drove up to their house. All was still. Paul's mother went to her room and slipped off her white fur coat. She had told her maid not to wait up for her. She heard her husband downstairs, mixing a whisky-and-soda.

And then, because of the strange anxiety at her heart, she stole upstairs to her son's room. Noiselessly she went along the upper corridor. Was there a faint noise? What was it?

She stood, with arrested muscles, outside his door, listening. There was a strange, heavy, and yet not loud noise. Her heart stood still. It was a soundless noise, yet rushing and powerful. Something huge, in violent, hushed motion. What was it? What in God's name was it? She ought to know. She felt that she knew the noise. She knew what it was.

Yet she could not place it. She couldn't say what it was. And on and on it went, like a madness.

Softly, frozen with anxiety and fear, she turned the door handle.

The room was dark. Yet in the space near the window, she heard and saw something plunging to and fro. She gazed in fear and amazement.

Then suddenly she switched on the light, and saw her son, in his green pyjamas, madly surging on the rocking horse. The blaze of light suddenly lit him up, as he urged the wooden horse, and lit her up, as she stood, blonde, in her dress of pale green and crystal, in the doorway.

"Paul!" she cried. "Whatever are you doing?"

"It's Malabar!" he screamed, in a powerful, strange voice. "It's Malabar."

His eyes blazed at her for one strange and senseless second, as he ceased urging his wooden horse. Then he fell with a crash to the ground, and she, all her tormented motherhood flooding upon her, rushed to gather him up.

But he was unconscious, and unconscious he remained, with some brain-fever. He talked and tossed, and his mother sat stonily by his side.

"Malabar! It's Malabar! Bassett, Bassett, I know! It's Malabar!"

So the child cried, trying to get up and urge the rocking horse that gave him his inspiration.

"What does he mean by Malabar?" asked the heart-frozen mother.

"I don't know," said the father stonily.

"What does he mean by Malabar?" she asked her brother Oscar.

"It's one of the horses running for the Derby," was the answer.

And, in spite of himself, Oscar Cresswell spoke to Bassett, and himself put a thousand on Malabar: at fourteen to one.

The third day of the illness was critical: they were waiting for a change. The boy, with his rather long, curly hair, was tossing ceaselessly on the pillow. He neither slept nor regained consciousness, and his eyes were like blue stones. His mother sat, feeling her heart had gone, turned actually into a stone.

In the evening, Oscar Cresswell did not come, but Bassett sent a message, saying could he come up for one moment, just one moment? Paul's mother was very angry at the intrusion, but on second thought she agreed. The boy was the same. Perhaps Bassett might bring him to consciousness.

The gardener, a shortish fellow with a little brown moustache, and sharp little brown eyes, tiptoed into the room, touched his imaginary cap to Paul's mother, and stole to the bedside, staring with glittering, smallish eyes, at the tossing, dying child.

"Master Paul!" he whispered. "Master Paul! Malabar come in first all right, a clean win. I did as you told me. You've made over seventy thousand pounds, you have; you've got over eighty thousand. Malabar came in all right, Master Paul."

"Malabar! Malabar! Did I say Malabar, mother? Did I say Malabar? Do you think I'm lucky, mother? I knew Malabar, didn't I? Over eighty thousand pounds! I call that lucky, don't you, mother? Over eighty thousand pounds! I knew, didn't I know I knew? Malabar came in all right. If I ride my horse till I'm sure, then I tell you, Bassett, you can go as high as you like. Did you go for all you were worth, Bassett?"

"I went a thousand on it, Master Paul."

"I never told you, mother, that if I can ride my horse, and get there, then I'm absolutely sure—oh, absolutely! Mother, did I ever tell you? I am lucky."

"No, you never did," said the mother.

But the boy died in the night.

And even as he lay dead, his mother heard her brother's voice saying to her: "My God, Hester, you're eighty-odd thousand to the good and a poor devil of a son to the bad. But, poor devil, poor devil, he's best gone out of a life where he rides his rocking horse to find a winner."

NATHANIEL HAWTHORNE

(*1804–1864*)

My Kinsman, Major Molineux

After the kings of Great Britain had assumed the right of appointing the colonial governors, the measures of the latter seldom met with the ready and general approbation which had been paid to those of their predecessors, under the original charters. The people looked with most jealous scrutiny to the exercise of power which did not emanate from themselves, and they usually rewarded their rulers with slender gratitude for the compliances by which, in softening their instructions from beyond the sea, they had incurred the reprehension of those who gave them. The annals of Massachusetts Bay will inform us, that of six governors in the space of about forty years from the surrender of the old charter, under James II, two were imprisoned by a popular insurrection; a third, as Hutchinson inclines to believe, was driven from the province by the whizzing of a musket-ball; a fourth, in the opinion of the same historian, was hastened to his grave by continual bickerings with the House of Representatives; and the remaining two, as well as their successors, till the Revolution, were favored with few and brief intervals of peaceful sway. The inferior members of the court party, in times of high political excitement, led scarcely a more desirable life. These remarks may serve as a preface to the following adventures, which chanced upon a summer night, not far from a hundred years ago. The reader, in order to avoid a long and dry detail of colonial affairs, is requested to dispense with an account of the train of circumstances that had caused much temporary inflammation of the popular mind.

It was near nine o'clock of a moonlight evening, when a boat crossed the ferry with a single passenger, who had obtained his conveyance at that unusual hour by the promise of an extra fare. While he stood on the landing-place, searching in either pocket for the means of fulfilling his agreement, the ferryman lifted a lantern, by the aid of which, and the newly risen moon, he took a very accurate survey of the stranger's figure. He was a youth of barely eighteen years, evidently country-bred, and now, as it should seem, upon his first visit to town. He was clad in a coarse gray coat, well worn, but in excellent repair; his under garments were durably constructed of leather, and fitted tight to a pair of serviceable and well-shaped limbs; his stockings of blue yarn were the incontrovertible work of a mother or a sister; and on his head was a three-cornered hat, which in its better days had perhaps sheltered the graver brow of the lad's father. Under his left arm was a heavy cudgel formed of an oak sapling, and retaining a part of the hardened root; and his equipment was completed by a wallet, not so abundantly stocked as to incommode the vigorous shoulders on which it hung. Brown, curly hair, well-shaped features, and bright, cheerful eyes were nature's gifts, and worth all that art could have done for his adornment.

The youth, one of whose names was Robin, finally drew from his pocket the half of a little province bill of five shillings, which, in the depreciation in that sort of currency, did but satisfy the ferryman's demand, with the surplus of a sexangular piece of parchment, valued a three pence. He then walked forward into the town, with as light a step as if his day's journey had not already exceeded thirty miles, and with as eager an eye as if he were entering London city, instead of the little metropolis of a New England colony. Before Robin had proceeded far, however, it occurred to him that he knew not whither to direct his steps; so he paused, and looked up and down the narrow street, scrutinizing the small and mean wooden buildings that were scattered on either side.

"This low hovel cannot be my kinsman's dwelling," thought he, "nor yonder old house, where the moonlight enters at the broken casement; and truly I see none hereabouts that might be worthy of him. It would have been wise to inquire my way of the ferryman, and doubtless he would have gone with me, and earned a shilling from the Major for his pains. But the next man I meet will do as well."

He resumed his walk, and was glad to perceive that the street now became wider, and the houses more respectable in their appearance. He soon discerned a figure moving on moderately in advance, and hastened his steps to overtake it. As Robin drew nigh, he saw that the passenger was a man in years, with a full periwig of gray hair, a wide-skirted coat of dark cloth, and silk stockings rolled above his knees. He carried a long and polished cane, which he struck down perpendicularly before him at every step; and at regular intervals he uttered two successive hems, of a peculiarly solemn and sepulchral intonation. Having made these observations, Robin laid hold of the skirt of the old man's coat, just when the light from the open door and windows of a barber's shop fell upon both their figures.

"Good evening to you, honored sir," said he, making a low bow, and still retaining his hold of the skirt. "I pray you tell me whereabouts is the dwelling of my kinsman, Major Molineux."

The youth's question was uttered very loudly; and one of the barbers, whose razor was descending on a well-soaped chin, and another who was dressing a Ramillies wig, left their occupations, and came to the door. The citizen, in the mean time, turned a long-favored countenance upon Robin, and answered him in a tone of excessive anger and annoyance. His two sepulchral hems, however, broke into the very centre of his rebuke, with most singular effect, like a thought of the cold grave obtruding among wrathful passions.

"Let go my garment, fellow! I tell you, I know not the man you speak of. What! I have authority, I have—hem, hem—authority; and if this be the respect you show for your betters, your feet shall be brought acquainted with the stocks by daylight, tomorrow morning!"

Robin released the old man's skirt, and hastened away, pursued by an ill-mannered roar of laughter from the barber's shop. He was at first considerably surprised by the result of his question, but, being a shrewd youth, soon thought himself able to account for the mystery.

"This is some country representative," was his conclusion, "who has never seen the inside of my kinsman's door, and lacks the breeding to answer a stranger civilly. The man is old, or verily—I might be tempted to turn back and smite him on the nose. Ah, Robin, Robin! even the barber's boys laugh at you for choosing such a guide! You will be wiser in time, friend Robin."

He now became entangled in a succession of crooked and narrow streets, which crossed each other, and meandered at no great distance from the water-side. The smell of tar was obvious to his nostrils, the masts of vessels pierced the moonlight above the tops of the buildings, and the numerous signs, which Robin paused to read, informed him that he was near the centre of business. But the streets were empty, the shops were closed, and lights were visible only in the second stories of a few dwelling-houses. At length, on the corner of a narrow lane, through which he was passing, he beheld the broad countenance of a British hero swinging before the door of an inn, whence proceeded the voices of many guests. The casement of one of the lower windows was thrown back, and a very thin curtain permitted Robin to distinguish a party at supper, round a well-furnished table. The fragrance of the good cheer steamed forth into the outer air, and the youth could not fail to recollect that the last remnant of his travelling stock of provision had yielded to his morning appetite, and that noon had found and left him dinnerless.

"Oh, that a parchment three-penny might give me a right to sit down at yonder table!" said Robin, with a sigh. "But the Major will make me welcome to the best of his victuals; so I will even step boldly in, and inquire my way to his dwelling."

He entered the tavern, and was guided by the murmur of voices and the fumes of tobacco to the public-room. It was a long and low apartment, with oaken walls, grown dark in the continual smoke, and a floor which was thickly sanded, but of no immaculate purity. A number of persons—the large part of whom appeared to be mariners, or in some way connected with the sea—occupied the wooden benches, or leather-bottomed chairs, conversing on various matters, and occasionally lending their attention to some topic of general interest. Three or four little groups were draining as many bowls of punch, which the West India trade had long since made a familiar drink in the colony. Others, who had the appearance of men who lived by regular and laborious handicraft, preferred the insulated bliss of an unshared potation, and became more taciturn under its influence. Nearly all, in short, evinced a predilection for the Good Creature in some of its various shapes, for this is a vice to which, as Fast Day sermons of a hundred years ago will testify, we have a long hereditary claim. The only guests to whom Robin's sympathies inclined him were two or three sheepish countrymen, who were using the inn somewhat after the fashion of a Turkish caravansary; they had gotten themselves into the darkest corner of the room, and heedless of the Nicotian atmosphere, were supping on the bread of their own ovens, and the bacon cured in their own chimney-smoke. But though Robin felt a sort of brotherhood with these strangers, his eyes were attracted from them to a person who stood near the door, holding whispered conversation with a group of ill-dressed associates. His features were separately striking almost to grotesqueness, and the whole face left a deep impression on the memory. The forehead bulged out into a double prominence, with a vale between; the nose came boldly forth in an irregular curve, and its bridge was of more than a finger's breadth; the eyebrows were deep and shaggy, and the eyes glowed beneath them like fire in a cave.

While Robin deliberated of whom to inquire respecting his kinsman's dwelling, he was accosted by the innkeeper, a little man in a stained white apron, who had come to pay his professional welcome to the stranger. Being in the second generation from a French Protestant, he seemed to have inherited the courtesy of his parent nation; but no variety of circumstances was ever known to change his voice from the one shrill note in which he now addressed Robin.

"From the country, I presume, sir?" said he, with a profound bow. "Beg leave to congratulate you on your arrival, and trust you intend a long stay with us. Fine town here, sir, beautiful buildings and much that may interest a stranger. May I hope for the honor of your commands in respect to supper?"

"The man sees a family likeness! the rogue has guessed that I am related to the Major!" thought Robin, who had hitherto experienced little superfluous civility.

All eyes were now turned on the country lad, standing at the door, in his worn three-cornered hat, gray coat, leather breeches, and blue yarn stockings, leaning on an oaken cudgel, and bearing a wallet on his back.

Robin replied to the courteous innkeeper, with such an assumption of confidence as befitted the Major's relative. "My honest friend," he said, "I shall make it a point to patronize your house on some occasion, when"—here he could not help lowering his voice—"when I may have more than a parchment three-pence in my pocket. My present business," continued he, speaking with lofty confidence, "is merely to inquire my way to the dwelling of my kinsman, Major Molineux."

There was a sudden and general movement in the room, which Robin interpreted as expressing the eagerness of each individual to become his guide. But the innkeeper turned his eyes to a written paper on the wall, which he read, or seemed to read, with occasional recurrences to the young man's figure.

"What have we here?" said he, breaking his speech into little dry fragments. " 'Left the house of the subscriber, bounden servant, Hezekiah Mudge,—had on, when he went away, gray coat, leather breeches, master's third-best hat. One proud currency reward to whosoever shall lodge him in any jail of the province.' Better trudge, boy; better trudge!"

Robin had begun to draw his hand towards the lighter end of the oak cudgel, but a strange hostility in every countenance induced him to relinquish his purpose of breaking the courteous inkeepers' head. As he turned to leave the room, he encountered a sneering glance from the bold-featured personage whom he had before noticed; and no sooner was he beyond the door, than he heard a general laugh, in which the innkeeper's voice might be distinguished, like the dropping of small stones into a kettle.

"Now, is it not strange," thought Robin, with his usual shrewdness,—"is it not strange that the confession of an empty pocket should outweigh the name of my kinsman, Major Molineux? Oh, if I had one of those grinning rascals in the woods, where I and my oak sapling grew up together, I would teach him that my arm is heavy though my purse be light!"

On turning the corner of the narrow lane, Robin found himself in a spacious street, with an unbroken line of lofty houses on each side, and a steepled building at the upper end, whence the ringing of a bell announced the hour of nine. The light of the moon, and the lamps from the numerous shop-windows, discovered people promenading on the pavement, and amongst them Robin hoped to recognize his hitherto inscrutable relative. The result of his former inquiries made him unwilling to hazard another, in a scene of such publicity, and he determined to walk slowly and silently up the street, thrusting his face close to that of every elderly gentleman, in search of the Major's lineaments. In his progress, Robin encountered many gay and gallant figures. Embroidered garments of showy colors, enormous periwigs, gold-laced hats, and silver-hilted swords glided past him and dazzled his optics. Travelled youths, imitators of the European fine gentlemen of the period, trod jauntily along, half dancing to the fashionable tunes which they hummed, and making poor Robin ashamed of his quiet and natural gait. At length, after many pauses to examine the gorgeous display of goods in the shop-windows, and after suffering some rebukes for the impertinence of his scrutiny into people's faces, the Major's kinsman found himself near the steepled building, still unsuccessful in his search. As yet, however, he had seen only one side of the thronged street; so Robin crossed, and continued the same sort of inquisition down the opposite pavement, with stronger hopes than the philosopher seeking an honest man, but with no better fortune. He had arrived about midway towards the lower end, from which his course began, when he overheard the approach of some one who struck down a cane on the flag-stones at every step, uttering, at regular intervals, two sepulchral hems.

"Mercy on us!" quoth Robin, recognizing the sound.

Turning a corner, which chanced to be close at his right hand, he hastened to pursue his researches in some other part of the town. His patience now was wearing low, and he seemed to feel more fatigue from his rambles since he crossed the ferry, than from his journey of several days on the other side. Hunger also pleaded loudly within him, and Robin began to balance the propriety of demanding, violently, and with lifted cudgel, the necessary guidance from the first solitary passenger whom he should meet. While a resolution to this effect was gaining strength, he entered a street of mean appearance, on either side of which a row of ill-built houses was straggling towards the harbor. The moonlight fell upon no passenger along the whole extent, but in the third domicile which Robin passed there was a half-opened door, and his keen glance detected a woman's garment within.

"My luck may be better here," said he to himself.

Accordingly, he approached the door, and beheld it shut closer as he did so; yet an open space remained, sufficing for the fair occupant to observe the stranger, without a corresponding display on her part. All that Robin could discern was a strip of scarlet petticoat, and the occasional sparkle of an eye, as if the moonbeams were trembling on some bright thing.

"Pretty mistress," for I may call her so with a good conscience, thought the shrewd youth, since I know nothing to the contrary,—"my sweet pretty mistress, will you be kind enough to tell me whereabouts I must seek the dwelling of my kinsman, Major Molineux?"

Robin's voice was plaintive and winning, and the female, seeing nothing to be shunned in the handsome country youth, thrust open the door, and came forth into the moonlight. She was a dainty little figure, with a white neck, round arms, and a slender waist, at the extremity of which her scarlet petticoat jutted out over a hoop, as if she were standing in a balloon. Moreover, her face was oval and pretty, her hair dark beneath the little cap, and her bright eyes possessed a sly freedom, which triumphed over those of Robin.

"Major Molineux dwells here," said this fair woman.

Now, her voice was the sweetest Robin had heard that night, the airy counterpart of a stream of melted silver; yet he could not help doubting whether that sweet voice spoke Gospel truth. He looked up and down the mean street, and then surveyed the house before which they stood. It was a small, dark edifice of two stories, the second of which projected over the lower floor, and the front apartment had the aspect of a shop for petty commodities.

"Now, truly, I am in luck," replied Robin, cunningly, "and so indeed is my kinsman, the Major, in having so pretty a housekeeper. But I prithee trouble him to step to the door; I will deliver him a message from his friends in the country, and then go back to my lodgings at the inn."

"Nay, the Major has been abed this hour or more," said the lady of the scarlet petticoat; "and it would be to little purpose to disturb him to-night, seeing his evening draught was of the strongest. But he is a kind-hearted man, and it would be as much as my life's worth to let a kinsman of his turn away from the door. You are the good old gentleman's very picture, and I could swear that was his rainy-weather hat. Also he has garments very much resembling those leather small-clothes. But come in, I pray, for I bid you hearty welcome in his name."

So saying, the fair and hospitable dame took our hero by the hand; and the touch was light, and the force was gentleness, and though Robin read in her eyes what he did not hear in her words, yet the slender-waisted woman in the scarlet petticoat proved stronger than the athletic country youth. She had drawn his half-willing footsteps nearly to the threshold, when the opening of a door in the neighborhood startled the Major's housekeeper, and, leaving the Major's kinsman, she vanished speedily into her own domicile. A heavy yawn preceded the appearance of a man, who, like the Moonshine of Pyramus and Thisbe, carried a lantern, needlessly aiding his sister luminary in the heavens. As he walked sleepily up the street, he turned his broad, dull face on Robin, and displayed a long staff, spiked at the end.

"Home, vagabond, home!" said the watchman, in accents that seemed to fall asleep as soon as they were uttered. "Home, or we'll set you in the stocks by peep of day!"

"This is the second hint of the kind," thought Robin. "I wish they would end my difficulties, by setting me there to-night."

Nevertheless, the youth felt an instinctive antipathy towards the guardian of midnight order, which at first prevented him from asking his usual question. But just when the man was about to vanish behind the corner, Robin resolved not to lose the opportunity, and shouted lustily after him,—

"I say, friend! will you guide me to the house of my kinsman, Major Molineux?"

The watchman made no reply, but turned the corner and was gone; yet Robin seemed to hear the sound of drowsy laughter stealing along the solitary street. At that moment, also, a pleasant titter saluted him from the open window above his head; he looked up, and caught the sparkle of a saucy eye; a round arm beckoned to him, and next he heard light footsteps descending the staircase within. But Robin, being of the household of a New England clergyman, was a good youth, as well as a shrewd one; so he resisted temptation, and fled away.

He now roamed desperately, and at random, through the town, almost ready to believe that a spell was on him, like that by which a wizard of his country had once kept three pursuers wandering, a whole winter night, within twenty paces of the cottage which they sought. The streets lay before him, strange and desolate, and the lights were extinguished in almost every house. Twice, however, little parties of men, among whom Robin distinguished individuals in outlandish attire, came hurrying along; but, though on both occasions they paused to address him, such intercourse did not at all enlighten his perplexity. They did but utter a few words in some language of which Robin knew nothing, and perceiving his inability to answer, bestowed a curse upon him in plain English and hastened away. Finally, the lad determined to knock at the door of every mansion that might appear worthy to be occupied by his kinsman, trusting that perseverance would overcome the fatality that had hitherto thwarted him. Firm in this resolve, he was passing beneath the walls of a church, which formed the corner of two streets, when, as he turned into the shade of its steeple, he encountered a bulky stranger, muffled in a cloak. The man was proceeding with the speed of earnest business, but Robin planted himself full before him, holding the oak with both hands across his body as a bar to further passage.

"Halt, honest man, and answer me a question," said he, very resolutely. "Tell me, this instant, whereabouts is the dwelling of my kinsman, Major Molineux!"

"Keep your tongue between your teeth, fool, and let me pass!" said a deep, gruff voice, which Robin partly remembered. "Let me pass, I say, or I'll strike you to the earth!"

"No, no, neighbor!" cried Robin, flourishing his cudgel, and then thrusting its larger end close to the man's muffled face. "No, no, I'm not the fool you take me for, nor do you pass till I have an answer to my question. Whereabouts is the dwelling of my kinsman, Major Molineux?"

The stranger, instead of attempting to force his passage, stepped back into the moonlight, unmuffled his face, and stared full into that of Robin.

"Watch here an hour, and Major Molineux will pass by," said he.

Robin gazed with dismay and astonishment on the unprecedented physiognomy of the speaker. The forehead with its double prominence, the broad hooked nose, the shaggy eyebrows, and fiery eyes were those which he had noticed at the inn, but the man's complexion had undergone a singular, or, more properly, a twofold change. One side of the face blazed an intense red, while the other was black as midnight, the division line being in the broad bridge of the nose; and a mouth which seemed to extend from ear to ear was black or red, in contrast to the color of the cheek. The effect was as if two individual devils, a fiend of fire and a fiend of darkness, had united themselves to form this infernal visage. The stranger grinned in Robin's face, muffled his parti-colored features, and was out of sight in a moment.

"Strange things we travellers see!" ejaculated Robin.

He seated himself, however, upon the steps of the church-door, resolving to wait the appointed time for his kinsman. A few moments were consumed in philosophical speculations upon the species of man who had just left him; but having settled this point shrewdly, rationally, and satisfactorily, he was compelled to look elsewhere for his amusement. And first he threw his eyes along the street. It was of more respectable appearance than most of those into which he had wandered, and the moon, creating, like the imaginative power, a beautiful strangeness in familiar objects, gave something of romance to a scene that might not have possessed it in the light of day. The irregular and often quaint architecture of the houses, some of whose roofs were broken into numerous little peaks, while others ascended, steep and narrow, into a single point, and others again were square; the pure snow-white of some of their complexions, the aged darkness of others, and the thousand sparkings, reflected from bright substances in the walls of many; these matters engaged Robin's attention for a while, and then began to grow wearisome. Next he endeavored to define the forms of distant objects, starting away, with almost ghostly indistinctness, just as his eye appeared to grasp them; and finally he took a minute survey of an edifice which stood on the opposite side of the street, directly in front of the church-door, where he was stationed. It was a large, square mansion, distinguished from its neighbors by a balcony, which rested on tall pillars, and by an elaborate Gothic window, communicating therewith.

"Perhaps this is the very house I have been seeking," thought Robin.

Then he strove to speed away the time, by listening to a murmur which swept continually along the street, yet was scarcely audible, except to an unaccustomed ear like his; it was a low, dull, dreamy sound, compounded of many noises, each of which was at too great a distance to be separately heard. Robin marvelled at this snore of a sleeping town, and marvelled more whenever its continuity was broken by now and then a distant shout, apparently loud where it originated. But altogether it was a sleep-inspiring sound, and, to shake off its drowsy influence, Robin arose, and climbed a window-frame, that he might view the interior of the church. There the moonbeams came trembling in, and fell down upon the deserted pews, and extended along the quiet aisles. A fainter yet more awful radiance was hovering around the pulpit, and one solitary ray had dared to rest upon the open page of the great Bible. Had nature, in that deep hour, become a worshipper in the house which man had builded? Or was that heavenly light the visible sanctity of the place,—visible because no earthly and impure feet were within the walls? The scene made Robin's heart shiver with a sensation of loneliness stronger than he had ever felt in the remotest depths of his native woods; so he turned away and sat down again before the door. There were graves around the church, and now an uneasy thought obtruded into Robin's breast. What if the object of his search, which had been so often and so strangely thwarted, were all the time mouldering in his shroud? What if his kinsman should glide through yonder gate, and nod and smile to him in dimly passing by?

"Oh that any breathing thing were here with me!" said Robin.

Recalling his thoughts from this uncomfortable track, he sent them over forest, hill, and stream, and attempted to imagine how that evening of ambiguity and weariness had been spent by his father's household. He pictured them assembled at the door, beneath the tree, the great old tree, which had been spared for its huge twisted trunk and venerable shade, when a thousand leafy brethren fell. There, at the going down of the summer sun, it was his father's custom to perform domestic worship, that the neighbors might come and join with him like brothers of the family, and that the wayfaring man might pause to drink at that fountain, and keep his heart pure by freshening the memory of home. Robin distinguished the seat of every individual of the little audience; he saw the good man in the midst, holding the Scriptures in the golden light that fell from the western clouds; he beheld him close the book and all rise up to pray. He heard the old thanksgivings for daily mercies, the old supplications for their continuance, to which he had so often listened in weariness, but which were now among his dear remembrances. He perceived the slight inequality of his father's voice when he came to speak of the absent one; he noted how his mother turned her face to the broad and knotted trunk; how his elder brother scorned, because the beard was rough upon his upper lip, to permit his features to be moved; how the younger sister drew down a low hanging branch before her eyes; and how the little one of all, whose sports had hitherto broken the decorum of the scene, understood the prayer for her playmate, and burst into clamorous grief. Then he saw them go in at the door; and when Robin would have entered also, the latch tinkled into its place, and he was excluded from his home.

"Am I here, or there?" cried Robin, starting; for all at once, when his thoughts had become visible and audible in a dream, the long, wide, solitary street shone out before him.

He aroused himself, and endeavored to fix his attention steadily upon the large edifice which he had surveyed before. But still his mind kept vibrating between fancy and reality; by turns, the pillars of the balcony lengthened into the tall, bare stems of pines, dwindled down to human figures, settled again into their true shape and size, and then commenced a new succession of changes. For a single moment, when he deemed himself awake, he could have sworn that a visage—one which he seemed to remember, yet could not absolutely name as his kinsman's—was looking towards him from the Gothic window. A deeper sleep wrestled with and nearly overcame him, but fled at the sound of footsteps along the opposite pavement. Robin rubbed his eyes, discerned a man passing at the foot of the balcony, and addressed him in a loud, peevish, and lamentable cry.

"Hallo, friend! must I wait here all night for my kinsman, Major Molineux?"

The sleeping echoes awoke, and answered the voice; and the passenger, barely able to discern a figure sitting in the oblique shade of the steeple, traversed the street to obtain a nearer view. He was himself a gentleman in his prime, of open, intelligent, cheerful, and altogether prepossessing countenance. Perceiving a country youth, apparently homeless and without friends, he accosted him in a tone of real kindness, which had become strange to Robin's ears.

"Well, my good lad, why are you sitting here?" inquired he. "Can I be of service to you in any way?"

"I am afraid not, sir," replied Robin, despondingly; "yet I shall take it kindly, if you'll answer me a single question. I've been searching, half the night, for one Major Molineux; now, sir, is there really such a person in these parts, or am I dreaming?"

"Major Molineux! The name is not altogether strange to me," said the the gentleman, smiling. "Have you any objection to telling me the nature of your business with him?"

Then Robin briefly related that his father was a clergyman, settled on a small salary, at a long distance back in the country, and that he and Major Molineux were brothers' children. The Major, having inherited riches, and acquired civil and military rank, had visited his cousin, in great pomp, a year or two before; had manifested much interest in Robin and an elder brother, and, being childless himself, had thrown out hints respecting the future establishment of one of them in life. The elder brother was destined to succeed to the farm which his father cultivated in the interval of sacred duties; it was therefore determined that Robin should profit by his kinsman's generous intentions, especially as he seemed to be rather the favorite, and was thought to possess other necessary endowments.

"For I have the name of being a shrewd youth," observed Robin, in this part of his story.

"I doubt not you deserve it," replied his new friend, good-naturedly; "but pray proceed."

"Well, sir, being nearly eighteen years old, and well grown, as you see," continued Robin, drawing himself up to his full height, "I thought it high time to begin the world. So my mother and sister put me in handsome trim, and my father gave me half the remnant of his last year's salary, and five days ago I started for this place, to pay the Major a visit. But, would you believe it, sir! I crossed the ferry a little after dark, and have yet found nobody that would show me the way to his dwelling; only, an hour of two since, I was told to wait here, and Major Molineux would pass by."

"Can you describe the man who told you this?" inquired the gentleman.

"Oh, he was a very ill-favored fellow, sir," replied Robin, "with two great bumps on his forehead, a hook nose, fiery eyes; and, what struck me as the strangest, his face was of two different colors. Do you happen to know such a man, sir?"

"Not intimately," answered the stranger, "but I chanced to meet him a little time previous to your stopping me. I believe you may trust his word, and that the Major will very shortly pass through this street. In the mean time, as I have a singular curiosity to witness your meeting, I will sit down here upon the steps and bear you company."

He seated himself accordingly, and soon engaged his companion in animated discourse. It was but of brief continuance, however, for a noise of shouting, which had long been remotely audible, drew so much nearer that Robin inquired its cause.

"What may be the meaning of this uproar?" asked he. "Truly, if your town be always as noisy, I shall find little sleep while I am an inhabitant."

"Why, indeed, friend Robin, there do appear to be three or four riotous fellows abroad to-night," replied the gentleman. "You must not expect all the stillness of your native woods here in our streets. But the watch will shortly be at the heels of these lads and"—

"Ay, and set them in the stocks by peep of day," interrupted Robin, recollecting his own encounter with the drowsy lantern-bearer. "But, dear sir, if I may trust my ears, an army of watchmen would never make head against such a multitude of rioters. There were at least a thousand voices went up to make that one shout."

"May not a man have several voices, Robin, as well as two complexions?" said his friend.

"Perhaps a man may; but Heaven forbid that a woman should!" responded the shrewd youth, thinking of the seductive tones of the Major's housekeeper.

The sounds of a trumpet in some neighboring street now became so evident and continual, that Robin's curiosity was strongly exicted. In addition to the shouts, he heard frequent bursts from many instruments of discord, and a wild and confused laughter filled up the intervals. Robin rose from the steps, and looked wistfully towards a point whither people seemed to be hastening.

"Surely some prodigious merry-making is going on," exclaimed he. "I have laughed very little since I left home, sir, and should be sorry to lose an opportunity. Shall we step round the corner by that darkish house, and take our share of the fun?"

"Sit down again, sit down, good Robin," replied the gentleman, laying his hand on the skirt of the gray coat. "You forget that we must wait here for your kinsman; and there is reason to believe that he will pass by, in the course of a very few moments."

The near approach of the uproar had now disturbed the neighborhood; windows flew open on all sides; and many heads, in the attire of the pillow, and confused by sleep suddenly broken, were protruded to the gaze of whoever had leisure to observe them. Eager voices hailed each other from house to house, all demanding the explanation, which not a soul could give. Half-dressed men hurried towards the unknown commotion, stumbling as they went over the stone steps that thrust themselves into the narrow foot-walk. The shouts, the laughter, and the tuneless bray, the antipodes of music, came onwards with increasing din, till scattered individuals, and then denser bodies, began to appear round a corner at the distance of a hundred yards.

"Will you recognize your kinsman, if he passes in this crowd?" inquired the gentleman.

"Indeed, I can't warrant it, sir; but I'll take my stand here, and keep a bright lookout," answered Robin, descending to the outer edge of the pavement.

A mighty stream of people now emptied into the street, and came rolling slowly towards the church. A single horseman wheeled the corner in the midst of them, and close behind him came a band of fearful wind-instruments, sending forth a fresher discord now that no intervening buildings kept it from the ear. Then a redder light disturbed the moonbeams, and a dense multitude of torches shone along the street, concealing, by their glare, whatever object they illuminated. The single horseman, clad in a military dress, and bearing a drawn sword, rode onward as the leader, and, by his fierce and variegated countenance, appeared like war personified; the red of one cheek was an emblem of fire and sword; the blackness of the other betokened the mourning that attends them. In his train were wild figures in the Indian dress, and many fantastic shapes without a model, giving the whole march a visionary air, as if a dream had broken forth from some feverish brain, and were sweeping visibly through the midnight streets. A mass of people, inactive, except as applauding spectators, hemmed the procession in; and several women ran along the sidewalk, piercing the confusion of heavier sounds with their shrill voices of mirth or terror.

"The double-faced fellow has his eye upon me," muttered Robin, with an indefinite but an uncomfortable idea that he was himself to bear a part in the pageantry.

The leader turned himself in the saddle, and fixed his glance full upon the country youth, as the steed went slowly by. When Robin had freed his eyes from those fiery ones, the musicians were passing before him, and the torches were close at hand; but the unsteady brightness of the latter formed a veil which he could not penetrate. The rattling of wheels over the stones sometimes found its way to his ear, and confused traces of a human form appeared at intervals, and then melted into the vivid light. A moment more, and the leader thundered a command to halt: the trumpets vomited a horrid breath, and then held their peace; the shouts and laughter of the people died away, and there remained only a universal hum, allied to silence. Right before Robin's eyes was an uncovered cart. There the torches blazed the brightest, there the moon shone out like day, and there, in tar-and-feathery dignity, sat his kinsman, Major Molineux!

He was an elderly man, of large and majestic person, and strong, square features, betokening a steady soul; but steady as it was, his enemies had found means to shake it. His face was pale as death, and far more ghastly; the broad forehead was contracted in his agony, so that his eyebrows formed one grizzled line; his eyes were red and wild, and the foam hung white upon his quivering lip. His whole frame was agitated by a quick and continual tremor, which his pride strove to quell even in those circumstances of overwhelming humiliation. But perhaps the bitterest pang of all was when his eyes met those of Robin; for he evidently knew him on the instant, as the youth stood witnessing the foul disgrace of a head grown gray in honor. They stared at each other in silence, and Robin's knees shook, and his hair bristled, with a mixture of pity and terror. Soon, however, a bewildering excitement began to seize upon his mind; the preceding adventures of the night, the unexpected appearance of the crowd, the torches, the confused din and the hush that followed, the spectre of his kinsman reviled by that great multitude,—all this, and, more than all, a perception of tremendous ridicule in the whole scene, affected him with a sort of mental inebriety. At that moment a voice of sluggish merriment saluted Robin's ears; he turned instinctively, and just behind the corner of the church stood the lantern-bearer, rubbing his eyes, and drowsily enjoying the lad's amazement. Then he heard a peal of laughter like the ringing of silvery bells; a woman twitched his arms, a saucy eye met his, and he saw the lady of the scarlet petticoat. A sharp, dry cachinnation appealed to his memory, and, standing on tiptoe in the crowd, with his white apron over his head, he beheld the courteous little innkeeper. And lastly, there sailed over the heads of the multitude a great, broad laugh, broken in the midst by two sepulchral hems; thus, "Haw, haw, haw,—hem, hem,—haw, haw, haw, haw!"

The sound proceeded from the balcony of the opposite edifice, and thither Robin turned his eyes. In front of the Gothic window stood the old citizen, wrapped in a wide gown, his gray periwig exchanged for a nightcap, which was thrust back from his forehead, and his silk stockings hanging about his legs. He supported himself on his polished cane in a fit of convulsive merriment, which manifested itself on his solemn old features like a funny inscription on a tombstone. Then Robin seemed to hear the voices of the barbers, of the guests of the inn, and of all who had made sport of him that night. The contagion was spreading among the multitude, when all at once, it seized upon Robin, and he sent forth a shout of laughter that echoed through the street,—every man shook his sides, every man emptied his lungs, but Robin's shout was the loudest there. The cloud-spirits peeped from their silvery islands, as the congregated mirth went roaring up the sky! The Man in the Moon heard the far bellow. "Oho," quoth he, "the old earth is frolicsome to-night!"

When there was a momentary calm in that tempestuous sea of sound, the leader gave the sign, the procession resumed its march. On they went, like fiends that throng in mockery around some dead potentate, mighty no more, but majestic still in his agony. On they went, in counterfeited pomp, in senseless uproar, in frenzied merriment, trampling all on an old man's heart. On swept the tumult, and left a silent street behind.

"Well, Robin, are you dreaming?" inquired the gentleman, laying his hand on the youth's shoulder.

Robin started, and withdrew his arm from the stone post to which he had instinctively clung, as the living stream rolled by him. His cheek was somewhat pale, and his eye not quite as lively as in the earlier part of the evening.

"Will you be kind enough to show me the way to the ferry?" said he, after a moment's pause.

"You have, then, adopted a new subject of inquiry?" observed his companion, with a smile.

"Why, yes, sir," replied Robin, rather dryly. "Thanks to you, and to my other friends, I have at last met my kinsman, and he will scarce desire to see my face again. I begin to grow weary of a town life, sir. Will you show me the way to the ferry?"

"No, my good friend Robin,—not to-night, at least," said the gentleman. "Some few days hence, if you wish it, I will speed you on your journey. Or, if you prefer to remain with us, perhaps, as you are a shrewd youth, you may rise in the world without the help of your kinsman, Major Molineux."

Humor and Pathos

Although humor is not easy to define, everybody knows about laughter. Man has a disposition toward the comic from infancy to the grave, and his responses range from a chuckle to a sidesplitting guffaw. The ideas, situations, and people he will laugh about are countless—and they include himself. As Max Eastman has reminded us, "Comedian and storyteller alike play continual tricks on their audiences, inventing ever new ways of tripping them playfully, and yet contriving that in their fall they alight upon some agreeable thought, image, or emotion." * Thus humor in its simplest form is a kind of pleasant and joyous irony; somebody falls, expects to land in a bed of thorns, and somehow lands in a bed of roses. The result is funny because it is the opposite of what we expect from a fall. And it is also funny if the pompous pretender to roses lands squarely in a bed of deflating thorns.

We know that humor has many faces and elicits many shades of response. Like the pathetic or the tragic, the comic depends upon some kind of incongruity: a discrepancy between appearance and reality, between form and content, between what one thinks himself to be and what one truly is. Often a very thin line separates humor from pathos, comedy from tragedy; we are sometimes hard put to know whether laughter or tears fill our eyes. Eastman states further: "The comic pleasure deriving from a fall is thus combined with innumerable other, often extremely serious, qualities of feeling. Contempt has its place here, but so also have pity and admiration. Hence arises the richness and infinite variety of humorous experience." The three selections that follow were chosen with this statement in mind.

First of all, these three stories make an attempt, through humor, to say something serious about people and their attitudes toward themselves and their responses to the world. This is to say that humor can make us think while we laugh, cause us to find values by ridiculing our pretensions, or bring us to the discovery of a serious idea beneath sheer nonsense. We first laugh with something like superior contempt at the characters in "Why I Live at the P.O." as they suppose they are making a proper

*From "Humor" in the *Dictionary of World Literature.*

impression but are actually doing the opposite. Gradually we learn to pity them in their human plight. After reading "The Tuxedos" we see both the laughable nonsense and pathetic implications in a family crisis where formal propriety attempts to counteract the highly informal arrangements between a boy and girl. Our feelings about "The Bull That Thought" are also mixed when we see a cantankerous bull turn into a superior "artist" and an inflated matador become a clumsy buffoon.

EUDORA WELTY

(*1909–*)

Why I Live at the P.O.

I was getting along fine with Mama, Papa-Daddy and Uncle Rondo until my sister Stella-Rondo just separated from her husband and came back home again. Mr. Whitaker! Of course I went with Mr. Whitaker first, when he first appeared here in China Grove, taking "Pose Yourself" photos, and Stella-Rondo broke us up. Told him I was onesided. Bigger on one side than the other, which is a deliberate, calculated falsehood: I'm the same. Stella-Rondo is exactly twelve months to the day younger than I am and for that reason she's spoiled.

She's always had anything in the world she wanted and then she'd throw it away. Papa-Daddy gave her this gorgeous Add-a-Pearl necklace when she was eight years old and she threw it away playing baseball when she was nine, with only two pearls.

So as soon as she got married and moved away from home the first thing she did was separate! From Mr. Whitaker! This photographer with the popeyes she said she trusted. Came home from one of those towns up in Illinois and to our complete surprise brought this child of two.

Mama said she like to made her drop dead for a second. "Here you had this marvelous blonde child and never so much as wrote your mother a word about it," says Mama. "I'm thoroughly ashamed of you." But of course she wasn't.

Stella-Rondo just calmly takes off this *hat,* I wish you could see it. She says, "Why, Mama, Shirley-T.'s adopted, I can prove it."

"How?" says Mama, but all I says was, "H'm!" There I was over the hot stove, trying to stretch two chickens over five people and a completely unexpected child into the bargain, without one moment's notice.

"What do you mean—'H'm!'?" says Stella-Rondo, and Mama says, "I heard that, Sister."

I said that oh, I didn't mean a thing, only that whoever Shirley-T. was, she was the spit-image of Papa-Daddy if he'd cut off his beard, which of course he'd never do in the world. Papa-Daddy's Mama's papa and sulks.

Stella-Rondo got furious! She said, "Sister, I don't need to tell you you got a lot of nerve and always did have and I'll thank you to make no future reference to my adopted child whatsoever."

"Very well," I said. "Very well, very well. Of course I noticed at once she looks like Mr. Whitaker's side too. That frown. She looks like a cross between Mr. Whitaker and Papa-Daddy."

"Well, all I can say is she isn't."

"She looks exactly like Shirley Temple to me," says Mama, but Shirley-T. just ran away from her.

So the first thing Stella-Rondo did at the table was turn Papa-Daddy against me.

"Papa-Daddy," she says. He was trying to cut up his meat. "Papa-Daddy!" I was taken completely by surprise. Papa-Daddy is about a million years old and's got this long-long beard. "Papa-Daddy, Sister says she fails to understand why you don't cut off your beard."

So Papa-Daddy l-a-y-s down his knife and fork! He's real rich. Mama says he is, he says he isn't. So he says, "Have I heard correctly? You don't understand why I don't cut off my beard?"

"Why," I says, "Papa-Daddy, of course I understand, I did not say any such of a thing, the idea!"

He says, "Hussy!"

I says, "Papa-Daddy, you know I wouldn't any more want you to cut off your beard than the man in the moon. It was the farthest thing from my mind! Stella-Rondo sat there and made that up while she was eating breast of chicken."

But he says, "So the postmistress fails to understand why I don't cut off my beard. Which job I got you through my influence with the government. 'Bird's nest'—is that what you call it?"

Not that it isn't the next to smallest P.O. in the entire state of Mississippi.

I says, "Oh, Papa-Daddy," I says, "I didn't say any such of a thing, I never dreamed it was a bird's nest, I have always been grateful though this is the next to smallest P.O. in the state of Mississippi, and I do not enjoy being referred to as a hussy by my own grandfather."

But Stella-Rondo says, "Yes, you did say it too. Anybody in the world could of heard you, that had ears."

"Stop right there," says Mama, looking at *me*.

So I pulled my napkin straight back through the napkin ring and left the table.

As soon as I was out of the room Mama says, "Call her back, or she'll starve to death," but Papa-Daddy says, "This is the beard I started growing on the Coast when I was fifteen years old." He would of gone on till nightfall if Shirley-T. hadn't lost the Milky Way she ate in Cairo.

So Papa-Daddy says, "I am going out and lie in the hammock, and you can all sit here and remember my words: I'll never cut off my beard as long as I live, even one inch, and I don't appreciate it in you at all." Passed right by me in the hall and went straight out and got in the hammock.

It would be a holiday. It wasn't five minutes before Uncle Rondo suddenly appeared in the hall in one of Stella-Rondo's flesh-colored kimonos, all cut on the bias, like something Mr. Whitaker probably throught was gorgeous.

"Uncle Rondo!" I says. "I didn't know who that was! Where are you going?"

"Sister," he says, "get out of my way, I'm poisoned."

"If you're poisoned stay away from Papa-Daddy," I says. "Keep out of the hammock. Papa-Daddy will certainly beat you on the head if you come within forty miles of him. He thinks I deliberately said he ought to cut off his beard after he got me the P.O., and I've told him and told him and told him, and he acts like he just don't hear me. Papa-Daddy must of gone stone deaf."

"He picked a fine day to do it then," says Uncle Rondo, and before you could say "Jack Robinson" flew out in the yard.

What he'd really done, he'd drunk another bottle of that prescription. He does it every single Fourth of July as sure as shooting, and it's horribly expensive. Then he falls over in the hammock and snores. So he insisted on zigzagging right on out to the hammock, looking like a half-wit.

Papa-Daddy woke up with this horrible yell and right there without moving an inch he tried to turn Uncle Rondo against me. I heard every word he said. Oh, he told Uncle Rondo I didn't learn to read till I was eight years old and he didn't see how in the world I ever got the mail put up at the P.O., much less read it all, and he said if Uncle Rondo could only fathom the lengths he had gone to to get me that job! And he said on the other hand he thought Stella-Rondo had a brilliant mind and deserved credit for getting out of town. All the time he was just lying there swinging as pretty as you please and looping out his beard, and poor Uncle Rondo was *pleading* with him to slow down the hammock, it was making him as dizzy as a witch to watch it. But that's what Papa-Daddy likes about a hammock. So Uncle Rondo was too dizzy to get turned against me for the time being. He's Mama's only brother and is a good case of a one-track mind. Ask anybody. A certified pharmacist.

Just then I heard Stella-Rondo raising the upstairs window. While she was married she got this peculiar idea that it's cooler with the windows shut and locked. So she has to raise the window before she can make a soul hear her outdoors.

So she raises the window and says, *"Oh!"* You would have thought she was mortally wounded.

Uncle Rondo and Papa-Daddy didn't even look up, but kept right on with what they were doing. I had to laugh.

I flew up the stairs and threw the door open! I says, "What in the wide world's the matter, Stella-Rondo? You mortally wounded?"

"No," she says, "I am not mortally wounded but I wish you would do me the favor of looking out that window there and telling me what you see."

So I shade my eyes and look out the window.

"I see the front yard," I says.

"Don't you see any human beings?" she says.

"I see Uncle Rondo trying to run Papa-Daddy out of the hammock," I says. "Nothing more. Naturally, it's so suffocating-hot in the house, with all the windows shut and locked, everybody who cares to stay in their right mind will have to go out and get in the hammock before the Fourth of July is over."

"Don't you notice anything different about Uncle Rondo?" asks Stella-Rondo.

"Why, no, except he's got on some terrible-looking flesh-colored contraption I wouldn't be found dead in, is all I can see," I says.

"Never mind, you won't be found dead in it, because it happens to be part of my trousseau, and Mr. Whitaker took several dozen photographs of me in it," says Stella-Rondo. "What on earth could Uncle Rondo *mean* by wearing part of my trousseau out in the broad open daylight without saying so much as 'Kiss my foot,' *knowing* I only got home this morning after my separation and hung my negligee up on the bathroom door, just as nervous as I could be?"

"I'm sure I don't know, and what do you expect me to do about it?" I says. "Jump out the window?"

"No. I expect nothing of the kind. I simply declare that Uncle Rondo looks like a fool in it, that's all," she says. "It makes me sick to my stomach."

"Well, he looks as good as he can," I says. "As good as anybody in reason could." I stood up for Uncle Rondo, please remember. And I said to Stella-Rondo, "I think I would do well not to criticize so freely if I were you and came home with a two-year-old child I had never said a word about, and no explanation whatever about my separation."

"I asked you the instant I entered this house not to refer one more time to my adopted child, and you gave me your word of honor you would not," was all Stella-Rondo would say, and started pulling out every one of her eyebrows with some cheap Kress tweezers.

So I merely slammed the door behind me and went down and made some green-tomato pickle. Somebody had to do it. Of course Mama had turned both the niggers loose; she always said no earthly power could hold one anyway on the Fourth of July, so she wouldn't even try. It turned out that Jaypan fell in the lake and came within a very narrow limit of drowning.

So Mama trots in. Lifts up the lid and says, "H'm! Not very good for your Uncle Rondo in his precarious condition, I must say. Or poor little adopted Shirley-T. Shame on you!"

That made me tired. I says, "Well, Stella-Rondo had better thank her lucky stars it was her instead of me came trotting in with that very peculiar-looking child. Now if it had been me that trotted in from Illinois and brought a peculiar-looking child of two, I shudder to think of the reception I'd of got, much less controlled the diet of an entire family."

"But you must remember, Sister, that you were never married to Mr. Whitaker in the first place and didn't go up to Illinois to live," says Mama, shaking a spoon in my face. "If you had I would of been just as overjoyed to see you and your little adopted girl as I was to see Stella-Rondo, when you wound up with your separation and came on back home."

"You would not," I says.

"Don't contradict me, I would," says Mama.

But I said she couldn't convince me though she talked till she was blue in the face. Then I said, "Besides, you know as well as I do that that child is not adopted."

"She most certainly is adopted," says Mama, stiff as a poker.

I says, "Why, Mama, Stella-Rondo had her just as sure as anything in this world, and just too stuck up to admit it."

"Why, Sister," said Mama. "Here I thought we were going to have a pleasant Fourth of July, and you start right out not believing a word your own baby sister tells you!"

"Just like Cousin Annie Flo. Went to her grave denying the facts of life," I remind Mama.

"I told you if you ever mentioned Annie Flo's name I'd slap your face," says Mama, and slaps my face.

"All right, you wait and see," I says.

"I," says Mama, *"I* prefer to take my children's word for anything when it's humanly possible." You ought to see Mama, she weighs two hundred pounds and has real tiny feet.

Just then something perfectly horrible occurred to me.

"Mama," I says, "can that child talk?" I simply had to whisper! "Mama, I wonder if that child can be—you know—in any way? Do you realize," I says, "that she hasn't spoken one single, solitary word to a human being up to this minute? This is the way she looks," I says, and I looked like this.

Well, Mama and I just stood there and stared at each other. It was horrible!

"I remember well that Joe Whitaker frequently drank like a fish," says Mama. "I believed to my soul he drank *chemicals*." And without another word she marches to the foot of the stairs and calls Stella-Rondo.

"Stella-Rondo? O-o-o-o-o! Stella-Rondo!"

"What?" says Stella-Rondo from upstairs. Not even the grace to get up off the bed.

"Can that child of yours talk?" asks Mama.

Stella-Rondo says, "Can she what?"

"Talk! Talk!" says Mama. "Burdyburdyburdyburdy!"

So Stella-Rondo yells back, "Who says she can't talk?"

"Sister says so," says Mama.

"You didn't have to tell me, I know whose word of honor don't mean a thing in this house," says Stella-Rondo.

And in a minute the loudest Yankee voice I ever heard in my life yells out, "OE'm Pop-OE the Sailor-r-r-r Ma-a-an!" and then somebody jumps up and down in the upstairs hall. In another second the house would of fallen down.

"Not only talks, she can tap-dance!" calls Stella-Rondo. "Which is more than some people I won't name can do."

"Why, the little precious darling thing!" Mama says, so surprised. "Just as smart as she can be!" Starts talking baby talk right there. Then she turns on me. "Sister, you ought to be thoroughly ashamed! Run upstairs this instant and apologize to Stella-Rondo and Shirley-T."

"Apologize for what?" I says. "I merely wondered if the child was normal, that's all. Now that she's proved she is, why, I have nothing further to say."

But Mama just turned on her heel and flew out, furious. She ran right upstairs and hugged the baby. She believed it was adopted. Stella-Rondo hadn't done a thing but turn her against me from upstairs while I stood there helpless over the hot stove. So that made Mama, Papa-Daddy and the baby all on Stella-Rondo's side.

Next, Uncle Rondo.

I must say that Uncle Rondo has been marvelous to me at various times in the past and I was completely unprepared to be made to jump out of my skin, the way it turned out. Once Stella-Rondo did something perfectly horrible to him—broke a chain letter from Flanders Field—and he took the radio back he had given her and gave it to me. Stella-Rondo was furious! For six months we all had to call her Stella instead of Stella-Rondo, or she wouldn't answer. I always thought Uncle Rondo had all the brains of the entire family. Another time he sent me to Mammoth Cave, with all expenses paid.

But this would be the day he was drinking that prescription, the Fourth of July.

So at supper Stella-Rondo speaks up and says she thinks Uncle Rondo ought to try to eat a little something. So finally Uncle Rondo said he would try a little cold biscuits and ketchup, but that was all. So *she* brought it to him.

"Do you think it wise to disport with ketchup in Stella-Rondo's flesh-colored kimono?" I says. Trying to be considerate! If Stella-Rondo couldn't watch out for her trousseau, somebody had to.

"Any objections?" asks Uncle Rondo, just about to pour out all the ketchup.

"Don't mind what she says, Uncle Rondo," says Stella-Rondo. "Sister has been devoting this solid afternoon to sneering out my bedroom window at the way you look."

"What's that?" says Uncle Rondo. Uncle Rondo has got the most terrible temper in the world. Anything is liable to make him tear the house down if it comes at the wrong time.

So Stella-Rondo says, "Sister says, 'Uncle Rondo certainly does look like a fool in that pink kimono!' "

Do you remember who it was really said that?

Uncle Rondo spills out all the ketchup and jumps out of his chair and tears off the kimono and throws it down on the dirty floor and puts his foot on it. It had to be sent all the way to Jackson to the cleaners and re-pleated.

"So that's your opinion of your Uncle Rondo, is it?" he says. "I look like a fool, do I? Well, that's the last straw. A whole day in this house with nothing to do, and then to hear you come out with a remark like that behind my back!"

"I didn't say any such of a thing, Uncle Rondo," I says, "and I'm not saying who did, either. Why, I think you look all right. Just try to take care of yourself and not talk and eat at the same time," I says. "I think you better go lie down."

"Lie down my foot," says Uncle Rondo. I ought to of known by that he was fixing to do something perfectly horrible.

So he didn't do anything that night in the precarious state he was in—just played Casino with Mama and Stella-Rondo and Shirley-T. and gave Shirley-T. a nickel with a head on both sides. It tickled her nearly to death, and she called him "Papa." But at 6:30 A.M. the next morning, he threw a whole five-cent package of some unsold one-inch firecrackers from the store as hard as he could into my bedroom and they every one went off. Not one bad one in the string. Anybody else, there'd be one that wouldn't go off.

Well, I'm just terribly susceptible to noise of any kind, the doctor has always told me I was the most sensitive person he had ever seen in his whole life, and I was simply prostrated. I couldn't eat! People tell me they heard it as far as the cemetery, and old Aunt Jep Patterson, that had been holding her own so good, thought it was Judgment Day and she was going to meet her whole family. It's usually so quiet here.

And I'll tell you it didn't take me any longer than a minute to make up my mind what to do. There I was with the whole entire house on Stella-Rondo's side and turned against me. If I have anything at all I have pride.

So I just decided I'd go straight down to the P.O. There's plenty of room there in the back, I says to myself.

Well! I made no bones about letting the family catch on to what I was up to. I didn't try to conceal it.

The first thing they knew, I marched in where they were all playing Old Maid and pulled the electric oscillating fan out by the plug, and everything got real hot. Next I snatched the pillow I'd done the needlepoint on right off the davenport from behind Papa-Daddy. He went "Ugh!" I beat Stella-Rondo up the stairs and finally found my charm bracelet in her bureau drawer under a picture of Nelson Eddy.

"So that's the way the land lies," says Uncle Rondo. There he was, piecing on the ham. "Well, Sister, I'll be glad to donate my army cot if you got any place to set it up, providing you'll leave right this minute and let me get some peace." Uncle Rondo was in France.

"Thank you kindly for the cot and 'peace' is hardly the word I would select if I had to resort to firecrackers at 6:30 A.M. in a young girl's bedroom," I says back to him. "And as to where I intend to go, you seem to forget my position as postmistress of China Grove, Mississippi," I says. "I've always got the P.O."

Well, that made them all sit up and take notice.

I went out front and started digging up some four-o'clocks to plant around the P.O.

"Ah-ah-ah!" says Mama, raising the window. "Those happen to be my four-o'clocks. Everything planted in that star is mine. I've never known you to make anything grow in your life."

"Very well," I says. "But I take the fern. Even you, Mama, can't stand there and deny that I'm the one watered that fern. And I happen to know where I can send in a box top and get a packet of one thousand mixed seeds, no two the same kind, free."

"Oh, where?" Mama wants to know.

But I says, "Too late. You 'tend to your house, and I'll 'tend to mine. You hear things like that all the time if you know how to listen to the radio. Perfectly marvelous offers. Get anything you want free."

So I hope to tell you I marched in and got that radio, and they could of all bit a nail in two, especially Stella-Rondo, that it used to belong to, and she well knew she couldn't get it back, I'd sue for it like a shot. And I very politely took the sewing-machine motor I helped pay the most on to give Mama for Christmas back in 1929, and a good big calendar, with the first-aid remedies on it. The thermometer and the Hawaiian ukulele certainly were rightfully mine, and I stood on the stepladder and got all my watermelon-rind preserves and every fruit and vegetable I'd put up, every jar. Then I began to pull the tacks out of the bluebird wall vases on the archway to the dining room.

"Who told you you could have those, Miss Priss?" says Mama, fanning as hard as she could.

"I bought 'em and I'll keep track of 'em," I says. "I'll tack 'em up one on each side of the post-office window, and you can see 'em when you come to ask me for your mail, if you're so dead to see 'em."

"Not I! I'll never darken the door to that post office again if I live to be a hundred," Mama says. "Ungrateful child! After all the money we spent on you at the Normal."

"Me either," says Stella-Rondo. "You can just let my mail lie there and *rot,* for all I care. I'll never come and relieve you of a single, solitary piece."

"I should worry," I says. "And who you think's going to sit down and write you all those big fat letters and postcards, by the way? Mr. Whitaker? Just because he was the only man ever dropped down in China Grove and you got him—unfairly—is he going to sit down and write you a lengthy correspondence after you come home giving no rhyme nor reason whatsoever for your separation and no explanation for the presence of that child? I may not have your brilliant mind, but I fail to see it."

So Mama says, "Sister, I've told you a thousand times that Stella-Rondo simply got homesick, and this child is far too big to be hers," and she says, "Now, why don't you all just sit down and play Casino?"

Then Shirley-T. sticks out her tongue at me in this perfectly horrible way. She has no more manners than the man in the moon. I told her she was going to cross her eyes like that some day and they'd stick.

"It's too late to stop me now," I says. "You should have tried that yesterday. I'm going to the P.O. and the only way you can possibly see me is to visit me there."

So Papa-Daddy says, "You'll never catch me setting foot in that post office, even if I should take a notion into my head to write a letter some place." He says, "I won't have you reachin' out of that little old window with a pair of shears and cuttin' off any beard of mine. I'm too smart for you!"

"We all are," says Stella-Rondo.

But I said, "If you're so smart, where's Mr. Whitaker?"

So then Uncle Rondo says, "I'll thank you from now on to stop reading all the orders I get on postcards and telling everybody in China Grove what you think is the matter with them," but I says, "I draw my own conclusions and will continue in the future to draw them." I says, "If people want to write their inmost secrets on penny postcards, there's nothing in the wide world you can do about it, Uncle Rondo."

"And if you think we'll ever *write* another postcard you're sadly mistaken," says Mama.

"Cutting off your nose to spite your face then," I says. "But if you're all determined to have no more to do with the U.S. mail, think of this: What will Stella-Rondo do now, if she wants to tell Mr. Whitaker to come after her?"

"Wah!" says Stella-Rondo. I knew she'd cry. She had a conniption fit right there in the kitchen.

"It will be interesting to see how long she holds out," I says. "And now—I am leaving."

"Good-bye," says Uncle Rondo.

"Oh, I declare," says Mama, "to think that a family of mine should quarrel on the Fourth of July, or the day after, over Stella-Rondo leaving old Mr. Whitaker and having the sweetest little adopted child! It looks like we'd all be glad!"

"Wah!" says Stella-Rondo, and has a fresh conniption fit.

"He left *her*—you mark my words," I says. "That's Mr. Whitaker. I know Mr. Whitaker. After all, I knew him first. I said from the beginning he'd up and leave her. I foretold every single thing that's happened."

"Where did he go?" asks Mama.

"Probably to the North Pole, if he knows what's good for him," I says.

But Stella-Rondo just bawled and wouldn't say another word. She flew to her room and slammed the door.

"Now look what you've gone and done, Sister," says Mama. "You go apologize."

"I haven't got time, I'm leaving," I says.

"Well, what are you waiting around for?" asks Uncle Rondo.

So I just picked up the kitchen clock and marched off, without saying "Kiss my foot" or anything, and never did tell Stella-Rondo goodbye.

There was a nigger girl going along on a little wagon right in front.

"Nigger girl," I says, "come help me haul these things down the hill, I'm going to live in the post office."

Took her nine trips in her express wagon. Uncle Rondo came out on the porch and threw her a nickel.

And that's the last I've laid eyes on any of my family or my family laid eyes on me for five solid days and nights. Stella-Rondo may be telling the most horrible tales in the world about Mr. Whitaker, but I haven't heard them. As I tell everybody, I draw my own conclusions.

But oh, I like it here. It's ideal, as I've been saying. You see, I've got everything cater-cornered, the way I like it. Hear the radio? All the war news. Radio, sewing machine, book ends, ironing board and that great big piano lamp—peace, that's what I like. Butter-bean vines planted all along the front where the strings are.

Of course, there's not much mail. My family are naturally the main people in China Grove, and if they prefer to vanish from the face of the earth, for all the mail they get or the mail they write, why, I'm not going to open my mouth. Some of the folks here in town are taking up for me and some turned against me. I know which is which. There are always people who will quit buying stamps just to get on the right side of Papa-Daddy.

But here I am, and here I'll stay. I want the world to know I'm happy.

And if Stella-Rondo should come to me this minute, on bended knees, and *attempt* to explain the incidents of her life with Mr. Whitaker, I'd simply put my fingers in both my ears and refuse to listen.

Study Guides

In this story the first-person narrator is also the major character. She delights in "telling all"—in dramatizing her family situation. She also remarks to her listener at the window of the post office that "the doctor has always told me I was the most sensitive person he had ever seen in his whole life." Therefore, in her role of observer, she is supersensitive to the faults of everybody around her, but ironically, she is insensitive to her own faults. In "telling all," she conveys to her listener far more about herself and her family than she herself realizes. She does not know that as she exposes her family she also displays her own petty pretensions and self-deceptions. Like the kimono in which Uncle Rondo disports in "broad open daylight," she too is "all cut on the bias." In defending herself and her actions, she condemns herself with every breath. This is the prevailing incongruity in Miss Welty's story. Sister is insular, self-centered, and willfully deceived about her own nature and the impression she makes upon the captive listener.

1. Examine the motivation behind each of Sister's acts and pronouncements. For example, she throws open Stella-Rondo's door and asks: "You mortally wounded?" Ostensibly she is expressing concern for Stella-Rondo's welfare, but what is her real motive? What motivation is actually behind her making green-tomato pickle? Her concern about the kimono while Uncle Rondo eats? Her solicitudes toward him after supper? Her concern over Shirley-T.'s inability to speak? Her warnings to Uncle Rondo to stay away from the hammock? Her rancor over Mr. Whitaker? Her insisting that Shirley-T. is not adopted? But is Shirley-T. adopted? How do you know?

2. The same sort of incongruity evident in Sister's behavior can be seen in the other members of the family. In one way or another each is pretentious, shortsighted, or ludicrous in the impression he makes. Explore the incongruities revealed in each of these vanities: (a) Papa-Daddy's

beard. What does it probably look like? What does he think it looks like? What is the basis of his pride in it and how may that pride be justified? (b) Mama's family pride. Why is Mama accused of "denying the facts of life" as did Cousin Annie Flo? What significance is there in Mama's insisting that Shirley-T. is adopted? Of believing Stella-Rondo is "brilliant" and Shirley-T. is "just as smart as she can be!"? What are the justifications for Mama's pride? Is it more reasonable than Papa-Daddy's pride in his beard? (c) Uncle Rondo's calling his drink a "prescription." What are his vanities and pretension? (d) Stella-Rondo's insisting on her own personal dignity and respectability. What does each of the following statements reveal? "Mr. Whitaker took several dozen photographs of me in it [the flesh-colored kimono]." " 'I asked you the instant I entered this house not to refer one more time to my adopted child, and you gave me your word of honor you would not,' was all Stella-Rondo would say, and started pulling out every one of her eyebrows with some cheap Kress tweezers." Uncle Rondo "gave Shirley-T. a nickel with a head on both sides. It tickled her nearly to death, and she called him 'Papa.' " (e) Sister's saying: "If I have anything at all I have pride." What does she have to be proud of?

3. The family squabbles in this story are inconsequential in the eyes of the world because the characters are so petty that they demand laughter instead of sympathy. That is, the average reader feels highly superior to the people of China Grove. At the same time we should perhaps be aware that in another degree, we may all correspond to them after a fashion. (Read "The Tuxedos," for example.) Thus one purpose of comedy—of satire in particular—is to "laugh us" into a recognition of some truth about ourselves. For in addition to providing amusement, comedy often fulfills the higher aim of creating a serious awareness. As for the setting (which includes time and place), consider the following: Could the identical situations and characters have existed in any other place except China Grove? Could the events have occurred in just the same way if there had not been a holiday? Why?

4. China Grove can be regarded as a microcosm of the world at large. What is the author possibly suggesting when she tells us Sister's family is the "main" one in China Grove? What happens in the macrocosm when disorder erupts in high places? The whole town of China Grove becomes embroiled in the family quarrel: "Some of the folks here in town are taking up for me and some turned against me." A kind of "revolutionary war" results from the family squabble and Sister's declaration of independence. What is the significance of "Hear the radio? All the war news"? What is the implication of time—"the Fourth of July, or day after"? Is there any implied commentary on the nature of our times in Sister's deserting her family for the "peace" and "cater-cornered" arrangement in the post office (a government agency)? What does this comic story tell us about the serious matter of civil strife?

5. Besides the comic incongruities which point to the irony of situation, the story makes use of other humorous discrepancies. One of these is overstatement. Sister makes trivial acts and petty emotions appear

ridiculously large because she overstates them. What, then, does her verbosity reveal about her lack of perspective and her self-dramatizing tendencies toward "martyrdom"?

6. On the other hand—also relating to language—there is a profusion of platitudes and clichés. What dangers and vices are suggested when characters habitually resort to these kinds of expressions? Point out specific examples and discuss them.

7. Try to determine exactly what the comic incongruities are in each of the following quotations and whether or not some contain an element of pathos:

> "I told you if you ever mentioned Annie Flo's name I'd slap your face," says Mama, and slaps my face.
>
> You ought to see Mama, she weighs two hundred pounds and has real tiny feet.
>
> Papa-Daddy's Mama's papa and sulks.
>
> "Papa-Daddy, you know I wouldn't any more want you to cut off your beard than the man in the moon."
>
> Stella-Rondo sat there and made that up while she was eating breast of chicken.
>
> He would of gone on till nightfall if Shirley-T. hadn't lost the Milky Way she ate in Cairo.
>
> He's Mama's only brother and is a good case of a one-track mind. Ask anybody. A certified pharmacist.
>
> "I believed to my soul he drank *chemicals.*"
>
> "Lie down my foot," says Uncle Rondo.

JEROME WEIDMAN

(1913–   )

The Tuxedos

Ever since the time, some ten years ago, when I worked for Mr. Brunschweig on Canal Street, I have been peculiarly sensitive to the half-hour of the day that comes between five-thirty and six o'clock in the late afternoon. Mr. Brunschweig was an excellent boss, as bosses go, except for one lamentable defect: he was a minute-pincher. He carried two large pocket watches and spent a good part of each day comparing them with each other and with the huge Seth Thomas on the wall. I am certain that he was a little terrified by the inexorableness of time and that his sensitivity to it was a direct result of the way he earned his living. Mr. Brunschweig rented tuxedos.

The tuxedo-renting business, as I knew it, was distinguished by two cardinal rules. First, the suits had to be made of the toughest and heaviest materials available. And second, it was necessary to deliver them as close to the moment of wearing as possible and even more imperative to pick them up as soon after they were taken off as the wearer would permit. Mr. Brunschweig's timing in this respect was so good and I was so nimble as a delivery boy that while many of his customers cursed him roundly for having delayed them in getting to a wedding, not one of them could say with honesty that he had worn a Brunschweig tuxedo to more than one affair for the price of a single renting.

My relations with Mr. Brunschweig were amicable if somewhat exhausting, but every day, as the hands of the clock crept around to half-past five, a definite tension would come into the atmosphere. My quitting time was six o'clock. As a general rule, Mr. Brunschweig arranged deliveries in such fashion that the last one carried me up to, or past, that hour. We had an understanding to the effect that if I took out a delivery at any time after five-thirty and could not get to my destination until six o'clock or a few minutes before, I did not have to return to the Canal Street store that night and was at liberty to go directly home. However, the possibility of his only employee departing for home five or ten minutes ahead of quitting time was so disturbing to Mr. Brunschweig that very often he would detain me in the store before I went out on my final delivery, talking about the weather or discussing the baseball scores, just to make sure that I could not possibly complete delivery before six o'clock.

Strangely enough, I did not resent these obvious subterfuges, because I sensed that Mr. Brunschweig was a little ashamed of them. What I did resent was that unconsciously I was being forced into practices I didn't approve of to combat him.

For instance, I would instinctively stall on any delivery after five-fifteen to make certain that I would not get back to the store in time to make another delivery before quitting. Or I would rush through a four-o'clock delivery to make sure that there would be ample time for still another one before six o'clock. In either case it was very unsettling, and scarcely a day went by that I didn't have a struggle with my conscience or the clock.

There were times, of course, when my energy overcame my caution. One day, in an industrious mood, I returned from an uptown delivery at twenty minutes to six. It had been a long trip and I could have stretched it for another twenty minutes with ease, but I had temporarily forgotten Mr. Brunschweig's vice and I did not realize my mistake until I came into the store. He was boxing an unusually large order, and I could tell from his cheery greeting that this one would carry me well past six o'clock. I was about to dismiss the occurrence as simply another occasion on which I had been outmaneuvered by Mr. Brunschweig when I saw that he had stacked six boxes, one on top of the other.

"Is that *one* delivery?" I asked in amazement.

The average delivery weighed well over ten pounds and consisted of a tuxedo, a shirt, a tie, studs, and a pair of patent-leather pumps, packed neatly into a heavy cardboard box. Two or three of these boxes were a load. Six of them were an incredible amount.

"Yeah," he said cheerfully. "Italian wedding. It all goes to one family. I'll give you a help to the subway."

I should have been grateful to him for this offer, I suppose, since it was an unusual move, but all I could think of was the prospect of juggling sixty pounds of tuxedos through the subway in the rush hour.

"Where's it going?" I asked.

"Brooklyn," he said. "It's just over the bridge. Won't take you long."

The boxes weighed so much I could scarcely raise them from the floor.

"Here," he said. "You take the hats. I'll take the suits till we get to the train."

I hadn't even thought about top hats. They were not very heavy, but they were the most perishable items in Mr. Brunschweig's stock and consequently were always packed with great care in individual boxes.

"We gotta hurry," Mr. Brunschweig said, handing me a slip of paper with an address on it. "It's the bride's family and I promised them early. Name is Lasquadro."

He took the lashed tuxedo boxes and I took the pile of hatboxes, tied one on top of another so that they resembled a small steamship funnel. In the street we paused for a moment while he locked the store and then we started off down Canal Street to the subway station.

The only satisfactory recollection I have of that evening is the brief memory of Mr. Brunschweig tottering along in front of me under the weight of six boxes of tuxedos and accessories. The rest was a nightmare. I remember being on the subway platform, between my two huge bundles, trying to get into train after train. I had to let seven or eight go by before I could wedge my way into one of them. Then I remember standing, perspiring and exhausted, outside the subway station in Brooklyn, looking at the two bundles and realizing that I could carry them no further. It had grown quite dark and I began to be worried, too, about being late with the delivery. Finally I worked out a plan. I dragged the tuxedos along the ground for a short distance, then went back for the hats, dragged them up to the tuxedos, and then repeated the process. It was an effective method but an extremely slow one. Though the address Mr. Brunschweig had given me was only three blocks from the Brooklyn subway station, it was almost twenty minutes later that I stopped, breathless, in front of the correct house number.

The street was deserted and dark; the house was a two-story brownstone affair and only the basement windows showed lights from behind drawn shades. As I wiped the perspiration from my face and tried to think of an excuse for being so late, I heard noises coming from the basement. Figures kept passing the windows quickly and the sounds of scuffling and angry voices reached me clearly. I was frightened and spent another precious minute trying to puzzle out a way of leaving my bundles without having to face the people inside the house.

Then, in a burst of nervous courage, I tumbled the bulky bundles down the steps that led to the basement door and knocked gently. There was no answer. The angry noises inside continued, and I knocked again. Still no answer. Then I discovered a push button on the wall beside the door, jabbed at it hastily, and a bell pealed shrilly somewhere inside the house. At once the door was pulled open and a small young man in shirt sleeves, with a tight, dark, scowling face, shot his head out and glared at me.

"What the hella *you* want?" he demanded harshly.

"The—the tuxedos," I said awkwardly. "I brought the tuxedos."

The young man turned his head and yelled at someone in the room behind him. "He brought the tuxedos! You hear that? He brought the tuxedos!"

He laughed unpleasantly and a man's voice replied from inside the room, "Tell him he knows what he can do with them!"

The young man in front of me reached for the door and started to slam it shut. The thought that I might have to drag those two bundles back to Canal Street that night was enough to make me forget my fright. I braced my shoulder against the door and held it open.

"I have to leave these here," I said quickly. "I have to—I have to get the receipt signed."

The little dark face glared at me and the hand on the door drew back threateningly. "Aah," he started to say, and then stopped. "O.K., O.K., come on. Bring 'em in and beat it."

He dragged the bundles in and the door swung shut behind me. As I began to fumble in my pocket for the receipt book, I stole a scared look at the scene in the room. It was a large, shabbily furnished living room, with a new radio in one corner, a huge potted rubber plant in another, and embroidered mottoes on the wall. A pretty, dark-haired girl in a white wedding gown was sitting at a table in the middle of the room. Five men, all in vests and shirt sleeves and all looking as if they must be brothers of the young man who had opened the door for me, were standing over her. One of the men held the girl and was twisting her arm behind her, and she was sobbing violently. A tiny old woman, with white hair in a knot at the back of her head and wearing a black alpaca apron, hovered on the outskirts of the group around the table, jabbering shrilly in Italian. The young man who had let me in joined his brothers. Nobody paid any attention to me.

"Come on," one of the men said, leaning over the girl. "What's his address? Give us that address!"

The girl shook her head and the man who was holding her arm gave it another twist. She screamed and dropped her head forward. Another man pushed his face down close to hers.

"Come on!" he yelled. "Give it to us. We're doing this for the family, ain't we? What's his address?"

The girl shook her head again; the little old lady chattered away. One of the brothers reached over and slapped the girl's face.

"Where was he when he called up?" he said. "Come on, tell us. We ain't gonna hurt him. We'll just murder the louse, that's all. Where was he?"

She didn't answer.

"Come on, you damn fool," the man who held her arm said. "Talk! You want him to go spreading it to the whole world he walked out on you an hour before the wedding?" He shook her angrily. "Where was he when he called up? Where does he live? We'll fix him so he won't talk. What's his address?"

The girl did not answer. He started to shake her again, then he saw me standing near the door. "Get that guy out of here," he said. The brother who had let me in came across the room in three steps and grabbed my shoulder. "Come on, kid," he said. "Beat it!"

I lifted my receipt book in front of his face. "The receipt," I said. "I must get my receipt signed. I can't leave the—" He snatched the book from me and fumbled in his vest pocket for a pencil. He couldn't find one. I held my own out to him and he scribbled his name in my receipt book.

"O.K., kid," he said sharply. "Outside!" and he shoved the receipt book and pencil at me. I took them and started toward the door. Suddenly the little old lady grabbed my arm and pulled me back.

"What the hellsa matter?" the young man asked angrily.

She gestured violently toward me and poured a stream of Italian at him.

"All right, all right," he said, and reached into his pocket, pulled out a coin, and tossed the tip to me. I caught it and turned toward the door again.

"Thanks," I said quickly. But before I could open the door the old lady was on me. She clawed at my hand until I opened it so she could see the coin. It was a quarter. She swung around to the young man and clutched his coat.

"What the hellsa matter now?" he cried. "I gave him the tip, didn't I?"

Again she started talking in Italian, pointing at the bundle of tuxedos and tapping off the boxes with her finger—one, two, three, four, five, six. She waved six fingers in his face and yelled at him. He bit his lip, dug into his pocket again, and slapped some more coins into my palm. At once the little old lady seized my hand again. Now there were two quarters, a dime, and a nickel in it. She counted them quickly, snatched up the nickel, and counted again. Sixty cents remained. Another glance at the tuxedos and another glance at the two quarters and dime in my hand. Six tuxedos. Sixty cents. She nodded sharply to herself. Now it was all right.

"Give us that address!" shouted one of the brothers. There was the sound of a slap and the girl screamed again. "Where was he when he called up?"

The little old lady pulled open the door, pushed me out roughly, and slammed it shut behind me.

RUDYARD KIPLING

(1865–1936)

The Bull That Thought

Westward from a town by the Mouths of the Rhône, runs a road so mathematically straight, so barometrically level, that it ranks among the world's measured miles and motorists use it for records.

I had attacked the distance several times, but always with a Mistral blowing, or the unchancy cattle of those parts on the move. But once, running from the East, into a high-piled, almost Egyptian, sunset, there came a night which it would have been sin to have wasted. It was warm with the breath of summer in advance; moonlit till the shadow of every rounded pebble and pointed cypress wind-break lay solid on that vast flat-floored waste; and my Mr. Leggatt, who had slipped out to make sure, reported that the road-surface was unblemished.

"Now," he suggested, "we might see what she'll do under strict road-conditions. She's been pullin' like the Blue de Luxe all day. Unless I'm all off, it's her night out."

We arranged the trial for after dinner—thirty kilometres as near as might be; and twenty-two of them without even a level crossing.

There sat beside me at table d'hôte an elderly, bearded Frenchman wearing the rosette of by no means the lowest grade of the Legion of Honour, who had arrived in a talkative Citroën. I gathered that he had spent much of his life in the French Colonial Service in Annam and Tonquin. When the War came, his years barring him from the front line, he had supervised Chinese woodcutters who, with axe and dynamite, deforested the centre of France for trench-props. He said my chauffeur had told him that I contemplated an experiment. He was interested in cars—had admired mine—would, in short, be greatly indebted to me if I permitted him to assist as an observer. One could not well refuse; and, knowing my Mr. Leggatt, it occurred to me there might also be a bet in the background.

While he went to get his coat, I asked the proprietor his name. "Voiron—Monsieur André Voiron," was the reply. "And his business?" "Mon Dieu! He is Voiron! He is all those things, there!" The proprietor waved his hands at brilliant advertisements on the dining-room walls, which declared that Voiron Frères dealt in wines, agricultural implements, chemical manures, provisions and produce throughout that part of the globe.

He said little for the first five minutes of our trip, and nothing at all for the next ten—it being, as Leggatt had guessed, Esmeralda's night out. But, when her indicator climbed to a certain figure and held there for three blinding kilometres, he expressed himself satisfied, and proposed to me that we should celebrate the event at the hotel. "I keep yonder," said he, "a wine on which I should value your opinion."

On our return, he disappeared for a few minutes, and I heard him rumbling in a cellar. The proprietor presently invited me to the dining-room, where, beneath one frugal light, a table had been set with local dishes of renown. There was, too, a bottle beyond most known sizes, marked black on red, with a date. Monsieur Voiron opened it, and we drank to the health of my car. The velvety, perfumed liquor, between fawn and topaz, neither too sweet nor too dry, creamed in its generous glass. But I knew no wine composed of the whispers of angels' wings, the breath of Eden and the foam and pulse of Youth renewed. So I asked what it might be.

"It is champagne," he said gravely.

"Then what have I been drinking all my life?"

"If you were lucky, before the War, and paid thirty shillings a bottle, it is possible you may have drunk one of our better-class *tisanes*."

"And where does one get this?"

"Here, I am happy to say. Elsewhere, perhaps, it is not so easy. We growers exchange these real wines among ourselves."

I bowed my head in admiration, surrender, and joy. There stood the most ample bottle, and it was not yet eleven o'clock. Doors locked and shutters banged throughout the establishment. Some last servant yawned on his way to bed. Monsieur Voiron opened a window and the moonlight flooded in from a small pebbled court outside. One could almost hear the town of Chambres breathing in its first sleep. Presently, there was a thick noise in the air, the passing of feet and hooves, lowings, and a stifled bark or two. Dust rose over the courtyard wall, followed by the strong smell of cattle.

"They are moving some beasts," said Monsieur Voiron, cocking an ear. "Mine, I think. Yes, I hear Christophe. Our beasts do not like automobiles—so we move at night. You do not know our country—the Crau, here, or the Camargue? I was—I am now, again—of it. All France is good; but this is the best." He spoke, as only a Frenchman can, of his own loved part of his own lovely land.

"For myself, if I were not so involved in all these affairs," he pointed to the advertisements—"I would live on our farm with my cattle, and worship them like a Hindu. You know our cattle of the Camargue, Monsieur. No? It is not an acquaintance to rush upon lightly. There are no beasts like them. They have a mentality superior to that of others. They graze and they ruminate, by choice, facing our Mistral, which is more than some automobiles will do. Also they have in them the potentiality of thought—and when cattle think—I have seen what arrives."

"Are they so clever as all that?" I asked idly.

"Monsieur, when your sportif chauffeur camouflaged your limousine so that she resembled one of your Army lorries, I would not believe her capacities. I bet him—ah—two to one—she would not touch ninety kilometres. It was proved that she could. I can give you no proof, but will you believe me if I tell you what a beast who thinks can achieve?"

"After the War," said I spaciously, "everything is credible."

"That is true! Everything inconceivable has happened; but still we learn nothing and we believe nothing. When I was a child in my father's house—before I became a Colonial Administrator—my interest and my affection were among our cattle. We of the old rock live here—have you seen?—in big farms like castles. Indeed, some of them may have been Saracenic. The barns group round them—great white-walled barns, and yards solid as our houses. One gate shuts all. It is a world apart; an administration of all that concerns beasts. It was there I learned something about cattle. You see, they are our playthings in the Camargue and the Crau. The boy measures his strength against the calf that butts him in play among the manure-heaps. He moves in and out among the cows, who are—not so amiable. He rides with the herdsmen in the open to shift the herds. Sooner or later, he meets as bulls the little calves that knocked him over. So it was with me—till it became necessary that I should go to our Colonies." He laughed. "Very necessary. That is a good time in youth, Monsieur, when one does these things which shock our parents. Why is it always Papa who is so shocked and has never heard of such things—and Mamma who supplies the excuses? . . . And when my brother—my elder who stayed and created the business—begged me to return and help him, I resigned my Colonial career gladly enough. I returned to our own lands, and my well-loved, wicked white and yellow cattle of the Camargue and the Crau. My Faith, I could talk of them all night, for this stuff unlocks the heart, without making repentance in the morning. . . . Yes! It was after the War that this happened. There was a calf, among Heaven knows how many of ours—a bull-calf—an infant indistinguishable from his companions. He was sick, and he had been taken up with his mother into the big farmyard at home with us. Naturally the children of our herdsmen practised on him from the first. It is in their blood. The Spaniards make a cult of bull-fighting. Our little devils down here bait bulls as automatically as the English child kicks or throws balls. This calf would chase them with his eyes open, like a cow when she hunts a man. They would take refuge behind our tractors and wine-carts in the centre of the yard: he would chase them in and out as a dog hunts rats. More than that, he would study their psychology, his eyes in their eyes. Yes, he watched their faces to divine which way they would run. He himself, also, would pretend sometimes to charge directly at a boy. Then he would wheel right or left—one could never tell—and knock over some child pressed against a wall who thought himself safe. After this, he would stand over him, knowing that his companions must come to his aid; and when they were all together, waving their jackets across his eyes and pulling his tail, he would scatter them—how he would scatter them! He could kick too, sideways like a cow. He knew his ranges as well as our gunners, and he was as quick on his feet as our Carpentier. I observed him often. Christophe—the man who passed just now—our chief herdsman, who had taught me to ride with our beasts when I was ten—Christophe told me that he was descended from a yellow cow of those days that had chased us once into the marshes. 'He kicks just like her,' said Christophe. 'He can side-kick as he jumps. Have you seen, too, that he is not deceived by the jacket when a boy waves it? He uses it to find the boy. They think they are feeling him. He is feeling them always. He thinks, that one.' I had come to the same conclusion. Yes—the creature was a thinker along the lines necessary to his sport; and he was a humorist also, like so many natural murderers. One knows the type among beasts as well as among men. It possesses a curious truculent mirth—almost indecent but infallibly significant——"

Monsieur Voiron replenished our glasses with the great wine that went better at each descent.

"They kept him for some time in the yards to practise upon. Naturally he became a little brutal; so Christophe turned him out to learn manners among his equals in the grazing lands, where the Camargue joins the Crau. How old was he then? About eight or nine months, I think. We met again a few months later—he and I. I was riding one of our little half-wild horses, along a road of the Crau, when I found myself almost unseated. It was he! He had hidden himself behind a wind-break till we passed, and had then charged my horse from behind. Yes, he had deceived even my little horse! But I recognised him. I gave him the whip across the nose, and I said: 'Apis, for this thou goest to Arles! It was unworthy of thee, between us two.' But that creature had no shame. He went away laughing, like an Apache. If he had dismounted me, I do not think it is I who would have laughed—yearling as he was."

"Why did you want to send him to Arles?" I asked.

"For the bull-ring. When your charming tourists leave us, we institute our little amusements there. Not a real bull-fight, you understand, but young bulls with padded horns, and our boys from hereabouts and in the city go to play with them. Naturally, before we send them we try them in our yards at home. So we brought up Apis from his pastures. He knew at once that he was among the friends of his youth—he almost shook hands with them—and he submitted like an angel to padding his horns. He investigated the carts and tractors in the yards, to choose his lines of defence and attack. And then—he attacked with an *élan,* and he defended with a tenacity and forethought that delighted us. In truth, we were so pleased that I fear we trespassed upon his patience. We desired him to repeat himself, which no true artist will tolerate. But he gave us fair warning. He went out to the centre of the yard, where there was some dry earth; he kneeled down and—you have seen a calf whose horns fret him thrusting and rooting into a bank? He did just that, very deliberately, till he had rubbed the pads off his horns. Then he rose, dancing on those wonderful feet that twinkled, and he said: 'Now, my friends, the buttons are off the foils. Who begins?' We understood. We finished at once. He was turned out again on the pastures till it should be time to amuse them at our little metropolis. But, some time before he went to Arles—yes, I think I have it correctly—Christophe, who had been out on the Crau, informed me that Apis had assassinated a young bull who had given signs of developing into a rival. That happens, of course, and our herdsmen should prevent it. But Apis had killed in his own style—at dusk, from the ambush of a wind-break—by an oblique charge from behind which knocked the other over. He had then disembowelled him. All very possible, *but*—the murder accomplished—Apis went to the bank of a wind-break, knelt, and carefully, as he had in our yard, cleaned his horns in the earth. Christophe, who had never seen such a thing, at once borrowed (do you know, it is most efficacious when taken that way?) some Holy Water from our little chapel in those pastures, sprinkled Apis (whom it did not affect), and rode in to tell me. It was obvious that a thinker of that bull's type would also be meticulous in his toilette; so, when he was sent to Arles, I warned our consignees to exercise caution with him. Happily, the change of scene, the music, the general attention, and the meeting again with old friends—all our bad boys attended—agreeably distracted him. He became for the time a pure *farceur* again; but his wheelings, his rushes, his rat-huntings were more superb than ever. There was in them now, you understand, a breadth of technique that comes of reasoned art, and, above all, the passion that arrives after experience. Oh, he had learned, out there on the Crau! At the end of his little turn, he was, according to local rules, to be handled in all respects except for the sword, which was a stick, as a professional bull who must die. He was manœuvred into, or he posed himself in, the proper attitude; made his rush; received the point on his shoulder and then—turned about and cantered toward the door by which he had entered the arena. He said to the world: 'My friends, the representation is ended. I thank you for your applause. I go to repose myself.' But our Arlesians, who are—not so clever as some, demanded an encore, and Apis was headed back again. We others from his country, we knew what would happen. He went to the centre of the ring, kneeled, and, slowly, with full parade, plunged his horns alternately in the dirt till the pads came off. Christophe shouts: 'Leave him alone, you straight-nosed imbeciles! Leave him before you must.' But they required emotion; for Rome has always debauched her loved Provincia with bread and circuses. It was given. Have you, Monsieur, ever seen a servant, with pan and broom, sweeping round the baseboard of a room? In a half-minute Apis has them all swept out and over the barrier. Then he demands once more that the door shall be opened to him. It is opened and he retires as though—which, truly, is the case—loaded with laurels."

Monsieur Voiron refilled the glasses, and allowed himself a cigarette, which he puffed for some time.

"And afterwards?" I said.

"I am arranging it in my mind. It is difficult to do it justice. Afterwards—yes, afterwards—Apis returned to his pastures and his mistresses and I to my business. I am no longer a scandalous old 'sportif' in shirtsleeves howling encouragement to the yellow son of a cow. I revert to Voiron Frères—wines, chemical manures, *et cetera*. And next year, through some chicane which I have not the leisure to unravel, and also, thanks to our patriarchal system of paying our older men out of the increase of the herds, old Christophe possesses himself of Apis. Oh, yes, he proves it through descent from a certain cow that my father had given his father before the Republic. Beware, Monsieur, of the memory of the illiterate man! An ancestor of Christophe had been a soldier under our Soult against your Beresford, near Bayonne. He fell into the hands of Spanish guerrillas. Christophe and his wife used to tell me the details on certain Saints' Days when I was a child. Now, as compared with our recent war, Soult's campaign and retreat across the Bidassoa——"

"But did you allow Christophe just to annex the bull?" I demanded.

"You do not know Christophe. He had sold him to the Spaniards before he informed me. The Spaniards pay in coin—douros of very pure silver. Our peasants mistrust our paper. You know the saying: 'A thousand francs paper; eight hundred metal, and the cow is yours.' Yes, Christophe sold Apis, who was then two and a half years old, and to Christophe's knowledge thrice at least an assassin."

"How was that?" I said.

"Oh, his own kind only; and always, Christophe told me, by the same oblique rush from behind, the same sideways overthrow, and the same swift disembowelment, followed by this levitical cleaning of the horns. In human life he would have kept a manicurist—this Minotaur. And so, Apis disappears from our country. That does not trouble me. I know in due time I shall be advised. Why? Because, in this land, Monsieur, not a hoof moves between Berre and the Saintes Maries without the knowledge of specialists such as Christophe. The beasts are the substance, and the drama of their lives to them. So when Christophe tells me, a little before Easter Sunday, that Apis makes his début in the bull-ring of a small Catalan town on the road to Barcelona, it is only to pack my car and trundle there across the frontier with him. The place lacked importance and manufactures, but it had produced a matador of some reputation, who was condescending to show his art in his native town. They were even running one special train to the place. Now our French railway system is only execrable, but the Spanish——"

"You went down by road, didn't you?" said I.

"Naturally. It was not too good. Villamarti was the matador's name. He proposed to kill two bulls for the honour of his birthplace. Apis, Christophe told me, would be his second. It was an interesting trip, and that little city by the sea was ravishing. Their bull-ring dates from the middle of the seventeenth century. It is full of feeling. The ceremonial too—when the horsemen enter and ask the Mayor in his box to throw down the keys of the bull-ring—that was exquisitely conceived. You know, if the keys are caught in the horseman's hat, it is considered a good omen. They were perfectly caught. Our seats were in the front row beside the gates where the bulls enter, so we saw everything.

Villamarti's first bull was not too badly killed. The second matador, whose name escapes me, killed his without distinction—a foil to Villamarti. And the third, Chisto, a laborious, middle-aged professional who had never risen beyond a certain dull competence, was equally of the background. Oh, they are as jealous as the girls of the Comédie Française, these matadors! Villamarti's troupe stood ready for his second bull. The gates opened, and we saw Apis, beautifully balanced on his feet, peer coquettishly round the corner, as though he were at home. A picador—a mounted man with the long lance-goad—stood near the barrier on his right. He had not even troubled to turn his horse, for the capeadors—the men with the cloaks—were advancing to play Apis—to feel his psychology and intentions, according to the rules that are made for bulls who do not think. . . . I did not realise the murder before it was accomplished! The wheel, the rush, the oblique charge from behind, the fall of horse and man were simultaneous. Apis leaped the horse, with whom he had no quarrel, and alighted, all four feet together (it was enough), between the man's shoulders, changed his beautiful feet on the carcass, and was away, pretending to fall nearly on his nose. Do you follow me? In that instant, by that stumble, he produced the impression that his adorable assassination was a mere bestial blunder. Then, Monsieur, I began to comprehend that it was an artist we had to deal with. He did not stand over the body to draw the rest of the troupe. He chose to reserve that trick. He let the attendants bear out the dead, and went on to amuse himself among the capeadors. Now to Apis, trained among our children in the yards, the cloak was simply a guide to the boy behind it. He pursued, you understand, the person, not the propaganda—the proprietor, not the journal. If a third of our electors of France were as wise, my friend! . . . But it was done leisurely, with humour and a touch of truculence. He romped after one man's cloak as a clumsy dog might do, but I observed that he kept the man on his terrible left side. Christophe whispered to me: 'Wait for his mother's kick. When he has made the fellow confident it will arrive.' It arrived in the middle of a gambol. My God! He lashed out in the air as he frisked. The man dropped like a sack, lifted one hand a little towards his head, and—that was all. So you see, a body was again at his disposition; a second time the cloaks ran up to draw him off, but a second time, Apis refused his grand scene. A second time he acted that his murder was accident and—he convinced his audience! It was as though he had knocked over a bridge-gate in the marshes by mistake. Unbelievable? I saw it."

The memory sent Monsieur Voiron again to the champagne, and I accompanied him.

"But Apis was not the sole artist present. They say Villamarti comes of a family of actors. I saw him regard Apis with a new eye. He, too, began to understand. He took his cloak and moved out to play him before they should bring on another picador. He had his reputation. Perhaps Apis knew it. Perhaps Villamarti reminded him of some boy with whom he had practised at home. At any rate Apis permitted it—up to a certain point; but he did not allow Villamarti the stage. He cramped him throughout. He dived and plunged clumsily and slowly, but always with menace and always closing in. We could see that the man was conforming to the bull—not the bull to the man; for Apis was playing him towards the centre of the ring, and, in a little while—I watched his face—Villamarti knew it. But I could not fathom the creature's motive. 'Wait,' said old Christophe. 'He wants that picador on the white horse yonder. When he reaches his proper distance he will get him. Villamarti is his cover. He used me once that way.' And so it was, my friend! With the clang of one of our own Seventy-fives, Apis dismissed Villamarti with his chest—breasted him over—and had arrived at his objective near the barrier. The same oblique charge; the head carried low for the sweep of the horns; the immense sideways fall of the horse, broken-legged and half-paralysed; the senseless man on the ground and—behold Apis between them, backed against the barrier—his right covered by the horse; his left by the body of the man at his feet. The simplicity of it! Lacking the carts and tractors of his early parade-grounds he, being a genius, had extemporised with the materials at hand, and dug himself in. The troupe closed up again, their left wing broken by the kicking horse, their right immobilised by the man's body which Apis bestrode with significance. Villamarti almost threw himself between the horns, but—it was more an appeal than an attack. Apis refused him. He held his base. A picador was sent at him—necessarily from the front, which alone was open. Apis charged—he who, till then, you realise, had not used the horn! The horse went over backwards, the man half beneath him. Apis halted, hooked him under the heart, and threw him to the barrier. We heard his head crack, but he was dead before he hit the wood. There was no demonstration from the audience. They, also, had begun to realise this Foch among bulls! The arena occupied itself again with the dead. Two of the troupe irresolutely tried to play him—God knows in what hope!—but he moved out to the centre of the ring. 'Look!' said Christophe. 'Now he goes to clean himself. That always frightened me.' He knelt down; he began to clean his horns. The earth was hard. He worried at it in an ecstasy of absorption. As he laid his head along and rattled his ears, it was as though he were interrogating the Devils themselves upon their secrets, and always saying impatiently: 'Yes, I know that—and *that*—and *that!* Tell me more—*more!'* In the silence that covered us, a woman cried: 'He digs a grave! Oh, Saints, he digs a grave!' Some others echoed this—not loudly—as a wave echoes in a grotto of the sea.

"And when his horns were cleaned, he rose up and studied poor Villamarti's troupe, eyes in eyes, one by one, with the gravity of an equal in intellect and the remote and merciless resolution of a master in his art. This was more terrifying than his toilette."

"And they—Villamarti's men?" I asked.

"Like the audience, were dominated. They had ceased to posture, or stamp, or address insults to him. They conformed to him. The two other matadors stared. Only Chisto, the oldest, broke silence with some call or other, and Apis turned his head towards him. Otherwise he was isolated, immobile—sombre—meditating on those at his mercy. Ah!

"For some reason the trumpet sounded for the *banderillas*—those gay hooked darts that are planted in the shoulders of bulls who do not think, after their neck-muscles are tired by lifting horses. When such bulls feel the pain, they check for an instant, and, in that instant, the men step gracefully aside. Villamarti's banderillero answered the trumpet mechanically—like one condemned. He stood out, poised the darts and stammered the usual patter of invitation. . . . And after? I do not assert that Apis shrugged his shoulders, but he reduced the episode to its lowest elements, as could only a bull of Gaul. With his truculence was mingled always—owing to the shortness of his tail—a certain Rabelaisian abandon, especially when viewed from the rear. Christophe had often commented upon it. Now, Apis brought that quality into play. He circulated round that boy, forcing him to break up his beautiful poses. He studied him from various angles, like an incompetent photographer. He presented to him every portion of his anatomy except his shoulders. At intervals he feigned to run in upon him. My God, he was cruel! But his motive was obvious. He was playing for a laugh from the spectators which should synchronise with the fracture of the human morale. It was achieved. The boy turned and ran towards the barrier. Apis was on him before the laugh ceased; passed him; headed him—what do I say?—herded him off to the left, his horns beside and a little in front of his chest: he did not intend him to escape into a refuge. Some of the troupe would have closed in, but Villamarti cried: 'If he wants him he will take him. Stand!' They stood. Whether the boy slipped or Apis nosed him over I could not see. But he dropped, sobbing. Apis halted like a car with four brakes, struck a pose, smelt him very completely and turned away. It was dismissal more ignominious than degradation at the head of one's battalion. The representation was finished. Remained only for Apis to clear his stage of the subordinate characters.

"Ah! His gesture then! He gave a dramatic start—this Cyrano of the Camargue—as though he was aware of them for the first time. He moved. All their beautiful breeches twinkled for an instant along the top of the barrier. He held the stage alone! But Christophe and I, we trembled! For, observe, he had now involved himself in a stupendous drama of which he only could supply the third act. And, except for an audience on the razor-edge of emotion, he had exhausted his material. Molière himself—we have forgotten, my friend, to drink to the health of that great soul—might have been at a loss. And Tragedy is but a step behind Failure. We could see the four or five Civil Guards, who are sent always to keep order, fingering the breeches of their rifles. They were but waiting a word from the Mayor to fire on him, as they do sometimes at a bull who leaps the barrier among the spectators. They would, of course, have killed or wounded several people —but that would not have saved Apis."

Monsieur Voiron drowned the thought at once, and wiped his beard.

"At that moment Fate—the Genius of France, if you will—sent to assist in the incomparable finale, none other than Chisto, the eldest, and, I should have said (but never again will I judge!) the least inspired of all; mediocrity itself but, at heart—and it is the heart that conquers always, my friend—at heart an artist. He descended stiffly into the arena, alone and assured. Apis regarded him, his eyes in his eyes. The man took stance, with his cloak, and called to the bull as to an equal: 'Now, Señor, we will show these honourable caballeros something together.' He advanced thus against this thinker who at a plunge—a kick—a thrust—could, we all knew, have extinguished him. My dear friend, I wish I could convey to you something of the unaffected bonhomie, the humour, the delicacy, the consideration bordering on respect even, with which Apis, the supreme artist, responded to this invitation. It was the Master, wearied after a strenuous hour in the atelier, unbuttoned and at ease with some not inexpert but limited disciple. The telepathy was instantaneous between them. And for good reason! Christophe said to me: 'All's well. That Chisto began among the bulls. I was sure of it when I heard him call just now. He has been a herdsman. He'll pull it off.' There was a little feeling and adjustment, at first, for mutual distances and allowances.

"Oh, yes! And here occurred a gross impertinence of Villamarti. He had, after an interval, followed Chisto—to retrieve his reputation. My Faith! I can conceive the elder Dumas slamming his door on an intruder precisely as Apis did. He raced Villamarti into the nearest refuge at once. He stamped his feet outside it, and he snorted: 'Go! I am engaged with an artist.' Villamarti went—his reputation left behind for ever.

"Apis returned to Chisto saying: 'Forgive the interruption. I am not always master of my time, but you were about to observe, my dear confrère . . . ?' Then the play began. Out of compliment to Chisto, Apis chose as his objective (every bull varies in his respect) the inner edge of the cloak—that nearest to the man's body. This allows but a few millimetres clearance in charging. But Apis trusted himself as Chisto trusted him, and this time, he conformed to the man, with inimitable judgment and temper. He allowed himself to be played into the shadow or the sun, as the delighted audience demanded. He raged enormously; he feigned defeat; he despaired in statuesque abandon, and thence flashed into fresh paroxysms of wrath—but always with the detachment of the true artist who knows he is but the vessel of an emotion whence others, not he, must drink. And never once did he forget that honest Chisto's cloak was to him the gauge by which to spare even a hair on the skin. He inspired Chisto too. My God! His youth returned to that meritorious beef-sticker—the desire, the grace, and the beauty of his early dreams. One could almost see that girl of the past for whom he was rising, rising to these present heights of skill and daring. It was his hour too—a miraculous hour of dawn returned to gild the sunset. All he knew was at Apis' disposition. Apis acknowledged it with all that he had learned at home, at Arles and in his lonely murders on our grazing-grounds. He flowed round Chisto like a river of death—round his knees, leaping at his shoulders, kicking just clear of one side or the other of his head; behind his back hissing as he shaved by; and once or twice—inimitable!—he reared wholly up before him while Chisto slipped back from beneath the avalanche of that instructed body. Those two, my dear friend, held five thousand people dumb with no sound but of their breathings—regular as pumps. It was unbearable. Beast and man realised together that we needed a change of note—a *détente*. They relaxed to pure buffoonery. Chisto fell back and talked to him outrageously. Apis pretended he had never heard such language. The audience howled with delight. Chisto slapped him; he took liberties with his short tail, to the end of which he clung while Apis pirouetted; he played about him in all postures; he had become the herdsman again—gross, careless, brutal, but comprehending. Yet Apis was always the more consummate clown. All that time (Christophe and I saw it) Apis drew off towards the gates of the *toril* where so many bulls enter but—have you ever heard of one that returned? *We* knew that Apis knew that as he had saved Chisto, so Chisto would save him. Life is sweet to us all; to the artist who lives many lives in one, sweetest. Chisto did not fail him. At the last, when none could laugh any longer, the man threw his cape across the bull's back, his arm round his neck. He flung up a hand at the gate, as Villamarti, young and commanding but *not* a herdsman, might have raised it, and he cried: 'Gentlemen, open to me and my honourable little donkey.' They opened—I have misjudged Spaniards in my time!—those gates opened to the man and the bull together, and closed behind them. And then? From the Mayor to the Guarda Civile they went mad for five minutes, till the trumpets blew and the fifth bull rushed out—an unthinking black Andalusian. I suppose some one killed him. My friend, my very dear friend, to whom I have opened my heart, I confess that I did not watch. Christophe and I we were weeping together like children of the same Mother. Shall we drink to Her?"

A Novella

At this point in his study of short fiction, the reader will have sampled twenty stories by nineteen authors. (Two stories by Eudora Welty are included because "A Worn Path" and "Why I Live at the P.O." exhibit, by contrast, the variety which may be reflected in one author's work.) These twenty stories provide a solid basis for reading short fiction critically and profitably. Nine additional stories for further reading are included, without comment, at the end of the book.

But first, before turning to that last section, the reader may find it worthwhile to look at "The Aspern Papers," Henry James's *novella,* or long short story, so that he may compare length, structure, plot, character development, and other characteristics of longer fiction with these same elements in the short story form. "The Aspern Papers" is a splendid example of a master craftsman's work on an extended piece of fiction—the work of an author who during his long career excelled in three major forms: the short story, the novella, and the novel. Readers should also keep in mind that James prepared two versions of "The Aspern Papers" for the press during his lifetime: the first in 1888, which is reprinted here; the second in 1909, for the "New York Edition" of his collected works. In a preface to the later version he discussed the background and genesis of the story, the revision of which provides an interesting exercise in textual analysis.

As a basis for an extended study or a research paper, a selected bibliography of collateral readings follows "The Aspern Papers." These are included for the reader interested in scholarly discussions of James's work and for the insights to be found in the writings of several critics.

HENRY JAMES

(1843–1916)

The Aspern Papers

CHAPTER I

I had taken Mrs. Prest into my confidence; in truth without her I should have made but little advance, for the fruitful idea in the whole business

Published by John Farquharson, Ltd.

dropped from her friendly lips. It was she who invented the short cut, who severed the Gordian knot. It is not supposed to be the nature of women to rise as a general thing to the largest and most liberal view—I mean of a practical scheme; but it has struck me that they sometimes throw off a bold conception—such as a man would not have risen to—with singular serenity. "Simply ask them to take you in on the footing of a lodger"—I don't think that unaided I should have risen to that. I was beating about the bush, trying to be ingenious, wondering by what combination of arts I might become an acquaintance, when she offered this happy suggestion that the way to become an acquaintance was first to become an inmate. Her actual knowledge of the Misses Bordereau was scarcely larger than mine, and indeed I had brought with me from England some definite facts which were new to her. Their name had been mixed up ages before with one of the greatest names of the century, and they lived now in Venice in obscurity, on very small means, unvisited, unapproachable, in a dilapidated old palace on an out-of-the-way canal: this was the substance of my friend's impression of them. She herself had been established in Venice for fifteen years and had done a great deal of good there; but the circle of her benevolence did not include the two shy, mysterious, and, as it was somehow supposed, scarcely respectable Americans (they were believed to have lost in their long exile all national quality, besides having had, as their name implied, some French strain in their origin), who asked no favours and desired no attention. In the early years of her residence she had made an attempt to see them, but this had been successful only as regards the little one, as Mrs. Prest called the niece; though in reality, as I afterwards learned, she was considerably the bigger of the two. She had heard Miss Bordereau was ill and had a suspicion that she was in want; and she had gone to the house to offer assistance, so that if there were suffering (and American suffering), she should at least not have it on her conscience. The "little one" received her in the great cold, tarnished Venetian sala, the central hall of the house, paved with marble and roofed with dim crossbeams, and did not even ask her to sit down. This was not encouraging for me, who wished to sit so fast, and I remarked as much to Mrs. Prest. She however replied with profundity, "Ah, but there's all the difference: I went to confer a favour and you will go to ask one. If they are proud you will be on the right side." And she offered to show me their house to begin with—to row me thither in her gondola. I let her know that I had already been to look at it half a dozen times; but I accepted her invitation, for it charmed me to hover about the place. I had made my way to it the day after my arrival in Venice (it had been described to me in advance by the friend in England to whom I owed definite information as to their possession of the papers), and I had besieged it with my eyes while I considered my plan of campaign. Jeffrey Aspern had never been in it that I knew of; but some note of his voice seemed to abide there by a roundabout implication, a faint reverberation.

Mrs. Prest knew nothing about the papers, but she was interested in my curiosity, as she was always interested in the joys and sorrows of her friends. As we went, however, in her gondola, gliding there under the sociable hood with the bright Venetian picture framed on either side by the movable window, I could see that she was amused by my infatuation, the way my interest in the papers had become a fixed idea. "One would think you expected to find in them the answer to the riddle of the universe," she said; and I denied the impeachment only by replying that if I had to choose between that precious solution and a bundle of Jeffrey Aspern's letters I knew indeed which would appear to me the greater boon. She pretended to make light of his genius and I took no pains to defend him. One doesn't defend one's god: one's god is in himself a defence. Besides, to-day, after his long comparative obscuration, he hangs high in the heaven of our literature, for all the world to see; he is a part of the light by which we walk. The most I said was that he was no doubt not a woman's poet: to which she rejoined aptly enough that he had been at least Miss Bordereau's. The strange thing had been for me to discover in England that she was still alive: it was as if I had been told Mrs. Siddons was, or Queen Caroline, or the famous Lady Hamilton, for it seemed to me that she belonged to a generation as extinct. "Why, she must be tremendously old—at least a hundred," I had said; but on coming to consider dates I saw that it was not strictly necessary that she should have exceeded by very much the common span. None the less she was very far advanced in life and her relations with Jeffrey Aspern had occurred in her early womanhood. "That is her excuse," said Mrs. Prest, half sententiously and yet also somewhat as if she were ashamed of making a speech so little in the real tone of Venice. As if a woman needed an excuse for having loved the divine poet! He had been not only one of the most brilliant minds of his day (and in those years, when the century was young, there were, as every one knows, many), but one of the most genial men and one of the handsomest.

The niece, according to Mrs. Prest, was not so old, and she risked the conjecture that she was only a grand-niece. This was possible; I had nothing but my share in the very limited knowledge of my English fellow-worshipper John Cumnor, who had never seen the couple. The world, as I say, had recognised Jeffrey Aspern, but Cumnor and I had recognised him most. The multitude, to-day, flocked to his temple, but of that temple he and I regarded ourselves as the ministers. We held, justly, as I think, that we had done more for his memory than any one else, and we had done it by opening lights into his life. He had nothing to fear from us because he had nothing to fear from the truth, which alone at such a distance of time we could be interested in establishing. His early death had been the only dark spot in his life, unless the papers in Miss Bordereau's hands should perversely bring out others. There had been an impression about 1825 that he had "treated her badly," just as there had been an impression that he had "served," as the London populace says, several other ladies in the same way. Each of these cases Cumnor and I had been able to investigate, and we had never failed to acquit him conscientiously of shabby behaviour. I judged him perhaps more indulgently than my friend; certainly, at any rate, it appeared to me that no man could have walked straighter in the given circumstances. These were almost always awkward. Half the women of his time, to speak liberally, had flung themselves at his head, and out of this pernicious fashion many complications, some of them grave, had not failed to arise. He was not a woman's poet, as I had said to Mrs. Prest, in the modern phase of his reputation; but the situation had been different when the man's own voice was mingled with his song. That voice, by every testimony, was one of the sweetest ever heard. "Orpheus and the Mænads!" was the exclamation that rose to my lips when I first turned over his correspondence. Almost all the Mænads were unreasonable and many of them insupportable; it struck me in short that he was kinder, more considerate than, in his place (if I could imagine myself in such a place!) I should have been.

It was certainly strange beyond all strangeness, and I shall not take up space with attempting to explain it, that whereas in all these other lines of research we had to deal with phantoms and dust, the mere echoes of echoes, the one living source of information that had lingered on into our time had been unheeded by us. Every one of Aspern's contemporaries had, according to our belief, passed away; we had not been able to look into a single pair of eyes into which his had looked or to feel a transmitted contact in any aged hand that his had touched. Most dead of all did poor Miss Bordereau appear, and yet she alone had survived. We exhausted in the course of months our wonder that we had not found her out sooner, and the substance of our explanation was that she had kept so quiet. The poor lady on the whole had had reason for doing so. But it was a revelation to us that it was possible to keep so quiet as that in the latter half of the nineteenth century—the age of newspapers and telegrams and photographs and interviewers. And she had taken no great trouble about it either: she had not hidden herself away in an undiscoverable hole; she had boldly settled down in a city of exhibition. The only secret of her safety that we could perceive was that Venice contained so many curiosities that were greater than she. And then accident had somehow favoured her, as was shown for example in the fact that Mrs. Prest had never happened to mention her to me, though I had spent three weeks in Venice—under her nose, as it were—five years before. Mrs. Prest had not mentioned this much to any one; she appeared almost to have forgotten she was there. Of course she had not the responsibilities of an editor. It was no explanation of the old woman's having eluded us to say that she lived abroad, for our researches had again and again taken us (not only by correspondence but by personal inquiry) to France, to Germany, to Italy, in which countries, not counting his important stay in England, so many of the too few years of Aspern's career were spent. We were glad to think at least that in all our publishings (some people consider I believe that we have overdone them), we had only touched in passing and in the most discreet manner on Miss Bordereau's connection. Oddly enough, even if we had had the material (and we often wondered what had become of it), it would have been the most difficult episode to handle.

The gondola stopped, the old palace was there; it was a house of the class which in Venice carries even in extreme dilapidation the dignified name. "How charming! It's gray and pink!" my companion exclaimed; and that is the most comprehensive description of it. It was not particularly old, only two or three centuries; and it had an air not so much of decay as of quiet discouragement, as if it had rather missed its career. But its wide front, with a stone balcony from end to end of the *piano nobile* or most important floor, was architectural enough, with the aid of various pilasters and arches; and the stucco with which in the intervals it had long ago been endued was rosy in the April afternoon. It overlooked a clean, melancholy, unfrequented canal, which had a narrow *riva* or convenient footway on either side. "I don't know why—there are no brick gables," said Mrs. Prest, "but this corner has seemed to me before more Dutch than Italian, more like Amsterdam than like Venice. It's perversely clean, for reasons of its own; and though you can pass on foot scarcely any one ever thinks of doing so. It has the air of a Protestant Sunday. Perhaps the people are afraid of the Misses Bordereau. I daresay they have the reputation of witches."

I forget what answer I made to this—I was given up to two other reflections. The first of these was that if the old lady lived in such a big, imposing house she could not be in any sort of misery and therefore would not be tempted by a chance to let a couple of rooms. I expressed this idea to Mrs. Prest, who gave me a very logical reply. "If she didn't live in a big house how could it be a question of her having rooms to spare? If she were not amply lodged herself you would lack ground to approach her. Besides, a big house here, and especially in this *quartier perdu,* proves nothing at all: it is perfectly compatible with a state of penury. Dilapidated old palazzi, if you will go out of the way for them, are to be had for five shillings a year. And as for the people who live in them—no, until you have explored Venice socially as much as I have you can form no idea of their domestic desolation. They live on nothing, for they have nothing to live on." The other idea that had come into my head was connected with a high blank wall which appeared to confine an expanse of ground on one side of the house. Blank I call it, but it was figured over with the patches that please a painter, repaired breaches, crumblings of plaster, extrusions of brick that had turned pink with time; and a few thin trees, with the poles of certain rickety trellises, were visible over the top. The place was a garden and apparently it belonged to the house. It suddenly occurred to me that if it did belong to the house I had my pretext.

I sat looking out on all this with Mrs. Prest (it was covered with the golden glow of Venice) from the shade of our *felze,* and she asked me if I would go in then, while she waited for me, or come back another time. At first I could not decide—it was doubtless very weak of me. I wanted still to think I *might* get a footing, and I was afraid to meet failure, for it would leave me, as I remarked to my companion, without another arrow for my bow. "Why not another?" she inquired, as I sat there hesitating and thinking it over; and she wished to know why even now and before taking the trouble of becoming an inmate (which might be wretchedly uncomfortable after all, even if it succeeded), I had not the resource of simply offering them a sum of money down. In that way I might obtain the documents without bad nights.

"Dearest lady," I exclaimed, "excuse the impatience of my tone when I suggest that you must have forgotten the very fact (surely I communicated it to you) which pushed me to throw myself upon your ingenuity. The old woman won't have the documents spoken of; they are personal, delicate, intimate, and she hasn't modern notions, God bless her! If I should sound that note first I should certainly spoil the game. I can arrive at the papers only by putting her off her guard, and I can put her off her guard only by ingratiating diplomatic practices. Hypocrisy, duplicity are my only chance. I am sorry for it, but for Jeffrey Aspern's sake I would do worse still. First I must take tea with her; then tackle the main job." And I told over what had happened to John Cumnor when he wrote to her. No notice whatever had been taken of his first letter, and the second had been answered very sharply, in six lines, by the niece. "Miss Bordereau requested her to say that she could not imagine what he meant by troubling them. They had none of Mr. Aspern's papers, and if they had should never think of showing them to any one on any account whatever. She didn't know what he was talking about and begged he would let her alone." I certainly did not want to be met that way.

"Well," said Mrs. Prest, after a moment, provokingly, "perhaps after all they haven't any of his things. If they deny it flat how are you sure?"

"John Cumnor is sure, and it would take me long to tell you how his conviction, or his very strong presumption—strong enough to stand against the old lady's not unnatural fib—has built itself up. Besides, he makes much of the internal evidence of the niece's letter."

"The internal evidence?"

"Her calling him 'Mr. Aspern.' "

"I don't see what that proves."

"It proves familiarity, and familiarity implies the possession of mementoes, of relics. I can't tell you how that 'Mr.' touches me—how it bridges over the gulf of time and brings our hero near to me—nor what an edge it gives to my desire to see Juliana. You don't say 'Mr.' Shakespeare."

"Would I, any more, if I had a box full of his letters?"

"Yes, if he had been your lover and some one wanted them!" And I added that John Cumnor was so convinced, and so all the more convinced by Miss Bordereau's tone, that he would have come himself to Venice on the business were it not that for him there was the obstacle that it would be difficult to disprove his identity with the person who had written to them, which the old ladies would be sure to suspect in spite of dissimulation and a change of name. If they were to ask him point-blank if he were not their correspondent it would be too awkward for him to lie; whereas I was fortunately not tied in that way. I was a fresh hand and could say no without lying.

"But you will have to change your name," said Mrs. Prest. "Juliana lives out of the world as much as it is possible to live, but none the less she has probably heard of Mr. Aspern's editors; she perhaps possesses what you have published."

"I have thought of that," I returned; and I drew out of my pocket-book a visiting-card, neatly engraved with a name that was not my own.

"You are very extravagant; you might have written it," said my companion.

"This looks more genuine."

"Certainly, you are prepared to go far! But it will be awkward about your letters; they won't come to you in that mask."

"My banker will take them in and I will go every day to fetch them. It will give me a little walk."

"Shall you only depend upon that?" asked Mrs. Prest. "Aren't you coming to see me?"

"Oh, you will have left Venice, for the hot months, long before there are any results. I am prepared to roast all summer—as well as hereafter, perhaps you'll say! Meanwhile, John Cumnor will bombard me with letters addressed, in my feigned name, to the care of the *padrona*."

"She will recognize his hand," my companion suggested.

"On the envelope he can disguise it."

"Well, you're a precious pair! Doesn't it occur to you that even if you are able to say you are not Mr. Cumnor in person they may still suspect you of being his emissary?"

"Certainly, and I see only one way to parry that."

"And what may that be?"

I hesitated a moment. "To make love to the niece."

"Ah," cried Mrs. Prest, "wait till you see her!"

CHAPTER II

"I must work the garden—I must work the garden," I said to myself, five minutes later, as I waited, upstairs, in the long, dusky sala, where the bare scagliola floor gleamed vaguely in a chink of the closed shutters. The place was impressive but it looked cold and cautious. Mrs. Prest had floated away, giving me a rendezvous at the end of half an hour by some neighbouring watersteps; and I had been let into the house, after pulling the rusty bell-wire, by a little red-headed, white-faced maid-servant, who was very young and not ugly and wore clicking pattens and a shawl in the fashion of a hood. She had not contented herself with opening the door from above by the usual arrangement of a creaking pulley, though she had looked down at me first from an upper window, dropping the inevitable challenge which in Italy precedes the hospitable act. As a general thing I was irritated by this survival of mediæval manners, though as I liked the old I suppose I ought to have liked it; but I was so determined to be genial that I took my false card out of my pocket and held it up to her, smiling as if it were a magic token. It had the effect of one indeed, for it brought her, as I say, all the way down. I begged her to hand it to her mistress, having first written on it in Italian the words, "Could you very kindly see a gentleman, an American, for a moment?" The little maid was not hostile, and I reflected that even that was perhaps something gained. She coloured, she smiled and looked both frightened and pleased. I could see that my arrival was a great affair, that visits were rare in that house, and that she was a person who would have liked a sociable place. When she pushed forward the heavy door behind me I felt that I had a foot in the citadel. She pattered across the damp, stony lower hall and I followed her up the high staircase—stonier still, as it seemed—without an invitation. I think she had meant I should wait for her below, but such was not my idea, and I took up my station in the sala. She flitted, at the far end of it, into impenetrable regions, and I looked at the place with my heart beating as I had known it to do in the dentist's parlour. It was gloomy and stately, but it owed its character almost entirely to its noble shape and to the fine architectural doors—as high as the doors of houses—which, leading into the various rooms, repeated themselves on either side at intervals. They were surmounted with old faded painted escutcheons, and here and there, in the spaces between them, brown pictures, which I perceived to be bad, in battered frames, were suspended. With the exception of several straw-bottomed chairs with their backs to the wall, the grand obscure vista contained nothing else to minister to effect. It was evidently never used save as a passage, and little even as that. I may add that by the time the door opened again through which the maid-servant had escaped, my eyes had grown used to the want of light.

I had not meant by my private ejaculation that I must cultivate the soil of the tangled enclosure which lay beneath the windows, but the lady who came toward me from the distance over the hard, shining floor might have supposed as much from the way in which, as I went rapidly to meet her, I exclaimed, taking care to speak Italian: "The garden, the garden—do me the pleasure to tell me if it's yours!"

She stopped short, looking at me with wonder; and then, "Nothing here is mine," she answered in English, coldly and sadly.

"Oh, you are English; how delightful!" I remarked, ingenuously. "But surely the garden belongs to the house?"

"Yes, but the house doesn't belong to me." She was a long, lean, pale person, habited apparently in a dull-coloured dressing-gown, and she spoke with a kind of mild literalness. She did not ask me to sit down, any more than years before (if she were the niece) she had asked Mrs. Prest, and we stood face to face in the empty pompous hall.

"Well then, would you kindly tell me to whom I must address myself? I'm afraid you'll think me odiously intrusive, but you know I *must* have a garden—upon my honour I must!"

Her face was not young, but it was simple; it was not fresh, but it was mild. She had large eyes which were not bright, and a great deal of hair which was not "dressed," and long fine hands which were—possibly—not clean. She clasped these members almost convulsively as, with a confused, alarmed look, she broke out, "Oh, don't take it away from us; we like it ourselves!"

"You have the use of it then?"

"Oh yes. If it wasn't for that!" And she gave a shy, melancholy smile.

"Isn't it a luxury, precisely? That's why, intending to be in Venice some weeks, possibly all summer, and having some literary work, some reading and writing to do, so that I must be quiet, and yet if possible a great deal in the open air—that's why I have felt that a garden it really indispensable. I appeal to your own experience," I went on, smiling, "Now can't I look at yours?"

"I don't know, I don't understand," the poor woman murmured, planted there and letting her embarrassed eyes wander all over my strangeness.

"I mean only from one of those windows—such grand ones as you have here—if you will let me open the shutters." And I walked toward the back of the house. When I had advanced half-way I stopped and waited, as if I took it for granted she would accompany me. I had been of necessity very abrupt, but I strove at the same time to give her the impression of extreme courtesy. "I have been looking at furnished rooms all over the place, and it seems impossible to find any with a garden attached. Naturally in a place like Venice gardens are rare. It's absurd if you like, for a man, but I can't live without flowers."

"There are none to speak of down there." She came nearer to me, as if, though she mistrusted me, I had drawn her by an invisible thread. I went on again, and she continued as she followed me: "We have a few, but they are very common. It costs too much to cultivate them; one has to have a man."

"Why shouldn't I be the man?" I asked. "I'll work without wages; or rather I'll put in a gardener. You shall have the sweetest flowers in Venice."

She protested at this, with a queer little sigh which might also have been a gush of rapture at the picture I presented. Then she observed, "We don't know you—we don't know you."

"You know me as much as I know you; that is, much more, because you know my name. And if you are English I am almost a countryman."

"We are not English," said my companion, watching me helplessly while I threw open the shutters of one of the divisions of the wide high window.

"You speak the language so beautifully: might I ask what you are?" Seen from above the garden was certainly shabby; but I perceived at a glance that it had great capabilities. She made no rejoinder, she was so lost in staring at me, and I exclaimed, "You don't mean to say you are also by chance American?"

"I don't know; we used to be."

"Used to be? Surely you haven't changed?"

"It's so many years ago—we are nothing."

"So many years that you have been living here? Well, I don't wonder at that; it's a grand old house. I suppose you all use the garden," I went on, "but I assure you I shouldn't be in your way. I would be very quiet and stay in one corner."

"We all use it?" she repeated after me, vaguely, not coming close to the window but looking at my shoes. She appeared to think me capable of throwing her out.

"I mean all your family, as many as you are."

"There is only one other; she is very old—she never goes down."

"Only one other, in all this great house!" I feigned to be not only amazed but almost scandalised. "Dear lady, you must have space then to spare!"

"To spare?" she repeated, in the same dazed way.

"Why, you surely don't live (two quiet women—I see you are quiet, at any rate) in fifty rooms!" Then with a burst of hope and cheer I demanded: "Couldn't you let me two or three? That would set me up!"

I had now struck the note that translated my purpose and I need not reproduce the whole of the tune I played. I ended by making my interlocutress believe that I was an honourable person, though of course I did not even attempt to persuade her that I was not an eccentric one. I repeated that I had studies to pursue; that I wanted quiet; that I delighted in a garden and had vainly sought one up and down the city; that I would undertake that before another month was over the dear old house should be smothered in flowers. I think it was the flowers that won my suit, for I afterwards found that Miss Tita (for such the name of this high tremulous spinster proved somewhat incongruously to be) had an insatiable appetite for them. When I speak of my suit as won I mean that before I left her she had promised that she would refer the question to her aunt. I inquired who her aunt might be and she answered, "Why, Miss Bordereau!" with an air of surprise, as if I might have been expected to know. There were contradictions like this in Tita Bordereau which, as I observed later, contributed to make her an odd and affecting person. It was the study of the two ladies to live so that the world should not touch them, and yet they had never altogether accepted the idea that it never heard of them. In Tita at any rate a grateful susceptibility to human contact had not died out, and contact of a limited order there would be if I should come to live in the house.

"We have never done anything of the sort; we have never had a lodger or any kind of inmate." So much as this she made a point of saying to me. "We are very poor, we live very badly. The rooms are very bare—that you might take; they have nothing in them. I don't know how you would sleep; how you would eat."

"With your permission, I could easily put in a bed and a few tables and chairs. *C'est la moindre des choses* and the affair of an hour or two. I know a little man from whom I can hire what I should want for a few months, for a trifle, and my gondolier can bring the things round in his boat. Of course in this great house you must have a second kitchen, and my servant, who is a wonderfully handy fellow" (this personage was an evocation of the moment), "can easily cook me a chop there. My tastes and habits are of the simplest; I live on flowers!" And then I ventured to add that if they were very poor it was all the more reason they should let their rooms. They were bad economists—I never heard of such a waste of material.

I saw in a moment that the good lady had never before been spoken to in that way, with a kind of humorous firmness which did not exclude sympathy but was on the contrary founded on it. She might easily have told me that my sympathy was impertinent, but this by good fortune did not occur to her. I left her with the understanding that she would consider the matter with her aunt and that I might come back the next day for their decision.

"The aunt will refuse; she will think the whole proceeding very *louche!*" Mrs. Prest declared shortly after this, when I had resumed my place in her gondola. She had put the idea into my head and now (so little are women to be counted on) she appeared to take a despondent view of it. Her pessimism provoked me and I pretended to have the best hopes; I went so far as to say that I had a distinct presentiment that I should succeed. Upon this Mrs. Prest broke out, "Oh, I see what's in your head! You fancy you have made such an impression in a quarter of an hour that she is dying for you to come and can be depended upon to bring the old one round. If you do get in you'll count it as a triumph."

I did count it as a triumph, but only for the editor (in the last analysis), not for the man, who had not the tradition of personal conquest. When I went back on the morrow the little maid-servant conducted me straight throught the long sala (it opened there as before in perfect perspective and was lighter now, which I thought a good omen) into the apartment from which the recipient of my former visit had emerged on that occasion. It was a large shabby parlour, with a fine old painted ceiling and a strange figure sitting alone at one of the windows. They come back to me now almost with the palpitation they caused, the successive feelings that accompanied my consciousness that as the door of the room closed behind me I was really face to face with the Juliana of some of Aspern's most exquisite and most renowned lyrics. I grew used to her afterwards, though never completely; but as she sat there before me my heart beat as fast as if the miracle of resurrection had taken place for my benefit. Her presence seemed somehow to contain his, and I felt nearer to him at that first moment of seeing her than I ever had been before or ever have been since. Yes, I remember my emotions in their order, even including a curious little tremor that took me when I saw that the niece was not there. With her, the day before, I had become sufficiently familiar, but it almost exceeded my courage (much as I had longed for the event) to be left alone with such a terrible relic as the aunt. She was too strange, too literally resurgent. Then came a check, with the perception that we were not really face to face, inasmuch as she had over her eyes a horrible green shade which for her, served almost as a mask. I believed for the instant that she had put it on expressly, so that from underneath it she might scrutinise me without being scrutinised herself. At the same time it increased the presumption that there was a ghastly death's-head lurking behind it. The divine Juliana as a grinning skull—the vision hung there until it passed. Then it came to me that she *was* tremendously old—so old that death might take her at any moment, before I had time to get what I wanted from her. The next thought was a correction to that; it lighted up the situation. She would die next week, she would die tomorrow —then I could seize her papers. Meanwhile she sat there neither moving nor speaking. She was very small and shrunken, bent forward, with her hands in her lap. She was dressed in black and her head was wrapped in a piece of old black lace which showed no hair.

My emotion keeping me silent she spoke first, and the remark she made was exactly the most unexpected.

CHAPTER III

"Our house is very far from the centre, but the little canal is very *comme il faut.*"

"It's the sweetest corner of Venice and I can imagine nothing more charming," I hastened to reply. The old lady's voice was very thin and weak, but it had an agreeable, cultivated murmur and there was wonder in the thought that that individual note had been in Jeffrey Aspern's ear.

"Please to sit down there. I hear very well," she said quietly, as if perhaps I had been shouting at her; and the chair she pointed to was at a certain distance. I took possession of it, telling her that I was perfectly aware that I had intruded, that I had not been properly introduced and could only throw myself upon her indulgence. Perhaps the other lady, the one I had had the honour of seeing the day before, would have explained to her about the garden. That was literally what had given me courage to take a step so unconventional. I had fallen in love at sight with the whole place (she herself probably was so used to it that she did not know the impression it was capable of making on a stranger), and I had felt it was really a case to risk something. Was her own kindness in receiving me a sign that I was not wholly out in my calculation? It would render me extremely happy to think so. I could give her my word of honour that I was a most respectable, inoffensive person and that as an inmate they would be barely conscious of my existence. I would conform to any regulations, any restrictions if they would only let me enjoy the garden. Moreover I should be delighted to give her references, guarantees; they would be of the very best, both in Venice and in England as well as in America.

She listened to me in perfect stillness and I felt that she was looking at me with great attention, though I could see only the lower part of her bleached and shrivelled face. Independently of the refining process of old age it had a delicacy which once must have been great. She had been very fair, she had had a wonderful complexion. She was silent a little after I had ceased speaking; then she inquired, "If you are so fond of a garden why don't you go to *terra firma,* where there are so many far better than this?"

"Oh, it's the combination!" I answered, smiling; and then, with rather a flight of fancy, "It's the idea of a garden in the middle of the sea."

"It's not in the middle of the sea; you can't see the water."

I stared a moment, wondering whether she wished to convict me of fraud. "Can't see the water? Why, dear madam, I can come up to the very gate in my boat."

She appeared inconsequent, for she said vaguely in reply to this, "Yes, if you have got a boat. I haven't any; it's many years since I have been in one of the gondolas." She uttered these words as if the gondolas were a curious faraway craft which she knew only by hearsay.

"Let me assure you of the pleasure with which I would put mine at your service!" I exclaimed. I had scarcely said this however before I became aware that the speech was in questionable taste and might also do me the injury of making me appear too eager, too possessed of a hidden motive.

But the old woman remained impenetrable and her attitude bothered me by suggesting that she had a fuller vision of me than I had of her. She gave me no thanks for my somewhat extravagant offer but remarked that the lady I had seen the day before was her niece; she would presently come in. She had asked her to stay away a little on purpose, because she herself wished to see me at first alone. She relapsed into silence and I asked myself why she had judged this necessary and what was coming yet; also whether I might venture on some judicious remark in praise of her companion. I went so far as to say that I should be delighted to see her again: she had been so very courteous to me, considering how odd she must have thought me—a declaration which drew from Miss Bordereau another of her whimsical speeches.

"She has very good manners; I bred her up myself!" I was on the point of saying that that accounted for the easy grace of the niece, but I arrested myself in time, and the next moment the old woman went on: "I don't care who you may be—I don't want to know; it signifies very little to-day." This had all the air of being a formula of dismissal, as if her next words would be that I might take myself off now that she had had the amusement of looking on the face of such a monster of indiscretion. Therefore I was all the more surprised when she added, with her soft, venerable quaver, "You may have as many rooms as you like—if you will pay a good deal of money."

I hesiated but for a single instant, long enough to ask myself what she meant in particular by this condition. First it struck me that she must have really a large sum in her mind; then I reasoned quickly that her idea of a large sum would probably not correspond to my own. My deliberation, I think, was not so visible as to diminish the promptitude with which I replied, "I will pay with pleasure and of course in advance whatever you may think it proper to ask me."

"Well then, a thousand francs a month," she rejoined instantly, while her baffling green shade continued to cover her attitude.

The figure, as they say, was startling and my logic had been at fault. The sum she had mentioned was, by the Venetian measure of such matters, exceedingly large; there was many an old palace in an out-of-the-way corner that I might on such terms have enjoyed by the year. But so far as my small means allowed I was prepared to spend money, and my decision was quickly taken. I would pay her with a smiling face what she asked, but in that case I would give myself the compensation of extracting the papers from her for nothing. Moreover if she had asked five times as much I should have risen to the occasion; so odious would it have appeared to me to stand chaffering with Aspern's Juliana. It was queer enough to have a question of money with her at all. I assured her that her views perfectly met my own and that on the morrow I should have the pleasure of putting three months' rent into her hand. She received this announcement with serenity and with no apparent sense that after all it would be becoming of her to say that I ought to see the rooms first. This did not occur to her and indeed her serenity was mainly what I wanted. Our little bargain was just concluded when the door opened and the younger lady appeared on the threshold. As soon as Miss Bordereau saw her niece she cried out almost gaily, "He will give three thousand—three thousand to-morrow!"

Miss Tita stood still, with her patient eyes turning from one of us to the other; then she inquired, scarcely above her breath, "Do you mean francs?"

"Did you mean francs or dollars?" the old woman asked of me at this.

"I think francs were what you said," I answered, smiling.

"That is very good," said Miss Tita, as if she had become conscious that her own question might have looked over-reaching.

"What do *you* know? You are ignorant," Miss Bordereau remarked; not with acerbity but with a strange, soft coldness.

"Yes, of money—certainly of money!" Miss Tita hastened to exclaim.

"I am sure you have your own branches of knowledge," I took the liberty of saying, genially. There was something painful to me, somehow, in the turn the conversation had taken, in the discussion of the rent.

"She had a very good education when she was young. I looked into that myself," said Miss Borderau. Then she added, "But she has learned nothing since."

"I have always been with you," Miss Tita rejoined very mildly, and evidently with no intention of making an epigram.

"Yes, but for that!" her aunt declared, with more satirical force. She evidently meant that but for this her niece would never have got on at all; the point of the observation however being lost on Miss Tita, though she blushed at hearing her history revealed to a stranger. Miss Bordereau went on, addressing herself to me: "And what time will you come to-morrow with the money?"

"The sooner the better. If it suits you I will come at noon."

"I am always here but I have my hours," said the old woman, as if her convenience were not to be taken for granted.

"You mean the times when you receive?"

"I never receive. But I will see you at noon, when you come with the money."

"Very good, I shall be punctual"; and I added, "May I shake hands with you, on our contract?" I thought there ought to be some little form, it would make me really feel easier, for I foresaw that there would be no other. Besides, though Miss Bordereau could not to-day be called personally attractive and there was something even in her wasted antiquity that bade one stand at one's distance, I felt an irresistible desire to hold in my own for a moment the hand that Jeffrey Aspern had pressed.

For a minute she made no answer and I saw that my proposal failed to meet with her approbation. She indulged in no movement of withdrawal, which I half expected; she only said coldly, "I belong to a time when that was not the custom."

I felt rather snubbed but I exclaimed good-humouredly to Miss Tita, "Oh, you will do as well!" I shook hands with her while she replied, with a small flutter, "Yes, yes, to show it's all arranged!"

"Shall you bring the money in gold?" Miss Bordereau demanded, as I was turning to the door.

I looked at her a moment. "Aren't you a little afraid, after all, of keeping such a sum as that in the house?" It was not that I was annoyed at her avidity but I was really struck with the disparity between such a treasure and such scanty means of guarding it.

"Whom should I be afraid of if I am not afraid of you?" she asked with her shrunken grimness.

"Ah well," said I, laughing, "I shall be in point of fact a protector and I will bring gold if you prefer."

"Thank you," the old woman returned with dignity and with an inclination of her head which evidently signified that I might depart. I passed out of the room, reflecting that it would not be easy to circumvent her. As I stood in the sala again I saw that Miss Tita had followed me and I supposed that as her aunt had neglected to suggest that I should take a look at my quarters it was her purpose to repair the omission. But she made no such suggestion; she only stood there with a dim, though not a languid smile, and with an effect of irresponsible, incompetent youth which was almost comically at variance with the faded facts of her person. She was not infirm, like her aunt, but she struck me as still more helpless, because her inefficiency was spiritual, which was not the case with Miss Bordereau's. I waited to see if she would offer to show me the rest of the house, but I did not precipitate the question, inasmuch as my plan was from this moment to spend as much of my time as possible in her society. I only observed at the end of a minute:

"I have had better fortune than I hoped. It was very kind of her to see me. Perhaps you said a good word for me."

"It was the idea of the money," said Miss Tita.

"And did you suggest that?"

"I told her that you would perhaps give a good deal."

"What made you think that?"

"I told her I thought you were rich."

"And what put that idea into your head?"

"I don't know; the way you talked."

"Dear me, I must talk differently now," I declared. "I'm sorry to say it's not the case."

"Well," said Miss Tita, "I think that in Venice the *forestieri,* in general, often give a great deal for something that after all isn't much." She appeared to make this remark with a comforting intention, to wish to remind me that if I had been extravagant I was not really foolishly singular. We walked together along the sala, and as I took its magnificent measure I said to her that I was afraid it would not form a part of my *quartiere.* Were my rooms by chance to be among those that opened into it? "Not if you go above, on the second floor," she answered with a little startled air, as if she had rather taken for granted I would know my proper place.

"And I infer that that's where your aunt would like me to be."

"She said your apartments ought to be very distinct."

"That certainly would be best." And I listened with respect while she told me that up above I was free to take whatever I liked; that there was another staircase, but only from the floor on which we stood, and that to pass from it to the garden-story or to come up to my lodging I should have in effect to cross the great hall. This was an immense point gained; I foresaw that it would constitute my whole leverage in my relations with the two ladies. When I asked Miss Tita how I was to manage at present to find my way up she replied with an access of that sociable shyness which constantly marked her manner.

"Perhaps you can't. I don't see—unless I should go with you." She evidently had not thought of this before.

We ascended to the upper floor and visited a long succession of empty rooms. The best of them looked over the garden; some of the others had a view of the blue lagoon, above the opposite rough-tiled housetops. They were all dusty and even a little disfigured with long neglect, but I saw that by spending a few hundred francs I should be able to convert three or four of them into a convenient habitation. My experiment was turning out costly, yet now that I had all but taken possession I ceased to allow this to trouble me. I mentioned to my companion a few of the things that I should put in, but she replied rather more precipitately than usual that I might do exactly what I liked; she seemed to wish to notify me that the Misses Bordereau would take no overt interest in my proceedings. I guessed that her aunt had instructed her to adopt this tone, and I may as well say now that I came afterwards to distinguish perfectly (as I believed) between the speeches she made on her own responsibility and those the old lady imposed upon her. She took no notice of the unswept condition of the rooms and indulged in no explanations nor apologies. I said to myself that this was a sign that Juliana and her niece (disenchanting idea!) were untidy persons, with a low Italian standard; but I afterwards recognized that a lodger who had forced an entrance had no *locus standi* as a critic. We looked out of a good many windows, for there was nothing within the rooms to look at, and still I wanted to linger. I asked her what several different objects in the prospect might be, but in no case did she appear to know. She was evidently not familiar with the view—it was as if she had not looked at it for years—and I presently saw that she was too preoccupied with something else to pretend to care for it. Suddenly she said—the remark was not suggested:

"I don't know whether it will make any difference to you, but the money is for me."

"The money?"

"The money you are going to bring."

"Why, you'll make me wish to stay here two or three years." I spoke as benevolently as possible, though it had begun to act on my nerves that with these women so associated with Aspern the pecuniary question should constantly come back.

"That would be very good for me," she replied, smiling.

"You put me on my honour!"

She looked as if she failed to understand this, but went on: "She wants me to have more. She thinks she is going to die."

"Ah, not soon, I hope!" I exclaimed, with genuine feeling. I had perfectly considered the possibility that she would destroy her papers on the day she should feel her end really approach. I believed that she would cling to them till then and I think I had an idea that she read Aspern's letters over every night or at least pressed them to her withered lips. I would have given a good deal to have a glimpse of the latter spectacle. I asked Miss Tita if the old lady were seriously ill and she replied that she was only very tired—she had lived so very, very long. That was what she said herself—she wanted to die for a change. Besides, all her friends were dead long ago; either they ought to have remained or she ought to have gone. That was another thing her aunt often said—she was not at all content.

"But people don't die when they like, do they?" Miss Tita inquired. I took the liberty of asking why, if there was actually enough money to maintain both of them, there would not be more than enough in case of her being left alone. She considered this difficult problem a moment and then she said, "Oh, well, you know, she takes care of me. She thinks that when I'm alone I shall be a great fool, I shall not know how to manage."

"I should have supposed rather that you took care of her. I'm afraid she is very proud."

"Why, have you discovered that already?" Miss Tita cried, with the glimmer of an illumination in her face.

"I was shut up with her there for a considerable time, and she struck me, she interested me extremely. It didn't take me long to make my discovery. She won't have much to say to me while I'm here."

"No, I don't think she will," my companion averred.

"Do you suppose she has some suspicion of me?"

Miss Tita's honest eyes gave me no sign that I had touched a mark. "I shouldn't think so—letting you in after all so easily."

"Oh, so easily! she has covered her risk. But where is it that one could take an advantage of her?"

"I oughtn't to tell you if I knew, ought I?" And Miss Tita added, before I had time to reply to this, smiling dolefully, "Do you think we have any weak points?"

"That's exactly what I'm asking. You would only have to mention them for me to respect them religiously."

She looked at me, at this, with that air of timid but candid and even gratified curiosity with which she had confronted me from the first; and then she said, "There is nothing to tell. We are terribly quiet. I don't know how the days pass. We have no life."

"I wish I might think that I should bring you a little."

"Oh, we know what we want," she went on. "It's all right."

There were various things I desired to ask her: how in the world they did live; whether they had any friends or visitors, any relations in America or in other countries. But I judged such an inquiry would be premature; I must leave it to a later chance. "Well, don't *you* be proud," I contented myself with saying. "Don't hide from me altogether."

"Oh, I must stay with my aunt," she returned, without looking at me. And at the same moment, abruptly, without any ceremony of parting, she quitted me and disappeared, leaving me to make my own way downstairs. I remained a while longer, wandering about the bright desert (the sun was pouring in) of the old house, thinking the situation over on the spot. Not even the pattering little *serva* came to look after me and I reflected that after all this treatment showed confidence.

CHAPTER IV

Perhaps it did, but all the same, six weeks later, towards the middle of June, the moment when Mrs. Prest undertook her annual migration, I had made no measureable advance. I was obliged to confess to her that I had no results to speak of. My first step had been unexpectedly rapid, but there was no appearance that it would be followed by a second. I was a thousand miles from taking tea with my hostesses—that privilege of which, as I reminded Mrs. Prest, we both had had a vision. She reproached me with wanting boldness and I answered that even to be bold you must have an opportunity: you may push on through a breach but you can't batter down a dead wall. She answered that the breach I had already made was big enough to admit an army and accused me of wasting precious hours in whimpering in her salon when I ought to have been carrying on the struggle in the field. It is true that I went to see her very often, on the theory that it would console me (I freely expressed my discouragement) for my want of success on my own premises. But I began to perceive that it did not console me to be perpetually chaffed for my scruples, especially when I was really so vigilant; and I was rather glad when my derisive friend closed her house for the summer. She had expected to gather amusement from the drama of my intercourse with the Misses Bordereau and she was disappointed that the intercourse, and consequently the drama, had not come off. "They'll lead you on to your ruin," she said before she left Venice. "They'll get all your money without showing you a scrap." I think I settled down to my business with more concentration after she had gone away.

It was a fact that up to that time I had not, save on a single brief occasion, had even a moment's contact with my queer hostesses. The exception had occured when I carried them according to my promise the terrible three thousand francs. Then I found Miss Tita waiting for me in the hall, and she took the money from my hand so that I did not see her aunt. The old lady had promised to receive me, but she apparently thought nothing of breaking that vow. The money was contained in a bag of chamois leather, of respectable dimensions, which my banker had given me, and Miss Tita had to make a big fist to receive it. This she did with extreme solemnity, though I tried to treat the affair a little as a joke. It was in no jocular strain, yet it was with simplicity, that she inquired, weighing the money in her two palms: "Don't you think it's too much?" To which I replied that that would depend upon the amount of pleasure I should get for it. Hereupon she turned away from me quickly, as she had done the day before, murmuring in a tone different from any she had used hitherto: "Oh, pleasure, pleasure—there's no pleasure in this house!"

After this, for a long time, I never saw her, and I wondered that the common chances of the day should not have helped us to meet. It could only be evident that she was immensely on her guard against them; and in addition to this the house was so big that for each other we were lost in it. I used to look out for her hopefully as I crossed the sala in my comings and goings, but I was not rewarded with a glimpse of the tail of her dress. It was as if she never peeped out of her aunt's apartment. I used to wonder what she did there week after week and year after year. I had never encountered such a violent *parti pris* of seclusion; it was more than keeping quiet—it was like hunted creatures feigning death. The two ladies appeared to have no visitors whatever and no sort of contact with the world. I judged at least that people could not have come to the house and that Miss Tita could not have gone out without my having some observation of it. I did what I disliked myself for doing (reflecting that it was only once in a way): I questioned my servant about their habits and let him divine that I should be interested in any information he could pick up. But he picked up amazingly little for a knowing Venetian: it must be added that where there is a perpetual fast there are very few crumbs on the floor. His cleverness in other ways was sufficient, if it was not quite all that I had attributed to him on the occasion of my first interview with Miss Tita. He had helped my gondolier to bring me round a boat-load of furniture; and when these articles had been carried to the top of the palace and distributed according to our associated wisdom he organised my household with such promptitude as was consistent with the fact that it was composed exclusively of himself. He made me in short as comfortable as I could be with my indifferent prospects. I should have been glad if he had fallen in love with Miss Bordereau's maid or, failing this, had taken her in aversion; either event might have brought about some kind of catastrophe and a catastrophe might have led to some parley. It was my idea that she would have been sociable, and I myself on various occasions saw her flit to and fro on domestic errands, so that I was sure she was accessible. But I tasted of no gossip from that fountain, and I afterwards learned that Pasquale's affections were fixed upon an object that made him heedless of other women. This was a young lady with a powdered face, a yellow cotton gown and much leisure, who used often to come to see him. She practised, at her convenience, the art of a stringer of beads (these ornaments are made in Venice, in profusion; she had her pocket full of them and I used to find them on the floor of my apartment), and kept an eye on the maiden in the house. It was not for me of course to make the domestics tattle, and I never said a word to Miss Bordereau's cook.

It seemed to me a proof of the old lady's determination to have nothing to do with me that she should never have sent me a receipt for my three month's rent. For some days I looked out for it and then, when I had given it up, I wasted a good deal of time in wondering what her reason had been for neglecting so indispensable and familiar a form. At first I was tempted to send her a reminder, after which I relinquished the idea (against my judgment as to what was right in the particular case), on the general ground of wishing to keep quiet. If Miss Bordereau suspected me of ulterior aims she would suspect me less if I should be businesslike, and yet I consented not to be so. It was possible she intended her omission as an impertinence, a visible irony, to show how she could overreach people who attempted to overreach her. On that hypothesis it was well to let her see that one did not notice her little tricks. The real reading of the matter, I afterwards perceived, was simply the poor old woman's desire to emphasise the fact that I was in the enjoyment of a favour as rigidly limited as it had been liberally bestowed. She had given me part of her house and now she would not give me even a morsel of paper with her name on it. Let me say that even at first this did not make me too miserable, for the whole episode was essentially delightful to me. I foresaw that I should have a summer after my own literary heart, and the sense of holding my opportunity was much greater than the sense of losing it. There could be no Venetian business without patience, and since I adored the place I was much more in the spirit of it for having laid in a large provision. That spirit kept me perpetual company and seemed to look out at me from the revived immortal face—in which all his genius shone—of the great poet who was my prompter. I had invoked him and he had come; he hovered before me half the time; it was as if his bright ghost had returned to earth to tell me that he regarded the affair as his own no less than mine and that we should see it fraternally, cheerfully to a conclusion. It was as if he had said, "Poor dear, be easy with her; she has some natural prejudices; only give her time. Strange as it may appear to you she was very attractive in 1820. Meanwhile are we not in Venice together, and what better place is there for the meeting of dear friends? See how it glows with the advancing summer; how the sky and the sea and the rosy air and the marble of the palaces all shimmer and melt together." My eccentric private errand became a part of the general romance and the general glory—I felt even a mystic companionship, a moral fraternity with all those who in the past had been in the service of art. They had worked for beauty, for a devotion; and what else was I doing? That element was in everything that Jeffery Aspern had written and I was only bringing it to the light.

I lingered in the sala when I went to and fro; I used to watch—as long as I thought decent—the door that led to Miss Bordereau's part of the house. A person observing me might have supposed I was trying to cast a spell upon it or attempting some odd experiment in hypnotism. But I was only praying it would open or thinking what treasure probably lurked behind it. I hold it singular, as I look back, that I should never have doubted for a moment that the sacred relics were there; never have failed to feel a certain joy at being under the same roof with them. After all they were under my hand—they had not escaped me yet; and they made my life continuous, in a fashion, with the illustrious life they had touched at the other end. I lost myself in this satisfaction to the point of assuming—in my quiet extravagance—that poor Miss Tita also went back, went back, as I used to phrase it. She did indeed, the gentle spinster, but not quite so far as Jeffrey Aspern, who was simple hearsay to her, quite as he was to me. Only she had lived for years with Juliana, she had seen and handled the papers and (even though she was stupid) some esoteric knowledge had rubbed off on her. That was what the old woman represented—esoteric knowledge; and this was the idea with which my editorial heart used to thrill. It literally beat faster often, of an evening, when I had been out, as I stopped with my candle in the re-echoing hall on my way up to bed. It was as if at such a moment as that, in the stillness, after the long contradiction of the day, Miss Bordereau's secrets were in the air, the wonder of her survival more palpable. These were the acute impressions. I had them in another form, with more of a certain sort of reciprocity, during the hours that I sat in the garden looking up over the top of my book at the closed windows of my hostess. In these windows no sign of life ever appeared; it was as if, for fear of my catching a glimpse of them, the two ladies passed their days in the dark. But this only proved to me that they had something to conceal; which was what I had wished to demonstrate. Their motionless shutters became as expressive as eyes consciously closed, and I took comfort in thinking that at all events though invisible themselves they saw me between the lashes.

I made a point of spending as much time as possible in the garden, to justify the picture I had originally given of my horticultural passion. And I not only spent time, but (hang it! as I said) I spent money. As soon as I had got my rooms arranged and could give the proper thought to the matter I surveyed the place with a clever expert and made terms for having it put in order. I was sorry to do this, for personally I liked it better as it was, with its weeds and its wild, rough tangle, its sweet, characteristic Venetian shabbiness. I had to be consistent, to keep my promise that I would smother the house in flowers. Moreover I formed this graceful project that by flowers I would make my way—I would succeed by big nosegays. I would batter the old woman with lilies—I would bombard their citadel with roses. Their door would have to yield to the pressure when a mountain of carnations should be piled up against it. The place in truth had been brutally neglected. The Venetian capacity for dawdling is of the largest, and for a good many days unlimited litter was all my gardener had to show for his ministrations. There was a great digging of holes and carting about of earth, and after a while I grew so impatient that I had thoughts of sending for my bouquets to the nearest stand. But I reflected that the ladies would see through the chinks of their shutters that they must have been bought and might make up their minds from this that I was a humbug. So I composed myself and finally, though the delay was long, perceived some appearances of bloom. This encouraged me and I waited serenely enough till they multiplied. Meanwhile the real summer days arrived and began to pass, and as I look back upon them they seem to me almost the happiest of my life. I took more and more care to be in the garden whenever it was not too hot. I had an arbour arranged and a low table and an armchair put into it; and I carried out books and portfolios (I had always some business of writing in hand), and worked and waited and mused and hoped, while the golden hours elapsed and the plants drank in the light and the inscrutable old palace turned pale and then, as the day waned, began to flush in it and my papers rustled in the wandering breeze of the Adriatic.

Considering how little satisfaction I got from it at first it is remarkable that I should not have grown more tired of wondering what mystic rites of ennui the Misses Bordereau celebrated in their darkened rooms; whether this had always been the tenor of their life and how in previous years they had escaped elbowing their neighbours. It was clear that they must have had other habits and other circumstances; that they must once have been young or at least middle-aged. There was no end to the questions it was possible to ask about them and no end to the answers it was not possible to frame. I had known many of my country-people in Europe and was familiar with the strange ways they were liable to take up there; but the Misses Bordereau formed altogether a new type of the American absentee. Indeed it was plain that the American name had ceased to have any application to them—I had seen this in the ten minutes I spent in the old woman's room. You could never have said whence they came, from the appearance of either of them; wherever it was they had long ago dropped the local accent and fashion. There was nothing in them that one recognised, and putting the question of speech aside they might have been Norwegian or Spaniards. Miss Bordereau, after all, had been in Europe nearly three-quarters of a century; it appeared by some verses addressed to her by Aspern on the occasion of his own second absence from America—verses of which Cumnor and I had after infinite conjecture established solidly enough the date—that she was even then, as a girl of twenty, on the foreign side of the sea. There was an implication in the poem (I hope not just for the phrase) that he had come back for her sake. We had no real light upon her circumstances at that moment, any more than we had upon her origin, which we believed to be of the sort usually spoken of as modest. Cumnor had a theory that she had been a governess in some family in which the poet visited and that, in consequence of her position, there was from the first something unavowed, or rather something positively clandestine, in their relations. I on the other hand had hatched a little romance according to which she was the daughter of an artist, a painter or a sculptor, who had left the western world when the century was fresh, to study in the ancient schools. It was essential to my hypothesis that this amiable man should have lost his wife, should have been poor and unsuccessful and should have had a second daughter, of a disposition quite different from Juliana's. It was also indispensable that he should have been accompanied to Europe by these young ladies and should have established himself there for the remainder of a struggling, saddened life. There was a further implication that Miss Bordereau had had in her youth a perverse and adventurous, albeit a generous and fascinating character, and that she had passed through some singular vicissitudes. By what passions had she been ravaged, by what sufferings had she been blanched, what store of memories had she laid away for the monotonous future?

I asked myself these things as I sat spinning theories about her in my arbour and the bees droned in the flowers. It was incontestable that, whether for right or for wrong, most readers of certain of Aspern's poems (poems not as ambiguous as the sonnets—scarcely more divine, I think—of Shakespeare) had taken for granted that Juliana had not always adhered to the steep footway of renunciation. There hovered about her name a perfume of reckless passion, an intimation that she had not been exactly as the respectable young person in general. Was this a sign that her singer had betrayed her, had given her away, as we say nowadays, to posterity? Certain it is that it would have been difficult to put one's finger on the passage in which her fair fame suffered an imputation. Moreover was not any fame fair enough that was so sure of duration and was associated with works immortal through their beauty? It was a part of my idea that the young lady had had a foreign lover (and an unedifying tragical rupture) before her meeting with Jeffrey Aspern. She had lived with her father and sister in a queer old-fashioned, expatriated, artistic Bohemia, in the days when the æsthetic was only the academic and the painters who knew the best models for a *contadina* and *pifferaro* wore peaked hats and long hair. It was a society less furnished than the coteries of to-day (in its ignorance of the wonderful chances, the opportunities of the early bird, with which its path was strewn), with tatters of old stuff and fragments of old crockery; so that Miss Bordereau appeared not to have picked up or have inherited many objects of importance. There was no enviable *bric-à-brac,* with its provoking legend of cheapness, in the room in which I had seen her. Such a fact as that suggested bareness, but none the less it worked happily into the sentimental interest I had always taken in the early movements of my countrymen as visitors to Europe. When Americans went abroad in 1820 there was something romantic, almost heroic in it, as compared with the perpetual ferryings of the present hour, when photography and other conveniences have annihilated surprise. Miss Bordereau sailed with her family on a tossing brig, in the days of long voyages and sharp differences; she had her emotions on the top of yellow diligences, passed the night at inns where she dreamed of travellers' tales, and was struck, on reaching the eternal city, with the elegance of Roman pearls and scarfs. There was something touching to me in all that and my imagination frequently went back to the period. If Miss Bordereau carried it there of course Jeffrey Aspern at other times had done so a great deal more. It was a much more important fact, if one were looking at his genius critically, that he had lived in the days before the general transfusion. It had happened to me to regret that he had known Europe at all; I should have liked to see what he would have written without that experience, by which he had incontestably been enriched. But as his fate had ordered otherwise I went with him—I tried to judge how the old world would have struck him. It was not only there, however, that I watched him; the relations he had entertained with the new had even a livelier interest. His own country after all had had most of his life, and his muse, as they said at that time, was essentially American. That was originally what I had loved him for: that at a period when our native land was nude and crude and provincial, when the famous "atmosphere" it is supposed to lack was not even missed, when literature was lonely there and art and form almost impossible, he had found means to live and write like one of the first; to be free and general and not at all afraid; to feel, understand and express everything.

CHAPTER V

I was seldom at home in the evening, for when I attempted to occupy myself in my apartments the lamplight brought in a swarm of noxious insects, and it was too hot for closed windows. Accordingly I spent the late hours either on the water (the moonlight of Venice is famous), or in the splendid square which serves as a vast forecourt to the strange old basilica of Saint Mark. I sat in front of Florian's *café*, eating ices, listening to music, talking with acquaintances: the traveller will remember how the immense cluster of tables and little chairs stretches like a promontory into the smooth lake of the Piazza. The whole place, of a summer's evening, under the stars and with all the lamps, all the voices and light footsteps on marble (the only sounds of the arcades that enclose it), is like an open-air saloon dedicated to cooling drinks and to a still finer degustation—that of the exquisite impressions received during the day. When I did not prefer to keep mine to myself there was always a stray tourist, disencumbered of his Baedeker, to discuss them with, or some domesticated painter rejoicing in the return of the season of strong effects. The wonderful church, with its low domes and bristling embroideries, the mystery of its mosaic and sculpture, looked ghostly in the tempered gloom, and the sea-breeze passed between the twin columns of the Piazzetta, the lintels of a door no longer guarded, as gently as if a rich curtain were swaying there. I used sometimes on these occasions to think of the Misses Bordereau and of the pity of their being shut up in apartments which in the Venetian July even Venetian vastness did not prevent from being stuffy. Their life seemed miles away from the life of the Piazza, and no doubt it was really too late to make the austere Juliana change her habits. But poor Miss Tita would have enjoyed one of Florian's ices, I was sure; sometimes I even had thoughts of carrying one home to her. Fortunately my patience bore fruit and I was not obliged to do anything so ridiculous.

One evening about the middle of July I came in earlier than usual—I forget what chance had led to this—and instead of going up to my quarters made my way into the garden. The temperature was very high; it was such a night as one would gladly have spent in the open air and I was in no hurry to go to bed. I had floated home in my gondola, listening to the slow splash of the oar in the narrow dark canals, and now the only thought that solicited me was the vague reflection that it would be pleasant to recline at one's length in the fragrant darkness on a garden bench. The odour of the canal was doubtless at the bottom of that aspiration and the breath of the garden, as I entered it, gave consistency to my purpose. It was delicious—just such an air as must have trembled with Romeo's vows when he stood among the flowers and raised his arms to his mistress's balcony. I looked at the windows of the palace to see if by chance the example of Verona (Verona being not far off) had been followed; but everything was dim, as usual, and everything was still. Juliana, on summer nights in her youth, might have murmured down from open windows at Jeffrey Aspern, but Miss Tita was not a poet's mistress any more than I was a poet. This however did not prevent my gratification from being great as I became aware on reaching the end of the garden that Miss Tita was seated in my little bower. At first I only made out an indistinct figure, not in the least counting on such an overture from one of my hostesses; it even occurred to me that some sentimental maid-servant had stolen in to keep a tryst with her sweetheart. I was going to turn away, not to frighten her, when the figure rose to its height and I recognised Miss Bordereau's niece. I must do myself the justice to say that I did not wish to frighten her either, and much as I had longed for some such accident I should have been capable of retreating. It was as if I had laid a trap for her by coming home earlier than usual and adding to that eccentricity by creeping into the garden. As she rose she spoke to me, and then I reflected that perhaps, secure in my almost inveterate absence, it was her nightly practice to take a lonely airing. There was no trap, in truth, because I had had no suspicion. At first I took for granted that the words she uttered expressed discomfiture at my arrival; but as she repeated them —I had not caught them clearly—I had the surprise of hearing her say, "Oh, dear, I'm so very glad you've come!" She and her aunt had in common the property of unexpected speeches. She came out of the arbour almost as if she were going to throw herself into my arms.

I hasten to add that she did nothing of the kind; she did not even shake hands with me. It was a gratification to her to see me and presently she told me why—because she was nervous when she was out-of-doors at night alone. The plants and bushes looked so strange in the dark, and there were all sorts of queer sounds—she could not tell what they were—like the noises of animals. She stood close to me, looking about her with an air of greater security but without any demonstration of interest in me as an individual. Then I guessed that nocturnal prowlings were not in the least her habit, and I was also reminded (I had been struck with the circumstance in talking with her before I took possession) that it was impossible to over-estimate her simplicity.

"You speak as if you were lost in the backwood," I said, laughing. "How you manage to keep out of his charming place when you have only three steps to take to get into it, is more than I have yet been able to discover. You hide away mighty well so long as I am on the premises, I know; but I had a hope that you peeped out a little at other times. You and your poor aunt are worse off than Carmelite nuns in their cells. Should you mind telling me how you exist without air, without exercise, without any sort of human contact? I don't see how you carry on the common business of life."

She looked at me as if I were talking some strange tongue and her answer was so little of an answer that I was considerably irritated.

"We go to bed very early—earlier than you would believe." I was on the point of saying that this only deepened the mystery when she gave me some relief by adding, "Before you came we were not so private. But I never have been out at night."

"Never in these fragrant alleys, blooming here under your nose?"

"Ah," said Miss Tita, "they were never nice till now!" There was an unmistakable reference in this and a flattering comparison, so that it seemed to me I had gained a small advantage. As it would help me to follow it up to establish a sort of grievance I asked her why, since she thought my garden nice, she had never thanked me in any way for the flowers I had been sending up in such quantities for the previous three weeks. I had not been discouraged—there had been, as she would have observed, a daily armful; but I had been brought up in the common forms and a word of recognition now and then would have touched me in the right place.

"Why I didn't know they were for me!"

"They were for both of you. Why should I make a difference?"

Miss Tita reflected as if she might be thinking of a reason for that, but she failed to produce one. Instead of this she asked abruptly, "Why in the world do you want to know us?"

"I ought after all to make a difference," I replied. "That question is your aunt's; it isn't yours. You wouldn't ask it if you hadn't been put up to it."

"She didn't tell me to ask you," Miss Tita replied, without confusion; she was the oddest mixture of the shrinking and the direct.

"Well, she has often wondered about it herself and expressed her wonder to you. She has insisted on it, so that she put the idea into your head that I am insufferably pushing. Upon my word I think I have been very discreet. And how completely your aunt must have lost every tradition of sociability, to see anything out of the way in the idea that respectable intelligent people, living as we do under the same roof, should occasionally exchange a remark! What could be more natural? We are of the same country and we have at least some of the same tastes, since, like you, I am intensely fond of Venice."

My interlocutress appeared incapable of grasping more than one clause in any proposition, and she declared quickly, eagerly, as if she were answering my whole speech: "I am not in the least fond of Venice. I should like to go far away!"

"Has she always kept you back so?" I went on, to show her that I could be as irrelevant as herself.

"She told me to come out to-night; she has told me very often," said Miss Tita. "It is I who wouldn't come. I don't like to leave her."

"Is she too weak, is she failing?" I demanded, with more emotion, I think, than I intended to show. I judged this by the way her eyes rested upon me in the darkness. It embarrassed me a little, and to turn the matter off I continued genially: "Do let us sit down together comfortably somewhere and you will tell me all about her."

Miss Tita made no resistance to this. We found a bench less secluded, less confidential, as it were, than the one in the arbour; and we were still sitting there when I heard midnight ring out from those clear bells of Venice which vibrate with a solemnity of their own over the lagoon and hold the air so much more than the chimes of other places. We were together more than an hour and our interview gave, as it struck me, a great lift to my undertaking. Miss Tita accepted the situation without a protest; she had avoided me for three months, yet now she treated me almost as if these three months had made me an old friend. If I had chosen I might have inferred from this that though she had avoided me she had given a good deal of consideration to doing so. She paid no attention to the flight of time—never worried at my keeping her so long away from her aunt. She talked freely, answering questions and asking them and not even taking advantage of certain longish pauses with which they inevitably alternated to say she thought she had better go in. It was almost as if she were waiting for something—something I might say to her—and intended to give me my opportunity. I was the more struck by this as she told me that her aunt had been less well for a good many days and in a way that was rather new. She was weaker; at moments it seemed as if she had no strength at all; yet more than ever before she wished to be left alone. That was why she had told her to come out—not even to remain in her own room, which was alongside; she said her niece irritated her, made her nervous. She sat still for hours together, as if she were asleep; she had always done that, musing and dozing; but at such times formerly she gave at intervals some small sign of life, of interest, liking her companion to be near her with her work. Miss Tita confided to me that at present her aunt was so motionless that she sometimes feared she was dead; moreover she took hardly any food—one couldn't see what she lived on. The great thing was that she still on most days got up; the serious job was to dress her, to wheel her out of her bedroom. She clung to as many of her old habits as possible and she had always, little company as they had received for years, made a point of sitting in the parlour.

I scarcely knew what to think of all this—of Miss Tita's sudden conversion to sociability and of the strange circumstance that the more the old lady appeared to decline toward her end the less she should desire to be looked after. The story did not hang together, and I even asked myself whether it were not a trap laid for me, the result of a design to make me show my hand. I could not have told why my companions (as they could only by courtesy be called) should have this purpose—why they should try to trip up so lucrative a lodger. At any rate I kept on my guard, so that Miss Tita should not have occasion again to ask me if I had an *arrière-pensée*. Poor woman, before we parted for the night my mind was at rest as to *her* capacity for entertaining one.

She told me more about their affairs than I had hoped; there was no need to be prying, for it evidently drew her out simply to feel that I listened, that I cared. She ceased wondering why I cared, and at last, as she spoke of the brilliant life they had led years before, she almost chattered. It was Miss Tita who judged it brilliant; she said that when they first came to live in Venice, years and years before (I saw that her mind was essentially vague about dates and the order in which events had occurred), there was scarcely a week that they had not some visitor or did not make some delightful *passeggio* in the city. They had seen all the curiosities; they had even been to the Lido in a boat (she spoke as if I might think there was a way on foot); they had had a collation there, brought in three baskets and spread out on the grass. I asked her what people they had known and she said, Oh! very nice ones—the Cavaliere Bombicci and the Contessa Altemura, with whom they had had a great friendship. Also English people—the Churtons and the Goldies and Mrs. Stock-Stock, whom they had loved dearly; she was dead and gone, poor dear. That was the case with most of their pleasant circle (this expression was Miss Tita's own), though a few were left, which was a wonder considering how they had neglected them. She mentioned the names of two or three Venetian old women; of a certain doctor, very clever, who was so kind—he came as a friend, he had really given up practice; of the *avvocato* Pochintesta, who wrote beautiful poems and had addressed one to her aunt. These people came to see them without fail every year, usually at the *capo d'anno,* and of old her aunt used to make them some little present —her aunt and she together: small things that she, Miss Tita, made herself, like paper lamp-shades or mats for the decanters of wine at dinner or those woollen things that in cold weather were worn on the wrists. The last few years there had not been many presents; she could not think what to make and her aunt had lost her interest and never suggested. But the people came all the same; if the Venetians liked you once they liked you for ever.

There was something affecting in the good faith of this sketch of former social glories; the picnic at the Lido had remained vivid through the ages and poor Miss Tita evidently was of the impression that she had had a brilliant youth. She had in fact had a glimpse of the Venetian world in its gossiping, home-keeping, parsimonious, professional walks; for I observed for the first time that she had acquired by contact something of the trick of the familiar, soft-sounding, almost infantile speech of the place. I judged that she had imbibed this inveterate dialect, from the natural way the names of things and people—mostly purely local—rose to her lips. If she knew little of what they represented she knew still less of anything else. Her aunt had drawn in—her failing interest in the table-mats and lamp-shades was a sign of that—and she had not been able to mingle in society or to entertain it alone; so that the matter of her reminiscences struck one as an old world altogether. If she had not been so decent her references would have seemed to carry one back to the queer rococo Venice of Casanova. I found myself falling into the error of thinking of her too as one of Jeffrey Aspern's contemporaries; this came from her having so little in common with my own. It was possible, I said to myself, that she had not even heard of him; it might very well be that Juliana had not cared to lift even for her the veil that covered the temple of her youth. In this case she perhaps would not know of the existence of the papers, and I welcomed that presumption—it made me feel more safe with her—until I remembered that we had believed the letter of disavowal received by Cumnor to be in the handwriting of the niece. If it had been dictated to her she had of course to know what it was about; yet after all the effect of it was to repudiate the idea of any connection with the poet. I held it probable at all events that Miss Tita had not read a word of his poetry. Moreover if, with her companion, she had always escaped the interviewer there was little occasion for her having got it into her head that people were "after" the letters. People had not been after them, inasmuch as they had not heard of them; and Cumnor's fruitless feeler would have been a solitary accident.

When midnight sounded Miss Tita got up; but she stopped at the door of the house only after she had wandered two or three times with me round the garden. "When shall I see you again?" I asked, before she went in; to which she replied with promptness that she should like to come out the next night. She added however that she should not come—she was so far from doing everything she liked.

"You might do a few things that *I* like," I said with a sigh.

"Oh, you—I don't believe you!" she murmured, at this, looking at me with her simple solemnity.

"Why don't you believe me?"

"Because I don't understand you."

"That is just the sort of occasion to have faith." I could not say more, though I should have liked to, as I saw that I only mystified her; for I had no wish to have it on my conscience that I might pass for having made love to her. Nothing less should I have seemed to do had I continued to beg a lady to "believe in me" in an Italian garden on a mid-summer night. There was some merit in my scruples, for Miss Tita lingered and lingered: I perceived that she felt that she should not really soon come down again and wished therefore to protract the present. She insisted too on making the talk between us personal to ourselves; and altogether her behavior was such as would have been possible only to a completely innocent woman.

"I shall like the flowers better now that I know they are also meant for me."

"How could you have doubted it? If you will tell me the kind you like best I will send a double lot of them."

"Oh, I like them all best!" Then she went on, familiarly: "Shall you study —shall you read and write—when you go up to your rooms?"

"I don't do that at night, at this season. The lamplight brings in the animals."

"You might have known that when you came."

"I did know it!"

"And in winter do you work at night?"

"I read a good deal, but I don't often write." She listened as if these details had a rare interest, and suddenly a temptation quite at variance with the prudence I had been teaching myself associated itself with her plain, mild face. Ah yes, she was safe and I could make her safer! It seemed to me from one moment to another that I could not wait longer—that I really must take a sounding. So I went on: "In general before I go to sleep—very often in bed (it's a bad habit, but I confess to it), I read some great poet. In nine cases out of ten it's a volume of Jeffrey Aspern."

I watched her well as I pronounced that name but I saw nothing wonderful. Why should I indeed—was not Jeffrey Aspern the property of the human race?

"Oh, we read him—we *have* read him," she quietly replied.

"He is my poet of poets—I know him almost by heart."

For an instant Miss Tita hesitated; then her sociability was too much for her.

"Oh, by heart—that's nothing!" she murmured, smiling. "My aunt used to know him—to know him"—she paused an instant and I wondered what she was going to say—"to know him as a visitor."

"As a visitor?" I repeated, staring.

"He used to call on her and take her out."

I continued to stare. "My dear lady, he died a hundred years ago!"

"Well," she said, mirthfully, "my aunt is a hundred and fifty."

"Mercy on us!" I exclaimed; "why didn't you tell me before? I should like so to ask her about him."

"She wouldn't care for that—she wouldn't tell you," Miss Tita replied.

"I don't care what she cares for! She *must* tell me—it's not a chance to be lost."

"Oh, you should have come twenty years ago: then she still talked about him."

"And what did she say?" I asked, eagerly.

"I don't know—that he liked her immensely."

"And she—didn't she like him?"

"She said he was a god." Miss Tita gave me this information flatly, without expression; her tone might have made it a piece of trivial gossip. But it stirred me deeply as she dropped the words into the summer night; it seemed such a direct testimony.

"Fancy, fancy!" I murmured. And then, "Tell me this, please—has she got a portrait of him? They are distressingly rare."

"A portrait? I don't know," said Miss Tita; and now there was discomfiture in her face. "Well, good-night!" she added; and she turned into the house.

I accompanied her into the wide, dusky, stone-paved passage which on the ground floor corresponded with our grand sala. It opened at one end into the garden, at the other upon the canal, and was lighted now only by the small lamp that was always left for me to take up as I went to bed. An extinguished candle which Miss Tita apparently had brought down with her stood on the same table with it. "Good-night, good-night!" I replied, keeping beside her as she went to get her light. "Surely you would know, shouldn't you, if she had one?"

"If she had what?" the poor lady asked, looking at me queerly over the flame of her candle.

"A portrait of the god. I don't know what I wouldn't give to see it."

"I don't know what she has got. She keeps her things locked up." And Miss Tita went away, toward the staircase, with the sense evidently that she had said too much.

I let her go—I wished not to frighten her—and I contented myself with remarking that Miss Bordereau would not have locked up such a glorious possession as that—a thing a person would be proud of and hang up in a prominent place on the parlour-wall. Therefore of course she had not any portrait. Miss Tita made no direct answer to this and candle in hand, with her back to me, ascended two or three stairs. Then she stopped short and turned round looking at me across the dusky space.

"Do you write—do you write?" There was a shake in her voice—she could scarcely bring out what she wanted to ask.

"Do I write? Oh, don't speak of my writing on the same day with Aspern's!"

"Do you write about *him*—do you pry into his life?"

"Ah, that's your aunt's question; it can't be yours!" I said, in a tone of slightly wounded sensibility.

"All the more reason then that you should answer it. Do you, please?"

I thought I had allowed for the falsehoods I should have to tell; but I found that in fact when it came to the point I had not. Besides, now that I had an opening there was a kind of relief in being frank. Lastly (it was perhaps fanciful, even fatuous), I guessed that Miss Tita personally would not in the last resort be less my friend. So after a moment's hesitation I answered, "Yes, I have written about him and I am looking for more material. In heaven's name have you got any?"

"Santo Dio!" she exclaimed, without heeding my question; and she hurried upstairs and out of sight. I might count upon her in the last resort, but for the present she was visibly alarmed. The proof of it was that she began to hide again, so that for a fortnight I never beheld her. I found my patience ebbing and after four or five days of this I told the gardener to stop the flowers.

CHAPTER VI

One afternoon, as I came down from my quarters to go out, I found Miss Tita in the sala: it was our first encounter on that ground since I had come to the house. She put on no air of being there by accident; there was an ignorance of such arts in her angular, diffident directness. That I might be quite sure she was waiting for me she informed me of the fact and told me that Miss Bordereau wished to see me: she would take me into the room at that moment if I had time. If I had been late for a love-tryst I would have stayed for this, and I quickly signified that I should be delighted to wait upon the old lady. "She wants to talk with you—to know you," Miss Tita said, smiling as if she herself appreciated that idea; and she led me to the door of her aunt's apartment. I stopped her a moment before she had opened it, looking at her with some curiosity. I told her that this was a great satisfaction to me and a great honour; but all the same I should like to ask what had made Miss Bordereau change so suddenly. It was only the other day that she wouldn't suffer me near her. Miss Tita was not embarrassed by my question; she had as many little unexpected serenities as if she told fibs, but the odd part of them was that they had on the contrary their source in her truthfulness. "Oh, my aunt changes," she answered; "it's so terribly dull—I suppose she's tired."

"But you told me that she wanted more and more to be alone."

Poor Miss Tita coloured, as if she found me over-insistent. "Well, if you don't believe she wants to see you—I haven't invented it! I think people often are capricious when they are very old."

"That's perfectly true. I only wanted to be clear as to whether you have repeated to her what I told you the other night."

"What you told me?"

"About Jeffrey Aspern—that I am looking for materials."

"If I had told her do you think she would have sent for you?"

"That's exactly what I want to know. If she wants to keep him to herself she might have sent for me to tell me so."

"She won't speak of him," said Miss Tita. Then as she opened the door she added in a lower tone, "I have told her nothing."

The old woman was sitting in the same place in which I had seen her last, in the same position, with the same mystifying bandage over her eyes. Her welcome was to turn her almost invisible face to me and show me that while she sat silent she saw me clearly. I made no motion to shake hands with her; I felt too well on this occasion that that was out of place for ever. It had been sufficiently enjoined upon me that she was too sacred for that sort of reciprocity—too venerable to touch. There was something so grim in her aspect (it was partly the accident of her green shade), as I stood there to be measured, that I ceased on the spot to feel any doubt as to her knowing my secret, though I did not in the least suspect that Miss Tita had not just spoken the truth. She had not betrayed me, but the old woman's brooding instinct had served her; she had turned me over and over in the long, still hours and she had guessed. The worst of it was that she looked terribly like an old woman who at a pinch would burn her papers. Miss Tita pushed a chair forward, saying to me, "This will be a good place for you to sit." As I took possession of it I asked after Miss Bordereau's health; expressed the hope that in spite of the very hot weather it was satisfactory. She replied that it was good enough—good enough; that it was a great thing to be alive.

"Oh, as to that, it depends upon what you compare it with!" I exclaimed, laughing.

"I don't compare—I don't compare. If I did that I should have given everything up long ago."

I liked to think that this was a subtle allusion to the rapture she had known in the society of Jeffrey Aspern—though it was true that such an allusion would have accorded ill with the wish I imputed to her to keep him buried in her soul. What it accorded with was my constant conviction that no human being had ever had a more delightful social gift than his, and what it seemed to convey was that nothing in the world was worth speaking of if one pretended to speak of that. But one did not! Miss Tita sat down beside her aunt, looking as if she had reason to believe some very remarkable conversation would come off between us.

"It's about the beautiful flowers," said the old lady; "you sent us so many—I ought to have thanked you for them before. But I don't write letters and I receive only at long intervals."

She had not thanked me while the flowers continued to come, but she departed from her custom so far as to send for me as soon as she began to fear that they would not come any more. I noted this; I remembered what an acquisitive propensity she had shown when it was a question of extracting gold from me, and I privately rejoiced at the happy thought I had had in suspending my tribute. She had missed it and she was willing to make a concession to bring it back. At the first sign of this concession I could only go to meet her. "I am afraid you have not had many, of late, but they shall begin again immediately—to-morrow, to-night."

"Oh, do send us some to-night!" Miss Tita cried, as if it were an immense circumstance.

"What else should you do with them? It isn't a manly taste to make a bower of your room," the old woman remarked.

"I don't make a bower of my room, but I am exceedingly fond of growing flowers, of watching their ways. There is nothing unmanly in that: it has been the amusement of philosophers, of statesmen in retirement; even I think of great captains."

"I suppose you know you can sell them—those you don't use," Miss Bordereau went on. "I daresay they wouldn't give you much for them; still, you could make a bargain."

"Oh, I have never made a bargain, as you ought to know. My gardener disposes of them and I ask no questions."

"I would ask a few, I can promise you!" said Miss Bordereau; and it was the first time I had heard her laugh. I could not get used to the idea that this vision of pecuniary profit was what drew out the divine Juliana most.

"Come into the garden yourself and pick them; come as often as you like; come every day. They are all for you," I pursued, addressing Miss Tita and carrying off this veracious statement by treating it as an innocent joke. "I can't imagine why she doesn't came down," I added, for Miss Bordereau's benefit.

"You must make her come; you must come up and fetch her," said the old woman, to my stupefaction. "That odd thing you have made in the corner would be a capital place for her to sit."

The allusion to my arbour was irreverent; it confirmed the impression I had already received that there was a flicker of impertinence in Miss Bordereau's talk, a strange mocking lambency which must have been a part of her adventurous youth and which had outlived passions and faculties. None the less I asked, "Wouldn't it be possible for you to come down there yourself? Wouldn't it do you good to sit there in the shade, in the sweet air?"

"Oh, sir, when I move out of this it won't be to sit in the air, and I'm afraid that any that may be stirring around me won't be particularly sweet! It will be a very dark shade indeed. But that won't be just yet," Miss Bordereau continued, cannily, as if to correct any hopes that this courageous allusion to the last receptacle of her mortality might lead me to entertain. "I have sat here many a day and I have had enough of arbours in my time. But I'm not afraid to wait till I'm called."

Miss Tita had expected some interesting talk, but perhaps she found it less genial on her aunt's side (considering that I had been sent for with a civil intention) than she had hoped. As if to give the conversation a turn that would put our companion in a light more favourable she said to me, "Didn't I tell you the other night that she had sent me out? You see that I can do what I like!"

"Do you pity her—do you teach her to pity herself?" Miss Bordereau demanded, before I had time to answer this appeal. "She has a much easier life than I had when I was her age."

"You must remember that it has been quite open to me to think you rather inhuman."

"Inhuman? That's what the poets used to call the women a hundred years ago. Don't try that; you won't do as well as they!" Juliana declared. "There is no more poetry in the world—that I know of at least. But I won't bandy words with you," she pursued, and I well remember the old-fashioned, artificial sound she gave to the speech. "You have made me talk, talk! It isn't good for me at all." I got up at this and told her I would take no more of her time; but she detained me to ask, "Do you remember, the day I saw you about the rooms, that you offered us the use of your gondola?" And when I assented, promptly, struck again with her disposition to make a "good thing" of my being there and wondering what she now had in her eye, she broke out, "Why don't you take that girl out in it and show her the place?"

"Oh dear aunt, what do you want to do with me?" cried the "girl," with a piteous quaver. "I know all about the place!"

"Well then, go with him as a cicerone!" said Miss Bordereau, with an effect of something like cruelty in her implacable power of retort—an incongruous suggestion that she was a sarcastic, profane, cynical old woman. "Haven't we heard that there have been all sorts of changes in all these years? You ought to see them and at your age (I don't mean because you're so young), you ought to take the chances that come. You're old enough, my dear, and this gentleman won't hurt you. He will show you the famous sunsets, if they still go on—*do* they go on? The sun set for me so long ago. But that's not a reason. Besides, I shall never miss you; you think you are too important. Take her to the Piazza; it used to be very pretty," Miss Bordereau continued, addressing herself to me. "What have they done with the funny old church? I hope it hasn't tumbled down. Let her look at the shops; she may take some money, she may buy what she likes."

Poor Miss Tita had got up, discountenanced and helpless, and as we stood there before her aunt it would certainly have seemed to a spectator of the scene that the old woman was amusing herself at our expense. Miss Tita protested, in a confusion of exclamations and murmurs; but I lost no time in saying that if she would do me the honour to accept the hospitality of my boat I would engage that she should not be bored. Or if she did not want so much of my company the boat itself, with the gondolier, was at her service; he was a capital oar and she might have every confidence. Miss Tita, without definitely answering this speech, looked away from me, out of the window, as if she were going to cry; and I remarked that once we had Miss Bordereau's approval we could easily come to an understanding. We would take an hour, whichever she liked, one of the very next days. As I made my obeisance to the old lady I asked her if she would kindly permit me to see her again.

For a moment she said nothing; then she inquired, "Is it very necessary to your happiness?"

"It diverts me more than I can say."

"You are wonderfully civil. Don't you know it almost kills *me?*"

"How can I believe that when I see you more animated, more brilliant than when I came in?"

"That is very true, aunt," said Miss Tita. "I think it does you good."

"Isn't it touching, the solicitude we each have that the other shall enjoy herself?" sneered Miss Bordereau. "If you think me brilliant to-day you don't know what you are talking about; you have never seen an agreeable woman. Don't try to pay me a compliment; I have been spoiled," she went on. "My door is shut, but you may sometimes knock."

With this she dismissed me and I left the room. The latch closed behind me, but Miss Tita, contrary to my hope, had remained within. I passed slowly across the hall and before taking my way downstairs I waited a little. My hope was answered; after a minute Miss Tita followed me. "That's a delightful idea about the Piazza," I said. "When will you go—to-night, to-morrow?"

She had been disconcerted, as I have mentioned, but I had already perceived and I was to observe again that when Miss Tita was embarrassed she did not (as most women would have done) turn away from you and try to escape, but came closer, as it were, with a deprecating, clinging appeal to be spared, to be protected. Her attitude was perpetually a sort of prayer for assistance, for explanation; and yet no woman in the world could have been less of a comedian. From the moment you were kind to her she depended on you absolutely; her self-consciousness dropped from her and she took the greatest intimacy, the innocent intimacy which was the only thing she could conceive, for granted. She told me she did not know what had got into her aunt; she had changed so quickly, she had got some idea. I replied that she must find out what the idea was and then let me know; we would go and have an ice together at Florian's and she should tell me while we listened to the band.

"Oh, it will take me a long time to find out!" she said, rather ruefully; and she could promise me this satisfaction neither for that night nor for the next. I was patient now, however, for I felt that I had only to wait; and in fact at the end of the week, one lovely evening after dinner, she stepped into my gondola, to which in honour of the occasion I had attached a second oar.

We swept in the course of five minutes into the Grand Canal; whereupon she uttered a murmur of ecstasy as fresh as if she had been a tourist just arrived. She had forgotten how splendid the great waterway looked on a clear, hot summer evening, and how the sense of floating between marble palaces and reflected lights disposed the mind to sympathetic talk. We floated long and far, and though Miss Tita gave no high-pitched voice to her satisfaction I felt that she surrendered herself. She was more than pleased, she was transported; the whole thing was an immense liberation. The gondola moved with slow strokes, to give her time to enjoy it, and she listened to the plash of the oars, which grew louder and more musically liquid as we passed into narrow canals, as if it were a revelation of Venice. When I asked her how long it was since she had been in a boat she answered, "Oh, I don't know; a long time—not since my aunt began to be ill." This was not the only example she gave me of her extreme vagueness about the previous years and the line which marked off the period when Miss Bordereau flourished. I was not at liberty to keep her out too long, but we took a considerable *giro* before going to the Piazza. I asked her no questions, keeping the conversation on purpose away from her domestic situation and the things I wanted to know; I poured treasures of information about Venice into her ears, described Florence and Rome, discoursed to her on the charms and advantages of travel. She reclined, receptive, on the deep leather cushions, turned her eyes conscientiously to everything I pointed out to her, and never mentioned to me till some time afterwards that she might be supposed to know Florence better than I, as she had lived there for years with Miss Bordereau. At last she asked, with the shy impatience of a child, "Are we not really going to the Piazza? That's what I want to see!" I immediately gave the order that we should go straight; and then we sat silent with the expectation of arrival. As some time still passed, however, she said suddenly, of her own movement, "I have found out what is the matter with my aunt: she is afraid you will go!"

"What has put that into her head?"

"She has had an idea you have not been happy. That is why she is different now."

"You mean she wants to make me happier?"

"Well, she wants you not to go; she wants you to stay."

"I suppose you mean on account of the rent," I remarked candidly.

Miss Tita's candour showed itself a match for my own. "Yes, you know; so that I shall have more."

"How much does she want you to have?" I asked, laughing. "She ought to fix the sum, so that I may stay till it's made up."

"Oh, that wouldn't please me," said Miss Tita. "It would be unheard of, your taking that trouble."

"But suppose I should have my own reasons for staying in Venice?"

"Then it would be better for you to stay in some other house."

"And what would your aunt say to that?"

"She wouldn't like it at all. But I should think you would do well to give up your reasons and go away altogether."

"Dear Miss Tita," I said, "it's not so easy to give them up!"

She made no immediate answer to this, but after a moment she broke out: "I think I know what your reasons are!"

"I daresay, because the other night I almost told you how I wish you would help me to make them good."

"I can't do that without being false to my aunt."

"What do you mean, being false to her?"

"Why, she would never consent to what you want. She has been asked, she has been written to. It made her fearfully angry."

"Then she *has* got papers of value?" I demanded, quickly.

"Oh, she has got everything!" sighed Miss Tita, with a curious weariness, a sudden lapse into gloom.

These words caused all my pulses to throb, for I regarded them as precious evidence. For some minutes I was too agitated to speak, and in the interval the gondola approached the Piazzetta. After we had disembarked I asked my companion whether she would rather walk round the square or go and sit at the door of the café; to which she replied that she would do whichever I liked best—I must only remember again how little time she had. I assured her there was plenty to do both, and we made the circuit of the long arcades. Her spirits revived at the sight of the bright shopwindows, and she lingered and stopped, admiring or disapproving of their contents, asking me what I thought of things, theorising about prices. My attention wandered from her; her words of a while before, "Oh, she has got everything!" echoed so in my consciousness. We sat down at last in the crowded circle at Florian's, finding an unoccupied table among those that were ranged in the square. It was a splendid night and all the world was out-of-doors; Miss Tita could not have wished the elements more auspicious for her return to society. I saw that she enjoyed it even more than she told; she was agitated with the multitude of her impressions. She had forgotten what an attractive thing the world is, and it was coming over her that somehow she had for the best years of her life been cheated of it. This did not make her angry; but as she looked all over the charming scene her face had, in spite of its smile of appreciation, the flush of a sort of wounded surprise. She became silent, as if she were thinking with a secret sadness of opportunities, for ever lost, which ought to have been easy; and this gave me a chance to say to her, "Did you mean a while ago that your aunt has a plan of keeping me on by admitting me occasionally to her presence?"

"She thinks it will make a difference with you if you sometimes see her. She wants you so much to stay that she is willing to make that concession."

"And what good does she consider that I think it will do me to see her?"

"I don't know; she thinks it's interesting," said Miss Tita, simply. "You told her you found it so."

"So I did; but every one doesn't think so."

"No, of course not, or more people would try."

"Well, if she is capable of making that reflection she is capable also of making this further one," I went on: "that I must have a particular reason for not doing as others do, in spite of the interest she offers—for not leaving her alone." Miss Tita looked as if she failed to grasp this rather complicated proposition; so I continued, "If you have not told her what I said to you the other night may she not at least have guessed it?"

"I don't know; she is very suspicious."

"But she has not been made so by indiscreet curiosity, by persecution?"

"No, no; it isn't that," said Miss Tita, turning on me a somewhat troubled face. "I don't know how to say it: it's on account of something—ages ago, before I was born—in her life."

"Something? What sort of thing?" I asked, as if I myself could have no idea.

"Oh, she has never told me," Miss Tita answered; and I was sure she was speaking the truth.

Her extreme limpidity was almost provoking, and I felt for the moment that she would have been more satisfactory if she had been less ingenuous. "Do you suppose it's something to which Jeffrey Aspern's letters and papers—I mean the things in her possession—have reference?"

"I daresay it is!" my companion exclaimed, as if this were a very happy suggestion. "I have never looked at any of those things."

"None of them? Then how do you know what they are?"

"I don't," said Miss Tita, placidly. "I have never had them in my hands. But I have seen them when she has had them out."

"Does she have them out often?"

"Not now, but she used to. She is very fond of them."

"In spite of their being compromising?"

"Compromising?" Miss Tita repeated, as if she was ignorant of the meaning of the word. I felt almost as one who corrupts the innocence of youth.

"I mean their containing painful memories."

"Oh, I don't think they are painful."

"You mean you don't think they affect her reputation?"

At this a singular look came into the face of Miss Bordereau's niece—a kind of confession of helplessness, an appeal to me to deal fairly, generously with her. I had brought her to the Piazza, placed her among charming influences, paid her an attention she appreciated, and now I seemed to let her perceive that all this had been a bribe—a bribe to make her turn in some way against her aunt. She was of a yielding nature and capable of doing almost anything to please a person who was kind to her; but the greatest kindness of all would be not to presume too much on this. It was strange enough, as I afterwards thought, that she had not the least air of resenting my want of consideration for her aunt's character, which would have been in the worst possible taste if anything less vital (from my point of view) had been at stake. I don't think she really measured it. "Do you mean that she did something bad?" she asked in a moment.

"Heaven forbid I should say so, and it's none of my business. Besides, if she did," I added, laughing, "it was in other ages, in another world. But why should she not destroy her papers?"

"Oh, she loves them too much."

"Even now, when she may be near her end?"

"Perhaps when she's sure of that she will."

"Well, Miss Tita," I said, "it's just what I should like you to prevent."

"How can I prevent it?"

"Couldn't you get them away from her?"

"And give them to you?"

This put the case very crudely, though I am sure there was no irony in her intention. "Oh, I mean that you might let me see them and look them over. It isn't for myself; there is no personal avidity in my desire. It is simply that they would be of such immense interest to the public, such immeasurable importance as a contribution to Jeffrey Aspern's history."

She listened to me in her usual manner, as if my speech were full of reference to things she had never heard of, and I felt particularly like the reporter of a newspaper who forces his way into a house of mourning. This was especially the case when after a moment she said, "There was a gentleman who some time ago wrote to her in very much those words. He also wanted her papers."

"And did she answer him?" I asked, rather ashamed of myself for not having her rectitude.

"Only when he had written two or three times. He made her very angry."

"And what did she say?"

"She said he was a devil," Miss Tita replied, simply.

"She used that expression in her letter?"

"Oh no; she said it to me. She made me write to him."

"And what did you say?"

"I told him there were no papers at all."

"Ah, poor gentleman!" I exclaimed.

"I knew there were, but I wrote what she bade me."

"Of course you had to do that. But I hope I shall not pass for a devil."

"It will depend upon what you ask me to do for you," said Miss Tita, smiling.

"Oh, if there is a chance of *your* thinking so my affair is in a bad way! I sha'n't ask you to steal for me, nor even to fib—for you can't fib, unless on paper. But the principal thing is this—to prevent her from destroying the papers."

"Why, I have no control of her," said Miss Tita. "It's she who controls me."

"But she doesn't control her own arms and legs, does she? The way she would naturally destroy her letters would be to burn them. Now she can't burn them without fire, and she can't get fire unless you give it to her."

"I have always done everything she has asked," my companion rejoined. "Besides, there's Olimpia."

I was on the point of saying that Olimpia was probably corruptible, but I thought it best not to sound that note. So I simply inquired if that faithful domestic could not be managed.

"Every one can be managed by my aunt," said Miss Tita. And then she observed that her holiday was over; she must go home.

I laid my hand on her arm, across the table, to stay her a moment. "What I want of you is a general promise to help me."

"Oh, how can I—how can I?" she asked, wondering and troubled. She was half surprised, half frightened at my wishing to make her play an active part.

"This is the main thing: to watch her carefully and warn me in time, before she commits that horrible sacrilege."

"I can't watch her when she makes me go out."

"That's very true."

"And when you do too."

"Mercy on us; do you think she will have done anything to-night?"

"I don't know; she is very cunning."

"Are you trying to frighten me?" I asked.

I felt this inquiry sufficiently answered when my companion murmured in a musing, almost envious way, "Oh, but she loves them—she loves them!"

This reflection, repeated with such emphasis, gave me great comfort; but to obtain more of that balm I said, "If she shouldn't intend to destroy the objects we speak of before her death she will probably have made some disposition by will."

"By will?"

"Hasn't she made a will for your benefit?"

"Why, she has so little to leave. That's why she likes money," said Miss Tita.

"Might I ask, since we are really talking things over, what you and she live on?"

"On some money that comes from America, from a lawyer. He sends it every quarter. It isn't much!"

"And won't she have disposed of that!"

My companion hesitated—I saw she was blushing. "I believe it's mine," she said; and the look and tone which accompanied these words betrayed so the absence of the habit of thinking of herself that I almost thought her charming. The next instant she added, "But she had a lawyer once, ever so long ago. And some people came and signed something."

"They were probably witnesses. And you were not asked to sign? Well then," I argued, rapidly and hopefully, "it is because you are the legatee; she has left all her documents to you!"

"If she has it's with very strict conditions," Miss Tita responded, rising quickly, while the movement gave the words a little character of decision. They seemed to imply that the bequest would be accompanied with a command that the articles bequeathed should remain concealed from every inquisitive eye and that I was very much mistaken if I thought she was the person to depart from an injunction so solemn.

"Oh, of course you will have to abide by the terms," I said; and she uttered nothing to mitigate the severity of this conclusion. None the less, later, just before we disembarked at her own door, on our return, which had taken place almost in silence, she said to me abruptly, "I will do what I can to help you." I was grateful for this—it was very well so far as it went; but it did not keep me from remembering that night in a worried waking hour that I now had her word for it to reinforce my own impression that the old woman was very cunning.

CHAPTER VII

The fear of what this side of her character might have led her to do made me nervous for days afterwards. I waited for an intimation from Miss Tita; I almost figured to myself that it was her duty to keep me informed, to let me know definitely whether or no Miss Bordereau had sacrificed her treasures. But as she gave no sign I lost patience and determined to judge so far as was possible with my own senses. I sent late one afternoon to ask if I might pay the ladies a visit, and my servant came back with surprising news. Miss Bordereau could be approached without the least difficulty; she had been moved out into the sala and was sitting by the window that overlooked the garden. I descended and found this picture correct; the old lady had been wheeled forth into the world and had a certain air, which came mainly perhaps from some brighter element in her dress, of being prepared again to have converse with it. It had not yet, however, begun to flock about her; she was perfectly alone and, though the door leading to her own quarters stood open, I had at first no glimpse of Miss Tita. The window at which she sat had the afternoon shade and, one of the shutters having been pushed back, she could see the pleasant garden, where the summer sun had by this time dried up too many of the plants—she could see the yellow light and the long shadows.

"Have you come to tell me that you will take the rooms for six months more?" she asked, as I approached her, startling me by something coarse in her cupidity almost as much as if she had not already given me a specimen of it. Juliana's desire to make our acquaintance lucrative had been, as I have sufficiently indicated, a false note in my image of the woman who had inspired a great poet with immortal lines; but I may say here definitely that I recognised after all that it behoved me to make a large allowance for her. It was I who had kindled the unholy flame; it was I who had put into her head that she had the means of making money. She appeared never to have thought of that; she had been living wastefully for years, in a house five times too big for her, on a footing that I could explain only by the presumption that, excessive as it was, the space she enjoyed cost her next to nothing and that small as were her revenues they left her, for Venice, an appreciable margin. I had descended on her one day and taught her to calculate, and my almost extravagant comedy on the subject of the garden had presented me irresistibly in the light of a victim. Like all persons who achieve the miracle of changing their point of view when they are old she had been intensely converted; she had seized my hint with a desperate, tremulous clutch.

I invited myself to go and get one of the chairs that stood, at a distance, against the wall (she had given herself no concern as to whether I should sit or stand); and while I placed it near her I began, gaily, "Oh, dear madam, what an imagination you have, what an intellectual sweep! I am a poor devil of a man of letters who lives from day to day. How can I take palaces by the year? My existence is precarious. I don't know whether six months hence I shall have bread to put in my mouth. I have treated myself for once; it has been an immense luxury. But when in comes to going on—!"

"Are your rooms too dear? if they are you can have more for the same money," Juliana responded. "We can arrange, we can *combinare,* as they say here."

"Well yes, since you ask me, they are too dear," I said. "Evidently you suppose me richer than I am."

She looked at me in her barricaded way. 'If you write books don't you sell them?"

"Do you mean don't people buy them? A little—not so much as I could wish. Writing books, unless one be a great genius—and even then!—is the last road to fortune. I think there is no more money to be made by literature."

"Perhaps you don't choose good subjects. What do you write about?" Miss Bordereau inquired.

"About the books of other people. I'm a critic, an historian, in a small way." I wondered what she was coming to.

"And what other people, now?"

"Oh, better ones than myself: the great writers mainly—the great philosophers and poets of the past; those who are dead and gone and can't speak for themselves."

"And what do you say about them?"

"I say they sometimes attached themselves to very clever women!" I answered, laughing. I spoke with great deliberation, but as my words fell upon the air they struck me as imprudent. However, I risked them and I was not sorry, for perhaps after all the old woman would be willing to treat. It seemed to be tolerably obvious that she knew my secret: why therefore drag the matter out? But she did not take what I had said as a confession; she only asked:

"Do you think it's right to rake up the past?"

"I don't know that I know what you mean by raking it up; but how can we get at it unless we dig a little? The present has such a rough way of treading it down."

"Oh, I like the past, but I don't like critics," the old woman declared, with her fine tranquillity.

"Neither do I, but I like their discoveries."

"Aren't they mostly lies?"

"The lies are what they sometimes discover," I said, smiling at the quiet impertinence of this. "They often lay bare the truth."

'The truth is God's, it isn't man's; we had better leave it alone. Who can judge of it—who can say?"

"We are terribly in the dark, I know," I admitted; "but if we give up trying what becomes of all the fine things? What becomes of the work I just mentioned, that of the great philosophers and poets? It is all vain words if there is nothing to measure it by!"

"You talk as if you were a tailor," said Miss Bordereau, whimsically; and then she added quickly, in a different manner, "This house is very fine; the proportions are magnificent. To-day I wanted to look at this place again. I made them bring me out here. When your man came, just now, to learn if

I would see you, I was on the point of sending for you, to ask if you didn't mean to go on. I wanted to judge what I'm letting you have. This sala is very grand," she pursued, like an auctioneer, moving a little, as I guessed, her invisible eyes. "I don't believe you often have lived in such a house, eh?"

"I can't often afford to!" I said.

"Well then, how much will you give for six months?"

I was on the point of exclaiming—and the air of excruciation in my face would have denoted a moral fact—"Don't, Juliana; for *his* sake, don't!" But I controlled myself and asked less passionately: "Why should I remain so long as that?"

"I thought you liked it," said Miss Bordereau, with her shrivelled dignity.

"So I thought I should."

For a moment she said nothing more, and I left my own words to suggest to her what they might. I half expected her to say, coldly enough, that if I had been disappointed we need not continue the discussion, and this in spite of the fact that I believed her now to have in her mind (however it had come there), what would have told her that my disappointment was natural. But to my extreme surprise she ended by observing: "If you don't think we have treated you well enough perhaps we can discover some way of treating you better." This speech was somehow so incongruous that it made me laugh again, and I excused myself by saying that she talked as if I were a sulky boy, pouting in the corner, to be "brought round." I had not a grain of complaint to make; and could anything have exceeded Miss Tita's graciousness in accompanying me a few nights before to the Piazza? At this the old woman went on: "Well, you brought it on yourself!" And then in a different tone, "She is a very nice girl." I assented cordially to this proposition, and she expressed the hope that I did so not merely to be obliging, but that I really liked her. Meanwhile I wondered still more what Miss Bordereau was coming to. "Except for me, to-day," she said, "she has not a relation in the world." Did she by describing her niece as amiable and unencumbered wish to represent her as a *parti?*

It was perfectly true that I could not afford to go on with my rooms at a fancy price and that I had already devoted to my undertaking almost all the hard cash I had set apart for it. My patience and my time were by no means exhausted, but I should be able to draw upon them only on a more usual Venetian basis. I was willing to pay the venerable woman with whom my pecuniary dealings were such a discord twice as much as any other *padrona di casa* would have asked, but I was not willing to pay her twenty times as much. I told her so plainly, and my plainness appeared to have some success, for she exclaimed, "Very good; you have done what I asked—you have made an offer!"

"Yes, but not for half a year. Only by the month."

"Oh, I must think of that then." She seemed disappointed that I would not tie myself to a period, and I guessed that she wished both to secure me and to discourage me; to say, severely, "Do you dream that you can get off with less than six months? Do you dream that even by the end of that time you will be appreciably nearer your victory?" What was more in my mind was that she had a fancy to play me the trick of making me engage myself when in fact she had annihilated the papers. There was a moment when my suspense on this point was so acute that I all but broke out with the question, and what kept it back was but a kind of instinctive recoil (lest it should be a mistake), from the last violence of self-exposure. She was such a subtle old witch that one could never tell where one stood with her. You may imagine whether it cleared up the puzzle when, just after she had said she would think of my proposal and without any formal transition, she drew out of her pocket with an embarrassed hand a small object wrapped in crumpled white paper. She held it there a moment and then she asked, "Do you know much about curiosities?"

"About curiosities?"

"About antiquities, the old gimcracks that people pay so much for to-day. Do you know the kind of price they bring?"

I thought I saw what was coming, but I said ingenuously, "Do you want to buy something?"

"No, I want to sell. What would an amateur give me for that? She unfolded the white paper and made a motion for me to take from her a small oval portrait. I possessed myself of it with a hand of which I could only hope that she did not perceive the tremor, and she added, "I would part with it only for a good price."

At the first glance I recognised Jeffrey Aspern, and I was well aware that I flushed with the act. As she was watching me however I had the consistency to exclaim, "What a striking face! Do tell me who it is."

"It's an old friend of mine, a very distinguished man in his day. He gave it to me himself, but I'm afraid to mention his name, lest you never should have heard of him, critic and historian as you are. I know the world goes fast and one generation forgets another. He was all the fashion when I was young."

She was perhaps amazed at my assurance, but I was surprised at hers; at her having the energy, in her state of health and at her time of life, to wish to sport with me that way simply for her private entertainment—the humour to test me and practice on me. This, at least, was the interpretation that I put upon her production of the portrait, for I could not believe that she really desired to sell it or cared for any information I might give her. What she wished was to dangle it before my eyes and put a prohibitive price on it. "The face comes back to me, it torments me," I said, turning the object this way and that and looking at it very critically. It was a careful but not a supreme work of art, larger than the ordinary miniature and representing a young man with a remarkably handsome face, in a high-collared green coat and a buff waistcoat. I judged the picture to have a valuable quality of resemblance and to have been painted when the model was about twenty-five years old. There are, as all the world knows, three other portraits of the poet in existence, but none of them is of so early a date as this elegant production. "I have never seen the original but I have seen other likenesses," I went on. "You expressed doubt of this generation having heard of the gentleman, but he strikes me for all the world as a celebrity. Now who is he? I can't put my finger on him—I can't give him a label. Wasn't he a writer? Surely he's a poet." I was determined that it should be she, not I, who should first pronounce Jeffrey Aspern's name.

My resolution was taken in ignorance of Miss Bordereau's extremely resolute character, and her lips never formed in my hearing the syllables that meant so much for her. She neglected to answer my question but raised her hand to take back the picture, with a gesture which though ineffectual was in a high degree peremptory. "It's only a person who should know for himself that would give me my price," she said with a certain dryness.

"Oh, then, you have a price?" I did not restore the precious thing; not from any vindictive purpose but because I instinctively clung to it. We looked at each other hard while I retained it.

"I know the least I would take. What it occurred to me to ask you about is the most I shall be able to get."

She made a movement, drawing herself together as if, in a spasm of dread at having lost her treasure, she were going to attempt the immense effort of rising to snatch it from me. I instantly placed it in her hand again, saying as I did so, "I should like to have it myself, but with your ideas I could never afford it."

She turned the small oval plate over in her lap, with its face down, and I thought I saw her catch her breath a little, as if she had had a strain or an escape. This however did not prevent her saying in a moment, "You would buy a likeness of a person you don't know, by an artist who has no reputation?"

"The artist may have no reputation, but that thing is wonderfully well painted," I replied, to give myself a reason.

"It's lucky you thought of saying that, because the painter was my father."

"That makes the picture indeed precious!" I exclaimed, laughing; and I may add that a part of my laughter came from my satisfaction in finding that I had been right in my theory of Miss Bordereau's origin. Aspern had of course met the young lady when he went to her father's studio as a sitter. I observed to Miss Bordereau that if she would entrust me with her property for twenty-four hours I should be happy to take advice upon it; but she made no answer to this save to slip it in silence into her pocket. This convinced me still more that she had no sincere intention of selling it during her lifetime, though she may have desired to satisfy herself as to the sum her niece, should she leave it to her, might expect eventually to obtain for it. "Well, at any rate I hope you will not offer it without giving me notice," I said, as she remained irresponsive. "Remember that I am a possible purchaser."

"I should want your money first!" she returned, with unexpected rudeness; and then, as if she bethought herself that I had just cause to complain of such an insinuation and wished to turn the matter off, asked abruptly what I talked about with her niece when I went out with her that way in the evening.

"You speak as if we had set up the habit," I replied. "Certainly I should be very glad if it were to become a habit. But in that case I should feel a still greater scruple at betraying a lady's confidence."

"Her confidence? Has she got confidence?"

"Here she is—she can tell you herself," I said; for Miss Tita now appeared on the threshold of the old woman's parlour. "Have you got confidence, Miss Tita? Your aunt wants very much to know."

"Not in her, not in her!" the younger lady declared, shaking her head with a dolefulness that was neither jocular nor affected. "I don't know what to do with her; she has fits of horrid imprudence. She is so easily tired—and yet she has begun to roam—to drag herself about the house." And she stood looking down at her immemorial companion with a sort of helpless wonder, as if all their years of familiarity had not made her perversities, on occasion, any more easy to follow.

"I know what I'm about. I'm not losing my mind. I daresay you would like to think so," said Miss Bordereau, with a cynical little sigh.

"I don't suppose you came out here yourself. Miss Tita must have had to lend you a hand," I interposed, with a pacifying intention.

"Oh, she insisted that we should push her; and when she insists!" said Miss Tita, in the same tone of apprehension; as if there were no knowing what service that she disapproved of her aunt might force her next to render.

"I have always got most things done I wanted, thank God! The people I have lived with have humoured me," the old woman continued, speaking out of the gray ashes of her vanity.

"I suppose you mean that they have obeyed you."

"Well, whatever it is, when they like you."

"It's just because I like you that I want to resist," said Miss Tita, with a nervous laugh.

"Oh I suspect you'll bring Miss Bordereau upstairs next, to pay me a visit," I went on; to which the old lady replied:

"Oh no; I can keep an eye on you from here!"

"You are very tired; you will certainly be ill tonight!" cried Miss Tita.

"Nonsense, my dear; I feel better at this moment than I have done for a month. To-morrow I shall come out again. I want to be where I can see this clever gentleman."

"Shouldn't you perhaps see me better in your sitting-room?" I inquired.

"Don't you mean shouldn't you have a better chance at me?" she returned, fixing me a moment with her green shade.

"Ah, I haven't that anywhere! I look at you but I don't see you."

"You excite her dreadfully—and that is not good," said Miss Tita, giving me a reproachful, appealing look.

"I want to watch you—I want to watch you!" the old lady went on.

"Well then, let us spend as much of our time together as possible—I don't care where—and that will give you every facility."

"Oh, I've seen you enough for to-day. I'm satisfied. Now I'll go home." Miss Tita laid her hands on the back of her aunt's chair and began to push, but I begged her to let me take her place. "Oh yes, you may move me this way—you sha'n't in any other!" Miss Bordereau exclaimed, as she felt herself propelled firmly and easily over the smooth, hard floor. Before we reached the door of her own apartment she commanded me to stop, and she took a long, last look up and down the noble sala. "Oh, it's a magnificent house!" she murmured; after which I pushed her forward. When we had entered the parlour Miss Tita told me that she should now be able to manage, and at the same moment the little red-haired *donna* came to meet her mistress. Miss Tita's idea was evidently to get her aunt immediately back to bed. I confess that in spite of this urgency I was guilty of the indiscretion of lingering; it held me there to think that I was nearer the documents I coveted—that they were probably put away somewhere in the faded, unsociable room. The place had indeed a bareness which did not suggest hidden treasures; there were no dusky nooks nor curtained corners, no massive cabinets nor chests with iron bands. Moreover it was possible, it was perhaps even probable, that the old lady had consigned her relics to her bedroom, to some battered box that was shoved under the bed, to the drawer of some lame dressing-table, where they would be in the range of vision by the dim night-lamp. None the less I scrutinised every article of furniture, every conceivable cover for a hoard, and noticed that there were half a dozen things with drawers, and in particular a tall old secretary, with brass ornaments of the style of the Empire—a receptacle somewhat rickety but still capable of keeping a great many secrets. I don't know why this article fascinated me so, inasmuch as I certainly had no definite purpose of breaking into it; but I stared at it so hard that Miss Tita noticed me and changed colour. Her doing this made me think I was right and that wherever they might have been before, the Aspern papers at that moment languished behind the peevish little lock of the secretary. It was hard to remove my eyes from the dull mahogany front when I reflected that a simple panel divided me from the goal of my hopes; but I remembered my prudence and with an effort took leave of Miss Bordereau. To make the effort graceful I said to her that I should certainly bring her an opinion about the little picture.

"The little picture?" Miss Tita asked, surprised.

"What do *you* know about it, my dear?" the old woman demanded. "You needn't mind. I have fixed my price."

"And what may that be?"

"A thousand pounds."

"Oh Lord!" cried poor Miss Tita, irrepressibly.

"Is that what she talks to you about?" said Miss Bordereau.

"Imagine your aunt's wanting to know!" I had to separate from Miss Tita with only those words, though I should have liked immensely to add, "For heaven's sake meet me to-night in the garden!"

CHAPTER VIII

As it turned out the precaution had not been needed, for three hours later, just as I had finished my dinner, Miss Bordereau's niece appeared, unannounced, in the open doorway of the room in which my simple repasts were served. I remember well that I felt no surprise at seeing her; which is not a proof that I did not believe in her timidity. It was immense, but a case in which there was a particular reason for boldness it never would have prevented her from running up to my rooms. I saw that she was now quite full of a particular reason; it threw her forward—made her seize me, as I rose to meet her, by the arm.

"My aunt is very ill; I think she is dying!"

"Never in the world," I answered, bitterly. "Don't you be afraid!"

"Do go for a doctor—do, do! Olimpia is gone for the one we always have, but she doesn't come back; I don't know what has happened to her. I told her that if he was not at home she was to follow him where he had gone; but apparently she is following him all over Venice. I don't know what to do—she looks so as if she were sinking."

"May I see her, may I judge?" I asked. "Of course I shall be delighted to bring some one; but hadn't we better send my man instead, so that I may stay with you?"

Miss Tita assented to this and I despatched my servant for the best doctor in the neighbourhood. I hurried downstairs with her, and on the way she told me than an hour after I quitted them in the afternoon Miss Bordereau had had an attack of "oppression," a terrible difficulty in breathing. This had subsided but had left her so exhausted that she did not come up: she seemed all gone. I repeated that she was not gone, that she would not go yet; whereupon Mis Tita gave me a sharper sidelong glance than she had ever directed at me and said, "Really, what do you mean? I suppose you don't accuse her of making-believe!" I forget what reply I made to this, but I grant that in my heart I thought the old woman capable of any weird manœuvre. Miss Tita wanted to know what I had done to her; her aunt had told her that I had made her so angry. I declared I had done nothing—I had been exceedingly careful; to which my companion rejoined that Miss Bordereau had assured her she had had a scene with me—a scene that had upset her. I answered with some resentment that it was a scene of her own making—that I couldn't think what she was angry with me for unless for not seeing my way to give a thousand pounds for the portrait of Jeffrey Aspern. "And did she show you that? Oh gracious—oh deary me!" groaned Miss Tita, who appeared to feel that the situation was passing out of her control and that the elements of her fate were thickening around her. I said that I would give anything to possess it, yet that I had not a thousand pounds; but I stopped when we came to the door of Miss Bordereau's room. I had an immense curiosity to pass it, but I thought it my duty to represent to Miss Tita that if I made the invalid angry she ought perhaps to be spared the sight of me. "The sight of you? Do you think she can *see?*" my companion demanded, almost with indignation. I did think so but forbore to say it, and I softly followed my conductress.

I remember that what I said to her as I stood for a moment beside the old woman's bed was, "Does she never show you her eyes then? Have you never seen them?" Miss Bordereau had been divested of her green shade, but (it was not my fortune to behold Juliana in her nightcap) the upper half of her face was covered by the fall of a piece of dingy lacelike muslin, a sort of extemporised hood which, wound round her head, descended to the end of her nose, leaving nothing visible but her white withered cheeks and puckered mouth, closed tightly and, as it were, consciously. Miss Tita gave me a glance of surprise, evidently not seeing a reason for my impatience. "You mean that she always wears something? She does it to preserve them."

"Because they are so fine?"

"Oh, to-day, to-day!" And Miss Tita shook her head, speaking low. "But they used to be magnificent!"

"Yes indeed, we have Aspern's word for that." And as I looked again at the old woman's wrappings I could imagine that she had not wished to allow people a reason to say that the great poet had overdone it. But I did not waste my time in considering Miss Bordereau, in whom the appearance of respiration was so slight as to suggest that no human attention could ever help her more. I turned my eyes all over the room, rummaging with them the closets, the chests of drawers, the tables. Miss Tita met them quickly and read, I think, what was in them; but she did not answer it, turning away restlessly, anxiously, so that I felt rebuked, with reason, for a preoccupation that was almost profane in the presence of our dying companion. All the same I took another look, endeavouring to pick out mentally the place to try first, for a person who should wish to put his hand on Miss Bordereau's papers directly after her death. The room was a dire confusion; it looked like the room of an old actress. There were clothes hanging over chairs, odd-looking, shabby bundles here and there, and various pasteboard boxes piled together, battered, bulging and discoloured, which might have been fifty years old. Miss Tita after a moment noticed the direction of my eyes again and, as if she guessed how I judged the air of the place (forgetting I had no business to judge it at all), said, perhaps to defend herself from the imputation of complicity in such untidiness:

"She likes it this way; we can't move things. There are old bandboxes she has had most of her life." Then she added, half taking pity on my real thought, "Those things were *there*." And she pointed to a small, low trunk which stood under a sofa where there was just room for it. It appeared to be a queer, superannuated coffer, of painted wood, with elaborate handles and shrivelled straps and with the colour (it had last been endued with a coat of light green) much rubbed off. It evidently had travelled with Juliana in the olden time—in the days of her adventures, which it had shared. It would have made a strange figure arriving at a modern hotel.

"*Were* there—they aren't now?" I asked, startled by Miss Tita's implication.

She was going to answer, but at that moment the doctor came in—the doctor whom the little maid had been sent to fetch and whom she had at last overtaken. My servant, going on his own errand, had met her with her companion in tow, and in the sociable Venetian spirit, retracing his steps with them, had also come up to the threshold of Miss Bordereau's room, where I saw him peeping over the doctor's shoulder. I motioned him away the more instantly that the sight of his prying face reminded me that I myself had almost as little to do there—an admonition confirmed by the sharp way the little doctor looked at me, appearing to take me for a rival who had the field before him. He was a short, fat, brisk gentleman who wore the tall hat of his profession and seemed to look at everything but his patient. He looked particularly at me, as if it struck him that I should be better for a dose, so that I bowed to him and left him with the women, going down to smoke a cigar in the garden. I was nervous; I could not go further; I could not leave the place. I don't know exactly what I thought might happen, but it seemed to me important to be there. I wandered about in the alleys—the warm night had come on—smoking cigar after cigar and looking at the light in Miss Bordereau's windows. They were open now, I could see; the situation was different. Sometimes the light moved, but not quickly; it did not suggest the hurry of a crisis. Was the old woman dying or was she already dead? Had the doctor said that there was nothing to be done at her tremendous age but to let her quietly pass away; or had he simply announced with a look a little more conventional that the end of the end had come? Were the other two women moving about to perform the offices that follow in such a case? It made me uneasy not to be nearer, as if I thought the doctor himself might carry away the papers with him. I bit my cigar hard as it came over me again that perhaps there were now no papers to carry!

I wandered about for an hour—for an hour and a half. I looked out for Miss Tita at one of the windows, having a vague idea that she might come there to give me some sign. Would she not see the red tip of my cigar moving about in the dark and feel that I wanted eminently to know what the doctor had said? I am afraid it is a proof my anxieties had made me gross that I should have taken in some degree for granted that at such an hour, in the midst of the greatest change that could take place in her life, they were uppermost also in poor Miss Tita's mind. My servant came down and spoke to me; he knew nothing save that the doctor had gone after a visit of half an hour. If he had stayed half an hour then Miss Bordereau was still alive: it could not have taken so much time as that to enunciate the contrary. I sent the man out of the house; there were moments when the sense of his curiosity annoyed me and this was one of them. *He* had been watching my cigartip from an upper window, if Miss Tita had not; he could not know what I was after and I could not tell him, though I was conscious he had fantastic private theories about me which he thought fine and which I, had I known them, should have thought offensive.

I went upstairs at last but I ascended no higher than the sala. The door of Miss Bordereau's apartment was open, showing from the parlour the dimness of a poor candle. I went toward it with a light tread and at the same moment Miss Tita appeared and stood looking at me as I approached. "She's better—she's better," she said, even before I had asked. "The doctor has given her something; she woke up, came back to life while he was there. He says there is no immediate danger."

"No immediate danger? Surely he thinks her condition strange!"

"Yes, because she had been excited. That affects her dreadfully."

"It will do so again then, because she excites herself. She did so this afternoon."

"Yes; she mustn't come out any more," said Miss Tita, with one of her lapses into a deeper placidity.

"What is the use of making such a remark as that if you begin to rattle her about again the first time she bids you?"

"I won't—I won't do it any more."

"You must learn to resist," I went on.

"Oh yes, I shall; I shall do so better if you tell me it's right."

"You mustn't do it for me; you must do it for yourself. It all comes back to you, if you are frightened."

"Well, I am not frightened now," said Miss Tita cheerfully. "She is very quiet."

"Is she conscious again—does she speak?"

"No, she doesn't speak, but she takes my hand. She holds it fast."

"Yes," I rejoined, "I can see what force she still has by the way she grabbed that picture this afternoon. But if she holds you fast how comes it that you are here?"

Miss Tita hesitated a moment; though her face was in deep shadow (she had her back to the light in the parlour and I had put down my own candle far off, near the door of the sala), I thought I saw her smile ingenuously. "I came on purpose—I heard your step."

"Why, I came on tiptoe, as inaudibly as possible."

"Well, I heard you," said Miss Tita.

"And is your aunt alone now?"

"Oh no; Olimpia is sitting there."

On my side I hesitated. "Shall we then step in there?" And I nodded at the parlour; I wanted more and more to be on the spot.

"We can't talk there—she will hear us."

I was on the point of replying that in that case we would sit silent, but I was too conscious that this would not do, as there was something I desired immensely to ask her. So I proposed that we should walk a little in the sala, keeping more at the other end, where we should not disturb the old lady. Miss Tita assented unconditionally; the doctor was coming again, she said, and she would be there to meet him at the door. We strolled through the fine superfluous hall, where on the marble floor—particularly as at first we said nothing—our footsteps were more audible than I had expected. When we reached the other end—the wide window, inveterately closed, connecting with the balcony that overhung the canal—I suggested that we should remain there, as she would see the doctor arrive still better. I opened the window and we passed out on the balcony. The air of the canal seemed even heavier, hotter, than that of the sala. The place was hushed and void; the quiet neighbourhood had gone to sleep. A lamp, here and there, over the narrow black water, glimmered in double; the voice of a man going homeward singing, with his jacket on his shoulder and his hat on his ear, came to us from a distance. This did not prevent the scene from being very *comme il faut,* as Miss Bordereau had called it the first time I saw her. Presently a gondola passed along the canal with its slow rhythmical plash, and as we listened we watched it in silence. It did not stop, it did not carry the doctor; and after it had gone on I said to Miss Tita:

"And where are they now—the things that were in the trunk?"

"In the trunk?"

"That green box you pointed out to me in her room. You said her papers had been there; you seemed to imply that she had transferred them."

"Oh yes; they are not in the trunk," said Miss Tita.

"May I ask if you have looked?"

"Yes, I have looked—for you."

"How for me, dear Miss Tita? Do you mean you would have given them to me if you had found them?" I asked, almost trembling.

She delayed to reply and I waited. Suddenly she broke out, "I don't know what I would do—what I wouldn't!"

"Would you look again—somewhere else?"

She had spoken with a strange, unexpected emotion, and she went on in the same tone: "I can't—I can't—while she lies there. It isn't decent."

"No, it isn't decent," I replied, gravely. "Let the poor lady rest in peace."

And the words, on my lips, were not hypocritical, for I felt reprimanded and shamed.

Miss Tita added in a moment, as if she had guessed this and were sorry for me, but at the same time wished to explain that I did drive her on or at least did insist too much: "I can't deceive her that way. I can't deceive her —perhaps on her deathbed."

"Heaven forbid I should ask you, though I have been guilty myself!"

"You have been guilty?"

"I have sailed under false colours." I felt now as if I must tell her that I had given her an invented name, on account of my fear that her aunt would have heard of me and would refuse to take me in. I explained this and also that I had really been a party to the letter written to them by John Cumnor months before.

She listened with great attention, looking at me with parted lips, and when I had made my confession she said, "Then your real name—what is it?" She repeated it over twice when I had told her, accompanying it with the exclamation "Gracious, gracious!" Then she added, "I like your own best."

"So do I," I said, laughing. "Ouf! it's a relief to get rid of the other."

"So it was a regular plot—a kind of conspiracy?"

"Oh, a conspiracy—we were only two," I replied, leaving out Mrs. Prest of course.

She hesitated; I thought she was perhaps going to say that we had been very base. But she remarked after a moment, in a candid, wondering way, "How much you must want them!"

"Oh, I do, passionately!" I conceded, smiling. And this chance made me go on, forgetting my compunction of a moment before. "How can she possibly have changed their place herself? How can she walk? How can she arrive at that sort of muscular exertion? How can she lift and carry things?"

"Oh, when one wants and when one has so much will!" said Miss Tita, as if she had thought over my question already herself and had simply had no choice but that answer—the idea that in the dead of night, or at some moment when the coast was clear, the old woman had been capable of a miraculous effort.

"Have you questioned Olimpia? Hasn't she helped her—hasn't she done for her?" I asked; to which Miss Tita replied promptly and positively that their servant had had nothing to do with the matter, though without admitting definitely that she had spoken to her. It was as if she were a little shy, a little ashamed now of letting me see how much she had entered into my uneasiness and had me on her mind. Suddenly she said to me, without any immediate relevance:

"I feel as if you were a new person, now that you have got a new name."

"It isn't a new one; it is a very good old one, thank heaven!"

She looked at me a moment. "I do like it better."

"Oh, if you didn't I would almost go on with the other!"

"Would you really?"

I laughed again, but for all answer to this inquiry I said, "Of course if she can rummage about that way she can perfectly have burnt them."

"You must wait—you must wait," Miss Tita moralised mournfully; and her tone ministered little to my patience, for it seemed after all to accept that wretched possibility. I would teach myself to wait, I declared nevertheless; because in the first place I could not do otherwise and in the second I had her promise, given me the other night, that she would help me.

"Of course if the papers are gone that's no use," she said; not as if she wished to recede, but only to be conscientious.

"Naturally. But if you could only find out!" I groaned, quivering again.

"I thought you said you would wait."

"Oh, you mean wait even for that?"

"For what then?"

"Oh, nothing," I replied, rather foolishly, being ashamed to tell her what had been implied in my submission to delay—the idea that she would do more than merely find out. I know not whether she guessed this; at all events she appeared to become aware of the necessity for being a little more rigid.

"I didn't promise to deceive, did I? I don't think I did."

"It doesn't much matter whether you did or not, for you couldn't!"

I don't think Miss Tita would have contested this even had she not been diverted by our seeing the doctor's gondola shoot into the little canal and approach the house. I noted that he came as fast as if he believed that Miss Bordereau was still in danger. We looked down at him while he disembarked and then went back into the sala to meet him. When he came up however I naturally left Miss Tita to go off with him alone, only asking her leave to come back later for news.

I went out of the house and took a long walk, as far as the Piazza, where my restlessness declined to quit me. I was unable to sit down (it was very late now but there were people still at the little tables in front of the cafés); I could only walk round and round, and I did so half a dozen times. I was uncomfortable, but it gave me a certain pleasure to have told Miss Tita who I really was. At last I took my way home again, slowly getting all but inextricably lost, as I did whenever I went out in Venice: so that it was considerably past midnight when I reached my door. The sala, upstairs, was as dark as usual and my lamp as I crossed it found nothing satisfactory to show me. I was disappointed, for I had notified Miss Tita that I would come back for a report, and I thought she might have left a light there as a sign. The door of the ladies' apartment was closed; which seemed an intimation that my faltering friend had gone to bed, tired of waiting for me. I stood in the middle of the place, considering, hoping she would hear me and perhaps peep out, saying to myself too that she would never go to bed with her aunt in a state so critical; she would sit up and watch—she would be in a chair, in her dressing-gown. I went nearer the door; I stopped there and listened. I heard nothing at all and at last I tapped gently. No answer came and after another minute I turned the handle. There was no light in the room; this ought to have prevented me from going in, but it had no such effect. If I have candidly narrated the importunities, the indelicacies, of which my desire to possess myself of Jeffrey Aspern's papers had rendered me capable I need not shrink from confessing this last indiscretion. I think it was the worst thing I did; yet there were extenuating circumstances. I was deeply though doubtless not disinterestedly anxious for more news of the old lady, and Miss Tita had accepted from me, as it were, a rendezvous which it might have been a point of honour with me to keep. It may be said that her leaving the place dark was a positive sign that she released me, and to this I can only reply that I desired not to be released.

The door of Miss Bordereau's room was open and I could see beyond it the faintness of a taper. There was no sound—my footstep caused no one to stir. I came further into the room; I lingered there with my lamp in my hand. I wanted to give Miss Tita a chance to come to me if she were with her aunt, as she must be. I made no noise to call her; I only waited to see if she would not notice my light. She did not, and I explained this (I found afterwards I was right) by the idea that she had fallen asleep. If she had fallen asleep her aunt was not on her mind, and my explanation ought to have led me to go out as I had come. I must repeat again that it did not, for I found myself at the same moment thinking of something else. I had no definite purpose, no bad intention, but I felt myself held to the spot by an acute, though absurd, sense of opportunity. For what I could not have said, inasmuch as it was not in my mind that I might commit a theft. Even if it had been I was confronted with the evident fact that Miss Bordereau did not leave her secretary, her cupboard and the drawers of her tables gaping. I had no keys, no tools and no ambition to smash her furniture. None the less it came to me that I was now, perhaps alone, unmolested, at the hour of temptation and secrecy, nearer to the tormenting treasure than I had ever been. I held up my lamp, let the light play on the different objects as if it could tell me something. Still there came no movement from the other room. If Miss Tita was sleeping she was sleeping sound. Was she doing so—generous creature—on purpose to leave me the field? Did she know I was there and was she just keeping quiet to see what I would do—what I *could* do? But what could I do, when it came to that? She herself knew even better than I how little.

I stopped in front of the secretary, looking at it very idiotically; for what had it to say to me after all? In the first place it was locked, and in the second it almost surely contained nothing in which I was interested. Ten to one the papers had been destroyed; and even if they had not been destroyed the old woman would not have put them in such a place as that after removing them from the green trunk—would not have transferred them, if she had the idea of their safety on her brain, from the better hiding place to the worse. The secretary was more conspicuous, more accessible in a room in which she could no longer mount guard. It opened with a key, but there was a little brass handle, like a button, as well; I saw this as I played my lamp over it. I did something more than this at that moment: I caught a glimpse of the possibility that Miss Tita wished me really to understand. If she did not wish me to understand, if she wished me to keep away, why had she not locked the door of communication between the sitting-room and the sala? That would have been a definite sign that I was to leave them alone. If I did not leave them alone she meant me to come for a purpose—a purpose now indicated by the quick, fantastic idea that to oblige me she had unlocked the secretary. She had not left the key, but the lid would probably move if I touched the button. This theory fascinated me, and I bent over very close to judge. I did not propose to do anything, not even—not in the least—to let down the lid; I only wanted to test my theory, to see if the cover *would* move. I touched the button with my hand—a mere touch would tell me; and as I did so (it is embarrassing for me to relate it), I looked over my shoulder. It was a chance, an instinct, for I had not heard anything. I almost let my luminary drop and certainly I stepped back, straightening myself up at what I saw. Miss Bordereau stood there in her night-dress, in the doorway of her room, watching me; her hands were raised, she had lifted the everlasting curtain that covered half her face, and for the first, the last, the only time I beheld her extraordinary eyes. They glared at me, they made me horribly ashamed. I never shall forget her strange little bent white tottering figure, with its lifted head, her attitude, her expression; neither shall I forget the tone in which as I turned, looking at her, she hissed out passionately, furiously:

"Ah, you publishing scoundrel!"

I know not what I stammered, to excuse myself, to explain; but I went towards her, to tell her I meant no harm. She waved me off with her old hands, retreating before me in horror; and the next thing I knew she had fallen back with a quick spasm, as if death had descended on her, into Miss Tita's arms.

CHAPTER IX

I left Venice the next morning, as soon as I learnt that the old lady had not succumbed, as I feared at the moment, to the shock I had given her—the shock I may also say she had given me. How in the world could I have supposed her capable of getting out of bed by herself? I failed to see Miss Tita before going; I only saw the *donna,* whom I entrusted with a note for her younger mistress. In this note I mentioned that I should be absent but for a few days. I went to Treviso, to Bassano, to Castelfranco; I took walks and drives and looked at musty old churches with ill-lighted pictures and spent hours seated smoking at the doors of cafés, where there were flies and yellow curtains, on the shady side of sleepy little squares. In spite of these pastimes, which were mechanical and perfunctory, I scantily enjoyed my journey: there was too strong a taste of the disagreeable in my life. It had been devilish awkward, as the young men say, to be found by Miss Bordereau in the dead of night examining the attachment of her bureau; and it had not been less so to have to believe for a good many hours afterward that it was highly probable I had killed her. In writing to Miss Tita I attempted to minimise these irregularities; but as she gave me no word of answer I could not know what impression I made upon her. It rankled in my mind that I had been called a publishing scoundrel, for certainly I did publish and certainly I had not been very delicate. There was a moment when I stood convinced that the only way to make up for this latter fault was to take myself away altogether on the instant; to sacrifice my hopes and relieve the two poor women for ever of the oppression of my intercourse. Then I reflected that I had better try a short absence first, for I must already have had a sense (unexpressed and dim) that in disappearing completely it would not be merely my own hopes that I should condemn to extinction. It would perhaps be sufficient if I stayed away long enough to give the elder lady time to think she was rid of me. That she would wish to be rid of me after this (if I was not rid of her) was now not to be doubted: that nocturnal scene would have cured her of the disposition to put up with my company for the sake of my dollars. I said to myself that after all I could not abandon Miss Tita, and I continued to say this even while I observed that she quite failed to comply with my earnest request (I had given her two or three addresses, at little towns, *poste restante*) that she would let me know how she was getting on. I would have made my servant write to me but that he was unable to manage a pen. It struck me there was a kind of scorn in Miss Tita's silence (little disdainful as she had ever been), so that I was uncomfortable and sore. I had scruples about going back and yet I had others about not doing so, for I wanted to put myself on a better footing. The end of it was that I did return to Venice on the twelfth day; and as my gondola gently bumped against Miss Bordereau's steps a certain palpitation of suspense told me that I had done myself a violence in holding off so long.

I had faced about so abruptly that I had not telegraphed to my servant. He was therefore not at the station to meet me, but he poked out his head from an upper window when I reached the house. "They have put her into the earth, *la vecchia,*" he said to me in the lower hall, while he shouldered my valise; and he grinned and almost winked, as if he knew I should be pleased at the news.

"She's dead!" I exclaimed, giving him a very different look.

"So it appears, since they have buried her."

"It's all over? When was the funeral?"

"The other yesterday. But a funeral you could scarcely call it, signore; it was a dull little passeggio of two gondolas. Poveretta!" the man continued, referring apparently to Miss Tita. His conception of funerals was apparently that they were mainly to amuse the living.

I wanted to know about Miss Tita—how she was and where she was—but I asked him no more questions till we had got upstairs. Now that the fact had met me I took a bad view of it, especially of the idea that poor Miss Tita had had to manage by herself after the end. What did she know about arrangements, about the steps to take in such a case? Poveretta indeed! I could only hope that the doctor had given her assistance and that she had not been neglected by the old friends of whom she had told me, the little band of the faithful whose fidelity consisted in coming to the house once a year. I elicited from my servant that two old ladies and an old gentleman had in fact rallied round Miss Tita and had supported her (they had come for her in a gondola of their own) during the journey to the cemetery, the little red-walled island of tombs which lies to the north of the town, on the way to Murano. It appeared from these circumstances that the Misses Bordereau were Catholics, a discovery I had never made, as the old woman could not go to church and her niece, so far as I perceived, either did not or went only to early mass in the parish, before I was stirring. Certainly even the priests respected their seclusion; I had never caught the whisk of the curato's skirt. That evening, an hour later, I sent my servant down with five words written on a card, to ask Miss Tita if she would see me for a few moments. She was not in the house, where he had sought her, he told me when he came back, but in the garden walking about to refresh herself and gathering flowers. He had found her there and she would be very happy to see me.

I went down and passed half an hour with poor Miss Tita. She had always had a look of musty mourning (as if she were wearing out old robes of sorrow that would not come to an end), and in this respect there was no appreciable change in her appearance. But she evidently had been crying, crying a great deal—simply, satisfyingly, refreshingly, with a sort of primitive, retarded sense of loneliness and violence. But she had none of the formalism or the self-consciousness of grief, and I was almost surprised to see her standing there in the first dusk with her hands full of flowers, smiling at me with her reddened eyes. Her white face, in the frame of her mantilla, looked longer, leaner than usual. I had had an idea that she would be a good deal disgusted with me—would consider that I ought to have been on the spot to advise her, to help her; and, though I was sure there was no rancour in her composition and no great conviction of the importance of her affairs, I had prepared myself for a difference in her manner, for some little injured look, half familiar, half estranged, which should say to my conscience, "Well, you are a nice person to have professed things!" But historic truth compels me to declare that Tita Bordereau's countenance expressed unqualified pleasure in seeing her late aunt's lodger. That touched him extremely and he thought it simplified his situation until he found it did not.

I was as kind to her that evening as I knew how to be, and I walked about the garden with her for half an hour. There was no explanation of any sort between us; I did not ask her why she had not answered my letter. Still less did I repeat what I had said to her in that communication; if she chose to let me suppose that she had forgotten the position in which Miss Bordereau surprised me that night and the effect of the discovery on the old woman I was quite willing to take it that way: I was grateful to her for not treating me as if I had killed her aunt.

We strolled and strolled and really not much passed between us save the recognition of her bereavement, conveyed in my manner and in a visible air that she had of depending on me now, since I let her see that I took an interest in her. Miss Tita had none of the pride that makes a person wish to preserve the look of independence; she did not in the least pretend that she knew at present what would become of her. I forbore to touch particularly on that however, for I certainly was not prepared to say that I would take charge of her. I was cautious; not ignobly, I think, for I felt that her knowledge of life was so small that in her unsophisticated vision there would be no reason why—since I seemed to pity her—I should not look after her. She told me how her aunt had died, very peacefully at the last, and how everything had been done afterwards by the care of her good friends (fortunately, thanks to me, she said, smiling, there was money in the house; and she repeated that when once the Italians like you they are your friends for life); and when we had gone into this she asked me about my *giro,* my impressions, the places I had seen. I told her what I could, making it up partly, I am afraid, as in my depression I had not seen much; and after she had heard me she exclaimed, quite as if she had forgotten her aunt and her sorrow, "Dear, dear, how much I should like to do such things—to take a little journey!" It came over me for the moment that I ought to propose some tour, say I would take her anywhere she liked; and I remarked at any rate that some excursion—to give her a change—might be managed: we would think of it, talk it over. I said never a word to her about the Aspern documents; asked no questions as to what she had ascertained or what had otherwise happened with regard to them before Miss Bordereau's death. It was not that I was not on pins and needles to know, but that I thought it more decent not to betray my anxiety so soon after the catastrophe. I hoped she herself would say something, but she never glanced that way, and I thought this natural at the time. Later however, that night, it occurred to me that her silence was somewhat strange; for if she had talked of my movements, of anything so detached as the Giorgione at Castelfranco, she might have alluded to what she could easily remember was in my mind. It was not to be supposed that the emotion produced by her aunt's death had blotted out the recollection that I was interested in that lady's relics, and I fidgeted afterwards as it came to me that her reticence might very possibly mean simply that nothing had been found. We separated in the garden (it was she who said she must go in); now that she was alone in the rooms I felt that (judged, at any rate, by Venetian ideas) I was on rather a different footing in regard to visiting her there. As I shook hands with her for good-night I asked her if she had any general plan—had thought over what she had better do. "Oh, yes, oh yes, but I haven't settled anything yet," she replied, quite cheerfully. Was her cheerfulness explained by the impression that I would settle for her?

I was glad the next morning that we had neglected practical questions, for this gave me a pretext for seeing her again immediately. There was a very practical question to be touched upon. I owed it to her to let her know formally that of course I did not expect her to keep me on as a lodger, and also to show some interest in her own tenure, what she might have on her hands in the way of a lease. But I was not destined, as it happened, to converse with her for more than an instant on either of these points. I sent her no message; I simply went down to the sala and walked to and fro there. I knew she would come out; she would very soon discover I was there. Somehow I preferred not to be shut up with her; gardens and big halls seemed better places to talk. It was a splendid morning, with something in the air that told of the waning of the long Venetian summer; a freshness from the sea which stirred the flowers in the garden and made a pleasant draught in the house, less shuttered and darkened now than when the old woman was alive. It was the beginning of autumn, of the end of the golden months. With this it was the end of my experiment—or would be in the course of half an hour, when I should really have learned that the papers had been reduced to ashes. After that there would be nothing left for me but to go to the station; for seriously (and as it struck me in the morning light) I could not linger there to act as guardian to a piece of middle-aged female helplessness. If she had not saved the papers wherein should I be indebted to her? I think I winced a little as I asked myself how much, if she *had* saved them, I should have to recognise and, as it were, to reward such a courtesy. Might not that circumstance after all saddle me with a guardianship? If this idea did not make me more uncomfortable as I walked up and down it was because I was convinced I had nothing to look to. If the old woman had not destroyed everything before she pounced upon me in the parlour she had done so afterwards.

It took Miss Tita rather longer than I had expected to guess that I was there; but when at last she came out she looked at me without surprise. I said to her that I had been waiting for her and she asked why I had not let her know. I was glad the next day that I had checked myself before remarking that I had wished to see if a friendly intuition would not tell her; it became a satisfaction to me that I had not indulged in that rather tender joke. What I did say was virtually the truth—that I was too nervous, since I cxpected her now to settle my fate.

"Your fate?" said Miss Tita, giving me a queer look; and as she spoke I noticed a rare change in her. She was different from what she had been the evening before—less natural, less quiet. She had been crying the day before and she was not crying now, and yet she struck me as less confident. It was as if something had happened to her during the night, or at least as if she had thought of something that troubled her—something in particular that affected her relations with me, made them more embarrassing and complicated. Had she simply perceived that her aunt's not being there now altered my position?

"I mean about our papers. *Are* there any? You must know now."

"Yes, there are a great many; more than I supposed." I was struck with the way her voice trembled as she told me this.

"Do you mean that you have got them in there—and that I may see them?"

"I don't think you can see them," said Miss Tita, with an extraordinary expression of entreaty in her eyes, as if the dearest hope she had in the world now was that I would not take them from her. But how could she expect me to make such a sacrifice as that after all that had passed between us? What had I come back to Venice for but to see them, to take them? My delight at learning they were still in existence was such that if the poor woman had gone down on her knees to beseech me never to mention them again I would have treated the proceeding as a bad joke. "I have got them but I can't show them," she added.

"Not even to me? Ah, Miss Tita!" I groaned, with a voice of infinite remonstrance and reproach.

She coloured and the tears came back to her eyes; I saw that it cost her a kind of anguish to take such a stand but that a dreadful sense of duty had descended upon her. It made me quite sick to find myself confronted with that particular obstacle; all the more had it appeared to me I had been extremely encouraged to leave it out of account. I almost considered that Miss Tita had assured me that if she had no greater hindrance than that—! "You don't mean to say you made her a deathbed promise? It was precisely against your doing anything of that sort that I thought I was safe. Oh, I would rather she had burned the papers outright than that!"

"No, it isn't a promise," said Miss Tita.

"Pray what is it then?"

She hesitated and then she said, "She tried to burn them, but I prevented it. She had hid them in her bed."

"In her bed?"

"Between the mattresses. That's where she put them when she took them out of the trunk. I can't understand how she did it, because Olimpia didn't help her. She tells me so and I believe her. My aunt only told her afterwards so that she shouldn't touch the bed—anything but the sheets. So it was badly made," added Miss Tita, simply.

"I should think so! And how did she try to burn them?"

"She didn't try much; she was too weak, those last days. But she told me—

she charged me. Oh, it was terrible! She couldn't speak after that night; she could only make signs."

"And what did you do?"

"I took them away. I locked them up."

"In the secretary?"

"Yes, in the secretary," said Miss Tita, reddening again.

"Did you tell her you would burn them?"

"No, I didn't—on purpose."

"On purpose to gratify me?"

"Yes, only for that."

"And what good will you have done me if after all you won't show them?"

"Oh, none; I know that—I know that."

"And did she believe you had destroyed them?"

"I don't know what she believed at the last. I couldn't tell—she was too far gone."

"Then if there was no promise and no assurance I can't see what ties you."

"Oh, she hated it so—she hated it so! She was so jealous. But here's the portrait—you may have that," Miss Tita announced, taking the little picture, wrapped up in the same manner in which her aunt had wrapped it, out of her pocket.

"I may have it—do you mean you give it to me?" I questioned, staring, as it passed into my hand.

"Oh yes."

"But it's worth money—a large sum."

"Well!" said Miss Tita, still with her strange look.

I did not know what to make of it, for it could scarcely mean that she wanted to bargain like her aunt. She spoke as if she wished to make me a present. "I can't take it from you as a gift," I said, "and yet I can't afford to pay you for it according to the ideas Miss Bordereau had of its value. She rated it at a thousand pounds."

"Couldn't we sell it?" asked Miss Tita.

"God forbid! I prefer the picture to the money."

"Well then keep it."

"You are very generous."

"So are you."

"I don't know why you should think so," I replied; and this was a truthful speech, for the singular creature appeared to have some very fine reference in her mind, which I did not in the least seize.

"Well, you have made a great difference for me," said Miss Tita.

I looked at Jeffrey Aspern's face in the little picture, partly in order not to look at that of my interlocutress, which had begun to trouble me, even to frighten me a little—it was so self-conscious, so unnatural. I made no answer to this last declaration; I only privately consulted Jeffrey Aspern's delightful eyes with my own (they were so young and brilliant, and yet so wise, so full of vision); I asked him what on earth was the matter with Miss Tita. He seemed to smile at me with friendly mockery, as if he were amused at my case. I had got into a pickle for him—as if he needed it! He was unsatisfactory, for the only moment since I had known him. Nevertheless, now that I held the little picture in my hand I felt that it would be a precious possession. "Is this a bribe to make me give up the papers?" I demanded in a moment, perversely. "Much as I value it, if I were to be obliged to choose, the papers are what I should prefer. Ah, but ever so much!"

"How can you choose—how can you choose?" Miss Tita asked, slowly, lamentably.

"I see! Of course there is nothing to be said, if you regard the interdiction that rests upon you as quite insurmountable. In this case it must seem to you that to part with them would be an impiety of the worst kind, a simple sacrilege!"

Miss Tita shook her head, full of her dolefulness. "You would understand if you had known her. I'm afraid," she quavered suddenly—"I'm afraid! She was terrible when she was angry."

"Yes, I saw something of that, that night. She was terrible. Then I saw her eyes. Lord, they were fine!"

"I see them—they stare at me in the dark!" said Miss Tita.

"You are nervous, with all you have been through."

"Oh yes, very—very!"

"You mustn't mind; that will pass away," I said, kindly. Then I added, resignedly, for it really seemed to me that I must accept the situation, "Well, so it is, and it can't be helped. I must renounce." Miss Tita, at this, looking at me, gave a low, soft moan, and I went on: "I only wish to heaven she had destroyed them; then there would be nothing more to say. And I can't understand why, with her ideas, she didn't."

"Oh, she lived on them!" said Miss Tita.

"You can imagine whether that makes me want less to see them," I answered, smiling. "But don't let me stand here as if I had it in my soul to tempt you to do anything base. Naturally you will understand I give up my rooms. I leave Venice immediately." And I took up my hat, which I had placed on a chair. We were still there rather awkwardly, on our feet, in the middle of the sala. She had left the door of the apartments open behind her but she had not led me that way.

A kind of spasm came into her face as she saw me take my hat. "Immediately—do you mean to-day?" The tone of the words was tragical—they were a cry of desolation.

"Oh no; not so long as I can be of the least service to you."

"Well, just a day or two more—just two or three days," she panted. Then controlling herself she added in another manner, "She wanted to say something to me—the last day—something very particular, but she couldn't."

"Something very particular?"

"Something more about the papers."

"And did you guess—have you any idea?"

"No, I have thought—but I don't know. I have thought all kinds of things."

"And for instance?"

"Well, that if you were a relation it would be different."

"If I were a relation?"

"If you were not a stranger. Then it would be the same for you as for me. Anything that is mine—would be yours, and you could do what you like. I couldn't prevent you—and you would have no responsibility."

She brought out this droll explanation with a little nervous rush, as if she were speaking words she had got by heart. They gave me an impression of subtlety and at first I failed to follow. But after a moment her face helped me to see further, and then a light came into my mind. It was embarrassing, and I bent my head over Jeffrey Aspern's portrait. What an odd expression was in his face! "Get out of it as you can, my dear fellow!" I put the picture into the pocket of my coat and said to Miss Tita, "Yes, I'll sell it for you. I sha'n't get a thousand pounds by any means, but I shall get something good."

She looked at me with tears in her eyes, but she seemed to try to smile as she remarked, "We can divide the money."

"No, no, it shall be all yours." Then I went on, "I think I know what your poor aunt wanted to say. She wanted to give directions that her papers should be buried with her."

Miss Tita appeared to consider this suggestion for a moment; after which she declared, with striking decision, "Oh no, she wouldn't have thought that safe!"

"It seems to me nothing could be safer."

"She had an idea that when people want to publish they are capable—" And she paused, blushing.

"Of violating a tomb? Mercy on us, what must she have thought of me!"

"She was not just, she was not generous!" Miss Tita cried with sudden passion.

The light that had come into my mind a moment before increased. "Ah, don't say that, for we *are* a dreadful race." Then I pursued, "If she left a will, that may give you some idea."

"I have found nothing of the sort—she destroyed it. She was very fond of me," Miss Tita added, incongruously. "She wanted me to be happy. And if any person should be kind to me—she wanted to speak of that."

I was almost awestricken at the astuteness with which the good lady found herself inspired, transparent astuteness as it was and sewn, as the phrase is, with white thread. "Depend upon it she didn't want to make any provision that would be agreeable to me."

"No, not to you but to me. She knew I should like it if you could carry out your idea. Not because she cared for you but because she did think of me," Miss Tita went on, with her unexpected, persuasive volubility. "You could see them—you could use them." She stopped, seeing that I perceived the sense of that conditional—stopped long enough for me to give some sign which I did not give. She must have been conscious however that though my face showed the greatest embarrassment that was ever painted on a human countenance it was not set as a stone, it was also full of compassion. It was a comfort to me a long time afterwards to consider that she could not have seen in me the smallest symptom of disrespect. "I don't know what to do; I'm too tormented, I'm too ashamed!" she continued, with vehemence. Then turning away from me and burying her face in her hands she burst into a flood of tears. If she did not know what to do it may be imagined whether I did any better. I stood there dumb, watching her while her sobs resounded in the great empty hall. In a moment she was facing me again, with her streaming eyes. "I would give you everything—and she would understand, where she is—she would forgive me!"

"Ah, Miss Tita—ah, Miss Tita," I stammered, for all reply. I did not know what to do, as I say, but at a venture I made a wild, vague movement, in consequence of which I found myself at the door. I remember standing there and staying, "It wouldn't do—it wouldn't do!" pensively, awkwardly, grotesquely, while I looked away to the opposite end of the sala as if there were a beautiful view there. The next thing I remember is that I was downstairs and out of the house. My gondola was there and my gondolier, reclining on the cushions, sprang up as soon as he saw me. I jumped in and to his usual *"Dove commanda?"* I replied, in a tone that made him stare, "Anywhere, anywhere; out into the lagoon!"

He rowed me away and I sat there prostrate, groaning softly to myself, with my hat pulled over my face. What in the name of the preposterous did she mean if she did not mean to offer me her hand? That was the price—that was the price! And did she think I wanted it, poor deluded, infatuated, extravagant lady? My gondolier, behind me, must have seen my ears red as I wondered, sitting there under the fluttering *tenda,* with my hidden face, noticing nothing as we passed—wondered whether her delusion, her infatuation had been my own reckless work. Did she think I had made love to her, even to get the papers? I had not, I had not; I repeated that over to myself for an hour, for two hours, till I was wearied if not convinced. I don't know where my gondolier took me; we floated aimlessly about on the lagoon, with slow, rare strokes. At last I became conscious that we were near the Lido, far up, on the right hand, as you turn your back to Venice, and I made him put me ashore. I wanted to walk, to move, to shed some of my bewilderment. I crossed the narrow strip and got to the sea-beach—I took my way toward Malamocco. But presently I flung myself down again on the warm sand, in the breeze, on the coarse dry grass. It took it out of me to think I had been so much at fault, that I had unwittingly but none the less deplorably trifled. But I had not given her cause—distinctly I had not. I had said to Mrs. Prest that I would make love to her; but it had been a joke without consequences and I had never said it to Tita Bordereau. I had been as kind as possible, because I really liked her; but since when had that become a crime where a woman of such an age and such an appearance was concerned? I am far from remembering clearly the succession of events and feelings during this long day of confusion, which I spent entirely in wandering about, without going home, until late at night; it only comes back to me that there were moments when I pacified my conscience and others when I lashed it into pain. I did not laugh all day—that I do recollect; the case, however it might have struck others, seemed to me so little amusing. It would have been better perhaps for me to feel the comic side of it. At any rate, whether I had given cause or not it went without saying that I could not pay the price. I could not accept. I could not, for a bundle of tattered papers, marry a ridiculous, pathetic, provincial old woman. It was a proof that she did not think the idea would come to me, her having determined to suggest it herself in that practical, argumentative, heroic way, in which the timidity however had been so much more striking than the boldness that her reasons appeared to come first and her feelings afterward.

As the day went on I grew to wish that I had never heard of Aspern's relics, and I cursed the extravagant curiosity that had put John Cumnor on the scent of them. We had more than enough material without them and my predicament was the just punishment of that most fatal of human follies, our not having known when to stop. It was very well to say it was no predicament, that the way out was simple, that I had only to leave Venice by the first train in the morning, after writing a note to Miss Tita, to be placed in her hand as soon as I got clear of the house; for it was a strong sign that I was embarrassed that when I tried to make up the note in my mind in advance (I would put it on paper as soon as I got home, before going to bed), I could not think of anything but. "How can I thank you for the rare confidence you have placed in me?" That would never do; it sounded exactly as if an acceptance were to follow. Of course I might go away without writing a word, but that would be brutal and my idea was still to exclude brutal solutions. As my confusion cooled I was lost in wonder at the importance I had attached to Miss Bordereau's crumpled scraps; the thought of them became odious to me and I was as vexed with the old witch for the superstition that had prevented her from destroying them as I was with myself for having already spent more money than I could afford in attempting to control their fate. I forget what I did, where I went after leaving the Lido and at what hour or with what recovery of composure I made my way back to my boat. I only know that in the afternoon, when the air was aglow with the sunset, I was standing before the church of Saints John and Paul and looking up at the small square-jawed face of Bartolommeo Colleoni, the terrible *condottiere* who sits so sturdily astride of his huge bronze horse, on the high pedestal on which Venetian gratitude maintains him. The statue is incomparable, the finest of all mounted figures, unless that of Marcus Aurelius, who rides benignant before the Roman Capitol, be finer: but I was not thinking of that; I only found myself staring at the triumphant captain as if he had an oracle on his lips. The western light shines into all his grimness at that hour and makes it wonderfully personal. But he continued to look far over my head, at the immersion of another day—he had seen so many go down into the lagoon through the centuries—and if he were thinking of battles and stratagems they were of a different quality from any I had to tell him of. He could not direct me what to do, gaze up at him as I might. Was it before this or after that I wandered about for an hour in the small canals, to the continued stupefaction of my gondolier, who had never seen me so restless and yet so void of a purpose and could extract from me no order but "Go anywhere—everywhere—all over the place"? He reminded me that I had not lunched and expressed therefore respectfully the hope that I would dine earlier. He had had long periods of leisure during the day, when I had left the boat and rambled, so that I was not obliged to consider him, and I told him that that day, for a change, I would touch no meat. It was an effect of poor Miss Tita's proposal, not altogether auspicious, that I had quite lost my appetite. I don't know why it happened that on this occasion I was more than ever struck with that queer air of sociability, of cousinship and family life, which makes up half the expression of Venice. Without streets and vehicles, the uproar of wheels, the brutality of horses, and with its little winding ways where people crowd together, where voices sound as in the corridors of a house, where the human step circulates as if it skirted the angles of furniture and shoes never wear out, the place has the character of an immense collective apartment, in which Piazza San Marco is the most ornamented corner and palaces and churches, for the rest, play the part of great divans of repose, tables of entertainment, expanses of decoration. And somehow the splendid common domicile, familiar, domestic and resonant, also resembles a theatre, with actors clicking over bridges and, in straggling processions, tripping along fondamentas. As you sit in your gondola the footways that in certain parts edge the canals assume to the eye the importance of a stage, meeting it at the same angle, and the Venetian figures, moving to and fro against the battered scenery of their little houses of comedy, strike you as members of an endless dramatic troupe.

I went to bed that night very tired, without being able to compose a letter to Miss Tita. Was this failure the reason why I became conscious the next morning as soon as I awoke of a determination to see the poor lady again the first moment she would receive me? That had something to do with it, but what had still more was the fact that during my sleep a very odd revulsion had taken place in my spirit. I found myself aware of this almost as soon as I opened my eyes; it made me jump out of my bed with the movement of a man who remembers that he has left the house-door ajar or a candle burning under a shelf. Was I still in time to save my goods? That question was in my heart; for what had now come to pass was that in the unconscious cerebration of sleep I had swung back to a passionate appreciation of Miss Bordereau's papers. They were now more precious than ever and a kind of ferocity had come into my desire to possess them. The condition Miss Tita had attached to the possession of them no longer appeared an obstacle worth thinking of, and for a hour, that morning, my repentant imagination brushed it aside. It was absurd that I should be able to invent nothing; absurd to renounce so easily and turn away helpless from the idea that the only way to get hold of the papers was to unite myself to her for life. I would not unite myself and yet I would have them. I must add that by the time I sent down to ask if she would see me I had invented no alternative, though to do so I had had all the time that I was dressing. This failure was humiliating, yet what could the alternative be? Miss Tita sent back word that I might come; and as I descended the stairs and crossed the sala to her door—this time she received me in her aunt's forlorn parlour—I hoped she would not think my errand was to tell her I accepted her hand. She certainly would have made the day before the reflection that I declined it.

As soon as I came into the room I saw that she had drawn this inference, but I also saw something which had not been in my forecast. Poor Miss Tita's sense of her failure had produced an extraordinary alteration in her, but I had been too full of my literary concupiscence to think of that. Now I perceived it; I can scarcely tell how it startled me. She stood in the middle of the room with a face of mildness bent upon me, and her look of forgiveness, of absolution made her angelic. It beautified her; she was younger; she was not a ridiculous old woman. This optical trick gave her a sort of phantasmagoric brightness, and while I was still the victim of it I heard a whisper somewhere in the depths of my conscience: "Why not, after all—why not?" It seemed to me I was ready to pay the price. Still more distinctly however than the whisper I heard Miss Tita's own voice. I was so struck with the different effect she made upon me that at first I was not clearly aware of what she was saying; then I perceived she had bade me good-bye—she said something about hoping I should be very happy.

"Good-bye—good-bye?" I repeated, with an inflection interrogative and probably foolish.

I saw she did not feel the interrogation, she only heard the words; she had strung herself up to accepting our separation and they fell upon her ear as a proof. "Are you going to-day?" she asked. "But it doesn't matter, for whenever you go I shall not see you again. I don't want to." And she smiled strangely, with an infinite gentleness. She had never doubted that I had left her the day before in horror. How could she, since I had not come back before night to contradict, even as a simple form, such an idea? And now she had the force of soul—Miss Tita with force of soul was a new conception—to smile at me in her humiliation.

"What shall you do—where shall you go?" I asked.

"Oh, I don't know. I have done the great thing. I have destroyed the papers."

"Destroyed them?" I faltered.

"Yes; what was I to keep them for? I burnt them last night, one by one, in the kitchen."

"One by one?" I repeated, mechanically.

"It took a long time—there were so many." The room seemed to go round me as she said this and a real darkness for a moment descended upon my eyes. When it passed Miss Tita was there still, but the transfiguration was over and she had changed back to a plain, dingy, elderly person. It was in this character she spoke as she said, "I can't stay with you longer, I can't;" and it was in this character that she turned her back upon me, as I had turned mine upon her twenty-four hours before, and moved to the door of her room. Here she did what I had not done when I quitted her—she paused long enough to give me one look. I have never forgotten it and I sometimes still suffer from it, though it was not resentful. No, there was no resentment, nothing hard or vindictive in poor Miss Tita; for when, later, I sent her in exchange for the portrait of Jeffrey Aspern a larger sum of money than I had hoped to be able to gather for her, writing to her that I had sold the picture, she kept it with thanks; she never sent it back. I wrote to her that I had sold the picture, but I admitted to Mrs. Prest at the time (I met her in London, in the autumn), that it hangs above my writing-table. When I look at it my chagrin at the loss of the letters becomes almost intolerable.

"The Aspern Papers": A Selected Bibliography

Canby, Henry S. *Turn West, Turn East: Mark Twain and Henry James.* Boston: Houghton Mifflin Company, 1951.

Dupee, F. W. *Henry James.* New York: William Sloane Associates, Inc., 1951; rev. ed. (Anchor Books), Garden City, N.Y.: Doubleday & Co., Inc., 1956.

Edel, Leon. "The Aspern Papers: Great Aunt Wycoff and Juliana Bordereau," *Modern Language Notes,* LXVII (June 1952), 392-95.

———, and Dan H. Laurence. *A Bibliography of Henry James.* London: Rupert Hart-Davis, Ltd., 1957.

Geismar, Maxwell. *Henry James and the Jacobites.* Boston: Houghton Mifflin Company, 1963.

Hoffman, Charles G. *The Short Novels of Henry James.* New York: Bookman Associates, 1957.

Holland, Laurence B. *The Expense of Vision: Essays on the Craft of Henry James.* Princeton, N.J.: Princeton University Press, 1964.

James, Henry. *The Art of the Novel: Critical Prefaces.* New York: Charles Scribner's Sons, 1946.

———. *The Novels and Tales of Henry James.* New York Edition, 26 vols. New York: Charles Scribner's Sons, 1907–1918.

Lehmann, John. "A Question of Covering One's Tracks," in *The Open Night.* London: Longmans, Green & Company, Ltd., 1952.

Matthiessen, F. O., and Kenneth Murdoch, eds. *The Notebooks of Henry James.* New York: Oxford University Press, Inc., 1947.

Neider, Charles. *Short Novels of the Masters.* New York: Holt, Rinehart & Winston, Inc., 1948.

Rahv, Philip. *The Great Short Novels of Henry James.* New York: The Dial Press, Inc., 1944.

Wallace, Irving. "The Real Juliana Bordereau," in *The Fabulous Originals.* New York: Alfred A. Knopf, Inc., 1955.

Nine Stories for Further Reading

SHERWOOD ANDERSON

(1876–1941)

I Want to Know Why

We got up at four in the morning, that first day in the east. On the evening before we had climbed off a freight train at the edge of town, and with the true instinct of Kentucky boys had found our way across town and to the racetrack and the stables at once. Then we knew we were all right. Hanley Turner right away found a nigger we knew. It was Bildad Johnson who in the winter works at Ed Becker's livery barn in our home town, Beckersville. Bildad is a good cook as almost all our niggers are and of course he, like everyone in our part of Kentucky who is anyone at all, likes the horses. In the spring Bildad begins to scratch around. A nigger from our country can flatter and wheedle anyone into letting him do most anything he wants. Bildad wheedles the stable men and the trainers from the horse farms in our country around Lexington. The trainers come into town in the evening to stand around and talk and maybe get into a poker game. Bildad gets in with them. He is always doing little favors and telling about things to eat, chicken browned in a pan, and how is the best way to cook sweet potatoes and corn bread. It makes your mouth water to hear him.

When the racing season comes on and the horses go to the races and there is all the talk on the streets in the evenings about the new colts, and everyone says when they are going over to Lexington or to the spring meeting at Churchill Downs or to Latonia, and the horsemen that have been down to New Orleans or maybe at the winter meeting at Havana in Cuba come home to spend a week before they start out again, at such a time when everything talked about in Beckersville is just horses and nothing else and the outfits start out and horse racing is in every breath of air you breathe, Bildad shows up with a job as cook for some outfit. Often when I think about it, his always going all season to the races and working in the livery barn in the winter where horses are and where men like to come and talk about horses, I wish I was a nigger. It's a foolish thing to say, but that's the way I am about being around horses, just crazy. I can't help it.

Well, I must tell you about what we did and let you in on what I'm talking about. Four of us boys from Beckersville, all whites and sons of men who live in Beckersville regular, made up our minds we were going to the races, not just to Lexington or Louisville, I don't mean, but to the big eastern track we were always hearing our Beckersville men talk about, to Saratoga. We were all pretty young then. I was just turned fifteen and I was the oldest of the four. It was my scheme. I admit that and I talked the others into trying it. There was Hanley Turner and Henry Rieback and Tom Tumberton and myself. I had thirty-seven dollars I had earned during the winter working nights and Saturdays in Enoch Myer's grocery. Henry Rieback had eleven dollars and the others, Hanley and Tom, had only a dollar or two each. We fixed it all up and laid low until the Kentucky spring meetings were over and some of our men, the sportiest ones, the ones we envied the most, had cut out—then we cut out too.

I won't tell you the trouble we had beating our way on freights and all. We went through Cleveland and Buffalo and other cities and saw Niagara Falls. We bought things there, souvenirs and spoons and cards and shells with pictures of the Falls on them for our sisters and mothers, but thought we had better not send any of the things home. We didn't want to put the folks on our trail and maybe be nabbed.

We got into Saratoga as I said at night and went to the track. Bildad fed us up. He showed us a place to sleep in hay over a shed and promised to keep still. Niggers are all right about things like that. They won't squeal on you. Often a white man you might meet, when you had run away from home like that, might appear to be all right and give you a quarter or a half dollar or something, and then go right and give you away. White men will do that, but not a nigger. You can trust them. They are squarer with kids. I don't know why.

At the Saratoga meeting that year there were a lot of men from home. Dave Williams and Arthur Mulford and Jerry Myers and others. Then there was a lot from Louisville and Lexington Henry Rieback knew but I didn't. They were professional gamblers and Henry Rieback's father is one too. He is what is called a sheet writer and goes away most of the year to tracks. In the winter when he is home in Beckersville he don't stay there much but goes away to cities and deals faro. He is a nice man and generous, is always sending Henry presents, a bicycle and a gold watch and a boy scout suit of clothes and things like that.

My own father is a lawyer. He's all right, but don't make much money and can't buy me things and anyway I'm getting so old now I don't expect it. He never said nothing to me against Henry, but Hanley Turner and Tom Tumberton's fathers did. They said to their boys that money so come by is no good and they didn't want their boys brought up to hear gamblers' talk and be thinking about such things and maybe embrace them.

That's all right and I guess the men know what they are talking about, but I don't see what it's got to do with Henry or horses either. That's what I'm writing this story about. I'm puzzled. I'm getting to be a man and want to think straight and be O.K., and there's something I saw at the race meeting at the eastern track I can't figure out.

I can't help it, I'm crazy about thoroughbred horses. I've always been that way. When I was ten years old and saw I was growing to be big and couldn't be a rider I was so sorry I nearly died. Harry Hellinfinger in Beckersville, whose father is Postmaster, is grown up and too lazy to work, but likes to stand around in the street and get up jokes on boys like sending them to a hardware store for a gimlet to bore square holes and other jokes like that. He played one on me. He told me that if I would eat a half a cigar I would be stunted and not grow any more and maybe could be a rider. I did it. When father wasn't looking I took a cigar out of his pocket and gagged it down some way. It made me awful sick and the doctor had to be sent for, and then it did no good. I kept right on growing. It was a joke. When I told what I had done and why most fathers would have whipped me but mine didn't.

Well, I didn't get stunted and didn't die. It serves Harry Hellinfinger right. Then I made up my mind I would like to be a stable boy, but had to give that up too. Mostly niggers do that work and I knew father wouldn't let me go into it. No use to ask him.

If you've never been crazy about thoroughbreds it's because you've never been around where they are much and don't know any better. They're beautiful. There isn't anything so lovely and clean and full of spunk and honest and everything as some race horses. On the big horse farms that are all around our town Beckersville there are tracks and the horses run in the early morning. More than a thousand times I've got out of bed before daylight and walked two or three miles to the tracks. Mother wouldn't of let me go but father always says, "Let him alone." So I got some bread out of the bread box and some butter and jam, gobbled it and lit out.

At the tracks you sit on the fence with men, whites and niggers, and they chew tobacco and talk, and then the colts are brought out. It's early and the grass is covered with shiny dew and in another field a man is plowing and they are frying things in a shed where the track niggers sleep, and you know how a nigger can giggle and laugh and say things that make you laugh. A white man can't do it and some niggers can't but a track nigger can every time.

And so the colts are brought out and some are just galloped by stable boys, but almost every morning on a big track owned by a rich man who lives maybe in New York, there are always, nearly every morning, a few colts and some of the old race horses and geldings and mares that are cut loose.

It brings a lump up into my throat when a horse runs. I don't mean all horses but some. I can pick them nearly every time. It's in my blood like in the blood of race-track niggers and trainers. Even when they just go slop-jogging along with a little nigger on their backs I can tell a winner. If my throat hurts and it's hard for me to swallow, that's him. He'll run like Sam Hill when you let him out. If he don't win every time it'll be a wonder and because they've got him in a pocket behind another or he was pulled or got off bad at the post or something. If I wanted to be a gambler like Henry Rieback's father I could get rich. I know I could and Henry says so too. All I would have to do is to wait 'til that hurt comes when I see a horse and then bet every cent. That's what I would do if I wanted to be a gambler, but I don't.

When you're at the tracks in the morning—not the race tracks but the training tracks around Beckersville—you don't see a horse, the kind I've been talking about, very often, but it's nice anyway. Any thoroughbred, that is sired right and out of a good mare and trained by a man that knows how, can run. If he couldn't what would he be there for and not pulling a plow?

Well, out of the stables they come and the boys are on their backs and it's lovely to be there. You hunch down on top of the fence and itch inside you. Over in the sheds the niggers giggle and sing. Bacon is being fried and coffee made. Everything smells lovely. Nothing smells better than coffee and manure and horses and niggers and bacon frying and pipes being smoked out of doors on a morning like that. It just gets you, that's what it does.

But about Saratoga. We was there six days and not a soul from home seen us and everything came off just as we wanted it to, fine weather and horses and races and all. We beat our way home and Bildad gave us a basket with fried chicken and bread and other eatables in, and I had eighteen dollars when we got back to Beckersville. Mother jawed and cried but Pop didn't say much. I told everything we done except one thing. I did and saw that alone. That's what I'm writing about. It got me upset. I think about it at night. Here it is.

At Saratoga we laid up nights in the hay in the shed Bildad had showed us and ate with the niggers early and at night when the race people had all gone away. The men from home stayed mostly in the grandstand and betting field, and didn't come out around the places where the horses are kept except to the paddocks just before a race when the horses are saddled.

At Saratoga they don't have paddocks under an open shed as at Lexington and Churchill Downs and other tracks down in our country, but saddle the horses right out in an open place under trees on a lawn as smooth and nice as Banker Bohon's front yard here in Beckersville. It's lovely. The horses are sweaty and nervous and shine and the men come out and smoke cigars and look at them and the trainers are there and the owners, and your heart thumps so you can hardly breathe.

Then the bugle blows for post and the boys that ride come running out with their silk clothes on and you run to get a place by the fence with the niggers.

I always am wanting to be a trainer or owner, and at the risk of being seen and caught and sent home I went to the paddocks before every race. The other boys didn't but I did.

We got to Saratoga on a Friday and on Wednesday the next week the big Mullford Handicap was to be run. Middlestride was in it and Sunstreak. The weather was fine and the track fast. I couldn't sleep the night before.

What had happened was that both these horses are the kind it makes my throat hurt to see. Middlestride is long and looks awkward and is a gelding. He belongs to Joe Thompson, a little owner from home who only has a half-dozen horses. The Mullford Handicap is for a mile and Middlestride can't untrack fast. He goes away slow and is always way back at the half, then he begins to run and if the race is a mile and a quarter he'll just eat up everything and get there.

Sunstreak is different. He is a stallion and nervous and belongs on the biggest farm we've got in our country, the Van Riddle place that belongs to Mr. Van Riddle of New York. Sunstreak is like a girl you think about sometimes but never see. He is hard all over and lovely too. When you look at his head you want to kiss him. He is trained by Jerry Tillford who knows me and has been good to me lots of times, lets me walk into a horse's stall to look at him close and other things. There isn't anything as sweet as that horse. He stands at the post quiet and not letting on, but he is just burning up inside. Then when the barrier goes up he is off like his name, Sunstreak. It makes you ache to see him. It hurts you. He just lays down and runs like a bird dog. There can't anything I ever see run like him except Middlestride when he gets untracked and stretches himself.

Gee! I ached to see that race and those two horses run, ached and dreaded it too. I didn't want to see either of our horses beaten. We had never sent a pair like that to the races before. Old men in Beckersville said so and the niggers said so. It was a fact.

Before the race I went over to the paddocks to see. I looked a last look at Middlestride, who isn't such a much standing in a paddock that way, then I went to see Sunstreak.

It was his day. I knew when I seen him. I forgot all about being seen myself and walked right up. All the men from Beckersville were there and no one noticed me except Jerry Tillford. He saw me and something happened. I'll tell you about that.

I was standing looking at that horse and aching. In some way, I can't tell how, I knew just how Sunstreak felt inside. He was quiet and letting the niggers rub his legs and Mr. Van Riddle himself put the saddle on, but he was just a raging torrent inside. He was like the water in the river at Niagara Falls just before it goes plunk down. That horse wasn't thinking about running. He don't have to think about that. He was just thinking about holding himself back 'til the time for the running came. I knew that. I could just in a way see right inside him. He was going to do some awful running and I knew it. He wasn't bragging or letting on much or prancing or making a fuss, but just waiting. I knew it and Jerry Tillford his trainer knew. I looked up and then that man and I looked into each other's eyes. Something happened to me. I guess I loved the man as much as I did the horse because he knew what I knew. Seemed to me there wasn't anything in the world but that man and the horse and me. I cried and Jerry Tillford had a shine in his eyes. Then I came away to the fence to wait for the race. The horse was better than me, more steadier, and now I know better than Jerry. He was the quietest and he had to do the running.

Sunstreak ran first of course and he busted the world's record for a mile. I've seen that if I never see anything more. Everything came out just as I expected. Middlestride got left at the post and was way back and closed up to be second, just as I knew he would. He'll get a world's record too some day. They can't skin the Beckersville country on horses.

I watched the race calm because I knew what would happen. I was sure. Hanley Turner and Henry Rieback and Tom Tumberton were all more excited than me.

A funny thing had happened to me. I was thinking about Jerry Tillford the trainer and how happy he was all through the race. I liked him that afternoon even more than I ever liked my own father. I almost forgot the horses thinking that way about him. It was because of what I had seen in his eyes as he stood in the paddocks beside Sunstreak before the race started. I knew he had been watching and working with Sunstreak since the horse was a baby colt, had taught him to run and be patient and when to let himself out and not to quit, never. I knew that for him it was like a mother seeing her child do something brave or wonderful. It was the first time I ever felt for a man like that.

After the race that night I cut out from Tom and Hanley and Henry. I wanted to be by myself and I wanted to be near Jerry Tillford if I could work it. Here is what happened.

The track in Saratoga is near the edge of town. It is all polished up and trees around, the evergreen kind, and grass and everything painted and nice. If you go past the track you get to a hard road made of asphalt for automobiles, and if you go along this for a few miles there is a road turns off to a little rummy-looking farmhouse set in a yard.

That night after the race I went along that road because I had seen Jerry and some other men go that way in an automobile. I didn't expect to find them. I walked for a ways and then sat down by a fence to think. It was the direction they went in. I wanted to be as near Jerry as I could. I felt close to him. Pretty soon I went up the side road—I don't know why—and came to the rummy farmhouse. I was just lonesome to see Jerry, like wanting to see your father at night when you are a young kid. Just then an automobile came along and turned in. Jerry was in it and Henry Rieback's father, and Arthur Bedford from home, and Dave Williams and two other men I didn't know. They got out of the car and went into the house, all but Henry Rieback's father who quarreled with them and said he wouldn't go. It was only about nine o'clock, but they were all drunk and the rummy-looking farmhouse was a place for bad women to stay in. That's what it was. I crept up along a fence and looked through a window and saw.

It's what gives me the fantods. I can't make it out. The women in the house were all ugly mean-looking women, not nice to look at or be near. They were homely too, except one who was tall and looked a little like the gelding Middlestride, but not clean like him, but with a hard ugly mouth. She had red hair. I saw everything plain. I got up by an old rosebush by an open window and looked. The women had on loose dresses and sat around in chairs. The men came in and some sat on the women's laps. The place smelled rotten and there was rotten talk, the kind a kid hears around a livery stable in a town like Beckersville in the winter but don't ever expect to hear talked when there are women around. It was rotten. A nigger wouldn't go into such a place.

I looked at Jerry Tillford. I've told you how I had been feeling about him on account of his knowing what was going on inside of Sunstreak in the minute before he went to the post for the race in which he made a world's record.

Jerry bragged in that bad-woman house as I know Sunstreak wouldn't never have bragged. He said that he made that horse, that it was him that won the race and made the record. He lied and bragged like a fool. I never heard such silly talk.

And then, what do you suppose he did! He looked at the woman in there, the one that was lean and hard-mouthed and looked a little like the gelding Middlestride, but not clean like him, and his eyes began to shine just as they did when he looked at me and at Sunstreak in the paddocks at the track in the afternoon. I stood there by the window—gee!—but I wished I hadn't gone away from the tracks, but had stayed with the boys and the niggers and the horses. The tall rotten-looking woman was between us just as Sunstreak was in the paddocks in the afternoon.

Then, all of a sudden, I began to hate that man. I wanted to scream and rush in the room and kill him. I never had such a feeling before. I was so mad clean through that I cried and my fists were doubled up so my finger-nails cut my hands.

And Jerry's eyes kept shining and he waved back and forth, and then he went and kissed that woman and I crept away and went back to the tracks and to bed and didn't sleep hardly any, and then next day I got the other kids to start home with me and never told them anything I seen.

I been thinking about it ever since. I can't make it out. Spring has come again and I'm nearly sixteen and go to the tracks mornings same as always, and I see Sunstreak and Middlestride and a new colt named Strident I'll bet will lay them all out, but no one thinks so but me and two or three niggers.

But things are different. At the tracks the air don't taste as good or smell as good. It's because a man like Jerry Tillford, who knows what he does, could see a horse like Sunstreak run, and kiss a woman like that the same day. I can't make it out. Darn him, what did he want to do like that for? I keep thinking about it and it spoils looking at horses and smelling things and hearing niggers laugh and everything. Sometimes I'm so mad about it I want to fight someone. It gives me the fantods. What did he do it for? I want to know why.

KATHERINE MANSFIELD

(1888–1923)

Her First Ball

Exactly when the ball began Leila would have found it hard to say. Perhaps her first real partner was the cab. It did not matter that she shared the cab with the Sheridan girls and their brother. She sat back in her own little corner of it, and the bolster on which her hand rested felt like the sleeve of an unknown young man's dress suit; and away they bowled, past waltzing lamp-posts and houses and fences and trees.

"Have you really never been to a ball before, Leila? But, my child, how too weird—" cried the Sheridan girls.

"Our nearest neighbour was fifteen miles," said Leila softly, gently opening and shutting her fan.

Oh, dear, how hard it was to be indifferent like the others! She tried not to smile too much; she tried not to care. But every single thing was so new and exciting . . . Meg's tuberoses, Jose's long loop of amber, Laura's little dark head, pushing above her white fur like a flower through snow. She would remember for ever. It even gave her a pang to see her cousin Laurie throw away the wisps of tissue paper he pulled from the fastenings of his new gloves. She would like to have kept those wisps as a keepsake, as a remembrance. Laurie leaned forward and put his hand on Laura's knee.

"Look here, darling," he said. "The third and the ninth as usual, Twig?"

Oh, how marvellous to have a brother! In her excitement Leila felt that if there had been time, if it hadn't been impossible, she couldn't have helped crying because she was an only child, and no brother had ever said "Twig?" to her; no sister would ever say, as Meg said to Jose that moment, "I've never known your hair go up more successfully than it has to-night!"

But, of course, there was no time. They were at the drill hall already; there were cabs in front of them and cabs behind. The road was bright on either side with moving fan-like lights, and on the pavement gay couples seemed to float through the air; little satin shoes chased each other like birds.

"Hold on to me, Leila; you'll get lost," said Laura.

"Come on, girls, let's make a dash for it," said Laurie.

Leila put two fingers on Laura's pink velvet cloak, and they were somehow lifted past the big golden lantern, carried along the passage, and pushed into the little room marked "Ladies." Here the crowd was so great there was hardly space to take off their things; the noise was deafening. Two benches on either side were stacked high with wraps. Two old women in white aprons ran up and down tossing fresh armfuls. And everybody was pressing forward trying to get at the little dressing-table and mirror at the far end.

A great quivering jet of gas lighted the ladies' room. It couldn't wait; it was dancing already. When the door opened again and there came a burst of tuning from the drill hall, it leaped almost to the ceiling.

Dark girls, fair girls were patting their hair, tying ribbons again, tucking handkerchiefs down the fronts of their bodices, smoothing marble-white gloves. And because they were all laughing it seemed to Leila that they were all lovely.

"Aren't there any invisible hair-pins?" cried a voice. "How most extraordinary! I can't see a single invisible hair-pin."

"Powder my back, there's a darling," cried someone else.

"But I must have a needle and cotton. I've torn simply miles and miles of the frill," wailed a third.

Then "Pass them along, pass them along!" The straw basket of programmes was tossed from arm to arm. Darling little pink-and-silver programmes, with pink pencils and fluffy tassels. Leila's fingers shook as she took one out of the basket. She wanted to ask someone, "Am I meant to have one too?" but she had just time to read: "Waltz 3. *Two, Two, in a Canoe.* Polka 4. *Making the Feathers Fly,*" when Meg cried, "Ready, Leila?" and they pressed their way through the crush in the passage towards the big double doors of the drill hall.

Dancing had not begun yet, but the band had stopped tuning, and the noise was so great it seemed that when it did begin to play it would never be heard. Leila, pressing close to Meg, looking over Meg's shoulder, felt that even the little quivering coloured flags strung across the ceiling were talking. She quite forgot to be shy; she forgot how in the middle of dressing she had sat down on the bed with one shoe off and one shoe on and begged her mother to ring up her cousins and say she couldn't go after all. And the rush of longing she had had to be sitting on the veranda of their forsaken up-country home, listening to the baby owls crying "More pork" in the moonlight, was changed to a rush of joy so sweet that it was hard to bear along. She clutched her fan, and, gazing at the gleaming, golden floor, the azaleas, the lanterns, the stage at one end with its red carpet and gilt chairs and the band in a corner, she thought breathlessly, "How heavenly; how simply heavenly!"

All the girls stood grouped together at one side of the doors, the men at the other, and the chaperones in dark dresses, smiling rather foolishly, walked with little careful steps over the polished floor towards the stage.

"This is my little country cousin Leila. Be nice to her. Find her partners; she's under my wing," said Meg, going up to one girl after another.

Strange faces smiled at Leila—sweetly, vaguely. Strange voices answered, "Of course, my dear." But Leila felt the girls didn't really see her. They were looking towards the men. Why didn't the men begin? What were they waiting for? There they stood, smoothing their gloves, patting their glossy hair and smiling among themselves. Then, quite suddenly, as if they had only just made up their minds that that was what they had to do, the men came gliding over the parquet. There was a joyful flutter among the girls. A tall, fair man flew up to Meg, seized her programme, scribbled something; Meg passed him on to Leila. "May I have the pleasure?" He ducked and smiled. There came a dark man wearing an eyeglass, then cousin Laurie with a friend, and Laura with a little freckled fellow whose tie was crooked. Then quite an old man—fat, with a big bald patch on his head—took her programme and murmured, "Let me see, let me see!" And he was a long time comparing his programme, which looked black with names, with hers. It seemed to give him so much trouble that Leila was ashamed. "Oh, please don't bother," she said eagerly. But instead of replying the fat man wrote something, glanced at her again. "Do I remember this bright little face?" he said softly. "Is it known to me of yore?" At that moment the band began playing; the fat man disappeared. He was tossed away on a great wave of music that came flying over the gleaming floor, breaking the groups up into couples, scattering them, sending them spinning. . . .

Leila had learned to dance at boarding school. Every Saturday afternoon the boarders were hurried off to a little corrugated iron mission hall where Miss Eccles (of London) held her "select" classes. But the difference between that dusty-smelling hall—with calico texts on the walls, the poor terrified little woman in a brown velvet toque with rabbit's ears thumping the cold piano, Miss Eccles poking the girls' feet with her long white wand—and this was so tremendous that Leila was sure if her partner didn't come and she had to listen to that marvellous music and to watch the others sliding, gliding over the golden floor, she would die at least, or faint, or lift her arms and fly out of one of those dark windows that showed the stars.

"Ours, I think—" Someone bowed, smiled, and offered her his arm; she hadn't to die after all. Someone's hand pressed her waist, and she floated away like a flower that is tossed into a pool.

"Quite a good floor, isn't it?" drawled a faint voice close to her ear.

"I think it's most beautifully slippery," said Leila.

"Pardon!" The faint voice sounded surprised. Leila said it again. And there was a tiny pause before the voice echoed. "Oh, quite!" and she was swung round again.

He steered so beautifully. That was the great difference between dancing with girls and men, Leila decided. Girls banged into each other, and stamped on each other's feet: the girl who was gentleman always clutched you so.

The azaleas were separate flowers no longer; they were pink and white flags streaming by.

"Were you at the Bells' last week?" the voice came again. It sounded tired. Leila wondered whether she ought to ask him if he would like to stop.

"No, this is my first dance," said she.

Her partner gave a little gasping laugh. "Oh, I say," he protested.

"Yes, it is really the first dance I've ever been to." Leila was most fervent. It was such a relief to be able to tell somebody. "You see, I've lived in the country all my life up until now. . . ."

At that moment the music stopped, and they went to sit on two chairs against the wall. Leila tucked her pink satin feet under and fanned herself, while she blissfully watched the other couples passing and disappearing through the swing doors.

"Enjoying yourself, Leila?" asked Jose, nodding her golden head.

Laura passed and gave her the faintest little wink; it made Leila wonder for a moment whether she was quite grown up after all. Certainly her partner did not say very much. He coughed, tucked his handkerchief away, pulled down his waistcoat, took a minute thread off his sleeve. But it didn't matter. Almost immediately the band started, and her second partner seemed to spring from the ceiling.

"Floor's not bad," said the new voice. Did one always begin with the floor? And then, "Were you at the Neaves' on Tuesday?" And again Leila explained. Perhaps it was a little strange that her partners were not more interested. For it was thrilling. Her first ball! She was only at the beginning of everything. It seemed to her that she had never known what the night was like before. Up till now it had been dark, silent, beautiful very often—oh, yes—but mournful somehow. Solemn. And now it would never be like that again—it had opened dazzling bright.

"Care for an ice?" said her partner. And they went through the swing doors, down the passage, to the supper room. Her cheeks burned, she was fearfully thirsty. How sweet the ices looked on little glass plates, and how cold the frosted spoon was, iced too! And when they came back to the hall there was the fat man waiting for her by the door. It gave her quite a shock again to see how old he was; he ought to have been on the stage with the fathers and mothers. And when Leila compared him with her other partners he looked shabby. His waistcoat was creased, there was a button off his glove, his coat looked as if it was dusty with French chalk.

"Come along, little lady," said the fat man. He scarcely troubled to clasp her, and they moved away so gently, it was more like walking than dancing. But he said not a word about the floor. "Your first dance, isn't it?" he murmured.

"How *did* you know?"

"Ah," said the fat man, "that's what it is to be old!" He wheezed faintly as he steered her past an awkward couple. "You see, I've been doing this kind of thing for the last thirty years."

"Thirty years?" cried Leila. Twelve years before she was born!

"It hardly bears thinking about, does it?" said the fat man gloomily. Leila looked at his bald head, and she felt quite sorry for him.

"I think it's marvellous to be still going on," she said kindly.

"Kind little lady," said the fat man, and he pressed her a little closer, and hummed a bar of the waltz. "Of course," he said, "you can't hope to last anything like as long as that. No-o," said the fat man, "long before that you'll be sitting up there on the stage, looking on, in your nice black velvet. And these pretty arms will have turned into little short fat ones, and you'll beat time with such a different kind of fan—a black bony one." The fat man seemed to shudder. "And you'll smile away like the poor old dears up there, and point to your daughter, and tell the elderly lady next to you how some dreadful man tried to kiss her at the club ball. And your heart will ache, ache"—the fat man squeezed her closer still, as if he really was sorry for that poor heart—"because no one wants to kiss you now. And you'll say how unpleasant these polished floors are to walk on, how dangerous they are. Eh, Mademoiselle Twinkletoes?" said the fat man softly.

Leila gave a light little laugh, but she did not feel like laughing. Was it—could it all be true? It sounded terribly true. Was this first ball only the beginning of her last ball after all? At that the music seemed to change; it sounded sad, sad; it rose upon a great sigh. Oh, how quickly things changed! Why didn't happiness last for ever? For ever wasn't a bit too long.

"I want to stop," she said in a breathless voice. The fat man led her to the door.

"No," she said, "I won't go outside. I won't sit down. I'll just stand here, thank you." She leaned against the wall, tapping with her foot, pulling up her gloves and trying to smile. But deep inside her a little girl threw her pinafore over her head and sobbed. Why had he spoiled it all?

"I say, you know," said the fat man, "you mustn't take me seriously, little lady."

"As if I should!" said Leila, tossing her small dark head and sucking her underlip. . . .

Again the couples paraded. The swing doors opened and shut. Now new music was given out by the bandmaster. But Leila didn't want to dance any more. She wanted to be home, or sitting on the veranda listening to those baby owls. When she looked through the dark windows at the stars, they had long beams like wings. . . .

But presently a soft, melting, ravishing tune began, and a young man with curly hair bowed before her. She would have to dance, out of politeness, until she could find Meg. Very stiffly she walked into the middle; very haughtily she put her hand on his sleeve. But in one minute, in one turn, her feet glided, glided. The lights, the azaleas, the dresses, the pink faces, the velvet chairs, all became one beautiful flying wheel. And when her next partner bumped into the fat man and he said, "Par*don*," she smiled at him more radiantly than ever. She didn't even recognize him again.

CARSON McCULLERS

(1917–   )

A Tree, A Rock, A Cloud

It was raining that morning, and still very dark. When the boy reached the streetcar café he had almost finished his route and he went in for a cup of coffee. The place was an all-night café owned by a bitter and stingy man called Leo. After the raw, empty street, the café seemed friendly and bright: along the counter there were a couple of soldiers, three spinners from the cotton mill, and in a corner a man who sat hunched over with his nose and

Reprinted from *The Ballad of the Sad Cafe* by Carson McCullers by permission of Houghton Mifflin Company.

half his face down in a beer mug. The boy wore a helmet such as aviators wear. When he went into the café he unbuckled the chin strap and raised the right flap up over his pink little ear; often as he drank his coffee someone would speak to him in a friendly way. But this morning Leo did not look into his face and none of the men were talking. He paid and was leaving the café when a voice called out to him:

"Son! Hey Son!"

He turned back and the man in the corner was crooking his finger and nodding to him. He had brought his face out of the beer mug and he seemed suddenly very happy. The man was long and pale, with a big nose and faded orange hair.

"Hey Son!"

The boy went toward him. He was an undersized boy of about twelve, with one shoulder drawn higher than the other because of the weight of the paper sack. His face was shallow, freckled, and his eyes were round child eyes.

"Yeah Mister?"

The man laid one hand on the paper boy's shoulders, then grasped the boy's chin and turned his face slowly from one side to the other. The boy shrank back uneasily.

"Say! What's the big idea?"

The boy's voice was shrill; inside the café it was suddenly very quiet.

The man said slowly, "I love you."

All along the counter the men laughed. The boy, who had scowled and sidled away, did not know what to do. He looked over the counter at Leo, and Leo watched him with a weary, brittle jeer. The boy tried to laugh also. But the man was serious and sad.

"I did not mean to tease you, Son," he said. "Sit down and have a beer with me. There is something I have to explain."

Cautiously, out of the corner of his eye, the paper boy questioned the men along the counter to see what he should do. But they had gone back to their beer or their breakfast and did not notice him. Leo put a cup of coffee on the counter and a little jug of cream.

"He is a minor," Leo said.

The paper boy slid himself up onto the stool. His ear beneath the upturned flap of the helmet was very small and red. The man was nodding at him soberly. "It is important," he said. Then he reached in his hip pocket and brought out something which he held up in the palm of his hand for the boy to see.

"Look very carefully," he said.

The boy stared, but there was nothing to look at very carefully. The man held in his big, grimy palm a photograph. It was the face of a woman, but blurred, so that only the hat and the dress she was wearing stood out clearly.

"See?" the man asked.

The boy nodded and the man placed another picture in his palm. The woman was standing on a beach in a bathing suit. The suit made her stomach very big, and that was the main thing you noticed.

"Got a good look?" He leaned over closer and finally asked: "You ever seen her before?"

The boy sat motionless, staring slantwise at the man. "Not so I know of."

"Very well." The man blew on the photographs and put them back into his pocket. "That was my wife."

"Dead?" the boy asked.

Slowly the man shook his head. He pursed his lips as though about to whistle and answered in a long-drawn way: "Nuuu—" he said. "I will explain."

The beer on the counter before the man was in a large brown mug. He did not pick it up to drink. Instead he bent down and, putting his face over the rim, he rested there for a moment. Then with both hands he tilted the mug and sipped.

"Some night you'll go to sleep with your big nose in a mug and drown," said Leo. "Prominent transient drowns in beer. That would be a cute death."

The paper boy tried to signal to Leo. While the man was not looking he screwed up his face and worked his mouth to question soundlessly: "Drunk?" But Leo only raised his eyebrows and turned away to put some pink strips of bacon on the grill. The man pushed the mug away from him, straightened himself, and folded his loose crooked hands on the counter. His face was sad as he looked at the paper boy. He did not blink, but from time to time the lids closed down with delicate gravity over his pale green eyes. It was nearing dawn and the boy shifted the weight of the paper sack.

"I am talking about love," the man said. "With me it is a science."

The boy half slid down from the stool. But the man raised his forefinger, and there was something about him that held the boy and would not let him go away.

"Twelve years ago I married the woman in the photograph. She was my wife for one year, nine months, three days, and two nights. I loved her. Yes. . . ." He tightened his blurred, rambling voice and said again: "I loved her. I thought also that she loved me. I was a railroad engineer. She had all home comforts and luxuries. It never crept into my brain that she was not satisfied. But do you know what happened?"

"Mgneeow!" said Leo.

The man did not take his eyes from the boy's face. "She left me. I came in one night and the house was empty and she was gone. She left me."

"With a fellow?" the boy asked.

Gently the man placed his palm down on the counter. "Why naturally, Son. A woman does not run off like that alone."

The café was quiet, the soft rain black and endless in the street outside. Leo pressed down the frying bacon with the prongs of his long fork. "So you have been chasing the floozie for eleven years. You frazzled old rascal!"

For the first time the man glanced at Leo. "Please don't be vulgar. Besides, I was not speaking to you." He turned back to the boy and said in a trusting and secretive undertone. "Let's not pay any attention to him. O.K.?"

The paper boy nodded doubtfully.

"It was like this," the man continued. "I am a person who feels many things. All my life one thing after another has impressed me. Moonlight. The leg of a pretty girl. One thing after another. But the point is that when I had enjoyed anything there was a peculiar sensation as though it was laying around loose in me. Nothing seemed to finish itself up or fit in with the other things. Women? I had my portion of them. The same. Afterwards laying around loose in me. I was a man who had never loved."

Very slowly he closed his eyelids, and the gesture was like a curtain drawn at the end of a scene in a play. When he spoke again his voice was excited and the words came fast—the lobes of his large, loose ears seemed to tremble.

"Then I met this woman. I was fifty-one years old and she always said she was thirty. I met her at a filling station and we were married within three days. And do you know what it was like? I just can't tell you. All I had ever felt was gathered together around this woman. Nothing lay around loose in me any more but was finished up by her."

The man stopped suddenly and stroked his long nose. His voice sank down to a steady and reproachful undertone: "I'm not explaining this right. What happened was this. There were these beautiful feelings and loose little pleasures inside me. And this woman was something like an assembly line for my soul. I run these little pieces of myself through her and I come out complete. Now do you follow me?"

"What was her name?" the boy asked.

"Oh," he said. "I called her Dodo. But that is immaterial."

"Did you try to make her come back?"

The man did not seem to hear. "Under the circumstances you can imagine how I felt when she left me."

Leo took the bacon from the grill and folded two strips of it between a bun. He had a gray face, with slitted eyes and a pinched nose saddled by faint blue shadows. One of the mill workers signaled for more coffee and Leo poured it. He did not give refills on coffee free. The spinner ate breakfast there every morning, but the better Leo knew his customers the stingier he treated them. He nibbled his own bun as though he grudged it to himself.

"And you never got hold of her again?"

The boy did not know what to think of the man, and his child's face was uncertain with mingled curiosity and doubt. He was new on the paper route; it was still strange to him to be out in the town in the black, queer early morning.

"Yes," the man said. "I took a number of steps to get her back. I went around trying to locate her. I went to Tulsa where she had folks. And to Mobile. I went to every town she had ever mentioned to me, and I hunted down every man she had formerly been connected with. Tulsa, Atlanta,

Chicago, Cheehaw, Memphis. . . . For the better part of two years I chased around the country trying to lay hold of her."

"But the pair of them had vanished from the face of the earth!" said Leo.

"Don't listen to him," the man said confidentially. "And also just forget those two years. They are not important. What matters is that around the third year a curious thing begun to happen to me."

"What?" the boy asked.

The man leaned down and tilted his mug to take a sip of beer. But as he hovered over the mug his nostrils fluttered slightly; he sniffed the staleness of the beer and did not drink. "Love is a curious thing to begin with. At first I thought only of getting her back. It was a kind of mania. But then as time went on I tried to remember her. But do you know what happened?"

"No," the boy said.

"When I laid myself down on a bed and tried to think about her my mind became a blank. I couldn't see her. I would take out her pictures and look. No good. Nothing doing. A blank. Can you imagine it?"

"Say Mac!" Leo called down the counter. "Can you imagine this bozo's mind a blank!"

Slowly, as though fanning away flies, the man waved his hand. His green eyes were concentrated and fixed on the shallow little face of the paper boy.

"But a sudden piece of glass on a sidewalk. Or a nickel tune in a music box. A shadow on a wall at night. And I would remember. It might happen in a street and I would cry or bang my head against a lamppost. You follow me?"

"A piece of glass . . ." the boy said.

"Anything. I would walk around and I had no power of how and when to remember her. You think you can put up a kind of shield. But remembering don't come to a man face forward—it corners around sideways. I was at the mercy of everything I saw and heard. Suddenly instead of me combing the countryside to find her she begun to chase me around in my very soul. *She* chasing *me*, mind you! And in my soul."

The boy asked finally: "What part of the country were you in then?"

"Ooh," the man groaned. "I was a sick mortal. It was like smallpox. I confess, Son, that I boozed. I fornicated. I committed any sin that suddenly appealed to me. I am loath to confess it but I will do so. When I recall that period it is all curdled in my mind, it was so terrible."

The man leaned his head down and tapped his forehead on the counter. For a few seconds he stayed bowed over in this position, the back of his stringy neck covered with orange furze, his hands with their long warped fingers held palm to palm in an attitude of prayer. Then the man straightened himself; he was smiling and suddenly his face was bright and tremulous and old.

"It was in the fifth year that it happened," he said. "And with it I started my science."

Leo's mouth jerked with a pale, quick grin. "Well none of we boys are getting any younger," he said. Then with sudden anger he balled up a dishcloth he was holding and threw it down hard on the floor. "You draggle-tailed old Romeo!"

"What happened?" the boy asked.

The old man's voice was high and clear: "Peace," he answered.

"Huh?"

"It is hard to explain scientifically, Son," he said. "I guess the logical explanation is that she and I had fleed around from each other for so long that finally we just got tangled up together and lay down and quit. Peace. A queer and beautiful blankness. It was spring in Portland and the rain came every afternoon. All evening I just stayed there on my bed in the dark. And that is how the science come to me."

The windows in the streetcar were pale blue with light. The two soldiers paid for their beers and opened the door—one of the soldiers combed his hair and wiped off his muddy puttees before they went outside. The three mill workers bent silently over their breakfasts. Leo's clock was ticking on the wall.

"It is this. And listen carefully. I meditated on love and reasoned it out. I realized what is wrong with us. Men fall in love for the first time. And what do they fall in love with?"

The boy's soft mouth was partly open and he did not answer.

"A woman," the old man said. "Without science, with nothing to go by, they undertake the most dangerous and sacred experience in God's earth. They fall in love with a woman. Is that correct, Son?"

"Yeah," the boy said faintly.

"They start at the wrong end of love. They begin at the climax. Can you wonder it is so miserable. Do you know how men should love?"

The old man reached over and grasped the boy by the collar of his leather jacket. He gave him a gentle little shake and his green eyes gazed down unblinking and grave.

"Son, do you know how love should be begun?"

The boy sat small and listening and still. Slowly he shook his head. The old man leaned closer and whispered:

"A tree. A rock. A cloud."

It was still raining outside in the street: a mild, gray, endless rain. The mill whistle blew for the six o'clock shift and the three spinners paid and went away. There was no one in the café but Leo, the old man, and the little paper boy.

"The weather was like this in Portland," he said. "At the time my science was begun. I meditated and I started very cautious. I would pick up something from the street and take it home with me. I bought a goldfish and I concentrated on the goldfish and I loved it. I graduated from one thing to another. Day by day I was getting this technique. On the road from Portland to San Diego——"

"Aw shut up!" screamed Leo suddenly. "Shut up! Shut up!"

The old man still held the collar of the boy's jacket; he was trembling and his face was earnest and bright and wild. "For six years now I have gone around by myself and built up my science. And now I am a master, Son. I can love anything. No longer do I have to think about it even. I see a street full of people and a beautiful light comes in me. I watch a bird in the sky. Or I meet a traveler on the road. Everything, Son. And anybody. All stranger and all loved! Do you realize what a science like mine can mean?"

The boy held himself stiffly, his hands curled tight around the counter edge. Finally he asked: "Did you ever really find that lady?"

"What? What say, Son?"

"I mean," the boy asked timidly. "Have you fallen in love with a woman again?"

The old man loosened his grasp on the boy's collar. He turned away and for the first time his green eyes had a vague and scattered look. He lifted the mug from the counter, drank down the yellow beer. His head was shaking slowly from side to side. Then finally he answered: "No, Son. You see that is the last step in my science. I go cautious. And I am not quite ready yet."

"Well!" said Leo. "Well well well!"

The old man stood in the open doorway. "Remember," he said. Framed there in the gray damp light of the early morning he looked shrunken and seedy and frail. But his smile was bright. "Remember I love you," he said with a last nod. And the door closed quietly behind him.

The boy did not speak for a long time. He pulled down the bangs on his forehead and slid his grimy little forefinger around the rim of his empty cup. Then without looking at Leo he finally asked:

"Was he drunk?"

"No," said Leo shortly.

The boy raised his clear voice higher. "Then was he a dope fiend?"

"No."

The boy looked up at Leo, and his flat little face was desperate, his voice urgent and shrill. "Was he crazy? Do you think he was a lunatic?" The paper boy's voice dropped suddenly with doubt. "Leo? Or not?"

But Leo would not answer him. Leo had run a night café for fourteen years, and he held himself to be a critic of craziness. There were the town characters and also the transients who roamed in from the night. He knew the manias of all of them. But he did not want to satisfy the questions of the waiting child. He tightened his pale face and was silent.

So the boy pulled down the right flap of his helmet and as he turned to leave he made the only comment that seemed safe to him, the only remark that could not be laughed down and despised:

"He sure has done a lot of traveling."

FLANNERY O'CONNOR

(1925–1964)

The Partridge Festival

Calhoun parked his small pod-shaped car in the driveway to his great-aunts' house and got out cautiously, looking to the right and left as if he expected the profusion of azalea blossoms to have a lethal effect upon him. Instead of a decent lawn, the old ladies had three terraces crammed with red and white azaleas, beginning at the sidewalk and running backwards to the very edge of their imposing unpainted house. The two of them were on the front porch, one sitting, the other standing.

"Here's our baby!" his Aunt Bessie intoned in a voice meant to reach the other one, two feet away but deaf. It turned the head of a girl in the next yard, who sat cross-legged under a tree, reading. She raised her spectacled face, stared at Calhoun, and then returned her attention—with what he saw plainly was a smirk—to the book. Scowling, he passed stolidly on to the porch to get over the preliminaries with his aunts. They would take his voluntary presence in Partridge at Azalea Festival time to be a sign that his character was improving.

They were box-jawed old ladies who looked like George Washington with his wooden teeth in. They wore black suits with large ruffled jabots and had dead-white hair pulled back. After each had embraced him, he dropped limply into a rocker and gave them a sheepish smile. He was here only because Singleton had captured his imagination, but he had told his Aunt Bessie over the telephone that he was coming to enjoy the festival.

The deaf one, Aunt Mattie, shouted, "Your great-grandfather would have been delighted to see you taking an interest in the festival, Calhoun. He initiated it himself, you know."

"Well," the boy yelled back, "what about the little extra excitement you've had this time?"

Ten days before the festival began, a man named Singleton had been tried by a mock court on the courthouse lawn for not buying an Azalea Festival Badge. During the trial he had been imprisoned in a pair of stocks and when convicted, had been locked in the "jail" together with a goat

Originally published in *The Critic,* 180 N. Wabash Ave., Chicago, Ill. Reprinted by permission of *The Critic* and the estate of the late Flannery O'Connor.

that had been tried and convicted previously for the same offense. The "jail" was an outdoor privy borrowed for the occasion by the Jaycees. Ten days later, Singleton had appeared in a side door on the courthouse porch and with a silent automatic pistol, had shot five of the dignitaries seated there and by mistake one person in the crowd. The innocent man received the bullet intended for the mayor who at that moment had reached down to pull up the tongue of his shoe.

"An unfortunate incident," his Aunt Mattie said. "It mars the festive spirit."

He heard the girl on the other lawn slam her book. The top of her rose into view above the hedge—a sloping-forward neck and a small face with a fierce expression, which she trained briefly on them before she disappeared. "It doesn't seem to have marred anything," he said. "As I passed through town I saw more people than ever before and all the flags were up. Partridge," he shouted, "will bury its dead but will not lose a nickel." The girl's front door slammed in the middle of the sentence.

His Aunt Bessie had gone into the house and come out again with a small leather box. "You look very like Father," she said and pulled up her chair beside him.

Without enthusiasm Calhoun opened the box, which shed a rust-colored dust over his knees, and removed the miniature of his great-grandfather. He was shown this every time he came. The old man—round-faced, bald, altogether unremarkable-looking—sat with his hands knotted on the head of a black stick. His expression was all innocence and determination. The master merchant, the boy thought, and flinched. "And what would this stalwart worthy think of Partridge today," he asked wryly, "with its festival in full swing after six citizens have been shot?"

"Father was progressive," his Aunt Bessie said, "—the most forward-looking merchant Partridge ever had. He would either have been one of the prominent men shot or he would have been the one to subdue the maniac."

The boy did not know how much of this he could stand. In the paper there had been pictures of the six "victims" and one of Singleton. Singleton's was the only distinctive face in the lot. It was broad but boney and bleak. One eye was more nearly round than the other and in the more nearly round one Calhoun had recognized the composure of the man who knows he will and who is willing to suffer for the right to be himself. A calculating contempt lurked in the regular eye but in the general expression there was the tortured look of the man who becomes maddened finally by the madness around him. The other six faces were of the same general stamp as his great-grandfather's.

"As you get older, you'll look more and more like Father," his Aunt Mattie prophesied. "You have his ruddy complexion and much the same expression."

"I'm a different type entirely," he said stiffly.

"Peaches and cream," his Aunt Bessie guffawed. "You're getting a little pot-tummy too," she said and took a lunge at his middle with her first. "How old is our baby now?"

"Twenty-three," he muttered, thinking that it could not go on like this for the whole visit, that once they had roughed him up a bit, they would leave off.

"And do you have a girl?" his Aunt Mattie asked.

"No," he said wearily. "I take it," he went on, "that around here Singleton is considered nothing but a mental case?"

"Yes," his Aunt Bessie said, "—peculiar. He never conformed. He was not like the rest of us here."

"A terrible drawback," the boy said. Though his eyes were not mismatched, the shape of his face was broad like Singleton's; but the real likeness between them was interior.

"Since he is insane, he is not responsible," his Aunt Bessie said.

The boy's eyes brightened. He sat forward and fixed the old lady with a narrow gaze. "And where then," he asked, "does the real guilt lie?"

"Father's head was as smooth as an infant's by the time he was thirty," she said. "You had better hurry and get you a girl. Ha ha. What are you going to do with yourself now?"

He reached into his pocket and withdrew his pipe and a sack of tobacco. You could not ask them questions in depth. They were both good low-church Episcopalians but they had amoral imaginations. "I think I shall write," he said and began to load the bowl.

"Well," his Aunt Bessie said, "that's fine. Maybe you'll be another Margaret Mitchell."

"I hope you'll do us justice," his Aunt Mattie shouted. "Few do."

"I'll do you justice all right," he said grimly. "I'm writing an expos. . . ." He stopped and put the pipe in his mouth and sat back. It would be ridiculous to tell *them*. He removed the pipe and said, "Well, that's too much to go into. It wouldn't interest you ladies."

His Aunt Bessie inclined her head significantly. "Calhoun," she said, "we wouldn't want to be disappointed in you." They eyed him as if it had just occurred to them that the pet snake they had been fondling might after all be poisonous.

"Know the truth," the boy said with his fiercest look, "and the truth shall make you free."

They appeared reassured at his quoting Scripture. "Isn't he sweet," his Aunt Mattie asked, "with his little pipe?"

"Better get you a girl, boy," his Aunt Bessie said.

He escaped them in a few minutes and took his bag upstairs and then came down again, ready to go out and immerse himself in his material. His intention was to spend the afternoon interviewing people about Singleton. He expected to write something that would vindicate the madman and he expected the writing of it to mitigate his own guilt, for his doubleness, his shadow, was cast before him more darkly than usual in the light of Singleton's purity.

For the three summer months of the year, he lived with his parents and sold air-conditioners, boats, and refrigerators so that for the other nine months he could afford to meet life naturally and bring his real self—the rebel-artist-mystic—to birth. During these other months he lived on the opposite side of the city in an unheated walk-up with two other boys who also did nothing. But guilt for the summer pursued him into the winter; the fact was, he could have fared without the orgy of selling he cast himself into in the summer.

When he had explained to them that he despised their values, his parents had looked at each other with a gleam of recognition as if this were what they had been expecting from what they had read, and his father had offered to give him a small allowance to finance the flat. He had refused it for the sake of his independence, but in the depths of himself, he knew it was not for his independence but because he *enjoyed* selling. In the face of a customer, he was carried outside himself; his face began to beam and sweat and all complexity left him; he was in the grip of a drive as strong as the drive of some men for liquor or a woman; and he was horribly good at it. He was so good at it that the company had given him an achievement scroll. He had put quotation marks around the word *achievement* and he and his friends used the scroll as a target for darts.

As soon as he had seen Singleton's picture in the paper, the face began to burn in his imagination like a dark reproachful liberating star. The next morning he had telephoned his aunts to expect him and he had driven the hundred and fifty miles to Partridge in a little short of four hours.

On his way out of the house, his Aunt Bessie halted him and said, "Be back by six, Baby Lamb, and we'll have a sweet surprise for you."

"Rice pudding?" he asked. They were terrible cooks.

"Sweeter by far!" the old lady said and rolled her eyes. He hastened away.

The girl next door had returned with her book to the lawn. He suspected that he might be supposed to know her. When he came for visits as a child, his aunts had always produced one of the neighbor's freak children to play with him—once a fat moron in a Girl Scout suit, another time a near-sighted boy who recited Bible verses, and another an almost square girl who had blackened his eye and left. He thanked God he was now grown and they would no longer dare to fill his time for him. The girl did not look up as he passed and he did not speak.

Once on the sidewalk, he was affected by the profusion of azaleas. They seemed to wash in tides of color across the lawns until they surged against the white house-fronts, crests of pink and crimson, crests of white and a mysterious shade that was not yet lavender, wild crests of yellow-red. The profusion of color almost stopped his breath with insidious pleasure. Moss hung from the old trees. The houses were the most picturesque types of run-down ante-bellum. The taint of the place was expressed in his great-grandfather's words which had survived as the town's motto: Beauty is Our Money Crop.

His aunts lived five blocks from the business section. He walked them quickly and came after a few minutes to the edge of the bare commercial scene, which had the ramshackle courthouse for its center. The sun beat down fiercely on the tops of cars parked in every available space. Flags, national, state, and confederate, flapped on every corner street light. People milled about. On the quiet shaded street where his aunts lived and the azaleas were best, he had not passed three people, but here they all were, staring avidly at the pathetic store displays and moving with languid reverence past the courthouse porch, the spot where blood had been spilled.

He wondered if any of them might think he was here for the same reason they were. He would have liked to start, in Socratic fashion, a street discussion about where the real guilt for the six deaths lay, but as he surveyed the scene, he saw no one who looked capable of any genuine interest in meaning. Without set purpose, he entered a drugstore. The place was dark and smelled of sour vanilla.

He sat down on the high stool at the counter and ordered a limeade. The boy preparing the drink had elaborate red sideburns and wore on his shirt-front an Azalea Festival Badge—the emblem which Singleton had refused to buy. Calhoun's eye fell on it at once. "I see you've paid your tribute to the god," he said.

The boy did not seem to get the significance of this.

"The badge," Calhoun said, "the badge."

The boy looked down at it and then back at Calhoun. He put the drink on the counter and continued to look at him as if he were serving someone with an interesting deformity.

"Are you enjoying the festive spirit?" Calhoun asked.

"All these doings?" the boy said.

"These grand events," Calhoun said, "commencing with, I believe, six deaths."

"Yessir," the boy said, "six in cold blood. And I knew four of them myself."

"You too have had your share of the glory then," Calhoun said. He felt suddenly a distinct hush fall on the street outside. He turned his eyes to the door just in time to see a hearse pass, followed by a line of slowly moving cars.

"That's the man that's having his funeral to himself," the boy said reverently. "The five that were supposed to get shot had theirs yesterday. One big one. But he didn't die in time for it."

"They have innocent as well as guilty blood on their hands," Calhoun said and glared at the boy.

"It wasn't no *they,*" the boy said. "One man done it all. A man named Singleton. He was bats."

"Singleton was only the instrument," Calhoun said. "Partridge itself is guilty." He finished his drink in a gulp and put down the glass.

The boy was looking at him as if he were mad. "Partridge can't shoot nobody," he said in a high exasperated voice.

Calhoun put his dime on the counter and left. The last car had turned at the end of the block. He thought he observed less activity. People had obviously hastened away at the sight of the hearse. Two doors from him an old man leaned out of a hardware store and glared up the street where the procession had disappeared. Calhoun's need to communicate was urgent. He approached diffidently. "I understand that was the last funeral," he said.

The old man put a hand behind his ear.

"The funeral of the innocent man," Calhoun shouted and nodded up the street.

The old man cleared his nostrils loudly. His expression was not affable. "The only bullet that went right," he said in a rasping voice. "Biller was a wastrel. Drunk at the time."

The boy scowled. "I suppose the other five were heroes?" he suggested archly.

"Fine men," the old man said. "Perished in the line of duty. We givem a hero's fu'nel—all five in one big service. Biller's folks tried to rush up the undertaker so they could get Biller in on it but we saw to it Biller didn't make it. Would have been a disgrace."

My God, the boy thought.

"The only thing Singleton ever did good was to rid us of Biller," the old man continued. "Now somebody ought to rid us of Singleton. There he is at Quincy, living in the laper luxury, laying in a cool bed at no expense, eating up your taxes and mine. They should have shot him on the spot."

This was so appalling that Calhoun was speechless.

"Going to keep him there, they ought to charge him board," the old man said.

With a contemptuous glance, the boy walked off. He crossed the street to the courthouse square, moving at an odd angle in order to put as much distance between himself and the old fool as quickly as possible. Here benches were scattered beneath the trees. He found an unoccupied one and sat down. To the side of the courthouse steps, several viewers stood admiring the "jail" where Singleton had been locked with the goat. The pathos of his friend's situation was borne in on him with a rush of empathy. He felt himself flung in the privy, the padlock clicked, he glared between the rotting planks at the fools howling and cavorting outside. The goat made an obscene noise; he saw that he was confined with the spirit of the community.

"Six men was shot here," an odd muffled voice close by said.

The boy jumped.

A small white girl whose tongue was curled in the mouth of a Coca-Cola bottle was sitting in a patch of sand at his feet, watching him with a detached gaze. Her eyes were the same green as the bottle. She was barefooted and had straight white hair. She withdrew her tongue from the bottle with an explosive sound. "A bad man did it," she said.

The boy felt the kind of frustration that accompanies contact with the certainty of children. "No," he said, "he was not a bad man."

The child put her tongue back in the bottle and withdrew it silently, her eyes on him.

"People were not good to him," he explained. "They were mean to him. They were cruel. What would you do if someone were cruel to you?"

"Shoot them," she said.

"Well, that's what he did," Calhoun said, frowning.

She continued to sit there and did not take her eyes off him. Her gaze might have been the depthless gaze of Partridge itself.

"You people persecuted him and finally drove him mad," the boy said. "He wouldn't buy a badge. Was that a crime? He was the Outsider here and you couldn't stand that. One of the fundamental rights of man," he said, glaring through the child's transparent stare, "is the right not to behave like a fool. The right to be different," he said hoarsely. "My God. The right to be yourself."

Without taking her eyes off him, she lifted one of her feet and set it on her knee.

"He was a bad bad bad man," she said.

Calhoun got up and walked off, glaring in front of him. His indignation swathed his vision in a kind of haze. He saw none of the activity around him distinctly. Two high-school girls in bright skirts and jackets swung into his path and shrilled, "Buy a ticket for the beauty contest tonight. See who'll be Miss Partridge Azalea!" He swerved sharply to the side and did not throw them so much as a glance. Their giggles followed him until he was past the courthouse and onto the block behind it. He stood there a moment, undecided what he would do next. He faced a barber shop which looked empty and cool. After a moment he entered it.

The barber, alone in the shop, raised his head from behind the paper he was reading. Calhoun asked for a haircut and sat down gratefully in the chair.

The barber was a tall emaciated fellow with eyes that might have faded from some deeper color. He looked to be a man who had suffered himself. He put the bib on the boy and stood staring at his round head as if it were a pumpkin he was wondering how to slice. Then he twirled the chair so that Calhoun faced the mirror. He was confronted with an image that was round-faced, unremarkable-looking and innocent. The boy's expression turned fierce. "Are you eating up this slop like the rest of them?" he asked belligerently.

"Come again?" the barber said.

"Do the tribal rites going on here improve the barber trade? All these doings, all these doings," he said impatiently.

"Well," the barber said, "last year it was a thousand extra people here and this year it looks to be more—on account," he said, "of the tragedy."

"The tragedy," the boy repeated and stretched his mouth.

"The six that was shot," the barber said.

"That tragedy," the boy said. "And what about the other tragedy—the man who was persecuted by these idiots until he shot six of them?"

"Oh him," the barber said.

"Singleton," the boy said. "Did he patronize your place?"

The barber began clipping his hair. A peculiar expression of disdain had come over his face at the mention of the name. "Tonight it's a beauty contest," he said, "tomorrow night it's a band concert, Thursday afternoon it's a big parade with Miss. . . ."

"Did you or didn't you know Singleton?" Calhoun interrupted.

"Known him well," the barber said and shut his mouth.

A tremor went through the boy as he realized that Singleton had probably sat in the chair he himself was now sitting in. He searched his face in the mirror desperately for its hidden likeness to the man. Slowly he saw it appear, a secret message brought to light by the heat of his feelings. "Did he patronize your shop?" he asked and held his breath for the answer.

"Him and me was related by marriage," the barber said indignantly, "but he never come in here. He was too big a skinflint to have his hair cut. He cut his own."

"An unpardonable crime," Calhoun said in a high voice.

"His second cousin married my sister-in-law," the barber said, "but he never known me on the street. Pass him as close as I am to you and he'd keep going. Kept his eyes on the ground all the time like he was following a bug."

"Preoccupied," the boy muttered. "He doubtless didn't know you were on the street."

"He known it," the barber said and his mouth curled unpleasantly. "He known it. I clip hair and he clipped coupons and that was that. I clip hair," he repeated as if this sentence had a particularly satisfying ring to his ears, "and he clipped coupons."

The typical have-not psychology, Calhoun thought. "Was the Singleton family once wealthy?" he asked.

"It wasn't but half of him Singleton," the barber said, "and the Singletons claimed there wasn't none of him Singleton. One of the Singleton girls gone off on a nine-months vacation and come back with him. Then they all died off and left him their money. It's no telling what the other half of him is. Something foreign I would judge." His tone insinuated more.

"I begin to get the picture," Calhoun said.

"He ain't clipping no coupons now," said the barber.

"No," Calhoun said and his voice rose, "now he's suffering. He's the scapegoat. He's laden with the sins of the community. Sacrificed for the guilt of others."

The barber paused, his mouth partway open. After a moment he said in a more respectful voice, "Reverend, you got him wrong. He wasn't a church-going man."

The boy reddened. "I'm not a church-going man myself," he said.

The barber seemed stopped again. He stood holding the scissors uncertainly.

"He was an individualist," Calhoun said. "A man who would not allow himself to be pressed into the mold of his inferiors. A non-conformist. He was a man of depth living among caricatures and they finally drove him mad, unleashed all his violence on themselves. Observe," he continued, "that they didn't try him. They simply had him committed at once to Quincy. Why? Because," he said, "a trial would have brought out his essential innocence and the real guilt of the community."

The barber's face lightened. "You're a lawyer, ain't you?" he asked.

"No," the boy said sullenly, "I'm a writer."

"Ohhh," the barber murmured. "I known it must be something like that." After a moment he said, "What you written?"

"He never married?" Calhoun went on rudely. "He lived alone in the Singleton place in the country?"

"What there was of it," the barber said. "He wouldn't have spent a nickel to keep it from falling down and no woman wouldn't have had him. That was the one thing he always had to pay for," he said and made a vulgar noise in his cheek.

"You know because you were always there," the boy said, barely able to control his disgust for this bigot.

"Naw," the barber said, "it was just common knowledge. I clip hair," he said, "but I don't live like a hog. I got plumbing in my house and a refrigerator that spits ice cubes into my wife's hand."

"He was not a materialist," Calhoun said. "There were things that meant more to him than plumbing. Independence, for instance."

"Ha," the barber snorted. "He wasn't so independent. Once lightning almost struck him and those that saw it said you should have seen him run. Took off like bees were swarming in his pants. They liked to died laughing," and he gave a hyena-like laugh himself and slapped his knee.

"Loathsome," the boy murmured.

"Another time," the barber continued, "somebody went out there and put a dead cat in his well. Somebody was always doing something to see if they could make him turn loose a little money. Another time. . . ."

Calhoun began fighting his way out of the bib as if it were a net he was caught in. When he was free of it, he thrust his hand in his pocket and brought out a dollar which he flung on the startled barber's shelf. Then he made for the door, letting it slam behind him in judgment on the place.

The walk back to his aunts' did not calm him. The colors of the azaleas had deepened with the approach of sundown and the trees rustled protectively over the old houses. No one here had a thought for Singleton, who lay on a cot in a filthy ward at Quincy. The boy felt now in a concrete way the force of his innocence, and he thought that to do justice to all the man had suffered, he would have to write more than a simple article. He would have to write a novel; he would have to show, not say, how primary injustice operated. Preoccupied with this, he went four doors past his aunts' house and had to turn and go back.

His Aunt Bessie met him at the door and drew him into the hall. "Told you we'd have a sweet surprise for you!" she said, pulling him by the arm into the parlor.

On the sofa sat a rangy-looking girl in a lime-green dress. "You remember Mary Elizabeth," his Aunt Mattie said, "—the cute little trick you took to the picture show once when you were here." Through his rage he recognized the girl who had been reading under the tree. "Mary Elizabeth is home for her spring holidays," his Aunt Mattie said. "Mary Elizabeth is a real scholar, aren't you, Mary Elizabeth?"

Mary Elizabeth scowled, indicating she was indifferent to whether she was a real scholar or not. She gave him a look which told him plainly she expected to enjoy this no more than he did.

His Aunt Mattie gripped the knob of her cane and began to lift herself from her chair. "We're going to have supper early," the other one said, "because Mary Elizabeth is going to take you to the beauty contest and it begins at seven."

"Great," the boy said in a tone that would be lost on them but he hoped not on Mary Elizabeth.

Throughout the meal he ignored the girl completely. His repartee with his aunts was markedly cynical but they did not have sense enough to understand his allusions and laughed like idiots at everything he said. Twice they called him "Baby Lamb" and the girl smirked. Otherwise she did nothing to suggest she was enjoying herself. Her round face was still childish behind her glasses. Retarded, Calhoun thought.

When the meal was over and they were on the way to the beauty contest, they continued to say nothing to each other. The girl, who was several inches taller than he, walked slightly in advance of him as if she would like to lose him on the way, but after two blocks she stopped abruptly and began to rummage in a large grass bag she carried. She took out a pencil and held it between her teeth while she continued to rummage. After a minute she brought up from the bottom of the bag two tickets and a stenographer's note pad. With these out, she closed the pocketbook and walked on.

"Are you going to take notes?" Calhoun inquired in a tone heavy with irony.

The girl looked around as if trying to identify the speaker. "Yes," she said, "I'm going to take notes."

"You appreciate this sort of thing?" Calhoun asked in the same tone. "You enjoy it?"

"It makes me vomit," she said, "I'm going to finish it off with one swift literary kick."

The boy looked at her blankly.

"Don't let me interfere with your pleasure in it," she said, "but this whole place is false and rotten to the core." Her voice came with a hiss of indignation. "They prostitute azaleas!"

Calhoun was astounded. After a moment he recovered himself. "It takes no great mind to come to that conclusion," he said haughtily. "What requires insight is finding a way to transcend it."

"You mean a form to express it in."

"It comes to the same thing," he said.

They walked the next two blocks in silence but both appeared shaken. When the courthouse was in view they crossed the street to it and Mary Elizabeth stuck the tickets at a boy who stood beside an entrance that had been formed by roping in the rest of the square. People were beginning to assemble on the grass inside.

"And do we stand here while you take notes?" Calhoun asked.

The girl stopped and faced him. "Look, Baby Lamb," she said, "you can do what you please. I'm going up to my father's office in the building where I can work. You can stay down here and help select Miss Partridge Azalea if you want to."

"I shall come," he said, controlling himself, "I'd like to observe a great female writer taking notes."

"Suit yourself," she said.

He followed her up the courthouse steps and through a side door. His irritation was so extreme that he did not realize he had passed through the very door where Singleton had stood to shoot. They walked through an empty barnlike hall and silently up a flight of tobacco-stained steps into another barnlike hall. Mary Elizabeth rooted in the grass bag for a key and then unlocked the door to her father's office. They entered a large threadbare room lined with lawbooks. As if he were an incompetent, the girl dragged two straight chairs from one wall to a window that overlooked the porch.

Then she sat down and stared out, apparently absorbed at once in the scene below.

Calhoun sat down in the other chair. To annoy her he began to look her over thoroughly. For what seemed at least five minutes, he did not take his eyes off her as she leaned with her elbows in the window. He stared at her so long that he was afraid her image would be etched forever on his retina. Finally he could stand the silence no longer. "What is your opinion of Singleton?" he asked abruptly.

She raised her head and appeared to look through him. "A Christ-figure," she said.

The boy was stunned.

"I mean as myth," she said scowling. "I'm not a Christian." She returned her attention to the scene outside. Below a bugle sounded. "Sixteen girls in bathing suits are about to appear," she drawled. "Surely this will be of interest to you?"

"Listen," Calhoun said fiercely, "get this through your head. I'm not interested in the damm festival or the damm azalea queen. I'm here only because of my sympathy for Singleton. I'm going to write about him. Possibly a novel."

"I intend to write a non-fiction study," the girl said in a tone that made it evident fiction was beneath her.

They looked at each other with open and intense dislike. Calhoun felt that if he probed sufficiently he would expose her essential shallowness. "Since our forms are different," he said, again with his ironical smile, "we might compare findings."

"It's quite simple," the girl said. "He was the scapegoat. While Partridge flings itself about selecting Miss Partridge Azalea, Singleton suffers at Quincy. He expiates . . ."

"I don't mean your abstract findings," the boy said. "I mean your concrete findings. Have you ever seen him? What did he look like? The novelist is not interested in narrow abstractions—particularly when they're obvious. He's . . ."

"How many novels have you written?" she asked.

"This will be my first," he said coldly. "Have you ever seen him?"

"No," she said, "that isn't necessary for me. What he looks like makes no difference—whether he has brown eyes or blue—that's nothing to a thinker."

"You are probably," he said, "afraid to look at him. The novelist is never afraid to look at the real object."

"I would not be afraid to look at him," the girl said angrily, "if it were at all necessary. Whether he has brown eyes or blue is nothing to me."

"There is more to it," Calhoun said, "than whether he has brown eyes or blue. You might find your theories enriched by the sight of him. And I don't mean by finding out the color of his eyes. I mean your existential encounter with his personality. The mystery of personality," he said, "is what interests the artist. Life does not abide in abstractions."

"Then what's keeping you from going and having a look at him?" she said. "What are you asking me what he looks like for? Go see for yourself."

The words fell on his head like a sack of rocks. After a moment he said, "Go see for yourself? Go see where?"

"At Quincy," the girl said. "Where do you think?"

"They wouldn't let me see him," he said. The suggestion was appalling to him; for some reason he could not at the moment understand, it struck him as unthinkable.

"They would if you said you were kin to him," she said. "It's only twenty miles from here. What's to stop you?"

He was about to say, "I'm not kin to him," but he stopped and reddened furiously on the edge of the betrayal. They were spiritual kin.

"Go see whether his eyes are brown or blue and have yourself a little old exis . . ."

"I take it," he said, "that if I go you would like to go along? Since you aren't afraid to see him."

The girl paled. "You won't go," she said. "You're not up to the old exis . . ."

"I will go," he said, seeing his opportunity to shut her up. "And if you care to go with me, you can be at my aunts' at nine in the morning. But I doubt," he added, "that I'll see you there."

She thrust forward her long neck and glared at him. "Oh yes you will," she said. "You'll see me there."

She returned her attention to the window and Calhoun looked at nothing. Each seemed sunk suddenly in some mammoth private problem. Raucous cheers came intermittently from outside. Every few minutes there was music and clapping but neither took any notice of it, or of each other. Finally the girl pulled away from the window and said, "If you've got the general idea, we can leave. I prefer to go home and read."

"I had the general idea before I came," Calhoun said.

He saw her to her door and when he had left her, his spirits lifted dizzily for an instant and then collapsed. He knew that the idea of going to see Singleton would never have occurred to him alone. It would be a torturing experience, but it might be his salvation. The sight of Singleton in his misery might cause him suffering sufficient to raise him once and for all from his commercial instincts. Selling was the only thing he had proved himself good at; yet it was impossible for him to believe that every man was not created equally an artist if he could but suffer and achieve it. As for the girl, he doubted if the sight of Singleton would do anything for her. She had that particular repulsive fanaticism peculiar to smart children—all brain and no emotion.

He spent a restless night, dreaming in snatches of Singleton. At one point he dreamed he was driving to Quincy to sell Singleton a refrigerator. When he awoke in the morning, a slow rain was descending indifferently. He turned his head to the grey window pane. He could not remember what he had dreamed but he sensed it had been unpleasant. A vision of the girl's flat face came to him. He thought of Quincy and saw rows and rows of low red buildings with rough heads sticking out of barred windows. He tried to concentrate on Singleton but his mind shied from the thought. He did not wish to go to Quincy. He remembered that it was a novel he was going to write. His desire to write a novel had gone down overnight like a defective tire.

While he lay in bed, the drizzle turned into a steady downpour. The rain might keep the girl from coming, or at least she might think she could use it as an excuse. He decided to wait until exactly nine o'clock and if she had not shown up by then to be off. He would not go to Quincy but would go home. It would be better to see Singleton at a later date when he would perhaps have responded to treatment. He got up and wrote the girl a note to be left with his aunts, saying he presumed she had decided, upon consideration, that she was not equal to the experience. It was a very concise note and he ended it, "Cordially yours."

She arrived at five minutes to nine and stood dripping in his aunts' hall, a tubular bundle of baby-blue plastic from which nothing showed but her face. She was holding a damp paper sack and her large mouth was twisted in an uncertain smile. Overnight she had apparently lost some of her self-assurance.

Calhoun was barely able to be polite. His aunts, who thought this was a romantic outing in the rain, kissed him out the door and stood on the porch idiotically waving their handkerchiefs until he and Mary Elizabeth were in the car and gone.

The girl was much too big for the small car. She kept shifting about and twisting inside her raincoat. "The rain has beat the azaleas down," she observed in a neutral tone.

Calhoun rudely kept silent. He was trying to obliterate her from his consciousness so that he could re-establish Singleton there. He had lost Singleton completely. The rain was coming down in grey swaths. When they reached the highway, they could barely see across the fields to a faint line of woods. The girl kept leaning forward, squinting into the opaque windshield. "If a truck were to come out of that," she said with a gawkish laugh, "that would be the end of us."

Calhoun stopped the car. "I'll be glad to take you back and go on by myself," he said.

"I have to go," she said hoarsely, staring at him. "I have to see him." Behind her spectacles, her eyes appeared larger than they should have been and suspiciously liquid. "I have to face this," she said.

Roughly, he started the car again.

"You have to prove to yourself that you can stand there and watch a man be crucified," she said. "You have to go through it with him. I thought about it all night."

"It may give you," Calhoun muttered, "a more balanced view of life."

"This is personal," she said. "You wouldn't understand," and she turned her head to the window.

Calhoun tried to concentrate on Singleton. Feature by feature, he brought the face together in his mind and each time he had it almost constructed, it fell apart and he was left with nothing. He drove in silence, at a reckless speed as if he would like to hit a hole in the road and see the girl go through the windshield. Every now and then she blew her nose weakly. After fifteen miles or so the rain slackened and stopped. The treeline on either side of them became black and clear and the fields intensely green. They would have an unmistakable view of the hospital grounds as soon as these should come in sight.

"Christ only had to take it three hours," the girl said all at once in a high voice, "but he'll be in this place the rest of his life!"

Calhoun cut his eyes toward her. There was a fresh wet line down the side of her face. He turned his eyes away, awed and furious. "If you can't stand this," he said, "I can still take you home and come back by myself."

"You wouldn't come back by yourself," she said, "and we're almost there." She blew her nose. "I want him to know that somebody takes his side. I want to say that to him no matter what it does to me."

Through his rage, the terrible thought occurred to the boy that he would have to *say* something to Singleton. What could he say to him in the presence of this woman? She had shattered the communion between them. "We've come to listen I hope you understand," he burst out. "I haven't driven all this way to hear you startle Singleton with your wisdom. I've come to listen to *him*."

"We should have brought a tape recorder!" she cried, "then we'd have what he says all our lives!"

"You don't have elementary understanding," Calhoun said, "if you think you approach a man like this with a tape recorder."

"Stop!" she shrieked, leaning toward the windshield, "that's it!"

Calhoun slammed on his brakes and looked forward wildly.

A cluster of low buildings, hardly noticeable, rose like a rich growth of warts on the hill to their right.

The boy sat helpless while the car, as if of its own volition, turned and headed toward the entrance. The letters QUINCY STATE HOSPITAL were cut in a concrete arch which it rolled effortlessly through.

"Abandon hope all ye who enter here," the girl murmured.

They had to stop within a hundred yards of the gate while a fat white-capped nurse led a line of patients, straggling like elderly schoolchildren, across the road in front of them. A snaggle-toothed woman in a candy-striped dress and black wool hat shook her fist at them and a baldheaded man waved energetically. A few threw malevolent looks as the line shuffled off across the green to another building.

After a moment the car rolled forward again. "Park in front of that center building," Mary Elizabeth directed.

"They won't let us see him," he mumbled.

"Not if you have anything to do with it," she said. "Park and let me out. I'll handle this." Her cheek had dried and her voice was businesslike. He parked and she got out. He watched her disappear into the building, thinking with grim satisfaction that she would soon turn into a full-grown ogre—false intellect, false emotions, maximum efficiency, all operating to produce the dominant hair-splitting Ph.D. Another line of patients passed in the road and several of them pointed at the small car. Calhoun did not look but he sensed he was being watched. "Hup up there," he heard the nurse say.

He looked again and gave a little cry. A gentle face, wrapped around with a green hand towel, was in his window, smiling toothlessly but with an agonizing tenderness.

"Get a move on, sweetie," the nurse said and the face retreated.

The boy rolled his window up rapidly but his heart was wrenched. He saw again the agonized face in the stocks—the slightly mismatched eyes, the wide mouth parted in a stifled useless cry. The vision lasted only a moment but when it passed, he was certain that the sight of Singleton was going to effect a change in him, that after this visit, some strange tranquility he had not before conceived of would be his. He sat for ten minutes with his eyes closed, knowing that a revelation was near and trying to prepare himself for it.

All at once the car door opened and the girl folded herself, panting, in beside him. Her face was pale. She held up two green permission slips and pointed to the names written on them: Calhoun Singleton on one, Mary Elizabeth Singleton on the other. For a moment they stared at the slips, then at each other. Both appeared to recognize that in their common kinship with him, a kinship with each other was unavoidable. Generously, Calhoun held out his hand. She shook it. "He's in the fifth building to the left," she said.

They drove to the fifth building and parked. It was a low red brick structure with barred windows, like all the others except that the outside of it was streaked with black stains. In one window two hands hung out, palms downward. Mary Elizabeth opened the paper sack she had brought and began to take out presents for Singleton. She had brought a box of candy, a carton of cigarets, and three books—a Modern Library *Thus Spake Zarathustra,* a paperback *Revolt of the Masses,* and a thin decorated volume of Housman. She handed the cigarets and the candy to Calhoun and got out of the car with the books herself. She started forward, but halfway to the door she stopped and put her hand to her mouth. "I can't take it," she murmured.

"Now now," Calhoun said kindly. He put his hand on her back and gave her a slight push and she began to move forward again.

They entered a stained linoleum-covered hall where a peculiar odor met them at once like an invisible official. There was a desk facing the door, behind which sat a frail harrassed-looking nurse whose eyes darted to right and left as if she expected ultimately to be hit from behind. Mary Elizabeth handed her the two green permits. The woman looked at them and groaned. "Go in yonder and wait," she said in a weary insult-bearing voice. "He'll have to be got ready. They shouldn't have give you these slips over there. What do they know about what goes on over here over there and what do them doctors care anyhow? If it was up to me the ones that don't cooperate wouldn't see nobody."

"We're his kin," Calhoun said. "We have every right to see him."

The nurse threw her head back in a soundless laugh and went off muttering.

Calhoun put his hand on the girl's back again and guided her into the waiting room where they sat down close together on a mammoth black leather sofa which faced an identical piece of furniture five feet away. There was nothing else in the room but a rickety table in one corner with an empty white vase on it. A barred window cast squares of damp light on the floor at their feet. There seemed an intense stillness about them although the place was anything but quiet. From one end of the building came a continuous mourning sound as delicate as the fluttering wail of owls; at the other end they heard rocketing peals of laughter. Closer at hand, a steady monotonous cursing broke the silence around it with a machine-like regularity. Each noise seemed to exist isolated from every other.

The two sat together as if they were waiting for some momentous event in their lives—a marriage or instantaneous deaths. They seemed already joined in a predestined convergence. At the same instant each made an involuntary motion as if to run but it was too late. Heavy footsteps were almost at the door and the machine-like curses were bearing down.

Two burly attendants entered with Singleton spider-like between them. He was holding his feet high up off the floor so that the attendants had to carry him. It was from him the curses were coming. He had on a hospital gown of the type that opens and ties up the back and his feet were stuck in black shoes from which the laces had been removed. On his head was a black hat, not the kind countrymen wear, but a black derby hat such as might be worn by a gunman in the movies. The two attendants came up to the empty sofa from behind and swung him over the back of it, then still holding him, each passed around the sofa arms and sat down beside him, grinning. They might have been twins for though one was blond and the other bald, they had identical looks of good-natured stupidity.

As for Singleton, he fixed Calhoun with his green slightly mismatched eyes. "Whadaya want with me?" he shrilled. "Speak up! My time is valuable." They were almost exactly the eyes that Calhoun had seen in the paper, except that the penetrating gleam in them had a slight reptilian quality.

The boy sat mesmerized.

After a moment, Mary Elizabeth said in a slow, hoarse, barely audible voice, "We came to say we understand."

The old man's glare shifted to her and for one instant his eyes remained absolutely still like the eyes of a treetoad that has sighted its prey. His throat appeared to swell. "Ahhh," he said as if he had just swallowed something pleasant, "eeeee."

"Mind out now, dad," one of the attendants said.

"Lemme sit with her," Singleton said and jerked his arm away from the attendant, who caught it again at once. "She knows what she wants."

"Let him sit with her," the blond attendant said, "she's his niece."

"No," the bald one said, "keep aholt to him. He's liable to pull off his frock. You know *him*."

But the other one had already let one of his wrists loose and Singleton was leaning outward toward Mary Elizabeth, straining away from the attendant who held him. The girl's eyes were glazed. The old man began to make suggestive noises through his teeth.

"Now now, dad," the idle attendant said.

"It's not every girl gets a chance at me," Singleton said. "Listen here, sister, I'm well-fixed. There's nobody in Partridge I can't skin. I own the place—as well as this hotel." His hand grasped toward her knee.

The girl gave a small stifled cry.

"And I got others elsewhere," he panted. "You and me are two of a kind. We ain't in their class. You're a queen. I'll put you on a float!" and at that moment he got his wrist free and lunged toward her but both attendants sprang after him instantly. As Mary Elizabeth crouched against Calhoun, the old man jumped nimbly over the sofa and began to speed around the room. The attendants, their arms and legs held wide apart to catch him, tried to close in on him from either side. They almost had him when he kicked off his shoes and leaped between them onto the table, sending the empty vase shattering to the floor. "Look girl!" he shrilled and began to pull the hospital gown over his head.

Mary Elizabeth was already dashing out the room and Calhoun ran behind her and thrust open the door just in time to prevent her crashing into it. They scrambled into the car and the boy drove it away as if his heart were the motor and would never go fast enough. The sky was bone-white and the slick highway stretched before them like a piece of the earth's exposed nerve. After five miles Calhoun pulled the car to the side of the road and stopped from exhaustion. They sat silently, looking at nothing until finally they turned and looked at each other. There each saw at once the likeness of their kinsman and flinched. They looked away and then back, as if with concentration they might find a more tolerable image. To Calhoun, the girl's face seemed to mirror the nakedness of the sky. In despair he leaned closer until he was stopped by a miniature visage which rose incorrigibly in her spectacles and fixed him where he was. Round, innocent, undistinguished as an iron link, it was the face whose gift of life had pushed straight forward to the future to raise festival after festival. Like a master salesman, it seemed to have been waiting there from all time to claim him.

JAMES JOYCE

(1882–1941)

Counterparts

The bell rang furiously and, when Miss Parker went to the tube, a furious voice called out in a piercing North of Ireland accent:

"Send Farrington here!"

Miss Parker returned to her machine, saying to a man who was writing at a desk:

"Mr. Alleyne wants you upstairs."

The man muttered *"Blast* him!" under his breath and pushed back his chair to stand up. When he stood up he was tall and of great bulk. He had a hanging face, dark wine-coloured, with fair eyebrows and moustache: his eyes bulged forward slightly and the whites of them were dirty. He lifted up the counter and, passing by the clients, went out of the office with a heavy step.

He went heavily upstairs until he came to the second landing, where a door bore a brass plate with the inscription *Mr. Alleyne.* Here he halted, puffing with labour and vexation, and knocked. The shrill voice cried:

"Come in!"

The man entered Mr. Alleyne's room. Simultaneously Mr. Alleyne, a little man wearing gold-rimmed glasses on a clean-shaven face, shot his head up over a pile of documents. The head itself was so pink and hairless it seemed like a large egg reposing on the papers. Mr. Alleyne did not lose a moment:

"Farrington? What is the meaning of this? Why have I always to complain of you? May I ask you why you haven't made a copy of that contract between Bodley and Kirwan? I told you it must be ready by four o'clock."

"But Mr. Shelley said, sir——"

"*Mr. Shelley said, sir.* . . . Kindly attend to what I say and not to what *Mr. Shelley says, sir.* You have always some excuse or another for shirking work. Let me tell you that if the contract is not copied before this evening I'll lay the matter before Mr. Crosbie. . . . Do you hear me now?"

"Yes, sir."

"Do you hear me now? . . . Ay and another little matter! I might as well be talking to the wall as talking to you. Understand once for all that you get a half an hour for your lunch and not an hour and a half. How many courses do you want, I'd like to know. . . . Do you mind me now?"

"Yes, sir."

Mr. Alleyne bent his head again upon his pile of papers. The man stared fixedly at the polished skull which directed the affairs of Crosbie & Alleyne, gauging its fragility. A spasm of rage gripped his throat for a few moments and then passed, leaving after it a sharp sensation of thirst. The man recognised the sensation and felt that he must have a good night's drinking. The middle of the month was passed and, if he could get the copy done in time, Mr. Alleyne might give him an order on the cashier. He stood still, gazing fixedly at the head upon the pile of papers. Suddenly Mr. Alleyne began to upset all the papers, searching for something. Then, as if he had been unaware of the man's presence till that moment, he shot up his head again, saying:

"Eh? Are you going to stand there all day? Upon my word, Farrington, you take things easy!"

"I was waiting to see . . ."

"Very good, you needn't wait to see. Go downstairs and do your work."

The man walked heavily towards the door and, as he went out of the room, he heard Mr. Alleyne cry after him that if the contract was not copied by evening Mr. Crosbie would hear of the matter.

He returned to his desk in the lower office and counted the sheets which remained to be copied. He took up his pen and dipped it in the ink but he continued to stare stupidly at the last words he had written: *In no case shall the said Bernard Bodley be* . . . The evening was falling and in a few minutes they would be lighting the gas: then he could write. He felt that he must slake the thirst in his throat. He stood up from his desk and, lifting the counter as before, passed out of the office. As he was passing out the chief clerk looked at him inquiringly.

"It's all right, Mr. Shelley," said the man, pointing with his finger to indicate the objective of his journey.

The chief clerk glanced at the hat-rack, but, seeing the row complete, offered no remark. As soon as he was on the landing the man pulled a shepherd's plaid cap out of his pocket, put it on his head and ran quickly down the rickety stairs. From the street door he walked on furtively on the inner side of the path towards the corner and all at once dived into a doorway. He was now safe in the dark snug of O'Neill's shop, and, filling up the little window that looked into the bar with his inflamed face, the colour of dark wine or dark meat, he called out:

"Here, Pat, give us a g.p., like a good fellow."

The curate brought him a glass of plain porter. The man drank it at a gulp and asked for a caraway seed. He put his penny on the counter and, leaving the curate to grope for it in the gloom, retreated out of the snug as furtively as he had entered it.

Darkness, accompanied by a thick fog, was gaining upon the dusk of February and the lamps in Eustace Street had been lit. The man went up by the houses until he reached the door of the office, wondering whether he could finish his copy in time. On the stairs a moist pungent odour of perfumes saluted his nose: evidently Miss Delacour had come while he was out in O'Neill's. He crammed his cap back again into his pocket and re-entered the office, assuming an air of absent-mindedness.

"Mr. Alleyne has been calling for you," said the chief clerk severely. "Where were you?"

The man glanced at the two clients who were standing at the counter as if to intimate that their presence prevented him from answering. As the clients were both male the chief clerk allowed himself a laugh.

"I know that game," he said. "Five times in one day is a little bit. . . . Well, you better look sharp and get a copy of our correspondence in the Delacour case for Mr. Alleyne."

This address in the presence of the public, his run upstairs and the porter he had gulped down so hastily confused the man and, as he sat down at his desk to get what was required, he realised how hopeless was the task of finishing his copy of the contract before half past five. The dark damp night was coming and he longed to spend it in the bars, drinking with his friends amid the glare of gas and the clatter of glasses. He got out the Delacour correspondence and passed out of the office. He hoped Mr. Alleyne would not discover that the last two letters were missing.

The moist pungent perfume lay all the way up to Mr. Alleyne's room. Miss Delacour was a middle-aged woman of Jewish appearance. Mr. Alleyne was said to be sweet on her or on her money. She came to the office often and stayed a long time when she came. She was sitting beside his desk now in an aroma of perfumes, smoothing the handle of her umbrella and nodding the great black feather in her hat. Mr. Alleyne had swivelled his chair round to face her and thrown his right foot jauntily upon his left knee. The man put the correspondence on the desk and bowed respectfully but neither Mr. Alleyne nor Miss Delacour took any notice of his bow. Mr. Alleyne tapped a finger on the correspondence and then flicked it towards him as if to say: "*That's all right: you can go.*"

The man returned to the lower office and sat down again at his desk. He started intently at the incomplete phrase: *In no case shall the said Bernard Bodley be . . .* and thought how strange it was that the last three words began with the same letter. The chief clerk began to hurry Miss Parker, saying she would never have the letters typed in time for post. The man listened to the clicking of the machine for a few minutes and then set to work to finish his copy. But his head was not clear and his mind wandered away to the glare and rattle of the public-house. It was a night for hot punches. He struggled on with his copy, but when the clock struck five he had still fourteen pages to write. Blast it! He couldn't finish it in time. He longed to execrate aloud, to bring his fist down on something violently. He was so enraged that he wrote *Bernard Bernard* instead of *Bernard Bodley* and had to begin again on a clean sheet.

He felt strong enough to clear out the whole office single-handed. His body ached to do something, to rush out and revel in violence. All the indignities of his life enraged him. . . . Could he ask the cashier privately for an advance? No, the cashier was no good, no damn good: he wouldn't give an advance. . . . He knew where he would meet the boys: Leonard and O'Halloran and Nosey Flynn. The barometer of his emotional nature was set for a spell of riot.

His imagination had so abstracted him that his name was called twice before he answered. Mr. Alleyne and Miss Delacour were standing outside the counter and all the clerks had turned round in anticipation of something. The man got up from his desk. Mr. Alleyne began a tirade of abuse, saying that two letters were missing. The man answered that he knew nothing about them, that he had made a faithful copy. The tirade continued: it was so bitter and violent that the man could hardly restrain his fist from descending upon the head of the manikin before him:

"I know nothing about any other two letters," he said stupidly.

"*You—know—nothing*. Of course you know nothing," said Mr. Alleyne. "Tell me," he added, glancing first for approval to the lady beside him, "do you take me for a fool? Do you think me an utter fool?"

The man glanced from the lady's face to the little egg-shaped head and back again; and, almost before he was aware of it, his tongue had found a felicitous moment:

"I don't think, sir," he said, "that that's a fair question to put to me."

There was a pause in the very breathing of the clerks. Everyone was astounded (the author of the witticism no less than his neighbours) and Miss Delacour, who was a stout amiable person, began to smile broadly. Mr. Alleyne flushed to the hue of a wild rose and his mouth twitched with a dwarf's passion. He shook his fist in the man's face till it seemed to vibrate like the knob of some electric machine:

"You impertinent ruffian! You impertinent ruffian! I'll make short work of you! Wait till you see! You'll apologise to me for your impertinence or you'll quit the office instanter! You'll quit this, I'm telling you, or you'll apologise to me!"

He stood in a doorway opposite the office watching to see if the cashier would come out alone. All the clerks passed out and finally the cashier came out with the chief clerk. It was no use trying to say a word to him when he was with the chief clerk. The man felt that his position was bad enough. He had been obliged to offer an abject apology to Mr. Alleyne for his impertinence but he knew what a hornet's nest the office would be for him. He could remember the way in which Mr. Alleyne had hounded little Peake out of the office in order to make room for his own nephew. He felt savage and thirsty and revengeful, annoyed with himself and with everyone else. Mr. Alleyne would never give him an hour's rest; his life would be a hell to him. He had made a proper fool of himself this time. Could he not keep his tongue in his cheek? But they had never pulled together from the first, he and Mr. Alleyne, ever since the day Mr. Alleyne had overheard him mimicking his North of Ireland accent to amuse Higgins and Miss Parker: that had been the beginning of it. He might have tried Higgins for the money, but sure Higgins never had anything for himself. A man with two establishments to keep up, of course he couldn't. . . .

He felt his great body again aching for the comfort of the public-house. The fog had begun to chill him and he wondered could he touch Pat in O'Neill's. He could not touch him for more than a bob—and a bob was no use. Yet he must get money somewhere or other: he had spent his last penny for the g.p. and soon it would be too late for getting money anywhere. Suddenly, as he was fingering his watch-chain, he thought of Terry Kelly's pawn-office in Fleet Street. That was the dart! Why didn't he think of it sooner?

He went through the narrow alley of Temple Bar quickly, muttering to himself that they could all go to hell because he was going to have a good night of it. The clerk in Terry Kelly's said *A crown!* but the consignor held out for six shillings; and in the end the six shillings was allowed him literally. He came out of the pawn-office joyfully, making a little cylinder of the coins between his thumb and fingers. In Westmoreland Street the footpaths were crowded with young men and women returning from business and ragged urchins ran here and there yelling out the names of the evening editions. The man passed through the crowd, looking on the spectacle generally with proud satisfaction and staring masterfully at the office-girls. His head was full of the noises of tram-gongs and swishing trolleys and his nose already sniffed the curling fumes of punch. As he walked on he preconsidered the terms in which he would narrate the incident to the boys:

"So, I just looked at him—coolly, you know, and looked at her. Then I looked back at him again—taking my time, you know. 'I don't think that that's a fair question to put to me,' says I."

Nosey Flynn was sitting up in his usual corner of Davy Byrne's and, when he heard the story, he stood Farrington a half-one, saying it was as smart a thing as ever he heard. Farrington stood a drink in his turn. After a while O'Halloran and Paddy Leonard came in and the story was repeated to them. O'Halloran stood tailors of malt, hot, all round and told the story of the retort he had made to the chief clerk when he was in Callan's of Fownes's Street; but, as the retort was after the manner of the liberal shepherds in the eclogues, he had to admit that it was not as clever as Farrington's retort. At this Farrington told the boys to polish off that and have another.

Just as they were naming their poisons who should come in but Higgins! Of course he had to join in with the others. The men asked him to give his version of it, and he did so with great vivacity for the sight of five small hot whiskies was very exhilarating. Everyone roared laughing when he showed the way in which Mr. Alleyne shook his fist in Farrington's face. Then he imitated Farrington, saying, *"And here was my nabs, as cool as you please,"* while Farrington looked at the company out of his heavy dirty eyes, smiling and at times drawing forth stray drops of liquor from his moustache with the aid of his lower lip.

When that round was over there was a pause. O'Halloran had money but neither of the other two seemed to have any; so the whole party left the shop somewhat regretfully. At the corner of Duke Street Higgins and Nosey Flynn bevelled off to the left while the other three turned back towards the city. Rain was drizzling down on the cold streets and, when they reached the Ballast Office, Farrington suggested the Scotch House. The bar was full of men and loud with the noise of tongues and glasses. The three men pushed past the whining match-sellers at the door and formed a little party at the corner of the counter. They began to exchange stories. Leonard introduced them to a young fellow named Weathers who was performing at the Tivoli as an acrobat and knockabout *artiste*. Farrington stood a drink all round. Weathers said he would take a small Irish and Apollinaris. Farrington, who had definite notions of what was what, asked the boys would they have an Apollinaris too; but the boys told Tim to make theirs hot. The talk became theatrical. O'Halloran stood a round and then Farrington stood another round, Weathers protesting that the hospitality was too Irish. He promised to get them in behind the scenes and introduce them to some nice girls. O'Halloran said that he and Leonard would go, but that Farrington wouldn't go because he was a married man; and Farrington's heavy dirty eyes leered at the company in token that he understood he was being chaffed. Weathers made them all have just one little tincture at his expense and promised to meet them later on at Mulligan's in Poolbeg Street.

When the Scotch House closed they went round to Mulligan's. They went into the parlour at the back and O'Halloran ordered small hot specials all round. They were all beginning to feel mellow. Farrington was just standing another round when Weathers came back. Much to Farrington's relief he drank a glass of bitter this time. Funds were getting low but they had enough to keep them going. Presently two young women with big hats and a young man in a check suit came in and sat at a table close by. Weathers saluted them and told the company that they were out of the Tivoli. Farrington's eyes wandered at every moment in the direction of one of the young women. There was something striking in her appearance. An immense scarf of peacock-blue muslin was wound round her hat and knotted in a great bow under her chin; and she wore bright yellow gloves, reaching to the elbow. Farrington gazed admiringly at the plump arm which she moved very often and with much grace; and when, after a little time, she answered his gaze he admired still more her large dark brown eyes. The oblique staring expression in them fascinated him. She glanced at him once or twice and, when the party was leaving the room, she brushed against his chair and said *"O, pardon!"* in a London accent. He watched her leave the room in the hope that she would look back to him, but he was disappointed. He cursed his want of money and cursed all the rounds he had stood, particularly all the whiskies and Apollinaris which he had stood to Weathers. If there was one thing that he hated it was a sponge. He was so angry that he lost count of the conversation of his friends.

When Paddy Leonard called him he found that they were talking about feats of strength. Weathers was showing his biceps muscle to the company and boasting so much that the other two had called on Farrington to uphold the national honour. Farrington pulled up his sleeve accordingly and showed his biceps muscle to the company. The two arms were examined and compared and finally it was agreed to have a trial of strength. The table was cleared and the two men rested their elbows on it, clasping hands. When Paddy Leonard said *"Go!"* each was to try to bring down the other's hand on to the table. Farrington looked very serious and determined.

The trial began. After about thirty seconds Weathers brought his opponent's hand slowly down on to the table. Farrington's dark wine-coloured face flushed darker still with anger and humiliation at having been defeated by such a stripling.

"You're not to put the weight of your body behind it. Play fair," he said.

"Who's not playing fair?" said the other.

"Come on again. The two best out of three."

The trial began again. The veins stood out on Farrington's forehead, and the pallor of Weathers' complexion changed to peony. Their hands and arms trembled under the stress. After a long struggle Weathers again brought his opponent's hand slowly on to the table. There was a murmur of applause from the spectators. The curate, who was standing beside the table, nodded his red head towards the victor and said with stupid familiarity:

"Ah! that's the knack!"

"What the hell do you know about it?" said Farrington fiercely, turning on the man. "What do you put in your gab for?"

"Sh, sh!" said O'Halloran, observing the violent expression of Farrington's face. "Pony up, boys. We'll have just one little smahan more and then we'll be off."

A very sullen-faced man stood at the corner of O'Connell Bridge waiting for the little Sandymount tram to take him home. He was full of smouldering anger and revengefulness. He felt humiliated and discontented; he did not even feel drunk; and he had only twopence in his pocket. He cursed everything. He had done for himself in the office, pawned his watch, spent all his money; and he had not even got drunk. He began to feel thirsty again and he longed to be back again in the hot reeking public-house. He had lost his reputation as a strong man, having been defeated twice by a mere boy. His heart swelled with fury and, when he thought of the woman in the big hat who had brushed against him and said *Pardon!* his fury nearly choked him.

His tram let him down at Shelbourne Road and he steered his great body along in the shadow of the wall of the barracks. He loathed returning to his home. When he went in by the side-door he found the kitchen empty and the kitchen fire nearly out. He bawled upstairs:

"Ada! Ada!"

His wife was a little sharp-faced woman who bullied her husband when he was sober and was bullied by him when he was drunk. They had five children. A little boy came running down the stairs.

"Who is that?" said the man, peering through the darkness.

"Me, pa."

"Who are you? Charlie?"

"No, pa. Tom."

"Where's your mother?"

"She's out at the chapel."

"That's right. . . . Did she think of leaving any dinner for me?"

"Yes, pa. I——"

"Light the lamp. What do you mean by having the place in darkness? Are the other children in bed?"

The man sat down heavily on one of the chairs while the little boy lit the lamp. He began to mimic his son's flat accent, saying half to himself: *"At the chapel. At the chapel, if you please!"* When the lamp was lit he banged his fist on the table and shouted:

"What's for my dinner?"

"I'm going . . . to cook it, pa," said the little boy.

The man jumped up furiously and pointed to the fire.

"On that fire! You let the fire out! By God, I'll teach you to do that again!"

He took a step to the door and seized the walking-stick which was standing behind it.

"I'll teach you to let the fire out!" he said, rolling up his sleeve in order to give his arm free play.

The little boy cried *"O, pa!"* and ran whimpering round the table, but the man followed him and caught him by the coat. The little boy looked about him wildly but, seeing no way of escape, fell upon his knees.

"Now, you'll let the fire out the next time!" said the man, striking at him vigorously with the stick. "Take that, you little whelp!"

The boy uttered a squeal of pain as the stick cut his thigh. He clasped his hands together in the air and his voice shook with fright.

"O, pa!" he cried. "Don't beat me, pa! And I'll . . . I'll say a *Hail Mary* for you. . . . I'll say a *Hail Mary* for you, pa, if you don't beat me. . . . I'll say a *Hail Mary*. . . ."

LORD DUNSANY

(1878–1957)

Mrs. Mulger

Her mother had been a lodging-house keeper before her. And now, in the same northern town, she too let lodgings, she too a widow now as her mother had been, and time still flying. Not that she thought of time as still flying; rather it seemed to have flown while she was not watching. For she was far on in the forties now, so it must have flown, looking at it that way. And yet with spring coming on, and two young men from the university, her lodgers, sitting at that table of theirs talking poetry, time mightn't have moved at all.

She had come into the sitting-room to see after her goldfish, and there they were talking away. And it might have been thirty years ago, which only seemed like yesterday, when her mother's young lodger had talked the very same stuff to her.

She couldn't help stopping a while to listen to them after she had fed her goldfish: it brought the years back so. No sense in it, any more than there had been in the talk of that other young man so long ago, but the same fervour, the same overwhelming certainty about something, whatever it was, as there is in the blackbird's voice in early April, when he seems so certain of spring.

So she stood still, smiling slightly, and listened as they talked to each other. Poetry as usual. And the curious thing about it was that though she could not understand a word of what they were saying, yet not a phrase was new to her. Sometimes she almost thought she could have completed their sentences for them. And then from the curious phrases one of them began to quote lines from an old poem. They were praising it with their queer words, lavishing praises upon it.

"I am afraid we are talking poetry, Mrs. Mulger," said one of them.

"Never mind, sir," she answered. "It doesn't do any harm."

Nor did it, if one kept away from it. Curiously enough, she might once have married a young man that wrote poetry, wrote it himself, that lodger of her mother's, a university student and all; but she knew what poetry led to. When she did marry she married the secretary of a branch of a trade union, a plumber in a good way of business; everybody wanted a plumber; and when he died he left her very well off. The other young man died long ago. The two men flashed through her thoughts all in a moment, like ghosts going home at cock-crow.

More talk and more lines quoted, and gradually the lines began to arrange themselves into a pattern that grew clear to the widow; not the meaning, whatever that might be, but the sound of them, and certain sounds and sights of springs that were gone, which seemed somehow to hang and glitter along the lines. It seemed funny to her what things would call up memories; you couldn't tell what would do it.

"The incomparable majesty of the Ode to a Rose," one of the young men was saying, and Mrs. Mulger was still standing there smiling slightly, and he turned to her rather sharply.

"But I am afraid," he said to her, "that the poem we are discussing is scarcely of interest to you, Mrs. Mulger."

For a moment her thoughts turned away from him down the years and came back again.

"You know," she said, "my name's Rose."

"A most perfect non-sequitur," said one to the other.

And when she had insisted on having it explained what that meant, and having got at the meaning, she said: "Not so much of a non-what-you-call-it as all that."

And there she stopped, thinking all of a sudden of a gun she had once heard fired in a wood, when she had gone five miles from the town to see the spring, and all the birds were singing; but at the sound of the gun their singing had ceased at once. She wouldn't stop their merry talk, she thought, as what she had been about to say would have stopped it. Never mind whether there was any sense in it or not; let them talk, and let the birds sing. So she ended up with: "It's a nice poem, I'm sure."

But that ode had been written to her.

WILLIAM COBB

(1937–)

The Stone Soldier

I

It was nine-thirty in the morning when he stepped off the train, and the first thing he did was to pull the wrinkled, big, red bandana out of his hip pocket and slowly wipe his face. He grunted under the heat and stood looking around—at the deserted platform with only one old Negro standing in the two-foot strip of shade next to the yellow wall, under the sign that said, in peeling whitish letters, HAMMOND; at the dusty street that ran away from the station, toward the east and toward the new sun; at the small frame buildings lining the street and the few brick ones; and halfway up the street, at the sign that said MADISON HOTEL, and under that, *Dining Room,* in smaller letters. He grunted again and looked at the Negro.

"Mornin, Uncle," he said. His white suit was stained under his armpits and wrinkled up the back; it was tight across his bulging belly, and the pants hugged his legs and made his thighs look like fat sausages under his belly. There was an early-morning stubble on his fleshy jowls, and he exuded an odor that was part sweat, part cheap bourbon, and part that universal smell of the fat person emerging from close quarters. His hat was pushed back to reveal a matted, yellow widow's peak over his squinting eyes as he looked at the small straw suitcase beside him, and then at the Negro, who hadn't answered him.

"I said mornin, Uncle," he said.

"I said mornin," the Negro answered. His face was in shadow, and the fat man couldn't tell by his tone of voice if he were trying to be smart with him. He paused a moment, looking around.

"The Lord doth send heat and make white and nigger alike sweat under it, don't he?" the fat man said. "Lord if he don't."

"Yes sir," the Negro said.

"But Goddam if a man got to stay out in it, has he? I'll just be gettin on up to the Madison Hotel for a bath and a shave, and then I'll be tendin to my business and be gettin on my way. But Lord if it ain't hot as the fires of almighty hell." The Negro said nothing, and the fat man widened his eyes and peered into the shadows at his face. The fat man's eyes bulged in their sockets; they looked as though they were loose inside his head. They kept moving back and forth, just slightly, a slight wiggle as if they might have been too well greased and he couldn't quite control them; it made him tilt his face slightly to the side and peer like an old woman trying to thread a needle. He stood there looking at the Negro for a minute, and he couldn't say anything. Because the Negro's lower lip was stretched, it hung down over his chin, glistening wetly, startlingly red against the dull, brown skin like the meat of a dog, torn open by buzzards, looks red against the bloated brown belly. The Negro moved his head, and the lip flapped, and his eyes bored into the fat man's with an incomprehensible message. The fat man felt the heat of the sun against the side of his sweating neck.

"It's open for business," the Negro said.

"What?"

"Madison Hotel," he said, and the lip flapped.

"My name is Lyman Sparks," the fat man said. He pulled out the bandana and swiped it around his neck; he reached into the folds of fat over his belly, into a pocket of his vest, and pulled out a small card and handed it to the Negro. The Negro didn't look at it; he just held it in his hand, at his side. "I do quite a bit of business with colored folks," the man said. "Not that that's what I'm here for, but you just well kill two birds with one stone, I always say." He looked slyly at the Negro, and a grin revealed blackened, twisted teeth. "And that's what the boss says too. Got to please the boss, ain't that right?"

The Negro moved out of the shadow. He was much taller than Sparks, with a high, slanting forehead and tight black hair sticking closely to his head; his arms hung loosely at his sides, and his legs were thin under the coarse cloth of his breeches. Sparks found himself looking at the soft, moist underlip, which was even more red when the sun hit it.

"Now," Sparks said, "what is your name?"

"Lip," the Negro said. His eyes bored into Sparks.

"Well now," Sparks said. "Well now. I reckon you're a freed man?"

"That's right," Lip said.

"Well then, I reckon I can talk to you man to man, or salesman, with somethin you need and want, to buyer who'd gointa be eternally grateful that I happened along. Ain't that right? Like, now that you your own boss, ain't no reason why you can't decide what you want to buy and what you don't, now is it?"

"It ain't much I want to buy," Lip said. Sparks grinned slyly at him again.

"Well now, suppose I was to take you in with me on the selling side? Suppose I didn't want you to buy anything. Suppose I wanted you to sell with me?"

Lip didn't answer him. He just stood there, his dark eyes level on Sparks.

"Course when I show you what I got, ain't no doubt in my mind that you gointa want one, too. And ain't no reason why I can't just give you one, long as we gone be partners, now is it?" He tilted his head to the side, as though he couldn't quite get Lip into focus. "Well now," he said, and he grunted as he knelt to open up the straw suitcase and began to rummage around among papers and pieces of clothing until he found what he was looking for, a small black book that was unmistakably a Bible.

"Now, I know you go to church, am I right? Sho you do, I know that by just lookin at you. And I can see you know what this here is I'm holdin in my hand. But reckon you do? Now just reckon you do?" He opened it and shoved it under Lip's nose, and the Negro took it and looked at the picture in front of him.

It was a well-known picture; Lip had seen it in the Episcopal church, made out of glass in a window; he had seen it when he helped Johnny Pope clean up down there. It was the one of Jesus, holding a little sheep in his arms and with other lambs around his feet rubbing up against his legs like cats will do. Only one thing was different. Jesus' face was dark, and his lips were thick, and his hair was darker, only still long and soft looking, and his hands holding the little sheep were dark, too.

Lip stood there looking down at it; he could hear Sparks breathing heavily beside him as he let the pages flip through his fingers, and it opened to the picture of the boy Jesus in the temple, when he was twelve years old. Here, too, he was a young colored boy, with some sand stuck to the paper that reflected the sunlight and made it look like a bright halo over the boy's head. The book seemed light and flimsy in Lip's hand; the pages were not slick like the ones in the Bible he had at home, but rough and coarse, and the printing was, in places, light and faded looking.

"Well?" Sparks said. And when the Negro didn't answer, he said, "Well, what do you think of it?"

"I reckon I already got a Bible," Lip said.

"But not like this one, I bet," Sparks said. He laughed, then. "Go on. Take it. I'm givin it to you, ain't gone charge you a cent for it. I do like that sometimes, good business, I always say. So you can just take it, and it don't obligate you in any way whatsoever. No sir." He looked slyly at Lip again and grinned. "Only thing is, I sho do think you ought to show it around. You know, show it to all your good friends, cause they gone sho want one, too, don't you reckon? After all, they freed men now too; ain't nobody to tell em what they can't have and what they can, and that's just what my company felt like after the war. Figured you colored folks ought to have products of your own, that's all."

"I don't know," Lip said.

"Hell, ahhh, Lip, I ain't askin you to sell for me. Nothing like that. Just let folks know that I got em, and where they can get em. That's all. You gone be doin them a favor."

Lip didn't answer. He just stood there, looking at the fat man with those deep eyes, large and red-rimmed, but steady.

"You understand that that ain't my business. Hell no. That's just a little sideline. A little service, you might say. A public service. I don't charge but a quarter for em, and that's some fine worksmanship goes into that artwork, you can see that. And hell, the quarter don't hardly pay for totin em around. No, I got other business round here, big business—but I figured I just might kill two birds with one stone."

He grinned again and tilted his head.

"Well, you just take that one, anyhow, hear? I want you to have it, free of charge. Let's just say, as a gift from a stranger who ain't never been in Hammond before. Maybe that'll bring me some luck on my other deal, my big deal." He winked at Lip and wiped his neck with the balled-up bandana. "I didn't come here just to sell no Bibles. No sir. But you just keep it, and you know where I'll be. The Madison Hotel. Ask for Mr. Sparks." He closed the straw suitcase and glanced up the sun-bright street to the hotel. A cotton wagon was coming slowly down the street, and the mule's hooves made little clouds of dust rise out of the motionless air. "Good to seen you, Lip. And that's Sparks, Lyman Sparks from Mobile." He pulled at his crotch, set his hat low over his eyes, and headed up the street on his sausage legs.

From where Dale Spivey was sitting, on the porch of the hotel, he could see Sparks leave the platform and start up the street. He had been watching while Sparks and the Negro were talking, his cane-bottom chair leaning back against a post at the edge of the porch. He was holding a pipe on his lap, and his eyes were half closed like the eyes of an old cow standing in the shade. He watched Sparks, lugging the straw suitcase, pass the wagon and tip his hat to the old Negro on the seat, and wipe at his neck with the red bandana.

"Walks straddle-legged like he scared some of that fat on his legs gone rub off his privates," Dale Spivey said.

He was speaking to Mr. Downey, who had been sitting in exactly the same position as Dale Spivey, only with his chair leaning back against the wall of the hotel.

"Who?" Mr. Downey said.

"That drummer."

Mr. Downey let his chair fall with a dull thump, and he leaned forward to look up the street at Sparks. Sparks came on slowly, already out of breath, bent at the waist and craning his short neck toward the two men on the porch. They watched him come up and stand in the street until he got his breath, wiping at his sweating face; then he came up the steps onto the porch.

"Mornin." His breath wheezed out around the word. "Lord if it ain't hot."

"Mornin," the two men said at the same time.

"My name is Sparks, Lyman Sparks," he said. "And I would assume you to be Mr. J. P. Downey, owner and proprietor of the Madison Hotel."

"That's right," Downey said.

"Well, I'm pleased to meet you," Sparks said. Then he looked at Dale, still leaning back in the cane-bottom chair, his eyes half closed and the cold pipe clenched between his teeth.

"That's Dale Spivey," Mr. Downey said.

"I'm happy to make your acquaintance, Mr. Spivey," Sparks said. Dale just nodded, and Mr. Sparks tilted his head to the side, and his eyes shifted; then he looked off up the street and at the building giving away to a few houses as the road ran down a hill. In the distance he could see the river, pale and shimmering under the sun, and the white-limerock ditches at the side of the street reflected the sun back at him. "Lord, it's gointa be another one, ain't it?" he said.

"It's September," Dale said.

"And rightly so. Rightly so," Sparks said. "But it sho nuff makes it uncomfortable for heavy folks." He sat in an empty chair and placed the straw suitcase carefully against the wall. The chair creaked under him as he pulled at and straightened his crotch. "Well now, Mr. Downey, I'll be wantin to put up with you for a while, but it's sho no hurry about it. I trust you do have room for me." Mr. Downey nodded. "I'll be transactin some business from here, but it's a mite early in the day to be talkin business deals, so I'll just set here for awhile with you all if you don't mind."

"Fine," Mr. Downey said.

They sat quietly for a while, and Sparks watched the heat waves rising off the road. An occasional wagon would go by, loaded with cotton, and the driver would raise his hand in greeting, and the men on the porch would do the same. Mr. Downey was a small man, with a thick, rough-looking shirt and a string tie, and a graying moustache; his face was sun-spotted and deeply tanned, and his eyes were small and bright and quick. Dale hardly moved at all; his heavy boots rested on the heels, and his breeches were drawn up his legs for the occasional slight breeze. His chin rested on his chest and his drooping eyes kept closing and opening and he kept taking the pipe from his mouth and putting it back. When he spoke suddenly, Sparks thought that someone else had come onto the porch.

"You had some business with John Thomas?" Dale said, and Sparks' eyes shifted to Dale.

"Who's that?" he said.

"John Thomas, the nigger down there at the station."

"Oh yes. Well, not business, I don't guess you'd say." He paused a minute. "That nigger told me his name was Lip."

"It is," Mr. Downey said. "John Thomas Lip."

"Oh," Sparks said. Then, after a minute, "Wonder what make his lip hang down like that?"

"He come right from Africa like that," Dale said. "One of them tribes in Africa, that he come from. They lips growed like that."

"Well, I declare," Sparks said. "Now don't that beat all? I never seen one of them before. I reckon you learn somethin ever day, don't you?"

"His mammy was like that too," Dale said. "Both of em belonged to Major Hammond. The old woman died before the war." Then his eyes closed.

"Well, I declare," Sparks said. "Beats all, don't it?"

Sparks watched Mr. Downey take a plug of tobacco from his pocket, pick a few pieces of lint off of it, cut a neat plug, and put it into his mouth. He waited until the hotel proprietor had chewed it a while, and he could see that Mr. Downey could talk.

"How is Major Hammond?" he asked, looking at Mr. Downey.

"Not good, I don't think," Mr. Downey said.

"Sick?"

"Well, he don't ever leave the house anymore. Miss Iva, she takes care of him, but he just sets there in the house and rocks."

"Well now, that's a pity," Sparks said. "That's sho bad. Man like that."

"You know the Major?" Dale asked, and his eyes opened a little. His chin came up off his chest a fraction.

"Well, no, not really. But Lord if I don't feel like I do. I heard enough about him." He wiped at his face. "Sho bad. Hear he lost ever thing he had. Sho bad."

Dale laughed. It was a low, muffled rumbling from out of his chest. "He could still write you a check for ten thousand dollars."

"Well now, I could too. I could write you a check for a million dollars, but that don't mean it'd be any good."

Sparks knew right then that he had moved too fast, and his eyes wiggled as he looked at Dale and then at Mr. Downey. They looked straight ahead, and he couldn't read their eyes. "But Lord, what does it matter?" he said. Mr. Downey let his chair fall again with a thump, and he leaned forward and spat a yellow stream over the edge of the porch. "Yes sir, I always say, what does it matter?" Sparks repeated.

But they didn't answer him. Sparks wiped at his face and neck and stood up. "Well, I just might get inta that room and get me a clean shirt on befo dinner, yes sir," he said. He picked up the suitcase and looked at Mr. Downey.

"Just tell the nigger," Mr. Downey said, hooking his thumb over his shoulder at the door. "He'll show you."

"Fine," said Sparks. He moved toward the door. "I hope you gentlemen will take dinner with me," he said. "In any case, I'll be down after a while. And it was certainly nice to've met cha." After he heaved through the door and into the gloom of the hotel, the two men sat without speaking for a while.

Then Dale said, "That son-of-a-bitch has got shifty eyes." And Mr. Downey just nodded and reached for his plug.

II

Sparks could feel the sweat running down the insides of his legs and down his collar as he walked through the town and he took out the fresh bandana, his third for the day, to mop his face. And then, at last, he was standing at the gate, looking up the sandy walk to the house and at the hint of lace curtains at the darkened windows and at the dusty verbena and smilax shading the veranda. The iron plowshare rattled on its chain as he pushed through the gate and puffed up the path to the porch. He knocked and then looked through the colored glass at the side of the door, cocking his head like a man trying to look at another man's woman without his knowing it, but when he saw the Negro woman coming up the hall, he snatched his hat from his head and stood, holding it over his belly, and waited for the door to open.

"Good afternoon," he said before the Negress could speak. "I was wonderin if I might have a audience with the Major. With Major Hammond."

The Negro woman was as big as he was; she stood blocking the door, looking levelly at him. Her broad face was bright yellow, and her skin was as moist and looked as soft as fresh baked bread; it shone dully over her broad nose, and her biceps bulged under the sleeves of a white house dress. She looked him up and down, at his dusty shoes and wrinkled suit, at his sweating face and matted hair.

"What?" she said.

"See him," he said. "See Major Hammond."

"The Major don't see nobody," she said and made a step back as though to close the door in his face.

"Well then," he said, "I'd like to see Miss Iva Ward Hammond, then, if you don't mind."

"Miss Ida restin," she said.

"Well now, this is a matter of great importance, Auntie, and I'd be glad to wait," he said and moved toward the door.

"You wait here," she said and pushed the door gently to. After a minute she reappeared and opened the door widely for him to enter.

"Miss Ida say for you to wait in the parlor," she said; "she be downstairs in a minute." She disappeared into the damp gloom of the hall toward the back of the house. Sparks realized with a sudden sense of pleasure that the house was much larger than it had looked from the outside; he went into the parlor and put his hat carefully on a deep-crimson sofa, slightly worn at the corners, and walked over to the window. He could see all the way down to the river from the window, to where the dusty road wound down to the landing and the big, stone storage barn that the young Negro at the hotel had told him was haunted because the walls ran water. But Dale Spivey had told him that the walls sweated because they had stored salt in it during the war. Then he looked around the room, at the two oil portraits over the mantel, in peeling gilt frames, the man looking stiff and staring, with steel-gray eyes and hair, and the woman looking stiff and rosy-cheeked, with a mountain of black curls piled over her head. He noticed the framed Stars and Bars on one wall, with black-edged holes in it, and brownish stains in one corner, and the bookcase crammed with leather-bound volumes between the windows. He took one of the books out and looked at the flyleaf; it was spotted and brown, and in faded ink was scrawled across the page: "Winslow Hammond, Rose Hill, 1834."

"My brother, Winslow, the oldest," he heard a voice say, and it startled him. He turned to see her standing just inside the parlor. "He was the only one of us that liked books and literature," she said. "Really liked them."

She came into the room and stood across from him, and his eyes flicked over her, from the dark dress, black or navy blue, down to the floor where he could hardly see the tiny shoes beneath, back to where her blouse gathered around her neck with white lace, to the face with the high white forehead that might have been chiseled from the limerock river bluff at the edge of town. Her gray-black hair was pulled back sharply to a knot at the back of her head. Her eyes were wide, but not staring, and were a clear, deep brown, steady on him as she came across the parlor. The thought that he had seen them before flickered into his consciousness and out again as she stopped and looked at him.

"I'm Iva Hammond," she said, and her lips were just a thin line over the strong, jutting chin. "Carla says that you'd like to see me, Mr. ——"

"Sparks, Lyman Sparks," he said. He looked at her eyes again, and there was the same question, the same look. He cleared his throat.

"I was hoping to see the Major, Miss Hammond," he said, "but I think you can help me."

"Won't you sit down, Mr. Sparks?" she said and sat herself on the slightly worn, red sofa. He took the rocker across from her, put his bulging legs out before him, and smiled his twisted smile at her. She looked steadily back at him, and he could read nothing in her face.

"Would you like a cool glass of water, Mr. Sparks?" she said. Before he could answer she called Carla, who came with a tray and a pitcher and two tall glasses and poured him a glass. He tasted it and smacked his lips.

"Ahhhh, that's good," he said. "I don't know when it's been so hot."

"It's the lime," she said.

"I beg your pardon, mam?" he said.

"The lime, in the water. Makes it so good. My father always used to say that that was one of the best advantages of this river bend, the lime water."

"It is good," Sparks said. He tilted the glass and had another swallow, and smiled at her, and said Ahhhh again. They sat quietly, and he could hear a clock ticking somewhere, and he heard Carla moving around in the back of the house.

"Well, Mr. Sparks, what was it you wanted to talk with me about?" she said.

"Well now," he said. He reached into his vest, pulled out a card, and leaning forward with effort, passed it to her. "Miss Iva—" He paused and grinned. "Miss Hammond, is your name Iva or Ida?"

A slight smile flickered at her thin lips, and she said, "It's Iva, Mr. Sparks. Though most of the Negroes call me Miss Ida. They have as long as I can remember."

"Well, Miss Iva," he said, grinning, "as you can see by my card, I represent the Dixie Monument Company, Mobile branch."

"Yes," she said.

"And I'm in this area, what you might call, solicitin for future buildin of monuments and callin on the most prominent citizens in each town to discuss it. Naturally, the first folks I'd call on in Hammond would be the Hammonds theirselves," he said, and he grinned and nodded to her.

"What sort of monuments would these be, sir?" she said.

"Why, Confederate monuments, Miss Iva, of course." Her expression didn't change, and the brown, deep eyes seemed even deeper. "Now we've sold one over at Livingston; it's possible that you've seen that one, and well, most of the towns are gointa be puttin em up sooner or later, and well, Miss Iva, we just feel like we got the best product for the people. Yes mam, ours is guaranteed to be standin long after a hundred years is up."

Miss Iva got up from the sofa and went to the window. His eyes followed her, and then turned inward as if he were examining what he would say next, or making it up, or trying to figure whether he had been too quick as he had been with Spivey and Mr. Downey. Then he fished into his coat and pulled out several pieces of paper, with drawings. They were slightly damp, and he brushed at the lint and bits of tobacco stuck on them, and heaved himself up from the rocker.

"You might like to look these over, Miss Ida. Of course, you'd want to see the real thing. But I can tell you, it's some fine art work goes into these statues, yes mam. And, too, right now we got cannons from about ever major battle in the war. Any one you want, you just name it and we'll supply. And it'll be the real thing, yes mam, the real thing. We don't believe in pushing off cannons made up there in some factory after the war like some of the companies are doin. Why, they's a company in Georgia claimed they had all the cannons from Chancellorsville for sale with their statues, and by God, they wasn't a one of em the real thing." He couldn't tell what she was thinking, or even if she was listening to him.

Then she turned from the window, and the dark eyes bored into him as she came back to the sofa and sat down.

"Mr. Sparks," she said, "I don't think you understand how scarce money is in Hammond right now. I don't think you know about our situation here."

He quickly arranged a sorrowful expression on his face. "Of course I do, Miss Ida. My company does, I mean. Why, we've taken that into consideration. Let me tell you, mam, that we've got a plan, yes mam, a plan for your whole town. Why, you can take up to fifty years to pay for it. We can arrange just about anything you want."

"Why?"

"I beg your pardon, mam?"

"I only asked why, Mr. Sparks," she said.

His eyes seemed to be jumping from one side of her face to the other.

"Never mind," she said. And then, "But why do you come to me?"

He grinned. "Why, well now, Miss Ida, you ought to know that. A man like me wants to do business with the right kind of people. And you know that if you, or the Major, said to the people of this town that they ought to buy one a these statues, which they sho ought, ain't no doubt about that, then they'd buy one. Now that's my business. I know what the people need, but I can't always get it over to em what they need. But the right kind of folks, you ain't got to sell, now ain't that right?"

"Well, I don't think that this is the time."

"Well, now, Miss Ida, you just ought to think about that. Now is the time to," and here he paused, "honor your dead. Our dead. Folks need to be reminded of those young boys that gave they lives for they country. Now, you sho believe that, now don't you?"

She glanced quickly at him, and he could detect that question in her eyes, that question that he'd seen before, and she said, "Mr. Sparks, I don't need to be reminded of the tragedy of the war."

"You don't, Miss Ida, now don't you think I know that? But what about all them folks that're gointa come after you? What about them? What about——"

He stopped, and his eyes were on the door to the parlor, and she knew even before she turned that her brother was standing there, and she knew what he looked like. Sparks' mouth was standing open and his eyes were active, and the beads of sweat were standing out on his face. And she thought about the Bible that Carla had told her about, the one the man had given Lip, and that Lip had brought to the kitchen door when he came to eat and had shown Carla, and that Carla had laughed at with the still strong laugh that echoed all over the house. And she disliked Mr. Sparks even more than she had before, because her brother was in the room now; she turned and looked at him.

He was leaning on the carved walking stick, in the old robe, his bad foot trailing behind him. He was small and frail, and his pale-blue eyes were so light as to look all white, except for the red rims and the tiny red veins. He had a high forehead, but his hair was thin and short and stuck out from his head in a mad tangle; his mouth hung open, and his head nodded forward and jerked. His hands on the cane were thin and wrinkled and the veins stood up on the backs. He hobbled slowly into the room and squinted at Sparks.

"This is my brother, Clayton Hammond, Mr. Sparks," she said. "He's not well," she added.

Sparks went forward toward her brother. "Why Major, I'm indeed happy to make your acquaintance. Why, I've heard so much about you, and well, it's a honor to meet a great officer like you."

The Major stood there like a weak sapling, his head moving slowly back and forth as he looked at Sparks. "What's your business, sir?" he said, and his voice grated like the bottom of a skiff when it's pulled out of the river onto sand.

"Mr. Sparks was just—" and she was going to say leaving.

But Sparks, moving with surprising quickness, was across the room in front of her brother, saying, "Sparks, Lyman Sparks, Major Hammond, and I'm happy to make your acquaintance. Yes, indeed, I really come to Hammond just to see you, and it woulda been a disappointment sho nuff if I hadn't got to talk with you."

The Major looked at him with his pale-blue eyes, and Sparks grinned. The Major's lips were thin and quivering, and sparse, gray whiskers clung to his wrinkled chin.

"Well now," Sparks said, rocking back on his heels to pat his bulging belly with both palms. "Well now, I reckon we can talk business now." And he glanced over at Miss Iva.

"No, I don't think we will, Mr. Sparks," she said.

"But, Miss Ida——"

"I've already told you, Mr. Sparks," she said. "We can't help you. It's not us that you ought to be talking to."

"Well now, Miss Ida," Sparks said, "I reckon the Major just ought to hear what I've got to say."

Miss Iva stood looking at him, one hand on the back of the rocker in front of her, her lips in a straight line and so tightly drawn as to be almost invisible. Sparks turned away from her smoldering eyes to the Major, who stood hunched over his cane.

"State your business, sir," the Major said.

And so Sparks told him about it, his eyes shifting from one to the other while Miss Iva stood watching him, watching him show the drawings to the Major, or rather, holding them in front of his face. He had begun to sweat with the effort and had pulled out a wrinkled, red bandana to pass it over his face from time to time. When he finished the whole spiel, he stood waiting, tilting his head at the Major.

"Chancellorsville," the Major said. "Chancellorsville."

"Yes, those fellers claimed they had the cannons from that battle, and Lord if they wasn't ever one a fake," Sparks chuckled.

Miss Iva crossed the room and stood beside her brother. "Mr. Sparks, I think my brother is tired now, so if you don't mind, I'll take him back."

But the old man stood rooted to the spot, looking at Sparks, and a gleam came into the dull eyes, a glimmer of understanding, and his old lips moved slowly.

"A soldier," he said. "A stone soldier?"

"Why that's right, Major Hammond," Sparks boomed. "That's right. A stone soldier, standin there guardin the town." And his finger pounded the drawings in his other hand. "Never thought of it like that, no sir."

And then the old man was crying, dry rasping sobs coming from deep down inside his body, so that his head shook, and two tiny tears made a path across his leathery cheek. Sparks straightened up, and Miss Iva put her arm across the withered shoulders.

"Why, Miss Ida," Sparks said. "Why, what did I say?"

"It was nothing you said, Mr. Sparks," she said. "He's just old, you understand."

The old man's head was down, and he was mumbling, something about Chancellorsville and a river, and Sparks backed up against the wall, suddenly afraid again, afraid for his deal, and he quickly wiped his face.

"Well now," he said, "I reckon I'm sorry."

Her eyes were on him for a moment before she spoke, and he looked away. She spoke quietly, "It's not your fault." She paused, and then she said, "It's not your fault that you're the way you are, Mr. Sparks, any more than it's his fault." She stopped speaking, and he hung his head, felt the clammy, wrinkled suit sticking to him. Carla had come to the door, and Miss Iva walked the old man over to her, and the servant disappeared down the hall with him; then Miss Iva crossed the room to the window, walking slowly, as though she had suddenly grown very tired, and Sparks, as quietly as he could, walked over to the sofa and picked up his hat and twisted it in his hands. Then she turned from the window and came toward him.

"Mr. Sparks," she said, "what you've brought here is no concern to me. If this town wants a monument, then it's all right with me, but it's not up to me to make the arrangements with you, do you understand?"

"Some great art work goes into these statues, Miss Ida," he said, a hint of a whine in his voice.

She was still standing across from him, a hand on the rocker. "You go to see George Mayhew, at the *Hammond Express,*" she said. "Talk to him. Tell him I sent you, if you want to."

He tilted his head to the side and saw her sharply and clearly, standing in the dim parlor as her eyes bore into him. And there was the question, the burning question; but he thought only of leaving, of fleeing, because he had what he had come for. There was nothing else for him in that house, the house that held the Major and his sister; he wanted only to get away, to complete his deal and get away. She had thrown open the door for him, but he couldn't understand why. He had only to walk out and put her behind him, to get on the train and walk into his boss's office and be patted on the back, and start getting his commission checks; but he stood looking at her. Instead of elation, there was a hollow, cold lump in the pit of his stomach, and he felt ugly and fat and sweating; he twisted his hat in his hands.

"Miss Ida," he began and stopped. After a long, hollow minute, he said, "Well now, it was a pleasure meeting you, Miss Ida," and he walked quickly across the room and down the hall and out the door. Once in the street he could see the Madison Hotel sign in the distance, through the rising waves of late afternoon heat. He began the long haul up the hill, in the dust, the sky red with sunset behind him. There was a tightness in his chest that was not caused by breathlessness; and he felt it again, stronger, when he passed a small frame building where some Negroes were sitting, and heard the low, ringing laugh. He looked at the faces; at the large, white eyes with the dark pupils and the shining white teeth; and at the one face that was not smiling, but was twisted grotesquely by the bulging, bulbous, red lip that hung down over his chin. Sparks turned his face toward the hotel and moved on, the sweat on his neck moving, unchecked, down over his collar and down the wrinkled back of the grayish suit, orange-tinted now in the dying sun.

III

He was standing on the platform, and he had just heard the 11:15 blowing before it crossed the trestle upriver, the trestle that Dale Spivey told him had been built by Bedford Forrest just a month before he was captured up at Gainesville. It would be a matter of minutes before Sparks would be away from Hammond, speeding toward Mobile. He stood squinting in the sun, his eyes red-rimmed from the bottle of corn whiskey that he'd drunk in his room in the hotel last night. He had been plagued by a sense of guilt that he could not understand, and he'd drunk the whiskey and had passed out, fully clothed, across the bed about daylight. George Mayhew had his ad for the *Hammond Express,* the one drawn up by his company in Mobile; he had the sanction of the leading citizen of Hammond (a fact that he had wasted no time in spreading around), and there was no doubt in his mind that he had made a sale. Once Hammond put up a statue, a stone soldier (that's what he thought of it as, now, because of the Major; and every time he thought about the stone soldier the image of Major Hammond leaning on the cane, sobbing quietly, would flash across his mind, but he would manage to put it quickly away, out of sight), he knew that the other towns across the state would soon follow suit and they would be his. Of course, the deal wasn't closed, but it would be. He allowed himself to smile, and he glanced around the platform and up the street toward the hotel, where he could make out Dale Spivey, tilted back in the chair on the porch; then he heard footsteps beside him and he looked around, and up, into the dark eyes, and his own eyes flickered over the lip and the white shirt with the sleeves torn out and with the collar missing.

"Well now, mornin, John Thomas," he said, squinting up in the near-noon sunlight. The Negro nodded to him, and after a moment held out his hand; Sparks looked, and there was the Bible. He'd almost forgotten about it, and it was a moment before he realized that the Negro wanted him to take it back.

"Why, that's all right, boy, you can keep it," he said, grinning. "You understand, I didn't come here for that, and well, I'm too busy for it anyway, and it don't matter that I didn't sell any. That one is yours to keep. I give it to you, and it's yours."

The Negro lowered his arm for a moment, and then held out the book to him again. "I don't want it, Mr. Sparks," he said. "I got a Bible give to me by Major Hammond a long time ago."

"But not like this'n," Sparks said.

He avoided looking into the Negro's eyes.

"I thank you," John Thomas said, "but I reckon I want you to take it back. I don't want it."

The train, with a roar, was approaching the platform now, and Sparks picked up the straw suitcase and wiped at his face.

"Well, Goddam, if a man don't take somethin give to him free, he don't deserve it, I don't reckon," and he took the Bible. "Well I see you, Lip," he said, and he moved toward the train.

From his seat he could look out onto the platform and the yellow station and the dusty street leading up the middle of the town. The train moved away, and the scene got smaller, and Sparks could see the Negro standing on the platform, moving back into the shadow against the wall. He was leaving, and the image of the Major and of Miss Iva standing in the dim parlor welled up in him, and he swallowed them down. The train was cool after the sun of the dusty street, and he looked down at the Bible in his hand. Then he opened the straw suitcase and put it back with the others, among the dirty shirts and wrinkled underwear and damp bandanas. He settled again in the seat, tugging at his crotch and pulling his breeches legs down so that they did not cut into his thighs. He placed the wrinkled hat in the other seat and relaxed, looking out at the rolling pastures and clumps of trees in the distance.

"I'll just never understand some folks," he said. And a sense of relief swept over him when he closed his eyes, for he realized, now that he was on his way back to Mobile, that he did not have to understand.

ANGUS WILSON

(1913–)

Realpolitik

John Hobday sat on the edge of his desk and swung his left leg with characteristic boyishness. He waited for the staff to get settled in their seats and then spoke with careful informality.

"I know how frightfully busy you are. As a matter of fact I am myself," he said with the half-humorous urchin smile that he used for such jokes. Only his secretary, Veronica, gave the helpful laugh he expected. It was not going to be an easy meeting, he decided. "So I'm not going to waste your time with a lot of talk," he went on. "I just thought. . . ." He paused and beat with his pencil against the desk whilst Mrs. Scrutton moved her chair fussily out of the sunlight. "Ready?" he asked with an over-elaborate smile. "Right. Then we'll start again. As I was saying, we're all very busy, but all the same I thought it was time we had a little meeting. I've been here a week now and although I've had some very helpful chats with each of you in turn, we've never had a chance to get together and outline our plans." None of the three who formed his audience made any response. Veronica, who remembered him taking over new departments at the Ministry during the war, thought he hasn't got the right tone, he doesn't realize that he's coming up against deeper loyalties with these people, loyalties to scholarship and ideas. She almost felt like letting him fend for himself, but old habits were too strong.

"I'm sure it's what everybody's been wanting," she said in her deep voice. She had gauged rightly, his moment of uncertainty had gone, her faithful bark had guided him at the crucial moment. Mrs. Scrutton tried to discomfort him. She rustled the papers on her lap and whispered audibly to Major Sarson, "Our plans. *His* plans for us would be more honest." But it was too late; she had missed her chance. John merely frowned at the interruption and it was Mrs. Scrutton who was left with burning cheeks, hiding her embarrassment by lighting a fresh cigarette.

"As you know," John went on, and Veronica could tell by the loud, trumpeting, rhetorical note of his voice that he was once more the confident salesman lost in the dream world of the grandiose schemes he was putting before them, "I've got some very big ideas for the Gallery. I'm not an expert in any way, as you people are, but I think that's possibly why Sir Harold's executors chose me for the job. They felt the Gallery had already got its full weight of scholars and experts, what it needed was a man with administrative experience, whose training had led him to take an over-all view of things, to think, shall I say, widely rather than deeply. That's why they got me in. But I'm going to be absolutely frank with you"—tossing a lock of brown, wavy hair from his forehead, he stared at his audience with a wide-eyed appeal—"I need *your* help; without my staff I can get nowhere."

Major Sarson winced slightly. All this theatricality and the loud pitch of John's voice got on his nerves, besides he could feel a draught round his legs. It's like some damned Methodist preacher fellow, he thought.

"You've been grand in this first week," John went on, "absolutely grand. I don't mind telling you now that when I arrived I was dead scared. You'd all been here for years, you knew the collections backwards, you had your own ways of running the place, and above all you'd had the inestimable advantage of knowing Sir Harold, of hearing exactly what was in his mind when he bought this picture or that object, of knowing what his ideals were in giving the public the benefit of his taste and experience. I felt sure you were bound to resent me as an outsider, and I knew I'd have done the same in your place."

The faces in front of him were quite unresponsive. He isn't going to get anywhere with sentimental appeals, thought Veronica, these people are idealists, there's nothing more hardboiled. The damned fools, thought John, they have the chance of turning this tin pot, cranky provincial gallery into a national institution and they won't play ball. Well, if they can't see which way their own chances lie, they're not getting in the way of mine. They'll have to come to heel or go. His voice became a little sharper, a shade less ingenuous and friendly.

"You've all told me your views in our various little chats. Sometimes we've agreed, sometimes we haven't. You've inclined to the feeling that all is for the best in the best of al possible worlds, I've felt that some changes were needed, that the scope of the work here wanted broadening, that the organization wanted, let's face it, bringing up to date a bit, and in all this the Board has agreed with me."

Tony Parnell's baby face had grown steadily more pouting and scowling as John had been speaking. To think of this mountebank in charge of the Gallery, a professional careerist, who understood nothing of Sir Harold's ideas and aims, who had even laughed when he'd spoken to him of the metaphysical aspects of technique in painting. He had banked so much on becoming Curator. Sir Harold had spoken so often of him as "my torch-bearer, the youngest member of our staff," and now these awful business-men who had got control of the estate had put this creature in. Major Sarson and Mrs. Scrutton were too old to fight these changes; he had promised before the meeting that *he* would make the challenge. Now was his opportunity. Red in the face, he opened his mouth, but in his nervousness his voice emerged a high falsetto. John smiled across at Veronica.

"The Board haven't had much opportunity of agreeing with us since they haven't heard our views," Tony squeaked.

"My dear Parnell," said John, and his tone was purposely patronizing and offensive. The old ones he regarded without rancour as dead wood to be cleared away, but Tony he disliked personally for his assumptions of scholarly disinterestedness and moral superiority. "Don't let that worry you. As soon as you've got your ideas clear come along and push them at the Board as much as you like. I shouldn't use too much of your favourite art jargon if I was you; the Board are anxious to help but they're only ordinary businessmen and they might not understand. If you follow my advice you'll come down to earth a bit, but of course that's entirely your affair."

Mrs. Scrutton fingered the buttons on her checked tweed coat nervously. "There's no need to bully Mr. Parnell," she said.

"Oh, come," said John jocosely, "if Parnell's going to have the ladies on his side I shall have to surrender." To his delight he saw that Tony was frowning with annoyance.

"Do let me deal with this in my own way," Parnell said to Mrs. Scrutton, whose lip began to tremble.

So that severe grey bobbed hair and man's collar and tie could dissolve early into tears, thought John, so much the better.

"Mrs. Scrutton was only trying to help you, Parnell," said Major Sarson. "Don't let us forget our manners, please."

John yawned slightly. "When the little civil war's over," he said, "I'd just like to outline our main functions. As I see them they're these: Relations with the Public, that's you, Parnell; Display, Mrs. Scrutton; Research, Major Sarson. Miss Clay," he indicated Veronica, "is maid of all work. And I, well, I'm the Aunt Sally, ready to stop the bricks and pass on the bouquets."

Major Sarson looked at his watch impatiently. "I quite agree with you,

Major," said John; "the sooner we get finished, the better. No true gentlemen continue to hold meetings after opening time." The old man's face twitched violently, no one before had referred overtly to his notorious weakness.

"I'd like to take the public first," said John. "You've done a first-rate job, Parnell—within its limits. But you haven't gone far enough. You've got real enthusiasm and that's half the battle—but only half. You give the public first-rate value in lectures and catalogues when they get here, but you don't try to get them to come. I know what you're going to say: 'They'll come if they're interested.' But aren't you being a bit hard on the poor, tired, pushed-around public of today? They've got to be told about the place. You've got to compete with the cinema, the football team *and* the fireside radio. In short you've got to advertise and you can't do that unless you have figures." Here John paused and picked up a file of papers.

"You have all the figures there," said Tony sulkily.

"I know," said John, "but don't you think they're just a bit too general? 'So many people visited the Gallery on August 5th, so many on November 3rd.' But what sort of people? Who are we catering for? Were they Chinamen, shopgirls, farmers, or just plain deaf-mutes? To tell us anything these figures want breaking down into groups—so many foreigners, so many over-forties, so many under-twenties. That's the way to build up a picture. Now supposing you run over these figures in the way that I suggest and we'll talk again."

Tony was about to protest that this task was impossible, but John held up his hand. "No, no, time's very short and there's one more point I want to raise before we pass on to display." Mrs. Scrutton drew her coat tightly round her. "It's about the lecture room. Sir Louis Crippen was saying something at the last Board meeting about its not being free for his archaeological society when he needed it. Do you know anything about that?"

Tony Parnell hesitated. "Well, actually," he said, "Mrs. Scrutton makes all the lecture hall arrangements."

"But isn't it the P.R.O.'s pigeon?" asked John.

"Yes," said Tony, "but . . . well . . . Mrs. Scrutton . . ."

"I see," said John coldly. "Perhaps you'd enlighten me, then, Mrs. Scrutton."

The grey bob shook as she answered, an involuntary shake that was to prove the prelude to age's palsy. "Sir Louis asked for Tuesday and Tuesdays are always booked by Miss Copley," she said.

"Miss Copley?"

Mrs. Scrutton guessed that he knew the answer and her reply attempted a rebuke. "Miss Copley is an old and true friend to the Gallery," she said. "She's been giving her lectures to Schools on Tuesdays for many years."

"No doubt," said John, "but I still think Sir Louis should have preference."

"I don't agree at all," said Major Sarson; "it would be most unfair."

"Yes, why should Sir Louis receive special treatment?" asked Mrs. Scrutton.

"Well, frankly," replied John, "because although Miss Copley may be a very old friend, Sir Louis is a very influential one and the Gallery needs influential friends."

Before Mrs. Scrutton there floated Sir Harold's features, like Erasmus she had thought him, the last of the humanists. Major Sarson too remembered his old friend's handshake and his firm clear voice. "Sarson," he had said, "this money came to me through false standards, false distinctions. There shall be no distinctions in its use but those of scholarship." The eyes of both these old people filled with tears.

John turned to Veronica. "You've nothing to do, Miss Clay," he said. "In future you will take on the lecture hall arrangements. Anything important you'll refer to me." Mrs. Scrutton made a gesture of protest. "No, no," said John. "I'm not going to let you wear yourself out on these minor details, you're far too valuable to the Gallery. Besides, you've got more than a full-time job with Display if it's properly carried out."

Tony Parnell half rose from his chair. "I thought the lecture hall arrangements came under Public Relations?"

"So did I," said John, "until you disillusioned me."

"Next we come to Display. I suppose no side of our work has been more revolutionized in recent years. The Philadelphia report, you know, and the Canadian Association series," he went on, smiling at Mrs. Scrutton. She suddenly felt very tired, she had seen these documents but had never been able to bring herself to read them. "But there's no need for me to mention these things to you," John continued. "Your arrangement of the miniature collection," and he sighed in wonder. "Well, I'm going to pay you a great compliment there. Your arrangement of the miniatures not only makes one want to look at them, it makes it impossible for one not to look at them. I'm sure, Mrs. Scrutton, you'll agree with my wish that some other sides of the collection had the same advantages as the miniatures—the jewellery, for instance, and the armour. But that's not your fault. There's just too much for one person, that's all there is to it. The same applies to the research. I'm not going to embarrass Major Sarson by talking about his position as a scholar"—he waved his hand towards the old man who went red round the ears—"suffice it to say what we all know, that the Gallery is honoured by the presence of the world's greatest authority on the Dutch school, and a great scholar of painting generally. Though I doubt, by the way, whether the Major's exactly fond of the moderns. I sometimes wish that the Gallery possessed only paintings, I'm sure Major Sarson does. Unfortunately that isn't the case. I fully sympathized with him when he spoke to me as he did of 'those wretched pots and pans' "—here John laughed patronizingly—"but I doubt if a ceramics man would. Frankly," he said, turning to Major

Sarson, "I consider it disgraceful that a scholar of your caliber should be taken off your real work in this way. Now how, you may ask, do I suppose to remedy the situation? Well, the answer is that I propose to treble the staff. From next month new staff will begin to arrive—some students from the Universities, some more experienced men from other galleries and museums."

There was silence for a minute, then Mrs. Scrutton spoke. "Does the Board know of this?

"Yes," said John, "they fully approve the scheme."

"Do they realize the expense involved?" asked Tony, the practical man.

"The Board are businessmen," said John; "they know that outlay must precede returns." He looked round at their faces. "Well, I think that's all," he said. "I know you will give the new members of the staff the same co-operation you have given me, whether it is a question of instructing and training them, or in some cases of working under them." His tone was openly sarcastic.

"Do I understand that people will be put over us?" asked Mrs. Scrutton.

"In cases where experts are brought in, it may be necessary to make revisions in seniority," said John.

"You realize, of course, that in such an eventuality we should resign," said Major Sarson.

"That would be a great loss to the Gallery, but we could not, of course, control your decisions," replied John, and opening the door, he bowed them out.

"Golly," said Veronica, "you do tell some lies, don't you? Or have the Board ratified your staff changes?"

"How many more times must I tell you, Veronica, that truth is relative," said John.

Veronica looked down for a minute. "I'll make you some coffee," she said.

"Yes," said John. "Victory always makes me thirsty. I cannot help being satisfied when I think of the well-merited unpleasant few weeks those three are going to have. The punishment of incompetence is always satisfactory."

"Mm," said Veronica doubtfully.

"What's that mean? You've not fallen for this sentimental stuff about Sir Harold, have you?"

"Good Lord, no," said Veronica. "It's not those misfits I'm worrying about, it's you."

"Me?" said John. "Why?"

"You're getting too fond of bullying," said Veronica; "it interferes with your charm, and charm's essential for your success." She went out to make the coffee.

What Veronica said was very true, thought John, and he made a note to be more detached in his attitude. All the same these criticisms were bad for his self-esteem. For all her loyalty Veronica knew him too well, got too near home. Charm was important to success, but self-esteem was more so. His imagination began to envisage further staff changes, perhaps a graduate secretary would really be more suitable now.

HERMAN MELVILLE

(1819–1891)

Bartleby the Scrivener

I am a rather elderly man. The nature of my avocations, for the last thirty years, has brought me into more than ordinary contact with what would seem an interesting and somewhat singular set of men, of whom, as yet, nothing, that I know of, has ever been written—I mean, the law-copyists, or scriveners. I have known very many of them, professionally and privately, and, if I pleased, could relate divers histories, at which good-natured gentlemen might smile, and sentimental souls might weep. But I waive the biographies of all other scriveners, for a few passages in the life of Bartleby, who was a scrivener, the strangest I ever saw, or heard of. While, of other law-copyists, I might write the complete life, of Bartleby nothing of that sort can be done. I believe that no materials exist, for a full and satisfactory biography of this man. It is an irreparable loss to literature. Bartleby was one of those beings of whom nothing is ascertainable, except from the original sources, and, in his case, those are very small. What my own astonished eyes saw of Bartleby, *that* is all I know of him, except, indeed, one vague report, which will appear in the sequel.

Ere introducing the scrivener, as he first appeared to me, it is fit I make some mention of myself, my *employés,* my business, my chambers, and general surroundings; because some such description is indispensable to an adequate understanding of the chief character about to be presented. Imprimis: I am a man who, from his youth upwards, has been filled with a profound conviction that the easiest way of life is the best. Hence, though I belong to a profession proverbially energetic and nervous, even to turbulence, at times, yet nothing of that sort have I ever suffered to invade my peace. I am one of those unambitious lawyers who never addresses a jury, or in any way draws down public applause; but, in the cool tranquillity of a snug retreat, do a snug business among rich men's bonds, and mortgages, and title-deeds. All who know me consider me an eminently *safe* man. The late John Jacob Astor, a personage little given to poetic enthusiasm, had no hesitation in pronouncing my first grand point to be prudence; my next, method. I do not speak it in vanity, but simply record the fact, that I was not unemployed in my profession by the late John Jacob Astor; a name which, I admit, I love to repeat; for it hath a rounded and orbicular sound to it, and rings like unto bullion. I will freely add, that I was not insensible to the late John Jacob Astor's good opinion.

Some time prior to the period at which this little history begins, my avocations had been largely increased. The good old office, now extinct in the State of New York, of a Master in Chancery, had been conferred upon me. It was not a very arduous office, but very pleasantly remunerative. I seldom lose my temper; much more seldom indulge in dangerous indignation at wrongs and outrages; but, I must be permitted to be rash here, and declare, that I consider the sudden and violent abrogation of the office of Master in Chancery, by the new Constitution, as a ——premature act; inasmuch as I had counted upon a life-lease of the profits, whereas I only received those of a few short years. But this is by the way.

My chambers were up stairs, at No.—Wall Street. At one end, they looked upon the white wall of the interior of a spacious sky-light shaft, penetrating the building from top to bottom.

This view might have been considered rather tame than otherwise, deficient in what landscape painters call "life." But, if so, the view from the other end of my chambers offered, at least, a contrast, if nothing more. In that direction, my windows commanded an unobstructed view of a lofty brick wall, black by age and everlasting shade; which wall required no spy-glass to bring out its lurking beauties, but, for the benefit of all near-sighted spectators, was pushed up to within ten feet of my window panes. Owing to the great height of the surrounding buildings, and my chambers being on the second floor, the interval between this wall and mine not a little resembled a huge square cistern.

At the period just preceding the advent of Bartleby, I had two persons as copyists in my employment, and a promising lad as an office-boy. First, Turkey; second, Nippers; third, Ginger Nut. These may seem names, the like of which are not usually found in the Directory. In truth, they were nicknames, mutually conferred upon each other by my three clerks, and were deemed expressive of their respective persons or characters. Turkey was a short, pursy Englishman, of about my own age—that is, somewhere not far from sixty. In the morning, one might say, his face was of a fine florid hue, but after twelve o'clock, meridian—his dinner hour—it blazed like a grate full of Christmas coals; and continued blazing—but, as it were, with a gradual wane—till six o'clock, P.M., or thereabouts; after which, I saw no more of the proprietor of the face, which, gaining its meridian with the sun, seemed to set with it, to rise, culminate, and decline the following day, with the like regularity and undiminished glory. There are many singular coincidences I have known in the course of my life, not the least among which was the fact, that, exactly when Turkey displayed his fullest beams from his red and radiant countenance, just then, too, at that critical moment, began the daily period when I considered his business capacities as seriously disturbed for the remainder of the twenty-four hours. Not that he was absolutely idle, or averse to business, then; far from it. The difficulty was, he was apt to be altogether too energetic. There was a strange, inflamed, flurried, flighty recklessness of activity about him. He would be incautious in dipping his pen into his inkstand. All his blots upon my documents were dropped there after twelve o'clock, meridian. Indeed, not only would he be reckless, and sadly given to making blots in the afternoon, but, some days, he went further, and was rather noisy. At such times, too, his face flamed with augmented blazonry, as if cannel coal had been heaped on anthracite. He made an unpleasant racket with his chair; spilled his sand-box; in mending his pens, impatiently split them all to pieces, and threw them on the floor in a sudden passion; stood up, and leaned over his table, boxing his papers about in a most indecorous manner, very sad to behold in an elderly man like him. Nevertheless, as he was in many ways a most valuable person to me, and all the time before twelve o'clock, meridian, was the quickest, steadiest creature, too, accomplishing a great deal of work in a style not easily to be matched—for these reasons, I was willing to overlook his eccentricities, though, indeed, occasionally, I remonstrated with him. I did this very gently, however, because, though the civilest, nay, the blandest and most reverential of men in the morning, yet, in the afternoon, he was disposed, upon provocation, to be slightly rash with his tongue—in fact, insolent. Now, valuing his morning services as I did, and resolved not to lose them—yet, at the same time, made uncomfortable by his inflamed ways after twelve o'clock—and being a man of peace, unwilling by my admonitions to call forth unseemly retorts from him, I took upon me, one Saturday noon (he was always worse on Saturdays) to hint to him, very kindly, that, perhaps, now that he was growing old, it might be well to abridge his labors; in short, he need not come to my chambers after twelve o'clock, but, dinner over, had best go home to his lodgings, and rest himself till tea-time. But no; he insisted upon his afternoon devotions. His countenance became intolerably fervid, as he oratorically assured me—gesticulating with a long ruler at the other end of the room—that if his services in the morning were useful, how indispensable, then, in the afternoon?

"With submission, sir," said Turkey, on this occasion, "I consider myself your right-hand man. In the morning I but marshal and deploy my columns; but in the afternoon I put myself at their head, and gallantly charge the foe, thus"—and he made a violent thrust with the ruler.

"But the blots, Turkey," intimated I.

"True; but, with submission, sir, behold these hairs! I am getting old. Surely, sir, a blot or two of a warm afternoon is not to be severely urged against gray hairs. Old age—even if it blot the page—is honorable. With submission, sir, we *both* are getting old."

This appeal to my fellow-feeling was hardly to be resisted. At all events, I saw that go he would not. So, I made up my mind to let him stay, resolving, nevertheless, to see to it that, during the afternoon, he had to do with my less important papers.

Nippers, the second on my list, was a whiskered, sallow, and, upon the whole, rather piratical-looking young man, of about five and twenty. I always deemed him the victim of two evil powers—ambition and indigestion. The ambition was evinced by a certain impatience of the duties of a mere copyist, an unwarrantable usurpation of strictly professional affairs, such as the original drawing up of legal documents. The indigestion seemed betokened in an occasional nervous testiness and grinning irritability, causing the teeth to audibly grind together over mistakes committed in copying; unnecessary maledictions, hissed, rather than spoken, in the heat of business; and especially by a continual discontent with the height of the table where he worked. Though of a very ingenious mechanical turn, Nippers could never get this table to suit him. He put chips under it, blocks of various sorts, bits of pasteboard, and at last went so far as to attempt an exquisite adjustment, by final pieces of folded blotting-paper. But no invention would answer. If, for the sake of easing his back, he brought the table lid at a sharp angle well up towards his chin, and wrote there like a man using the steep roof of a Dutch house for his desk, then he declared that it stopped the circulation in his arms. If now he lowered the table to his waistbands, and stooped over it in writing, then there was a sore aching in his back. In short, the truth of the matter was, Nippers knew not what he wanted. Or, if he wanted anything, it was to be rid of a scrivener's table altogether. Among the manifestations of his diseased ambition was a fondness he had for receiving visits from certain ambiguous-looking fellows in seedy coats, whom he called his clients. Indeed, I was aware that not only was he, at times, considerable of a ward-politician, but he occasionally did a little business at the Justices' courts, and was not unknown on the steps of the Tombs. I have good reason to believe, however, that one individual who called upon him at my chambers, and who, with a grand air, he insisted was his client, was no other than a dun, and the alleged title-deed, a bill. But, with all his failings, and the annoyances he caused me, Nippers, like his compatriot Turkey, was a very useful man to me; wrote a neat, swift hand; and, when he chose, was not deficient in a gentlemanly sort of deportment. Added to this, he always dressed in a gentlemanly sort of way; and so, incidentally, reflected credit upon my chambers. Whereas, with respect to Turkey, I had much ado to keep him from being a reproach to me. His clothes were apt to look oily, and smell of eating-houses. He wore his pantaloons very loose and baggy in summer. His coats were exercrable; his hat not to be handled. But while the hat was a thing of indifference to me, inasmuch as his natural civility and deference, as a dependent Englishman, always led him to doff it the moment he entered the room, yet his coat was another matter. Concerning his coats, I reasoned with him; but with no effect. The truth was, I suppose, that a man with so small an income could not afford to sport such a lustrous face and a lustrous coat at one and the same time. As Nippers once observed, Turkey's money went chiefly for red ink. One winter day, I presented Turkey with a highly respectable-looking coat of my own—a padded gray coat, of a most comfortable warmth, and which buttoned straight up from the knee to the neck. I thought Turkey would appreciate the favor, and abate his rashness and obstreperousness of afternoons. But no; I verily believe that buttoning himself up in so downy and blanket-like a coat had a pernicious effect upon him—upon the same principle that too much oats are bad for horses. In fact, precisely as a rash, restive horse is said to feel his oats, so Turkey felt his coat. It made him insolent. He was a man whom prosperity harmed.

Though, concerning the self-indulgent habits of Turkey, I had my own private surmises, yet, touching Nippers, I was well persuaded that, whatever might be his faults in other respects, he was, at least, a temperate young man. But, indeed, nature herself seemed to have been his vintner, and, at his birth, charged him so thoroughly with an irritable, brandy-like disposition, that all subsequent potations were needless. When I consider how, amid the stillness of my chambers, Nippers would sometimes impatiently rise from his seat, and stooping over his table, spread his arms wide apart, seize the whole desk, and move it, and jerk it, with a grim, grinding motion on the floor, as if the table were a perverse voluntary agent, intent on thwarting and vexing him, I plainly perceive that, for Nippers, brandy-and-water were altogether superfluous.

It was fortunate for me that, owing to its peculiar cause—indigestion—the irritability and consequent nervousness of Nippers were mainly observable in the morning, while in the afternoon he was comparatively mild. So that, Turkey's paroxysms only coming on about twelve o'clock, I never had to do with their eccentricities at one time. Their fits relieved each other, like guards. When Nippers's was on, Turkey's was off; and *vice versa*. This was a good natural arrangement, under the circumstances.

Ginger Nut, the third on my list, was a lad, some twelve years old. His father was a car-man, ambitious of seeing his son on the bench instead of a cart, before he died. So he sent him to my office, as student at law, errand-boy, cleaner and sweeper, at the rate of one dollar a week. He had a little desk to himself, but he did not use it much. Upon inspection, the drawer exhibited a great array of the shells of various sorts of nuts. Indeed, to this quick-witted youth, the whole noble science of the law was contained in a nut-shell. Not the least among the employments of Ginger Nut, as well as one which he discharged with the most alacrity, was his duty as cake and apple purveyor for Turkey and Nippers. Copying law-papers being proverbially a dry, husky sort of business, my two scriveners were fain to moisten their mouths very often with Spitzenbergs, to be had at the numerous stalls nigh the Custom House and Post Office. Also, they sent Ginger Nut very frequently for that peculiar cake—small, flat, round, and very spicy—after which he had been named by them. Of a cold morning, when business was but dull, Turkey would gobble up scores of these cakes, as if they were mere wafers—indeed, they sell them at the rate of six or eight for a penny—the scrape of his pen blending with the crunching of the crisp particles in his mouth. Of all the fiery afternoon blunders and flurried rashnesses of Turkey, was his once moistening a ginger-cake between his lips, and clapping it on to a mortgage, for a seal. I came within an ace of dismissing him then. But he mollified me by making an oriental bow, and saying—

"With submission, sir, it was generous of me to find you in stationery on my own account."

Now my original business—that of a conveyancer and title hunter, and drawer-up of recondite documents of all sorts—was considerably increased by receiving the master's office. There was now great work for scriveners. Not only must I push the clerks already with me, but I must have additional help.

In answer to my advertisement, a motionless young man one morning stood upon my office threshold, the door being open, for it was summer. I can see that figure now—pallidly neat, pitiably respectable, incurably forlorn! It was Bartleby.

After a few words touching his qualifications, I engaged him, glad to have among my corps of copyists a man of so singularly sedate an aspect, which I thought might operate beneficially upon the flightly temper of Turkey, and the fiery one of Nippers.

I should have stated before that ground glass folding-doors divided my premises into two parts, one of which was occupied by my scriveners, the other by myself. According to my humor, I threw open these doors, or closed them. I resolved to assign Bartleby a corner by the folding-doors, but on my side of them, so as to have this quiet man within easy call, in case any trifling thing was to be done. I placed his desk close up to a small side-window in that part of the room, a window which originally had afforded a lateral view of certain grimy back-yards and bricks, but which owing to subsequent erections, commanded at present no view at all, though it gave some light. Within three feet of the panes was a wall, and the light came down from far above, between two lofty buildings, as from a very small opening in a dome. Still further to a satisfactory arrangement, I procured a high green folding screen, which might entirely isolate Bartleby from my sight, though not remove him from my voice. And thus, in a manner, privacy and society were conjoined.

At first, Bartleby did an extraordinary quantity of writing. As if long famishing for something to copy, he seemed to gorge himself on my documents. There was no pause for digestion. He ran a day and night line, copying by sun-light and by candle-light. I should have been quite delighted with his application, had he been cheerfully industrious. But he wrote on silently, palely, mechanically.

It is, of course, an indispensable part of a scrivener's business to verify the accuracy of his copy, word by word. Where there are two or more scriveners in an office, they assist each other in this examination, one reading from the copy, the other holding the original. It is a very dull, wearisome, and lethargic affair. I can readily imagine that, to some sanguine temperaments, it would be altogether intolerable. For example, I cannot credit that the mettlesome poet, Byron, would have contentedly sat down with Bartleby to examine a law document of, say five hundred pages, closely written in a crimpy hand.

Now and then, in the haste of business, it had been my habit to assist in comparing some brief document myself, calling Turkey or Nippers for this purpose. One object I had, in placing Bartleby so handy to me behind the screen, was, to avail myself of his services on such trivial occasions. It was on the third day, I think, of his being with me, and before any necessity had arisen for having his own writing examined, that, being much hurried to complete a small affair I had in hand, I abruptly called to Bartleby. In my haste and natural expectancy of instant compliance, I sat with my head bent over the original on my desk, and my right hand sideways, and somewhat nervously extended with the copy, so that, immediately upon emerging from his retreat, Bartleby might snatch it and proceed to business without the least delay.

In this very attitude did I sit when I called to him, rapidly stating what it was I wanted him to do—namely, to examine a small paper with me. Imagine my surprise, nay, my consternation, when, without moving from his privacy, Bartleby, in a singularly mild, firm voice, replied, "I would prefer not to."

I sat awhile in perfect silence, rallying my stunned faculties. Immediately it occurred to me that my ears had deceived me, or Bartleby had entirely misunderstood my meaning. I repeated my request in the clearest tone I could assume; but in quite as clear a one came the previous reply, "I would prefer not to."

"Prefer not to," echoed I, rising in high excitement, and crossing the room with a stride. "What do you mean? Are you moon-struck? I want you to help me compare this sheet here—take it," and I thrust it towards him.

"I would prefer not to," said he.

I looked at him steadfastly. His face was leanly composed; his gray eye dimly calm. Not a wrinkle of agitation rippled him. Had there been the least uneasiness, anger, impatience or impertinence in his manner; in other words, had there been any thing ordinarily human about him, doubtless I should have violently dismissed him from the premises. But as it was, I should have as soon thought of turning my pale plaster-of-paris bust of Cicero out of doors. I stood gazing at him awhile, as he went on with his own writing, and then reseated myself at my desk. This is very strange, thought I. What had one best do? But my business hurried me. I concluded to forget the matter for the present, reserving it for my future leisure. So calling Nippers from the other room, the paper was speedily examined.

A few days after this, Bartleby concluded four lengthy documents, being quadruplicates of a week's testimony taken before me in my High Court of Chancery. It became necessary to examine them. It was an important suit, and great accuracy was imperative. Having all things arranged, I called Turkey, Nippers, and Ginger Nut, from the next room, meaning to place the four copies in the hands of my four clerks, while I should read from the original. Accordingly, Turkey, Nippers, and Ginger Nut had taken their seats in a row, each with his document in his hand, when I called to Bartleby to join this interesting group.

"Bartleby! quick, I am waiting."

I heard a slow scrape of his chair legs on the uncarpeted floor, and soon he appeared standing at the entrance of his hermitage.

"What is wanted?" said he, mildly.

"The copies, the copies," said I, hurriedly. "We are going to examine them. There"—and I held towards him the fourth quadruplicate.

"I would prefer not to," he said, and gently disappeared behind the screen.

For a few moments I was turned into a pillar of salt, standing at the head of my seated column of clerks. Recovering myself, I advanced towards the screen, and demanded the reason for such extraordinary conduct.

"*Why* do you refuse?"

"I would prefer not to."

With any other man I should have flown outright into a dreadful passion, scorned all further words, and thrust him ignominiously from my presence. But there was something about Bartleby that not only strangely disarmed me, but, in a wonderful manner, touched and disconcerted me. I began to reason with him.

"These are your own copies we are about to examine. It is labor saving to you, because one examination will answer for your four papers. It is common usage. Every copyist is bound to help examine his copy. Is it not so? Will you not speak? Answer!"

"I prefer not to," he replied in a flute-like tone. It seemed to me that, while I had been addressing him, he carefully revolved every statement that I made; fully comprehended the meaning; could not gainsay the irresistible conclusion; but, at the same time, some paramount consideration prevailed with him to reply as he did.

"You are decided, then, not to comply with my request—a request made according to common usage and common sense?"

He briefly gave me to understand, that on that point my judgment was sound. Yes: his decision was irreversible.

It is not seldom the case that, when a man is browbeaten in some unprecedented and violently unreasonable way, he begins to stagger in his own plainest faith. He begins, as it were, vaguely to surmise that, wonderful as it may be, all the justice and all the reason is on the other side. Accordingly, if any disinterested persons are present, he turns to them for some reinforcement of his own faltering mind.

"Turkey," said I, "what do you think of this? Am I not right?"

"With submission, sir," said Turkey, in his blandest tone, "I think that you are."

"Nippers," said I, "what do *you* think of it?"

"I think I should kick him out of the office."

(The reader, of nice perceptions, will here perceive that, it being morning, Turkey's answer is couched in polite and tranquil terms, but Nippers replies in ill-tempered ones. Or, to repeat a previous sentence, Nippers' ugly mood was on duty and Turkey's off.)

"Ginger Nut," said I, willing to enlist the smallest suffrage in my behalf, "what do *you* think of it?"

"I think, sir, he's a little *luny,*" replied Ginger Nut, with a grin.

"You hear what they say," said I, turning towards the screen, "come forth and do your duty."

But he vouchsafed no reply. I pondered a moment in sore perplexity. But once more business hurried me. I determined again to postpone the consideration of this dilemma to my future leisure. With a little trouble we made out to examine the papers without Bartleby, though at every page or two Turkey deferentially dropped his opinion, that this proceeding was quite out of the common; while Nippers, twitching in his chair with a dyspeptic nervousness, ground out, between his set teeth, occasional hissing maledictions against the stubborn oaf behind the screen. And for his (Nippers's) part, this was the first and the last time he would do another man's business without pay.

Meanwhile Bartleby sat in his hermitage, oblivious to everything but his own peculiar business there.

Some days passed, the scrivener being employed upon another lengthy work. His late remarkable conduct led me to regard his ways narrowly. I observed that he never went to dinner; indeed, that he never went anywhere. As yet I had never, of my personal knowledge, known him to be outside of my office. He was a perpetual sentry in the corner. At about eleven o'clock though, in the morning, I noticed that Ginger Nut would advance toward the opening in Bartleby's screen, as if silently beckoned thither by a gesture invisible to me where I sat. The boy would then leave the office, jingling a few pence, and reappear with a handful of ginger-nuts, which he delivered in the hermitage, receiving two of the cakes for his trouble.

He lives, then, on ginger-nuts, thought I; never eats a dinner, properly speaking; he must be a vegetarian, then; but no! he never eats even vegetables, he eats nothing but ginger-nuts. My mind then ran on in reveries concerning the probable effects upon the human constitution of living entirely on ginger-nuts. Ginger-nuts are so called, because they contain ginger as one of their peculiar constituents, and the final flavoring one. Now, what was ginger? A hot, spicy thing. Was Bartleby hot and spicy? Not at all. Ginger, then, had no effect upon Bartleby. Probably he preferred it should have none.

Nothing so aggravates an earnest person as a passive resistance. If the individual so resisted be of a not inhumane temper, and the resisting one perfectly harmless in his passivity, then, in the better moods of the former, he will endeavor charitably to construe to his imagination what proves impossible to be solved by his judgment. Even so, for the most part, I regarded Bartleby and his ways. Poor fellow! thought I, he means no mischief; it is plain he intends no insolence; his aspect sufficiently evinces that his eccentricities are involuntary. He is useful to me. I can get along with him. If I turn him away, the chances are he will fall in with some less-indulgent employer, and then he will be rudely treated, and perhaps driven forth miserably to starve. Yes. Here I can cheaply purchase a delicious self-approval. To befriend Bartleby, to humor him in his strange willfulness, will cost me little or nothing, while I lay up in my soul what will eventually prove a sweet morsel for my conscience. But this mood was not invariable with me. The passiveness of Bartleby sometimes irritated me. I felt strangely goaded on to encounter him in new opposition—to elicit some angry spark from him answerable to my own. But, indeed, I might as well have essayed to strike fire with my knuckles against a bit of Windsor soap. But one afternoon the evil impulse in me mastered me, and the following little scene ensued:

"Bartleby," said I, "when those papers are all copied, I will compare them with you."

"I would prefer not to."

"How? Surely you do not mean to persist in that mulish vagary?"

No answer.

I threw open the folding-doors near by, and, turning upon Turkey and Nippers, exclaimed:

"Bartleby a second time says, he won't examine his papers. What do you think of it, Turkey?"

It was afternoon, be it remembered. Turkey sat glowing like a brass boiler; his bald head steaming; his hands reeling among his blotted papers.

"Think of it?" roared Turkey; "I think I'll just step behind his screen, and black his eyes for him!"

So saying, Turkey rose to his feet and threw his arms into a pugilistic position. He was hurrying away to make good his promise, when I detained him, alarmed at the effect of incautiously rousing Turkey's combativeness after dinner.

"Sit down, Turkey," said I, "and hear what Nippers has to say. What do you think of it, Nippers? Would I not be justified in immediately dismissing Bartleby?"

"Excuse me, that is for you to decide, sir. I think his conduct quite unusual, and, indeed, unjust, as regards Turkey and myself. But it may only be a passing whim."

"Ah," exclaimed I, "you have strangely changed your mind, then—you speak very gently of him now."

"All beer," cried Turkey; "gentleness is effects of beer—Nippers and I dined together to-day. You see how gentle *I* am, sir. Shall I go and black his eyes?"

"You refer to Bartleby, I suppose. No, not to-day, Turkey," I replied; "pray, put up your fists."

I closed the doors, and again advanced towards Bartleby. I felt additional incentives tempting me to my fate. I burned to be rebelled against again. I remembered that Bartleby never left the office.

"Bartleby," said I, "Ginger Nut is away; just step around to the Post Office, won't you? (it was but a three minutes' walk), and see if there is anything for me."

"I would prefer not to."

"You *will* not?"

"I *prefer* not."

I staggered to my desk, and sat there in a deep study. My blind inveteracy returned. Was there any other thing in which I could procure myself to be ignominiously repulsed by this lean, penniless wight?—my hired clerk? What added thing is there, perfectly reasonable, that he will be sure to refuse to do?

"Bartleby!"

No answer.

"Bartleby," in a louder tone.

No answer.

"Bartleby," I roared.

Like a very ghost, agreeable to the laws of magical invocation, at the third summons, he appeared at the entrance of his hermitage.

"Go to the next room, and tell Nippers to come to me."

"I prefer not to," he respectfully and slowly said, and mildly disappeared.

"Very good, Bartleby," said I, in a quiet sort of serenely-severe self-possessed tone, intimating the unalterable purpose of some terrible retribution very close at hand. At the moment I half intended something of the kind. But upon the whole, as it was drawing towards my dinner-hour, I thought it best to put on my hat and walk home for the day, suffering much from perplexity and distress of mind.

Shall I acknowledge it? The conclusion of this whole business was, that it soon became a fixed fact of my chambers, that a pale young scrivener, by the name of Bartleby, had a desk there; that he copied for me at the usual rate of four cents a folio (one hundred words); but he was permanently exempt from examining the work done by him, that duty being transferred to Turkey and Nippers, out of compliment, doubtless, to their superior acuteness; moreover, said Bartleby was never, on any account, to be dispatched on the most trivial errand of any sort; and that even if entreated to take upon him such a matter, it was generally understood that he would "prefer not to"—in other words, that he would refuse point-blank.

As days passed on, I became considerably reconciled to Bartleby. His steadiness, his freedom from all dissipation, his incessant industry (except when he chose to throw himself into a standing revery behind his screen), his great stillness, his unalterableness of demeanor under all circumstances, made him a valuable acquisition. One prime thing was this—*he was always there*—first in the morning, continually through the day, and the last at night. I had a singular confidence in his honesty. I felt my most precious papers perfectly safe in his hands. Sometimes, to be sure, I could not, for the very soul of me, avoid falling into sudden spasmodic passions with him. For it was exceeding difficult to bear in mind all the time those strange peculiarities, privileges, and unheard of exemptions, forming the tacit stipulations on Bartleby's part under which he remained in my office. Now and then, in the eagerness of dispatching pressing business, I would inadvertently summon Bartleby, in a short, rapid tone, to put his finger, say, on the incipient tie of a bit of red tape with which I was about compressing some papers. Of course, from behind the screen the usual answer, "I prefer not to," was sure to come; and then, how could a human creature, with the common infirmities of our nature, refrain from bitterly exclaiming upon such perverseness—such unreasonableness. However, every added repulse of this sort which I received only tended to lessen the probability of my repeating the inadvertence.

Here it must be said, that according to the custom of most legal gentlemen occupying chambers in densely-populated law buildings, there were several keys to my door. One was kept by a woman residing in the attic, which person weekly scrubbed and daily swept and dusted my apartments. Another was kept by Turkey for convenience sake. The third I sometimes carried in my own pocket. The fourth I knew not who had.

Now, one Sunday morning I happened to go to Trinity Church, to hear a celebrated preacher, and finding myself rather early on the ground I thought I would walk around to my chambers for a while. Luckily I had my key with me; but upon applying it to the lock, I found it resisted by something inserted from the inside. Quite surprised, I called out; when to my consternation a key was turned from within; and thrusting his lean visage at me, and holding the door ajar, the apparition of Bartleby appeared, in his shirt sleeves, and otherwise in a strangely tattered deshabille, saying quietly that he was sorry, but he was deeply engaged just then, and—preferred not admitting me at present. In a brief word or two, he moreover added, that perhaps I had better walk around the block two or three times, and by that time he would probably have concluded his affairs.

Now, the utterly unsurmised appearance of Bartleby, tenanting my law-chambers of a Sunday morning, with his cadaverously gentlemanly *nonchalance,* yet withal firm and self-possessed, had such a strange effect upon me, that incontinently I slunk away from my own door, and did as desired. But not without sundry twinges of impotent rebellion against the mild effrontery of this unaccountable scrivener. Indeed, it was his wonderful mildness chiefly, which not only disarmed me, but unmanned me as it were. For I consider that one, for the time, is a sort of unmanned when he tranquilly permits his hired clerk to dictate to him, and order him away from his own premises. Furthermore, I was full of uneasiness as to what Bartleby could possibly be doing in my office in his shirt sleeves, and in an otherwise dismantled condition of a Sunday morning. Was anything amiss going on? Nay, that was out of the question. It was not to be thought of for a moment that Bartleby was an immoral person. But what could he be doing there?—copying? Nay again, whatever might be his eccentricities, Bartleby was an eminently decorous person. He would be the last man to sit down to his desk in any state approaching to nudity. Besides, it was Sunday; and there was something about Bartleby that forbade the supposition that he would by any secular occupation violate the proprieties of the day.

Nevertheless, my mind was not pacified; and full of a restless curiosity, at last I returned to the door. Without hindrance I inserted my key, opened it, and entered. Bartleby was not to be seen. I looked round anxiously, peeped behind his screen; but it was very plain that he was gone. Upon more closely examining the place, I surmised that for an indefinite period Bartleby must have ate, dressed, and slept in my office, and that too without plate, mirror, or bed. The cushioned seat of a rickety old sofa in one corner bore the faint impress of a lean, reclining form. Rolled away under his desk, I found a blanket; under the empty grate, a blacking box and brush; on a chair, a tin basin, with soap and a ragged towel; in a newspaper a few crumbs of ginger-nuts and a morsel of cheese. Yes, thought I, it is evident enough that Bartleby has been making his home here, keeping bachelor's hall all by himself. Immediately then the thought came sweeping across me, what miserable friendlessness and loneliness are here revealed! His poverty is great; but his solitude, how horrible! Think of it. Of a Sunday, Wall Street is deserted as Petra; and every night of every day it is an emptiness. This building, too, which of week-days hums with industry and life, at nightfall echoes with sheer vacancy, and all through Sunday is forlorn. And here Bartleby makes his home; sole spectator of a solitude which he has seen all populous—a sort of innocent and transformed Marius brooding among the ruins of Carthage!

For the first time in my life a feeling of over-powering stinging melancholy seized me. Before, I had never experienced aught but a not unpleasing sadness. The bond of a common humanity now drew me irresistibly to gloom. A fraternal melancholy! For both I and Bartleby were sons of Adam. I remembered the bright silks and sparkling faces I had seen that day, in gala trim, swan-like sailing down the Mississippi of Broadway; and I contrasted them with the pallid copyist, and thought to myself, Ah, happiness courts the light, so we deem the world is gay; but misery hides aloof, so we deem that misery there is none. These sad fancyings—chimeras, doubtless, of a sick and silly brain—led on to other and more special thoughts, concerning the eccentricities of Bartleby. Presentiments of strange discoveries hovered round me. The scrivener's pale form appeared to me laid out, among uncaring strangers, in its shivering winding sheet.

Suddenly I was attracted by Bartleby's closed desk, the key in open sight left in the lock.

I mean no mischief, seek the gratification of no heartless curiosity, thought I; besides, the desk is mine, and its contents, too, so I will make bold to look within. Everything was methodically arranged, the papers smoothly placed. The pigeon holes were deep, and removing the files of documents, I groped into their recesses. Presently I felt something there, and dragged it out. It was an old bandanna handkerchief, heavy and knotted. I opened it, and saw it was a savings bank.

I now recalled all the quiet mysteries which I had noted in the man. I remembered that he never spoke but to answer; that, though at intervals he had considerable time to himself, yet I had never seen him reading—no, not even a newspaper; that for long periods he would stand looking out, at his pale window behind the screen, upon the dead brick wall; I was quite sure he never visited any refectory or eating house; while his pale face clearly indicated that he never drank beer like Turkey, or tea and coffee even, like other men; that he never went anywhere in particular that I could learn; never went out for a walk, unless, indeed, that was the case at present; that he had declined telling who he was, or whence he came, or whether he had any relatives in the world; that though so thin and pale, he never complained of ill health. And more than all, I remembered a certain unconscious air of pallid—how shall I call it?—of pallid haughtiness, say, or rather an austere reserve about him, which had positively awed me into my tame compliance with his eccentricities, when I had feared to ask him to do the slightest incidental thing for me, even though I might know, from his long-continued motionlessness, that behind his screen he must be standing in one of those dead-wall reveries of his.

Revolving all these things, and coupling them with the recently discovered fact, that he made my office his constant abiding place and home, and not forgetful of his morbid moodiness; revolving all these things, a prudential feeling began to steal over me. My first emotions had been those of pure melancholy and sincerest pity; but just in proportion as the forlornness of Bartleby grew and grew to my imagination, did that same melancholy merge into fear, that pity into repulsion. So true it is, and so terrible, too, that up to a certain point the thought or sight of misery enlist our best affections; but, in certain special cases, beyond that point it does not. They err who would assert that invariably this is owing to the inherent selfishness of the human heart. It rather proceeds from a certain hopelessness of remedying excessive and organic ill. To a sensitive being, pity is not seldom pain. And when at last it is perceived that such pity cannot lead to effectual succor, common sense bids the soul be rid of it. What I saw that morning persuaded me that the scrivener was the victim of innate and incurable disorder. I might give alms to his body; but his body did not pain him; it was his soul that suffered, and his soul I could not reach.

I did not accomplish the purpose of going to Trinity Church that morning. Somehow, the things I had seen disqualified me for the time from church-going. I walked homeward, thinking what I would do with Bartleby. Finally, I resolved upon this—I would put certain calm questions to him the next morning, touching his history, etc., and if he declined to answer them openly and unreservedly (and I supposed he would prefer not), then to give him a twenty dollar bill over and above whatever I might owe him, and tell him his services were no longer required; but that if in any other way I could assist him, I would be happy to do so, especially if he desired to return to his native place, wherever that might be, I would willingly help to defray the expenses. Moreover, if, after reaching home, he found himself at any time in want of aid, a letter from him would be sure of a reply.

The next morning came.

"Bartleby," said I, gently calling to him behind his screen.

No reply.

"Bartleby," said I, in a still gentler tone, "come here; I am not going to ask you to do anything you would prefer not to do—I simply wish to speak to you."

Upon this he noiselessly slid into view.

"Will you tell me, Bartleby, where you were born?"

"I would prefer not to."

"Will you tell me *anything* about yourself?"

"I would prefer not to."

"But what reasonable objection can you have to speak to me? I feel friendly towards you."

He did not look at me while I spoke, but kept his glance fixed upon my bust of Cicero, which, as I then sat, was directly behind me, some six inches above my head.

"What is your answer, Bartleby?" said I, after waiting a considerable time for a reply, during which his countenance remained immovable, only there was the faintest conceivable tremor of the white attenuated mouth.

"At present I prefer to give no answer," he said, and retired into his hermitage.

It was rather weak in me I confess, but his manner, on this occasion, nettled me. Not only did there seem to lurk in it a certain calm disdain, but his perverseness seemed ungrateful, considering the undeniable good usage and indulgence he had received from me.

Again I sat ruminating what I should do. Mortified as I was at his behavior, and resolved as I had been to dismiss him when I entered my office, nevertheless I strangely felt something superstitious knocking at my heart, and forbidding me to carry out my purpose, and denouncing me for a villain if I dared to breathe one bitter word against this forlornest of mankind. At last, familiarly drawing my chair behind his screen, I sat down and said: "Bartleby, never mind, then, about revealing your history; but let me entreat you, as a friend, to comply as far as may be with the usages of this office. Say now, you will help to examine papers to-morrow or next day: in short, say now, that in a day or two you will begin to be a little reasonable:—say so, Bartleby."

"At present I would prefer not to be a little reasonable," was his mildly cadaverous reply.

Just then the folding-doors opened, and Nippers approached. He seemed suffering from an unusually bad night's rest, induced by severer indigestion than common. He overheard those final words of Bartleby.

"Prefer not, eh?" gritted Nippers—"I'd *prefer* him, if I were you, sir," addressing me—"I'd *prefer* him; I'd give him preferences, the stubborn mule! What is it, sir, pray, that he *prefers* not to do now?"

Bartleby moved not a limb.

"Mr. Nippers," said I, "I'd prefer that you would withdraw for the present."

Somehow, of late, I had got into the way of involuntarily using this word "prefer" upon all sorts of not exactly suitable occasions. And I trembled to think that my contact with the scrivener had already and seriously affected me in a mental way. And what further and deeper aberration might it not yet produce? This apprehension had not been without efficacy in determining me to summary measures.

As Nippers, looking very sour and sulky, was departing, Turkey blandly and deferentially approached.

"With submission, sir," said he, "yesterday I was thinking about Bartleby here, and I think that if he would but prefer to take a quart of good ale every day, it would do much towards mending him, and enabling him to assist in examining his papers."

"So you have got the word, too," said I, slightly excited.

"With submission, what word, sir?" asked Turkey, respectfully crowding himself into the contracted space behind the screen, and by so doing, making me jostle the scrivener. "What word, sir?"

"I would prefer to be left alone here," said Bartleby, as if offended at being mobbed in his privacy.

"That's the word, Turkey," said I—*"that's* it."

"Oh, *prefer?* oh yes—queer word. I never use it myself. But, sir, as I was saying, if he would but prefer—"

"Turkey," interrupted I, "you will please withdraw."

"Oh, certainly, sir, if you prefer that I should."

As he opened the folding-door to retire, Nippers at his desk caught a glimpse of me, and asked whether I would prefer to have a certain paper copied on blue paper or white. He did not in the least roguishly accent the word prefer. It was plain that it involuntarily rolled from his tongue. I thought to myself, surely I must get rid of a demented man, who already has in some degree turned the tongues, if not the heads of myself and clerks. But I thought it prudent not to break the dismission at once.

The next day I noticed that Bartleby did nothing but stand at his window in his dead-wall revery. Upon asking him why he did not write, he said that he had decided upon doing no more writing.

"Why, how now? what next?" exclaimed I, "do no more writing?"

"No more."

"And what is the reason?"

"Do you not see the reason for yourself?" he indifferently replied.

I looked steadfastly at him, and perceived that his eyes looked dull and glazed. Instantly it occurred to me, that his unexampled diligence in copying by his dim window for the first few weeks of his stay with me might have temporarily impaired his vision.

I was touched. I said something in condolence with him. I hinted that of course he did wisely in abstaining from writing for a while; and urged him to embrace that opportunity of taking wholesome exercise in the open air. This, however, he did not do. A few days after this, my other clerks being absent, and being in a great hurry to dispatch certain letters by the mail, I thought that, having nothing else earthly to do, Bartleby would surely be less inflexible than usual, and carry these letters to the Post Office. But he blankly declined. So, much to my inconvenience, I went myself.

Still added days went by. Whether Bartleby's eyes improved or not, I could not say. To all appearance, I thought they did. But when I asked him if they did, he vouchsafed no answer. At all events, he would do no copying. At last, in reply to my urgings, he informed me that he had permanently given up copying.

"What!" exclaimed I; "suppose your eyes should get entirely well—better than ever before—would you not copy then?"

"I have given up copying," he answered, and slid aside.

He remained as ever, a fixture in my chamber. Nay—if that were possible

—he became still more of a fixture than before. What was to be done? He would do nothing in the office; why should he stay there? In plain fact, he had now become a millstone to me, not only useless as a necklace, but afflictive to bear. Yet I was sorry for him. I speak less than truth when I say that, on his own account, he occasioned me uneasiness. If he would but have named a single relative or friend, I would instantly have written, and urged their taking the poor fellow away to some convenient retreat. But he seemed alone, absolutely alone in the universe. A bit of wreck in the mid-Atlantic. At length, necessities connected with my business tyrannized over all other considerations. Decently as I could, I told Bartleby that in six days time he must unconditionally leave the office. I warned him to take measures, in the interval, for procuring some other abode. I offered to assist him in this endeavor, if he himself would but take the first step towards a removal. "And when you finally quit me, Bartleby," added I, "I shall see that you go not away entirely unprovided. Six days from this hour, remember."

At the expiration of that period, I peeped behind the screen, and lo! Bartleby was there.

I buttoned up my coat, balanced myself; advanced slowly towards him, touched his shoulder, and said, "The time has come; you must quit this place; I am sorry for you; here is money; but you must go."

"I would prefer not," he replied, with his back still towards me.

"You *must.*"

He remained silent.

Now I had an unbounded confidence in this man's common honesty. He had frequently restored to me sixpences and shillings carelessly dropped upon the floor, for I am apt to be very reckless in such shirt-button affairs. The proceeding, then, which followed will not be deemed extraordinary.

"Bartleby," said I, "I owe you twelve dollars on account; here are thirty-two; the odd twenty are yours—Will you take it?" and I handed the bills towards him.

But he made no motion.

"I will leave them here, then," putting them under a weight on the table. Then taking my hat and cane and going to the door, I tranquilly turned and added—"After you have removed your things from these offices, Bartleby, you will of course lock the door—since every one is now gone for the day but you—and if you please, slip your key underneath the mat, so that I may have it in the morning. I shall not see you again; so good-by to you. If, hereafter, in your new place of abode, I can be of any service to you, do not fail to advise me by letter. Good-by, Bartleby, and fare you well."

But he answered not a word; like the last column of some ruined temple, he remained standing mute and solitary in the middle of the otherwise deserted room.

As I walked home in a pensive mood, my vanity got the better of my pity. I could not but highly plume myself on my masterly management in getting rid of Bartleby. Masterly I call it, and such it must appear to any dispassionate thinker. The beauty of my procedure seemed to consist in its perfect quietness. There was no vulgar bullying, no bravado of any sort, no choleric hectoring, and striding to and fro across the apartment, jerking out vehement commands for Bartleby to bundle himself off with his beggarly traps. Nothing of the kind. Without loudly bidding Bartleby depart—as an inferior genius might have done—I *assumed* the ground that depart he must; and upon that assumption built all I had to say. The more I thought over my procedure, the more I was charmed with it. Nevertheless, next morning, upon awakening, I had my doubts—I had somehow slept off the fumes of vanity. One of the coolest and wisest hours a man has, is just after he awakes in the morning. My procedure seemed as sagacious as ever—but only in theory. How it would prove in practice—there was the rub. It was truly a beautiful thought to have assumed Bartleby's departure; but, after all, that assumption was simply my own, and none of Bartleby's. The great point was, not whether I had assumed that he would quit me, but whether he would prefer so to do. He was more a man of preferences than assumptions.

After breakfast, I walked down town, arguing the probabilities *pro* and *con*. One moment I thought it would prove a miserable failure, and Bartleby would be found all alive at my office as usual; the next moment it seemed certain that I should find his chair empty. And so I kept veering about. At the corner of Broadway and Canal Street, I saw quite an excited group of people standing in earnest conversation.

"I'll take odds he doesn't," said a voice as I passed.

"Doesn't go?—done!" said I, "put up your money."

I was instinctively putting my hand in my pocket to produce my own, when I remembered that this was an election day. The words I had overheard bore no reference to Bartleby, but to the success or non-success of some candidate for the mayoralty. In my intent frame of mind, I had, as it were, imagined that all Broadway shared in my excitement, and were debating the same question with me. I passed on, very thankful that the uproar of the street screened my momentary absent-mindedness.

As I had intended, I was earlier than usual at my office door. I stood listening for a moment. All was still. He must be gone. I tried the knob. The door was locked. Yes, my procedure had worked to a charm; he indeed must be vanished. Yet a certain melancholy mixed with this: I was almost sorry for my brilliant success. I was fumbling under the door mat for the key, which Bartleby was to have left there for me, when accidentally my knee knocked against a panel, producing a summoning sound, and in response a voice came to me from within—"Not yet; I am occupied."

It was Bartleby.

I was thunderstruck. For an instant I stood like the man who, pipe in mouth, was killed one cloudless afternoon long ago in Virginia, by summer lightning; at his own warm open window he was killed, and remained leaning out there upon the dreamy afternoon, till some one touched him, when he fell.

"Not gone!" I murmured at last. But again obeying that wondrous ascendancy which the inscrutable scrivener had over me, and from which ascendancy, for all my chafing, I could not completely escape, I slowly went down stairs and out into the street, and while walking round the block, considered what I should next do in this unheard-of perplexity. Turn the man out by an actual thrusting I could not; to drive him away by calling him hard names would not do; calling in the police was an unpleasant idea; and yet, permit him to enjoy his cadaverous triumph over me—this, too, I could not think of. What was to be done? or, if nothing could be done, was there anything further that I could *assume* in the matter? Yes, as before I had prospectively assumed that Bartleby would depart, so now I might retrospectively assume that departed he was. In the legitimate carrying out of this assumption, I might enter my office in a great hurry, and pretending not to see Bartleby at all, walk straight against him as if he were air. Such a proceeding would in a singular degree have the appearance of a home-thrust. It was hardly possible that Bartleby could withstand such an application of the doctrine of assumptions. But upon second thoughts the success of the plan seemed rather dubious. I resolved to argue the matter over with him again.

"Bartleby," said I, entering the office, with a quietly severe expression, "I am seriously displeased. I am pained, Bartleby. I had thought better of you. I had imagined you of such a gentlemanly organization, that in any delicate dilemma a slight hint would suffice—in short, an assumption. But it appears I am deceived. Why," I added, unaffectedly starting, "you have not even touched that money yet," pointing to it, just where I had left it the evening previous.

He answered nothing.

"Will you, or will you not, quit me?" I now demanded in a sudden passion, advancing close to him.

"I would prefer *not* to quit you," he replied, gently emphasizing the *not*.

"What earthly right have you to stay here? Do you pay any rent? Do you pay my taxes? Or is this property yours?"

He answered nothing.

"Are you ready to go on and write now? Are your eyes recovered? Could you copy a small paper for me this morning? or help examine a few lines? or step round to the Post Office? In a word, will you do anything at all, to give a coloring to your refusal to depart the premises?"

He silently retired into his hermitage.

I was now in such a state of nervous resentment that I thought it but prudent to check myself at present from further demonstrations. Bartleby and I were alone. I remembered the tragedy of the unfortunate Adams and the still more unfortunate Colt in the solitary office of the latter; and how poor Colt, being dreadfully incensed by Adams, and imprudently permitting himself to get wildly excited, was at unawares hurried into his fatal act—an act which certainly no man could possibly deplore more than the actor himself. Often it had occurred to me in my ponderings upon the subject, that had that altercation taken place in the public street, or at a private residence, it would not have terminated as it did. It was the circumstance of being alone in a solitary office, up stairs, of a building entirely unhallowed by humanizing domestic associations—an uncarpeted office, doubtless, of a dusty, haggard sort of appearance—this it must have been, which greatly helped to enhance the irritable desperation of the hapless Colt.

But when this old Adam of resentment rose in me and tempted me concerning Bartleby, I grappled him and threw him. How? Why, simply by recalling the divine injunction: "A new commandment give I unto you, that ye love one another." Yes, this it was that saved me. Aside from higher considerations, charity often operates as a vastly wise and prudent principle—a great safeguard to its possessor. Men have committed murder for jealousy's sake, and anger's sake, and hatred's sake, and selfishness' sake, and spiritual pride's sake; but no man, that ever I heard of, ever committed a diabolical murder for sweet charity's sake. Mere self-interest, then, if no better motive can be enlisted, should, especially with high-tempered men, prompt all beings to charity and philanthropy. At any rate, upon the occasion in question, I strove to drown my exasperated feelings towards the scrivener by benevolently construing his conduct. Poor fellow, poor fellow! thought I, he don't mean anything; and besides, he has seen hard times, and ought to be indulged.

I endeavored, also, immediately to occupy myself, and at the same time to comfort my despondency. I tried to fancy, that in the course of the morning, at such time as might prove agreeable to him, Bartleby, of his own free accord, would emerge from his hermitage and take up some decided line of march in the direction of the door. But no. Half-past twelve o'clock came; Turkey began to glow in the face, overturn his inkstand, and become generally obstreperous; Nippers abated down into quietude and courtesy; Ginger Nut munched his noon apple; and Bartleby remained standing at his window in one of his profoundest dead-wall reveries. Will it be credited? Ought I to acknowledge it? That afternoon I left the office without saying one further word to him.

Some days now passed, during which, at leisure intervals I looked a little into "Edwards on the Will," and "Priestly on Necessity." Under the circumstances, those books induced a salutary feeling. Gradually I slid into the persuasion that these troubles of mine, touching the scrivener, had been all predestinated from eternity, and Bartleby was billeted upon me for some mysterious purpose of an all-wise Providence, which it was not for a mere mortal like me to fathom. Yes, Bartleby, stay there behind your screen, thought I; I shall persecute you no more; you are harmless and noiseless as any of these old chairs; in short, I never feel so private as when I know you are here. At last I see it, I feel it; I penetrate to the predestinated purpose of my life. I am content. Others may have loftier parts to enact; but my mission in this world, Bartleby, is to furnish you with office-room for such period as you may see fit to remain.

I believe that this wise and blessed frame of mind would have continued with me, had it not been for the unsolicited and uncharitable remarks obtruded upon me by my professional friends who visited the rooms. But thus it often is, that the constant friction of illiberal minds wears out at last the best resolves of the more generous. Though to be sure, when I reflected upon it, it was not strange that people entering my office should be struck by the peculiar aspect of the unaccountable Bartleby, and so be tempted to throw out some sinister observations concerning him. Sometimes an attorney, having business with me, and calling at my office, and finding no one but the scrivener there, would undertake to obtain some sort of precise information from him touching my whereabouts; but without heeding his idle talk, Bartleby would remain standing immovable in the middle of the room. So after contemplating him in that position for a time, the attorney would depart, no wiser than he came.

Also, when a reference was going on, and the room full of lawyers and witnesses, and business driving fast, some deeply-occupied legal gentleman present, seeing Bartleby wholly unemployed, would request him to run round to his (the legal gentleman's) office and fetch some papers for him. Thereupon, Bartleby would tranquilly decline, and yet remain idle as before. Then the lawyer would give a great stare, and turn to me. And what could I say? At last I was made aware that all through the circle of my professional acquaintance, a whisper of wonder was running round, having reference to the strange creature I kept at my office. This worried me very much. And as the idea came upon me of his possibly turning out a long-lived man, and keep occupying my chambers, and denying my authority; and perplexing my visitors; and scandalizing my professional reputation; and casting a general gloom over the premises; keeping soul and body together to the last upon his savings (for doubtless he spent but half a dime a day), and in the end perhaps outlive me, and claim possession of my office by right of his perpetual occupancy: as all these dark anticipations crowded upon me more and more, and my friends continually intruded their relentless remarks upon the apparition in my room, a great change was wrought in me. I resolved to gather all my faculties together, and forever rid me of this intolerable incubus.

Ere evolving any complicated project, however, adapted to this end,

I first simply suggested to Bartleby the propriety of his permanent departure. In a calm and serious tone, I commended the idea to his careful and mature consideration. But, having taken three days to meditate upon it, he apprised me, that his original determination remained the same; in short, that he still preferred to abide with me.

What shall I do? I now said to myself, buttoning up my coat to the last button. What shall I do? what ought I to do? what does conscience say I *should* do with this man, or, rather, ghost. Rid myself of him, I must; go, he shall. But how? You will not thrust him, the poor, pale, passive mortal—you will not thrust such a helpless creature out of your door? you will not dishonor yourself by such cruelty? No, I will not, I cannot do that. Rather would I let him live and die here, and then mason up his remains in the wall. What, then, will you do? For all your coaxing, he will not budge. Bribes he leaves under your own paper-weight on your table; in short, it is quite plain that he prefers to cling to you.

Then something severe, something unusual must be done. What! surely you will not have him collared by a constable, and commit his innocent pallor to the common jail? And upon what ground could you procure such a thing to be done?—a vagrant, is he? What! he a vagrant, a wanderer, who refuses to budge? It is because he will *not* be a vagrant, then, that you seek to count him *as* a vagrant. That is too absurd. No visible means of support: there I have him. Wrong again: for indubitably he *does* support himself, and that is the only unanswerable proof that any man can show of his possessing the means so to do. No more, then. Since he will not quit me, I must quit him. I will change my offices; I will move elsewhere, and give him fair notice, that if I find him on my new premises I will then proceed against him as a common trespasser.

Acting accordingly, next day I thus addressed him: "I find these chambers too far from the City Hall; the air is unwholesome. In a word, I propose to remove my offices next week, and shall no longer require your services. I tell you this now, in order that you may seek another place."

He made no reply, and nothing more was said.

On the appointed day I engaged carts and men, proceeded to my chambers, and, having but little furniture, everything was removed in a few hours. Throughout, the scrivener remained standing behind the screen, which I directed to be removed the last thing. It was withdrawn; and, being folded up like a huge folio, left him the motionless occupant of a naked room. I stood in the entry watching him a moment, while something from within me upbraided me.

I re-entered, with my hand in my pocket—and—and my heart in my mouth.

"Good-by, Bartleby; I am going—good-by, and God some way bless you; and take that," slipping something in his hand. But it dropped upon the floor, and then—strange to say—I tore myself from him whom I had so longed to be rid of.

Established in my new quarters, for a day or two I kept the door locked, and started at every footfall in the passages. When I returned to my rooms, after any little absence, I would pause at the threshold for an instant, and attentively listen, ere applying my key. But these fears were needless. Bartleby never came nigh me.

I thought all was going well, when a perturbed-looking stranger visited me, inquiring whether I was the person who had recently occupied rooms at No. — Wall Street.

Full of forebodings, I replied that I was.

"Then, sir," said the stranger, who proved a lawyer, "you are responsible for the man you left there. He refuses to do any copying; he refuses to do anything; he says he prefers not to; and he refuses to quit the premises."

"I am very sorry, sir," said I, with assumed tranquillity, but an inward tremor, "but, really, the man you allude to is nothing to me—he is no relation or apprentice of mine, that you should hold me responsible for him."

"In mercy's name, who is he?"

"I certainly cannot inform you. I know nothing about him. Formerly I employed him as a copyist; but he has done nothing for me now for some time past."

"I shall settle him, then—good morning, sir."

Several days passed, and I heard nothing more; and, though I often felt a charitable prompting to call at the place and see poor Bartleby, yet a certain squeamishness, of I know not what, withheld me.

All is over with him, by this time, thought I, at last, when, through another week, no further intelligence reached me. But, coming to my room the day after, I found several persons waiting at my door in a high state of nervous excitement.

"That's the man—here he comes," cried the foremost one, whom I recognized as the lawyer who had previously called upon me alone.

"You must take him away, sir, at once," cried a portly person among them, advancing upon me, and whom I knew to be the handlord of No. — Wall Street. "These gentlemen, my tenants, cannot stand it any longer; Mr. B——," pointing to the lawyer, "has turned him out of his room, and he now persists in haunting the building generally, sitting upon the banisters of the stairs by day, and sleeping in the entry by night. Everybody is concerned; clients are leaving the offices; some fears are entertained of a mob; something you must do, and that without delay."

Aghast at this torrent, I fell back before it, and would fain have locked myself in my new quarters. In vain I persisted that Bartleby was nothing to me—no more than to any one else. In vain—I was the last person known to have anything to do with him, and they held me to the terrible account. Fearful, then, of being exposed in the papers (as one person present obscurely threatened), I considered the matter, and, at length, said, that if the lawyer would give me a confidential interview with the scrivener, in his (the lawyer's) own room, I would, that afternoon, strive my best to rid them of the nuisance they complained of.

Going up stairs to my old haunt, there was Bartleby silently sitting upon the banister at the landing.

"What are you doing here, Bartleby?" said I.

"Sitting upon the banister," he mildly replied.

I motioned him into the lawyer's room, who then left us.

"Bartleby," said I, "are you aware that you are the cause of great tribulation to me, by persisting in occupying the entry after being dismissed from the office?"

No answer.

"Now one of two things must take place. Either you must do something, or something must be done to you. Now what sort of business would you like to engage in? Would you like to re-engage in copying for some one?"

"No; I would prefer not to make any change."

"Would you like a clerkship in a dry-good store?"

"There is too much confinement about that. No, I would not like a clerkship; but I am not particular."

"Too much confinement," I cried, "why you keep yourself confined all the time!"

"I would prefer not to take a clerkship," he rejoined, as if to settle that little item at once.

"How would a bar-tender's business suit you? There is no trying of the eye-sight in that."

"I would not like it at all; though, as I said before, I am not particular."

His unwonted wordiness inspirited me. I returned to the charge.

"Well, then, would you like to travel through the country collecting bills for the merchants? That would improve your health."

"No, I would prefer to be doing something else."

"How, then, would going as a companion to Europe, to entertain some young gentleman with your conversation—how would that suit you?"

"Not at all. It does not strike me that there is anything definite about that. I like to be stationary. But I am not particular."

"Stationary you shall be, then," I cried, now losing all patience, and, for the first time in all my exasperating connection with him, fairly flying into a passion. "If you do not go away from these premises before night, I shall feel bound—indeed, I *am* bound—to—to—to quit the premises myself!" I rather absurdly concluded, knowing not with what possible threat to try to frighten his immobility into compliance. Despairing of all further efforts, I was precipitately leaving him, when a final thought occurred to me—one which had not been wholly unindulged before.

"Bartleby," said I, in the kindest tone I could assume under such exciting circumstances, "will you go home with me now—not to my office, but my dwelling—and remain there till we can conclude upon some convenient arrangement for you at our leisure? Come, let us start now, right away."

"No: at present I would prefer not to make any change at all."

I answered nothing; but, effectually dodging every one by the suddenness and rapidity of my flight, rushed from the building, ran up Wall Street towards Broadway, and jumping into the first omnibus, was soon removed from pursuit. As soon as tranquillity returned, I distinctly perceived that I had now done all that I possibly could, both in respect to the demands of the landlord and his tenants, and with regard to my own desire and sense of duty, to benefit Bartleby, and shield him from rude persecution. I now strove to be entirely care-free and quiescent; and my conscience justified me in the attempt; though, indeed, it was not so successful as I could have wished. So fearful was I of being again hunted out by the incensed landlord and his exasperated tenants, that, surrendering my business to Nippers, for a few days, I drove about the upper part of the town and through the suburbs, in my rockaway; crossed over to Jersey City and Hoboken, and paid fugitive visits to Manhattanville and Astoria. In fact, I almost lived in my rockaway for the time.

When again I entered my office, lo, a note from the landlord lay upon the desk. I opened it with trembling hands. It informed me that the writer had sent to the police, and had Bartleby removed to the Tombs as a vagrant. Moreover, since I knew more about him than any one else, he wished me to appear at that place, and make a suitable statement of the facts. These tidings had a conflicting effect upon me. At first I was indignant; but, at last, almost approved. The landlord's energetic, summary disposition, had led him to adopt a procedure which I do not think I would have decided upon myself; and yet, as a last resort, under such peculiar circumstances, it seemed the only plan.

As I afterwards learned, the poor scrivener, when told that he must be conducted to the Tombs, offered not the slightest obstacle, but, in his pale, unmoving way, silently acquiesced.

Some of the compassionate and curious bystanders joined the party; and headed by one of the constables arm in arm with Bartleby, the silent procession filed its way through all the noise, and heat, and joy of the roaring thoroughfares at noon.

The same day I received the note, I went to the Tombs, or, to speak more properly, the Halls of Justice. Seeking the right officer, I stated the purpose of my call, and was informed that the individual I described was, indeed, within. I then assured the functionary that Bartleby was a perfectly honest man, and greatly to be compassionated, however unaccountably eccentric.

I narrated all I knew, and closed by suggesting the idea of letting him remain in as indulgent confinement as possible, till something less harsh might be done—though, indeed, I hardly knew what. At all events, if nothing else could be decided upon, the alms-house must receive him. I then begged to have an interview.

Being under no disgraceful charge, and quite serene and harmless in all his ways, they had permitted him freely to wander about the prison, and, especially, in the inclosed grass-platted yards thereof. And so I found him there, standing all alone in the quietest of the yards, his face towards a high wall, while all around, from the narrow slits of the jail windows, I thought I saw peering out upon him the eyes of murderers and thieves.

"Bartleby!"

"I know you," he said, without looking round—"and I want nothing to say to you."

"It was not I that brought you here, Bartleby," said I, keenly pained at his implied suspicion. "And to you, this should not be so vile a place. Nothing reproachful attaches to you by being here. And see, it is not so sad a place as one might think. Look, there is the sky, and here is the grass."

"I know where I am," he replied, but would say nothing more, and so I left him.

As I entered the corridor again, a broad meat-like man, in an apron, accosted me, and, jerking his thumb over his shoulder, said—"Is that your friend?"

"Yes."

"Does he want to starve? If he does, let him live on the prison fare, that's all."

"Who are you?" asked I, not knowing what to make of such an unofficially speaking person in such a place.

"I am the grub-man. Such gentlemen as have friends here, hire me to provide them with something good to eat."

"Is this so?" said I, turning to the turnkey.

He said it was.

"Well, then," said I, slipping some silver into the grub-man's hands (for so they called him), "I want you to give particular attention to my friend there; let him have the best dinner you can get. And you must be as polite to him as possible."

"Introduce me, will you?" said the grub-man, looking at me with an expression which seemed to say he was all impatience for an opportunity to give a specimen of his breeding.

Thinking it would prove of benefit to the scrivener, I acquiesced; and, asking the grub-man his name, went up with him to Bartleby.

"Bartleby, this is a friend; you will find him very useful to you."

"Your sarvant, sir, your sarvant," said the grub-man, making a low salutation behind his apron. "Hope you find it pleasant here, sir; nice grounds—cool apartments—hope you'll stay with us sometime—try to make it agreeable. What will you have for dinner to-day?"

"I prefer not to dine to-day," said Bartleby, turning away. "It would disagree with me; I am unused to dinners." So saying, he slowly moved to the other side of the inclosure, and took up a position fronting the dead-wall.

"How's this?" said the grub-man, addressing me with a stare of astonishment. "He's odd, ain't he?"

"I think he is a little deranged," said I, sadly.

"Deranged? deranged is it? Well, now, upon my word, I thought that friend of yourn was a gentleman forger; they are always pale and genteel-like, them forgers. I can't help pity 'em—can't help it, sir. Did you know Monroe Edwards?" he added, touchingly, and paused. Then, laying his hand piteously on my shoulder, sighed, "he died of consumption at Sing-Sing. So you weren't acquainted with Monroe?"

"No, I was never socially acquainted with any forgers. But I cannot stop longer. Look to my friend yonder. You will not lose by it. I will see you again."

Some few days after this, I again obtained admission to the Tombs, and went through the corridors in quest of Bartleby; but without finding him.

"I saw him coming from his cell not long ago," said a turnkey, "may be he's gone to loiter in the yards."

So I went in that direction.

"Are you looking for the silent man?" said another turnkey, passing me. "Yonder he lies—sleeping in the yard there. 'Tis not twenty minutes since I saw him lie down."

The yard was entirely quiet. It was not accessible to the common prisoners. The surrounding walls, of amazing thickness, kept off all sounds behind them. The Egyptian character of the masonry weighed upon me with its gloom. But a soft imprisoned turf grew under foot. The heart of the eternal pyramids, it seemed, wherein, by some strange magic, through the clefts, grass-seed, dropped by birds, had sprung.

Strangely huddled at the base of the wall, his knees drawn up, and lying on his side, his head touching the cold stones, I saw the wasted Bartleby. But nothing stirred. I paused; then went close up to him; stooped over, and saw that his dim eyes were open; otherwise he seemed profoundly sleeping. Something prompted me to touch him. I felt his hand, when a tingling shiver ran up my arm and down my spine to my feet.

The round face of the grub-man peered upon me now. "His dinner is ready. Won't he dine to-day, either? Or does he live without dining?"

"Lives without dining," said I, and closed the eyes.

"Eh!—He's asleep, ain't he?"

"With kings and counselors," murmured I.

There would seem little need for proceeding further in this history. Imagination will readily supply the meagre recital of poor Bartleby's interment. But, ere parting with the reader, let me say, that if this little narrative has sufficiently interested him, to awaken curiosity as to who Bartleby was, and what manner of life he led prior to the present narrator's making his acquaintance, I can only reply, that in such curiosity I fully share, but am wholly unable to gratify it. Yet here I hardly know whether I should divulge one little item of rumor, which came to my ear a few months after the scrivener's decease. Upon what basis it rested, I could never ascertain; and hence, how true it is I cannot now tell. But, inasmuch as this vague report has not been without a certain suggestive interest to me, however sad, it may prove the same with some others; and so I will briefly mention it. The report was this: that Bartleby had been a subordinate clerk in the Dead Letter Office at Washington, from which he had been suddenly removed by a change in the administration. When I think over this rumor, hardly can I express the emotions which seize me. Dead letters! does it not sound like dead men? Conceive a man by nature and misfortune prone to a pallid hopelessness, can any business seem more fitted to heighten it than that of continually handling these dead letters, and assorting them for the flames? For by the cart-load they are annually burned. Sometimes from out the folded paper the pale clerk takes a ring—the finger it was meant for, perhaps, moulders in the grave; a bank-note sent in swiftest charity—he whom it would relieve, nor eats nor hungers any more; pardon for those who died despairing; hope for those who died unhoping; good tidings for those who died stifled by unrelieved calamities. On errands of life, these letters speed to death.

Ah, Bartleby! Ah, humanity!

Glossary of Literary Terms

Abstraction: An idea or quality withdrawn from the particular act or concrete object in which it originally inhered. Numbers, classes, and attributes are all abstractions and do not exist by themselves but subsist in objects and actions. The senses perceive concrete things; the mind may make abstract meanings of them. For example, Melville's narrator in "Bartleby the Scrivener" draws out of the concrete act (" . . . restored to me sixpences and shillings carelessly dropped upon the floor . . .") the abstraction which he expresses as "this man's common *honesty.*" In much modern fiction abstractions are avoided so that the richness, complexity, and preciseness of a specific act or object may be presented. Abstract ideas are provoked, of course, but they are substantiated by concrete *circumstantiality.* The theme of a story is not the story but is abstracted from it, and the theme is relatively meaningless until it is perceived in the specific instance from which it is drawn. See also *Image* and *Circumstantiality.*

Action: The literal chain of events in a story, especially the movement from disturbance to equilibrium. As distinguished from plot, action denotes the events themselves, not the unifying arrangement of those events. See also *Plot.*

Allegory: A narrative in which, point to point, abstractions are represented by specific characters, actions, or objects. An allegory may or may not reflect, on the literal level, normal human experiences. But it always reflects a "higher" meaning, whether intellectual, moral, religious, or political. And it must correspond strictly and consistently at every point to the higher meaning—the idea or system of ideas—it is reflecting. A successful allegory, then, must meet three requirements: (1) the literal events, characters, and objects must make for effective, though not necessarily versimilar, narrative; (2) the narrative details must be continuously consistent with their abstract equivalents; (3) the higher meaning to which the details point must be applicable to broad or universal human experience. See pages 169–70.

Allusion: A brief reference, either tacit or overt, to a person, place, event, or well-known work of art. The associations evoked by the reference add clarification and often depth of meaning. An allusion may also suggest comparison or contrast to some aspect of the story in which the allusion is made.

Ambiguity: In literature, a figurative use of language, closely allied to a pun; multiple meanings of a word or phrase are intended and one meaning is as valid in context as is another. It may also signify, in fiction, the intentional manipulation of elements in a story so as to deliver multiple, sometimes even contradictory, interpretations and significances. See pages 151, 170, 207–8.

Antagonist: See *Plot* and *Character.*

Atmosphere: The over-all mood or feeling aroused by setting (time and place), characters, events, imagery, and theme. Atmosphere may arouse tensions and expectations in the reader and provide the inclusive surroundings befitting the events that transpire and the characters involved in them. Atmosphere is allied with, but is to be distinguished from, tone and setting. See pages 1–2, 16–18, 45–46.

Attitude: The author's and/or narrator's prevailing disposition toward his subject (characters, events, and theme), toward himself, and toward his audience.

Carpe diem: Literally, "seize the day." A common theme in literature which urges the value and necessity of making the fullest use of time and opportunity before they are taken away. Frequently appears in combination with *ubi sunt* theme or motif. See *Motif, Theme,* and page 144.

Catastrophe: See *Plot.*

Character: Denotes the actors in imaginative literature and their particular traits and personalities. They may be in conflict with one another or with some force such as Nature, Fate, Destiny, or their own dual nature. The character who commands our chief interest and who is most affected by the conflict of the story is the *protagonist,* or hero. The *protagonist* need not necessarily be good, noble, or virtuous; he may be mean and despicable. However, he is usually, in varying degrees, a combination of both virtue and vice—that is, a *rounded character,* as opposed to a *stock* or *flat character* who represents only a single trait, motive, quality, or class. (A stock character may exhibit more than one trait, but he lacks any significant individuality that would distinguish him as a particular human entity rather than a type or class. Stock characters are *stereotypes,* such as the jolly Mammy; the go-getting, golf-playing Man in the Gray Flannel Suit; the Southern Belle; etc. But such stereotypes may often be depicted by employing *caricature,* a comic and satiric representation wherein some feature or trait of character is exaggerated and excessively distorted to create a ludicrous incongruity.) The character or force opposed to the protagonist is the *antagonist.* Again, like the protangonist, he may be either good, bad, or both, and whether he acts as protagonist or antagonist is determined by whether he is of primary or secondary interest in the story. The antagonist is usually the chief embodiment of whatever opposition confronts the central character. *Background characters,* as part of the general world surrounding the main characters, are usually flat and undeveloped in ratio to the completeness of *motivation* and personality given the central figures. This is necessary in a short story because of severely limited space; however, in a novella or novel the background characters may be given full individuality and more complete motives and characteristics. With a fully developed character, individual motivation must be clear and seen as the result of moral, ethical, or religious values working in conjunction with personality traits and idiosyncrasies of temper, humor, prevailing disposition, virtues, and vices. The character's action and response to the situation, which he creates or in which he finds himself by chance, must be completely consistent with his nature so that the action grows out of his personality and is the inevitable consequence of his characteristics. In fiction a character can be inconsistent only to the degree that there is an element of inconsistency in all people; however, the grounds for a character's inconsistency must be made apparent. A fully rounded character, like a human being, has a certain opaqueness and has the ability to act somewhat unexpectedly, though his actions should always be believable in terms of the traits identifying his nature. A character may be *static* (unchanged by the conflict he endures) or *developing* (transformed by the experience dramatized in the story) as determined by the initial flexibility ascribed to his nature at the beginning of his struggle. See pages 68–69, 107–8, 116, 132–34, 153.

Circumstantiality: The specific and particular details of imagery and action in a narrative from which a reader infers a situation or circumstance. It may provide the particulars of an unstated generalization. For instance: "James flicked imaginary ashes off his cigarette. He saw the sweep hand of his watch make a half circle before he rose again to look out the window." From these details we know that James is nervous and impatient. In addition, circumstantiality is a primary means of creating an illusion of reality, for it is in the circumstances of an event that we ourselves perceive conscious experience.

Cliché: A trite, overused phrase or expression, usually metaphorical in origin, but dulled by too frequent repetition; for example, "rained cats and dogs," "the old man" (for father or husband), "tickled to death," "quick on the trigger." The term may also apply to a stock situation, character, conflict, or resolution which has been used and reused until hackneyed. A wagon train drawn up in a circle and fighting off Indians only to be saved in the "nick of time" (a verbal cliché) by the sudden appearance of a troop of cavalry is a cliché of situation.

Climax: See *Plot.*

Coincidence: A chance occurrence of events. Its use is condemned in fiction if it serves illogically to solve the problem presented in the story. See pages 48–49, 69–70, and *Plot.*

Comedy: See pages 250, 261–63.

Complication: See *Plot.*

Compression: See *Density.*

Conceit: A figure of speech—a metaphorical image—which creates an elaborate (and sometimes shocking) parallel between objects and ideas which, on the surface, may appear to be dissimilar. See *Imagery.*

Concentration: See *Density.*

Concrete: See *Abstraction* and *Circumstantiality.*

Conflict: See *Plot.*

Convention: Any technique, device, or rule which by common agreement and practice is accepted; an artificiality that is considered proper and correct. A convention is usually condemned when used for its own sake and when it fails to deliver fresh insight and awareness.

Denouement: See *Plot.*

Density: The quality of compactness, compression, and concentration resulting from a strict economy in presentation and a skillful use of such devices as *symbol, ambiguity, irony,* and *allusion.* The ultimate degree of density is to be found in poetry, where emotion and meaning are compressed into the least space. Most short stories are characterized by a considerable degree of density. The greater the degree of density the greater the degree of *intensity;* just as a spring, compressed to its smallest size, reacts with greatest intensity and force when it is released, so the impact of a short story achieves much of its force from its concentrated and compact method of presentation.

Deus ex machina: "God from the machine"—the appearance of a god from the machinery which lowered him onto the stage in Greek drama so that he might solve the principal problem in the play. Thus the term denotes the direct hand of Fate or an agency of Destiny; it is also used at times to mean an artificial contrivance or coincidence which "illegitimately" resolves the tensions in a story.

Didactic: Fiction designed to persuade, argue, or propagandize rather than convey honest experience and objective meaning. See *Objectivity.*

Discovery: See *Plot.* See also pages 69, 93, 143–44.

Dramatic: An adjective used to denote fiction marked by powerful tensions, clear-cut conflicts, a high degree of concreteness rather than abstractness, and little or no authorial commentary on the significance of events in the work. See *Point of view.*

Dramatic irony: See *Irony.*

Enveloping action: The social background or milieu which surrounds the characters in a story. It may represent moral, social, and environmental conditions of the society in which a character exists, and though not specifically a part of the dramatized events of the story, enveloping action may exert force upon the characters involved and partially relate their actions to a broader social significance. It may be thought of as an aspect of atmosphere. See *Plot.*

Epilogue: A concluding or summarizing statement following the main body of a work. In classical drama, this speech was delivered by the chorus or an actor.

Epiphany: See pages 143–44, 150–54, 161–62.

Episodic: Fiction is episodic when the relationship between one episode and the next is tenuous and lacking in basic continuity, or when one action is largely independent of the action that come before and after. A journeying hero, such as Huckleberry Finn traveling down the Mississippi and encountering various crises along the river, usually imparts an episodic structure to fiction. See *Structure* and pages 169, 194–95, 203–4.

Exposition: The presentation of necessary information concerning characters and events as they existed prior to the first dramatized action in a narrative; background information needed to comprehend developing situations; part of *rising action* and *enveloping action.* See *Plot.*

Expressionism: See *Impressionism.*

Fable: A short moral tale, often preposterous at the literal level. Usually it illustrates some simple characteristic or aspect of human nature. See *Allegory, Symbol, Myth,* and pages 169–70, 194–95, 203–6, 221–22.

Falling action: See *Plot.*

Focus: The particular aspect of event or character toward which the author directs the reader's attention. Analogous to a "closeup" in a movie, one episode or event out of several is given special attention and becomes the center of concentration beside which all other aspects are relatively underdeveloped and secondary. The focus may shift from point to point throughout the story or it may remain fixed. A story as a whole may be focused primarily on character, setting, or theme; and the individual parts of the story may have their separate focus. For example, in "The Fall of the House of Usher" the story as a whole focuses on atmosphere, and within parts of the story there is focus on the setting (the fissure and windows in the house), on the action (the moments directly before Madeline emerges from the tomb), on character (Roderick's hypersensitivity). *Focus of character* answers the question "Whose story is it?" That is, focus of character directs the sequence of events directly to the person who is most intimately involved. *Focus of narrative* relates to the angle of vision from which the events and characters are seen and is thus equated with *point of view.* See pages 116, 132–33.

Foreshadowing: A hint or forewarning of significant events that are to emerge as the story progresses. Foreshadowing may appear in the form of motifs, symbols, allusions, recurrent images, or direct statement. See pages 2, 17–18, 33–34, 93, 144.

Form: See *Structure* and pages xi–xii, 94, 203–4.

Function: See pages xii–xiii, 1, 17–19, 169–70.

Genre: A distinctive type or category of literature, each with its own characteristics and forms, such as epic, lyric, tragedy, short story, novel, etc.

Hybris (*or Hubris*): See page 93.

Hyperbole: Overstatement and exaggeration for ironic effect. Opposite of *litotes.* See *Irony.*

Image: A verbal expression that makes a direct sensory appeal, calling to mind a sight, sound, smell, touch, taste, etc. It may be a direct description of a concrete object or act delivered in its specifics and particulars, or it may be a figure of speech—a metaphor, simile, personification, or symbol, wherein two things are compared. An image is always concrete and perceivable by the physical senses, though it may be equated with an abstraction. "Death," for instance, is not an image; "a skeleton draped in black and carrying a scythe in his hand" is a personification of death and is an image.

Impressionism, Impressionistic: A literary technique which for present purposes may be equated with *expressionism.* The impressionistic writer attempts to represent objects as they appear to the narrator or to a character during a particular moment or mood and from a given position. Little effort is made to represent an object in its literal reality. Advanced techniques of impressionism present a view of the world as it appears to the *inner* sight of a troubled or even abnormal individual; impressionism frequently attempts to depict the semiconscious or subconscious workings of a mind, or a "stream of consciousness." It relies heavily on imagery and lets the quality of the images reveal the emotional state of the perceiver.

In medias res: [Beginning] in the middle of the action.

Intensity: See *Density.*

Irony: A literary effect characterized by a discrepancy between appearance and reality, form and content, or the expression of a statement and the intention of that statement. Sarcasm—praise that implies disapproval, or disapproval that implies praise—is a simple form of *verbal irony,* a discrepancy that inheres in a word, an expression, or in their usage. Words and expressions with dual meanings, paradoxical statements, and verbal ambiguity belong to this type of irony, as does *understatement* or *litotes* (the deliberate underplaying of an emotion or situation). A second type is *dramatic irony,* wherein a character, for some reason, acts without awareness of the knowledge possessed by the reader, who perceives the full implications of a situation or the real dangers confronting the character. This sort of irony presents a discrepancy—which is often (but not always) comic—between what a character says and what the audience knows to be true. (See "Why I Live at the P.O." as an example of dramatic irony.) A third type of irony is called *situational irony,* or *irony of fate,* or *cosmic irony.* Here we find an incongruity between expectation and reward, between the appearance of events and their actuality. Events may appear to be leading a character to great success, whereas actually they are progressively directing him to ruin. *Reversals,* caused by quirks of Fate, or Chance, or powers of Nature that have not been taken into consideration, are frequently examples of situational irony. The *ironic view* is a term which may be used to denote a highly objective, disinvolved, godlike view of a character by an author who, with detachment and dispassion, sees all sides to all things. In this usage irony is equated with total awareness and complete objectivity. A character who attempts but fails to arrive at total awareness is the narrator in "The Aspern Papers." James reserves this awareness for only the reader.

Law of economy: See *Density* and pages xiii, 1.

Mood: The aspect of *attitude* which is emotional; the author and/or narrator's emotional reaction toward his subject. Also used to refer to the emotional response that the story creates in the reader. Rather loosely used as synonym for *attitude,* and sometimes *atmosphere.*

Motif: A lesser theme that is part of a larger theme; or a subsidiary theme that is recurrently stated throughout a work to reinforce the major theme (for example the recurring *ubi sunt* theme in "Youth"). Motif may also be used to designate a frequently recurring word, phrase, incident, idea, or character common in general literature; for instance, the "Cinderella" motif, the "Horatio Alger" motif, and the "Babe-in-the-Woods" (uninitiated stranger) motif. Motif may also apply to a conscious repetition of significant words or images in a given work. See pages 93–96.

Motivation: See *Character.*

Myth: A narrative embodying beliefs subscribed to by the people for whom and by whom the story was created. Originally tales involving men and gods, myths attempted to embody an interpretation of natural, psychological, and spiritual experience; thus they are always highly symbolical or allegorical. Belief in the truth of the idea which the narrative symbolized was often transferred to the acts and actors themselves, whom nonbelievers regarded as obviously imaginary. Thus the sacred truths of pagans, who believed in their mythic narratives, were false to Christians, just as the Christian myth was false to the pagans, even though both Christians and pagans may have subscribed to a common idea embodied in both their myths. Hence arises the basis for contradictory and confusing uses of the term. In common usage, myth is "a person or thing having only an imaginary or unverifiable existence" or "an ill-founded belief held uncritically, especially by an interested group." However, in literary usage, myth is a fictional construct that embodies and expresses man's most profound intuitional knowledge and/or instinctive awareness of fundamental truth. Thus in this usage a story, novel, or tale which approaches myth achieves the ultimate degree of universality, profundity, and density to which fiction can attain. See pages 169–70, 194–96, 203–8, 221–22.

Narrative: A series of unified events. See *Action* and *Plot.*

Narrator: See *Point of view.*

Novella: An extended prose narrative occupying a place in fiction midway between the short story and the novel—longer than a short story but shorter than most novels. Like a novel, it gives full development to characters, setting, and thematic implications; but like a short story, it usually maintains great compression and a strict unity of effect.

Objectivity: A work of art is said to be objective when it omits editorializing or generalizing commentary, when the action is set forth in deed and gesture and the reader is permitted to draw his own conclusions without direct assistance from the author or a character who acts as his proxy. Objectivity is thus a term used to describe the disinvolvement of the author from his materials and the dramatization of ideas and concepts. Objectivity is also used to designate the totality of an author's view of the subject he chooses to write about and in this connection is synonymous with the *ironic view.* See also *Dramatic* and *Irony.* The opposite of objectivity is *subjectivity,* a presentation marked by the personal opinions of the author and delivered with little dramatization. See *Point of view.*

Parable: A short moral tale, usually allegorical, but lacking the same systematic correspondences as allegory. See *Fable, Myth, Allegory,* and pages 169–70, 204–6.

Pathos: A justified response of pity or sympathetic concern. When not justified by the events that evoke it, pathos becomes *sentimentality* (emotion unwarranted by the situation). Pathos should also be distinguished from *tragedy* on the basis of the magnitude of the events and characters who inspire the emotion. In pathetic situations suffering and/or harm is experienced by passive, innocent, or weak characters whose struggle is neither of heroic proportion nor of far-reaching consequence. Tragic situations involve a character of great potential or worth, but who is not innocent, who struggles bravely, nobly, and violently against finally overwhelming odds; upon the outcome of his struggle hang fated consequences of first importance to many others. The pathetic produces an emotion of pity; the tragic brings a feeling more akin to terror.

Peripety: A reversal. See *Plot.*

Plot: The arrangement of narrative events which reveals their unity and clarifies their significance. Plot should be distinguished from *action* or *conflict,* although both are contributing ingredients. Plot is the ordering of action and the revelation, as well as the resolution, of conflict. Events, for instance, invariably occur in a chronological sequence and with almost infinite detail; whereas plot may not present specific actions in a strict chronological arrangement. Also, plot will avoid all details that do not reveal some planned significance. The basis of a plot is *conflict,* the collision of opposing forces; the collision may occur between the *protagonist* (see *Character*) and his social or natural environment, between the protagonist and another person (*antagonist*), or between conflicting values, ideals, or emotions within a single individual. An undramatized explanation of the background from which the conflict arises is a part of plot called *exposition;* it supplies the reader with the information necessary to understand what has occurred before the central action takes place. When exposition is partially dramatized by dialogue or by references that characters make to some significant action and circumstances connecting the central action to a broad, encompassing conflict, this background is designated *enveloping action.* Both exposition and enveloping action are part of the *rising action* or *complication*—that part of plot that brings the conflicting forces to their greatest strength, peril and *tension.* When the conflict has reached its greatest dimensions, the *climax* occurs and the highest point of *suspense* is reached. The *falling action* immediately follows the climax; tensions start toward resolution and the forces in opposition begin to subside to a state of adjustment. Falling action involves *peripety* or *reversal* (the change from one state or condition to its opposite, from good fortune to bad, from failure to success, from imbalance to balance). The reversal brings about a *denouement,* an unknotting of all the problems. If the denouement is tragic, it is called *catastrophe.* And with the denouement there is usually a *discovery,* "a change from ignorance to knowledge, and thus to either love or hate, in the personages marked for good or evil fortune." Sometimes this discovery is called *epiphany.* See also pages 48, 68–70, 92–93.

Point of view: The angle of vision and authority from which a story is told. Seldom does the author tell a story in his own person. Instead he assumes a *persona,* or voice of an imaginary narrator, who relates the events and describes the scenes from his particular view—both physical and mental.

Basically there are two points of view: first person and third person; but each can have a number of variations and refinements. The first-person narrator can be a major character or a minor character; but he can relate events only from his own angle of vision; he can report only what he has seen, heard, felt, imagined, or been told. (See "Why I Live at the P.O.")

The third-person point of view is impersonal and has three divisions: (1) *omniscient*—which allows the all-knowing narrator complete freedom to move from one place to another, in and out of characters' minds, to comment directly on events (see "The Haunted Palace"); (2) *limited omniscient*—also in the third person, but related strictly from the physical and mental viewpoint of one character, either major or minor, in the story itself (see "A Sense of Shelter"); (3) *dramatic,* or *objective*—third person still, but using the sound camera technique as the angle of vision; it is very close to drama though it allows the camera to rove beyond the limits of the proscenium to record a story; as it records it never makes comment; neutral and dispassionate, it never enters the thoughts of characters. (See "A Tree, A Rock, A Cloud," which uses this technique with minor exceptions.) Consistency in point of view is considered imperative in the highly wrought modern short story, which achieves much of its force from establishing and maintaining unity through one of the above angles of vision.

Prologue: The preface or introduction to a dramatic action wherein the theme is intimated and the setting and chief characters may be identified. See page 93.

Resolution: The concluding and "unknotting" of thematic implications; thus resolution is to theme what denouement is to plot. Usually occurs with the denouement and is sometimes loosely equated with it.

Reversal: See *Plot.*

Rising action: Complication. See *Plot.*

Sentimentality: See *Pathos.*

Setting: See *Atmosphere* and pages 1–2, 16–19, 33–35, 44–46.

Situational irony: See *Irony.*

Stereotype: See *Character.*

Stock character: See *Character.*

Structure: An inexact but useful term to refer to the architecture of a story, which may be built of fairly simple chronological sequences, or constructed of flashbacks and other patterns of action, forward and backward. It is often argued that the essential structure of a short story consists of *rising action, climax,* and *denouement.* But this is too simple a formula by which to categorize most successful stories.

We may also think of structure in these terms: (1) Episodic—a series of loosely related actions held together by a central hero. Examples include the adventures of Tom Jones and Huckleberry Finn. (2) Circular or round robin—the protagonist departs from a certain place, ventures far, but returns (with fresh knowledge) to the original place. Conrad's "Youth" approximates this circular structure. (3) Scenic—a pattern of alternating scenes much like those in drama. As in "The Aspern Papers," scenes may shift from house to garden, from a public locale to a private room, etc.

Subjectivity: See *Objectivity.*

Suspense: Anxiety and uncertainty created by unanswered questions and increased by a recurring process of answering a question only to introduce immediately another more momentous one.

Symbol: An object, person, or action that embodies several meanings in addition to its denotative or literal meaning. See pages 17–18, 34, 93–95, 134, 143–44, 150–54, 169–70, 195, 205.

Tension: A highly technical literary term meaning, generally, the interplay and counterbalancing of the parts to the whole and with each other. However, when the term is applied to fiction, it usually is synonymous with conflict, particularly thematic conflict wherein one aspect of a theme tends to contradict another. Sometimes equated with ambiguity.

Theme: The cogent and unifying idea, along with its pertinent implications, which, in combination with emotional attitudes, is the final effect of a short story. See pages xi–xiii, 16–18, 44–47, 92–93, 96, 107, 115–19, 132–34, 143–44, 150–54, 193–96, 204–8.

Tone: Synonym for attitude; also a description of the effect achieved through a combination of attitude and mood. See *Attitude, Mood,* and pages 17, 33, 45, 115, 132.

Tragedy: See *Pathos* and page 93.

Ubi sunt: Elegiac theme or motif lamenting the passing of something of great value; literally means "where are?" or "whither flown?" as in "where are the snows of yesteryear?" or "where are the days that are no more?" See *Motif* and pages 144, 193–94.

Voice: The *persona* or created character who serves as narrator, or as an imaginary character in the role of author, but is not the author himself. The omniscient narrator who speaks in "What You Hear From 'Em?" is not the author, Peter Taylor, but is a *persona* who voices attitudes toward the events of the story and its characters.